BRITISH POSTMARKS

by Dr J T Whitney

THE HANDBOOK TO
BRITISH POSTAL MARKINGS
AND THEIR VALUES

Seventh Edition Edited by Colin G Peachey and V Brian Crookes

ⓒ Published by the
British Postmark Society at
19 Moorland Road,
Hemel Hempstead, Herts HP1 1NH, 1997

ISBN 0 900214 09 0

1st Edition February 1979
Reprinted August 1979
2nd edition (Picton Publishing) May 1980
3rd Edition (Longman Group Limited) May 1983
4th Edition (Published by the Author) January 1987
5th Edition (Published by the Author) January 1990
6th Edition (Published by the British Postmark Society) Summer 1993
7th Edition (Published by the British Postmark Society) Summer 1997

Acknowledgements

Acknowledgement for illustrations is given to the British Post Office, Mr E W Proud of Proud-Bailey Co Ltd, the Railway Philatelic Group, Robson Lowe and especially to the House of Alcock for illustrations from "The Postmarks of GB and Ireland" by R C Alcock and F C Holland (1940). The individual numbers of these illustrations are as published in the 5th edition (though we have revised the numbering in the Sixth Edition and again in this edition) and copyright of these is now reserved by Mr E W Proud of Proud-Bailey Co Ltd.

Thanks are also expressed to "Parsons, Peachey and Pearson" for permission to use their reference numbers in chapter 11 "Slogan Postmarks" and to the British Postmark Society for permission to use, in chapter 12, the reference numbers of "Special Event Postmarks of the UK" by G R Pearson. (This permission was granted by Colin Peachey, now involved as co-Editor of this book, at an earlier date.)

We are grateful to all collectors who have been kind enough to submit ideas and material that has helped us produce the Seventh Edition. The following list may not be exhaustive but we extend our thanks to these and to others who earlier helped with the Sixth Edition :

David Allison, Patrick Awcock, Rev C M Beaver, Alicia Belsey, Russell Biggs, Grahame Blackman, Tony Bosworth, John Bradley, Derrick Burney, Bob Carpenter, Ron Carpenter, Stan Challis, W G Clarke, Norman Claydon, F B Coates, S F Cohen, Dr Peter Coldrey, Mr & Mrs L Coppock, John Cowell, Nigel Davidson of Bay Stamps, P J Dawling, John Daynes, Ken Dee, Philip Densham, Keith Downing, Judith Dowsett, Roger Dymond, Barrie Evans of "Messengers", Gerard Fletcher, Peter Forrestier-Smith, G W Fortey, John Frost, Phil Gains, Bill Garrard, Dr Tony Goodbody, Martin Grier, Ray Haffner of "Postings", Eric Harris, Walter Harris, John Holman, G B Horton, Roger Hosking, Roger Hudson, Alan Kane, Alistair Kennedy, Eric Langdon, Colin Langston, Ron Kirby, Don Little, Stuart Mackenzie, Eric Mein, Glenn Morgan, Alan Munford, John Newcomb, Tony Osmond, John Owen, J A Pasquill MBE, Julia Petty, F Pilborough, W (Bill) T Pipe, Daphne Pullan, Arthur Roberts, Pete Roberts, Christopher Riding, Brian Rowley, F W Scott, Ken Smith, Bernard Snook, Anthony Staniland, Rev Jim Stothers, Fred Taylor, Ray Tear, Norman Towers, Dr David Trapnell, Bill Varnham, Alan Violet, J J Waterman, S Webb, Ron Wedgerfield, Chris Whitehead, R S Williamson, Harold Wilson, the Forces Postal History Society, the Railway Philatelic Group and the Welsh Philatelic Society, Roger Bowden of Jersey Philatelic Bureau, and numerous members of Royal Mail staff throughout the country (for help with the town listing in chapter 10).

A particular Thank You is due to Michael Goodman who has helped with improved illustrations for both the Sixth and Seventh Editions ...

... and a further Thank You to Colin's good friend Roger Dymond and his PC for their help in producing page 1, chapter headings and for other make-up work.

Foreword

In building further on Tim Whitney's excellent work, we are delighted with the positive and encouraging reactions we received following publication of the Sixth Edition in 1993. Since then we have strived to reach a new level of accuracy and completeness. This latter word should be used with care since this is not an encyclopaedia and it does not set out to be complete on every postmark that can be found covering 300 years and more. The main purpose of the book is to enable a collector, with cover (ie an envelope or entire) in hand, to identify the postmark and determine a minimum value.

Once again we are only too pleased to maintain Tim Whitney's name as the author of the book and we continue to do so with the full knowledge of and support from Diana, Tim's widow. We use "author" in the loosest sense of the word, acknowledging that the book brings together parts of existing works for a wider postmark-collecting audience, a task which Tim did with amazing success.

Since the Sixth Edition we have continued to liaise with authors of works of postal history topics relevant to this work, to publicise their work and include a summary of these works in return. In this way we have been able to update, for example, both the RAF section of chapter 16 and the Land's End section of chapter 24. We have received a large number of comments from other collectors, sometimes identifying new items. These have affected, in particular, chapters 3 and 7. Over the last four years we have thoroughly reviewed chapters 10 (the list of towns), 13, 14 (coastal steamers), 15 (modern FPOs and Camps), 17, 20, 23, and 24, and some of these have been the subject of several re-drafts over that period. Last and by no means least come the new chapters 1A "Free Franks" and 4 "Early Scotland", almost worth a volume on its own, as promised in the Sixth Edition. Once again we have to take a "tough line" on space as we wish the book to remain a handbook and do not want it to reach encyclopaedic proportions.

How do we maintain the book as a "Postmarks Simplified"? Taking chapter 17 (Islands) for example, to further clarify a page that included items of 18th, 19th and 20th centuries, we added some dates. Have we in the process made the listing too complex? It is tempting to add either counties or dates to the list of stations in chapter 13, but we fear the simplicity of the listing would be spoiled in the process. After all, Pipe & Blackman's excellent book gives this detail. We are keen to maintain the strengths of this book. What are your views?

The overall format has been maintained as established in the Sixth Edition. The formula is 80% of A4 with the illustrations and text reduced together though the detailed listings are inevitably in smaller print, about as small as we dare!

Our work is not finished. We heralded a new version of chapter 5 (early Irish) and with much work already done the results will be included in the Eighth Edition. At the other end of the time scale a summary of mechanised offices is planned for chapter 27 so as to show which TOWNS are involved in mechanised sorting and which facilities were used at each. Thus we anticipate producing yet a further Edition (probably our "Millennium Edition"!) with more new material.

Not surprisingly, we have given a thorough review to prices in most chapters, though for the more expensive items specimens are elusive and the valuation depends on such items coming up at auctions. Help with noting auction realisations is always welcome but please remember the condition of the item at auction might not match the standard we have defined in the following pages!

Ideas for further improvement and development of this much loved volume would always be welcome. Please write and give us feedback but please do not forget to include an SAE or International Reply Coupon.

Thanks

We thank most sincerely our respective wives Valerie and Vicki for their encouragement and forbearance during the years we have worked on this Edition.

Colin Peachey and Brian Crookes

4

CONTENTS

Introduction

1. Using this book

In introducing our Seventh Edition, the principle of previous editions remains unchanged, in that the book is designed as a 'Postmarks Simplified'. It can be used by readers with little or no previous knowledge, by the "average level" collector, or by specialists who will find it useful for ready reference or for fields outside their area of specialisation. For the beginner we hope the brief explanatory paragraphs will prove useful. For the specialist we have checked the data carefully, improved it where possible and revised the prices.

It is important to realise that, in many instances, this is a Catalogue of postmark types rather than actual postmarks. Behind a single entry there may be several hundred or even thousands of postmarks, varying in value depending on the date and place of use. Even where lists have been given, variations such as punctuation and the size of the mark have been ignored or the lists would be just too long. Thus the price is a <u>minimum</u> for each type of postmark and **each price should be treated as though the word 'From' is printed before it.**

An important change in this Edition is that EACH entry in the main lists is numbered not just those that are pictured. We hope thereby that "CBP ref numbers" can become more of an "industry standard", used by collectors, dealers and auctioneers alike. We apologise for having to change the numbers from the Sixth Edition in order to achieve this, but we promise NOT to change them again (unless perhaps a chapter or section receives a wholesale revision) and we acknowledge we will have to use "A" numbers if necessary in future. Numbers remain related to the chapters in which they appear, thus chapter 7 starts with 7/1, 7/2 and so on.

In describing postmarks, where / appears in the list it separates lines of type (though not used universally). All postmarks are in black unless stated otherwise. A postmark on cover may be shown ⊠ , △ on piece, ○ on loose stamp. The term 'postmark' is used for convenience to describe all kinds of marks applied in the processing of the mails though the function may vary considerably, e.g. cancelling the stamps, giving information, advertising an event, raising a surcharge etc. A cancellation is slightly different in that it is a mark used for cancelling a stamp, thus frequently 'postmark', 'mark' and 'cancellation' can be used synonymously. The term 'cachet' is used to describe explanatory rubber stamps but specifically those that do NOT cancel the stamps. (Note : terminology is different in USA where a special event cover is termed "cacheted cover")

2. How to price a cover.

2.1 Prices given are generally for clear strikes on a clean card or cover. Exceptions are for parcel marks on "piece", or documents including registration receipts. The latter are worth less than a complete envelope. * (asterisk) denotes <u>"items seldom seen so difficult to value"</u> or "top end of price scale, depends on auction realisations".

Some dealers describe the quality of a mark with a 4-star rating, others attempt more precision by the use of percentages.

<u>Prices stated are for at least Three Star or 85% quality.</u>

: Halve prices for Two Star or 55%
: Quarter prices for One Star or when less than half the mark is clear

Collectors are strongly advised to insist on these standards when purchasing items. Covers in pristine condition or with other attractive features will command a premium above catalogue value. Covers from which stamps have been removed are usually almost worthless, even if with valuable postmarks. "Grubby" or "dog eared" covers, those roughly opened, or those with biro addresses across which the postmark has fallen, are only of one or two star quality and their value is affected accordingly.

2.2   Postmarks, in the editors' opinion, should always be collected on full entire, cover or card (or on a piece as large as an envelope in the case of parcel or packet marks).

: Fronts are often worth only one third of Catalogue value.
: Pieces (or 'squares') are worth 20-25% of Catalogue value.
: Loose stamps on which a substantial (at least half) part of the
  postmark can be positively identified are usually worth only 10% of
  Catalogue value.

2.3 To assess the basic value of a cover –

: First check the value of all postmarks on the cover in this handbook
: Take the highest value and add to it half the value of other marks
  priced over £5, ignoring others.
: Then check the value of the stamps in a stamp catalogue. If the market value of the stamp (say one quarter catalogue value) is greater than the postmark then the value of the stamp will prevail, otherwise add a premium to take account of the value of the stamp if above, say, £10.

2.4 One last factor is that of "genuineness". A postal history collector will usually favour an envelope or card that is addressed and appears to have travelled through the mails. A commercial cover, with handwritten or typed address, is normally preferred to a "philatelic" one ie clearly prepared by a collector, and this may be reflected in the price of the cover. "By favour" items, with postmarks stamped on plain unaddressed cards etc., are be viewed with suspicion since forgery is possible.

3. SID handstamps

SIDs (Self inking datestamps) are spreading across the country in the 1990s and we do NOT claim to have included them in all the relevant lists. Where they are already there (e.g. South Kensington Station and Reading Barracks in  chapters 13 and 15 respectively of the Sixth Edition) we have left them, but they have not been added to the Jersey, Isle of Wight or Scottish Islands sections of chapter 17. See illustrations here for two examples.

PLEASE REMEMBER : THIS HANDBOOK IS AN OVERALL GUIDE, WE DO NOT PLAN TO INCLUDE EVERY POSTMARK!! SO WRITE TO US WITH VALUES AND IDEAS BY ALL MEANS, BUT NOT TO TELL US ONE POSTMARK IS MISSING!!

All correspondence should be addressed to Colin Peachey at 19 Moorland Road, Hemel Hempstead, Herts HP1 1NH. Please send photocopies of any postmark about which you have a query and enclose a SAE or International Reply Coupon.

1.   The General Post to 1839

Early Stages of the Postal System

We include this summary as a brief background to early postal history and to show the steps that led to the first postal markings shown in the pages of chapter 1 that follow.

Henry I (1100-1135) appointed messengers to carry Government letters. Later, messengers were appointed by Barons, Church dignitaries and others.

Henry III (1216-1272) provided uniforms for King's Messengers.

Edward I (1272-1307) instituted fixed places (Posting Houses) where horses were available for the carriage of letters.

Edward II (1307-1327). The first manuscript postal marking appeared on covers: "Haste, post haste".

Henry VIII (1509-1547) appointed Brian Tuke as "Master of the Postes".

Elizabeth I (1558-1603) appointed Thomas Randolph as "Chief Postmaster" for Inland and Foreign mail.

Charles I (1625-1649) appointed Thomas Witherings as "Chief Postmaster". He set up the nucleus of the modern system with regular post roads, post houses, staff and fixed rates.

Charles II (1660-1685) appointed Henry Bishop as "Postmaster General". Following complaints of delays to letters, the first postal handstamp "Bishop mark" was introduced in April 1661. The "Franking system" also started whereby letters from MPs and others were sent and received free of postal charges.

The General Post (GPO London)

The Postmaster General administered six main post roads which radiated from London to post towns in England and Wales. They were named Bristol, Chester, Kent, North, Western and Yarmouth. Additionally, the North Road continued to Edinburgh for destinations in Scotland. The Chester Road continued to Holyhead where Packet Boats took mail to Dublin for destinations in Ireland.

Handstamps were struck in London on the date of posting there or on the date of receipt.

Bishop Marks:

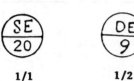

Note :
In this example
I used for J,
V for U, thus
IV = JU = June

1/1	1/2	1/3	1/4

1/1	London Bishop Marks with month in top section (14mm), 1661-66	300.00
1/2	As above but 1667-1713, sans serif from 1673	125.00
1/3	As above but day in top section and larger (19mm), 1713-19 ..	60.00
1/4	As above but 1720-87	25.00

Note : the year can only be determined from contents of the letter

Later Datestamps:

| 1/5 | 1/6 | 1/8 | 1/10 | 1/13 | 1/14 |

1/5	Double circle type, Jan-April 1787	100.00
1/6	Double circle with month, day and year, with or without code letters, 1787-98	10.00
1/7	As above, but with S above for Sunday	250.00
1/8	New type, single or double rim, 1795-99	5.00
1/9	As above, but year in 3 or 4 figures, 1800-39	3.50
1/10	Coded type, single or double rim, several types, red, 1799-1839 .	1.00
1/11	As above but coded S for Sunday	75.00
1/12	As above but without code for Late Fees	60.00
1/13	Boxed types for Late Fees, 1797-1839	15.00
1/14	Sunday stamp, various colours, 1832-39	25.00

Branch Offices :

1/15

1/15 Branch offices (with or without PAID) from 1829:

Borough (B)	7.50	Old Cavendish Street (O.C.S)	7.50
Charing Cross (CH, CX or C†)	5.00	Vere St. (VS)	7.50
Lombard St. (LS)	5.00		

Early Receiving House Miscellaneous Marks:

    THE·POST FOR·ALL·KENT GOES·EVERY NIGHT·FROM THE·ROVND·HO VSE·IN·LOVE LANE & COMES EVERY·MOR (NING)

    1/16   **1/17**   **1/18**   **1/19**

1/16 Send Answer By the Post at the Round House in Love Lane Neare
      Billinsgate, oval, 1661-63
1/17 The Post For all Kent Goes Every Night From the Round House in
      Love Lane & Comes Every Mor(ning), circular, 1661-62
1/18 Essex Post Goes and Coms Every Day, circular, 1674-75
1/19 S.X. Post Goes & Comes Every Day, 1675

These marks (not shown to scale) were used to advertise the posts which ran on the Kent and Essex roads. They are very rare and are each worth several thousand pounds. A specimen of **1/18** realised £4,400 at auction in 1989.

Receiving Houses :

    1/20   **1/22**   Partington

1/20 Initials of Receiver, usually circled, black 10.00
1/21   as above but red 45.00

    Surname of Receiver:
1/22   Partington (lower case letters) 60.00
1/23   Walter (upper case letters) 150.00

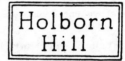
    G·P·O WHITE CHAPEL   **Holborn Hill**

    1/24   **1/25**   **1/26**

1/24 Address with circle or double circle:

Borough	£250	Tottenham Court Road	£150
Union St. Borough	£250	Vigo Lane	£100
Charles St. Soho	£150	Wapping	£250
Gt. Knightrider St.	£150	Whitechapel	£150
Temple	£150		

1/25 G.P.O. above Receiving House name:

Finsbury Square	£250	Pall Mall	£250
Gt. Surrey St.	£250	Wapping	£250
King St. Tower Hill	£250	Whitechapel	£250

1/26 Office name within frame, single or double, many types   5.00

Paid Marks:

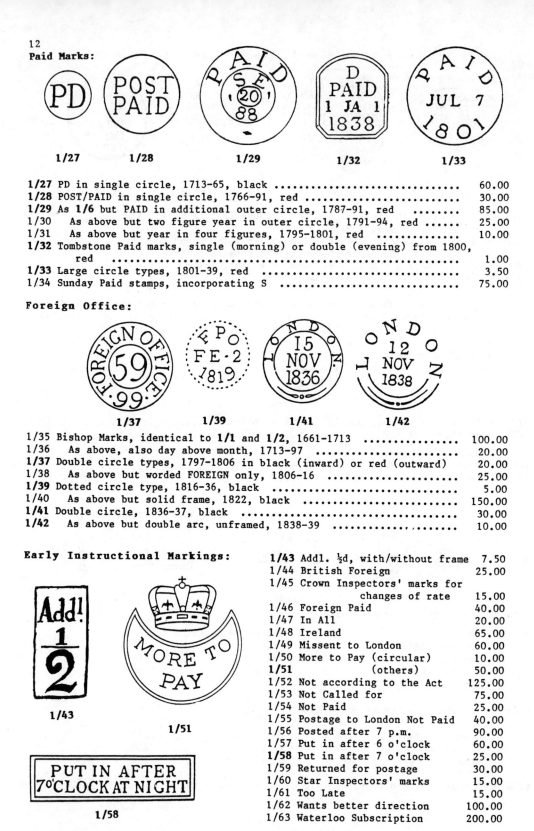

| 1/27 | 1/28 | 1/29 | 1/32 | 1/33 |

1/27 PD in single circle, 1713-65, black 60.00
1/28 POST/PAID in single circle, 1766-91, red 30.00
1/29 As 1/6 but PAID in additional outer circle, 1787-91, red 85.00
1/30   As above but two figure year in outer circle, 1791-94, red 25.00
1/31   As above but year in four figures, 1795-1801, red 10.00
1/32 Tombstone Paid marks, single (morning) or double (evening) from 1800,
     red 1.00
1/33 Large circle types, 1801-39, red 3.50
1/34 Sunday Paid stamps, incorporating S 75.00

Foreign Office:

| 1/37 | 1/39 | 1/41 | 1/42 |

1/35 Bishop Marks, identical to 1/1 and 1/2, 1661-1713 .... 100.00
1/36   As above, also day above month, 1713-97 .... 20.00
1/37 Double circle types, 1797-1806 in black (inward) or red (outward) . 20.00
1/38   As above but worded FOREIGN only, 1806-16 .... 25.00
1/39 Dotted circle type, 1816-36, black 5.00
1/40   As above but solid frame, 1822, black 150.00
1/41 Double circle, 1836-37, black 30.00
1/42   As above but double arc, unframed, 1838-39 .... 10.00

Early Instructional Markings:

1/43 Addl. ½d, with/without frame   7.50
1/44 British Foreign   25.00
1/45 Crown Inspectors' marks for
                     changes of rate 15.00
1/46 Foreign Paid   40.00
1/47 In All   20.00
1/48 Ireland   65.00
1/49 Missent to London   60.00
1/50 More to Pay (circular)   10.00
1/51   (others)   50.00
1/52 Not according to the Act   125.00
1/53 Not Called for   75.00
1/54 Not Paid   25.00
1/55 Postage to London Not Paid   40.00
1/56 Posted after 7 p.m.   90.00
1/57 Put in after 6 o'clock   60.00
1/58 Put in after 7 o'clock   25.00
1/59 Returned for postage   30.00
1/60 Star Inspectors' marks   15.00
1/61 Too Late   15.00
1/62 Wants better direction   100.00
1/63 Waterloo Subscription   200.00

1/43

1/51

PUT IN AFTER
7°CLOCK AT NIGHT

1/58

1A.   Free Franks

England and Wales

It was as early as 1652 that the Council of State set down rules under which correspondence to and from Members of Parliament and specified Officers of State could be sent without payment of a postal charge. Such letters were known as FRANKS.   Initially the local Postmaster had to be able to recognise, from the sender's seal or the recipient's name, the eligibility. Later it became necessary for the sender's place of residence, date and signature to be written on the address panel. Various other restrictions were imposed from time to time, including maximum weight (1 ounce) and daily number of letters received (15) or sent (10).

In 1764 the Franking Office within London Chief Office introduced a FREE handstamp. This was applied to eligible letters arriving or departing London or in transit.

Frank letters were not exempted from provincial Penny Post charges, nor from the London Two Penny Post. Handstamp instructional markings concerning these Posts and other matters first appeared in the early 1800s. They were struck <u>instead of</u> a FREE mark.

On 10 January 1840 the Uniform Penny Post was introduced and the Free Franking system abolished. The final date of the FREE system was 11 January to allow for the latest possible eligible posting.

1A/1	1A/2	1A/3

1A/1	Single circle, large F, red, 1764-66	150.00
1A/2	as above, but uniform letters, red, 1765-88	30.00
1A/3	Double circle, with stamper's code letter A,C,P or S at centre, brown or red, 1787-92	100.00

1A/4	1A/5	1A/6

1A/4	Single circle, with code letter, brown or red, 1789-91	100.00
1A/5	Hooded wreath circle, with code letter, purple or red, 1790-91	150.00
1A/6	Treble circle, with date & code letter, red, 1791-97	75.00
1A/7	as above, but without code letter, single or double rim, red, 1797-99	100.00
1A/8	Fancy Experimental types, with FREE and date, 1799	100.00

1A/9

1A/10

1A/11

1A/9 Single circle, crown inside, single or double rim, red, 1800-07   50.00
1A/10 Single circle, crown on top, red, 1807 .... *
1A/11 Single circle, with single rim (morning duty) or double rim
      (evening duty), crown breaking top of circle, many varieties,
      red, 1807-39 (see note 4 at end of chapter) 10.00
1A/12   as above, with simple cross below date, red, 1815-39 ...... 10.00
1A/13   as above, with Maltese Cross or letter 'E' below date, 1837-39 50.00
1A/14   as above, with letter 'N' below date, 1837-39 .... 75.00
1A/15   as above, with space below date, 1838-39 .... 50.00
1A/16 Any of the above, but January 1840 .... double values

TO PAY
ONLY
D
2

1A/17

TO PAY
2d
ONLY

1A/18

TO PAY 1ᴰ ONLY

1A/19

To Pay
1ᵈ Only

1A/20

1A/17 TO PAY ONLY D 2, framed, black, 1803-17 .... 150.00
1A/18 TO PAY 2d ONLY, framed, several varieties, black, brown or red,
    1817-39 .... 10.00
1A/19 TO PAY 1D ONLY, framed, several varieties, black, brown or red,
    1817-36 .... 30.00
1A/20   as above, but unframed, 1835-39 .... 75.00

Above Privilege
Number

1A/21

ABOVE NUMBER

1A/22

Above Weight

1A/23

ABOVE WEIGHT

1A/24

1A/21 Above Privilege, Above Privilige Number or Above Number, in script,
    framed or unframed, black, purple or red, 1797-1830 ..... 150.00
1A/22   as above, but capitals, black or red, 1819-35 .... 150.00
1A/23 Above Weight, script, purple or red, 1814-25 .... 150.00
1A/24   as above, but capitals, framed or unframed, black, brown,
    green, purple or red, 1818-36 .... 150.00

Scotland

The system was similar to that for England and Wales. However, many fewer letters were routed via the Edinburgh Chief Office and only one FREE handstamp was ever used – during the period 1771 to 1792. Only two handstamp instructional markings are occasionally seen, one of which was used at the Glasgow Branch Office.

TO PAY
ONE PENNY

To Pay
ONE PENNY

1A/25   1A/26   1A/27

1A/25 Single circle with 'E' below FREE, red, 1771-92 .... *
1A/26 TO PAY ONE PENNY, unframed, black, Edinburgh Chief Office, 1827-39 100.00
1A/27 To Pay ONE PENNY, unframed, black, Glasgow Branch Office, 1835-39 150.00

Ireland

The system was similar to that for England and Wales. Many letters were routed through the Dublin Chief Office and from there to London, so two different FREE marks may be found on one cover. More than 10 handstamp instructional markings have been recorded, but little is known of them. Readers are invited to send a photocopy of any unlisted mark and of covers which extend the periods of use.

    Free   FREE

1A/28   1A/29 (two)   1A/30

1A/28 Single circle, with shamrock leaves above and below FREE, black,
       1706-10 .... *
1A/29 Free, unframed, upper or lower case, black, 1707-84 .... 150.00
1A/30 Single circle, with FREE and 'D' (Dublin) below, red or purple,
       1769-84 .... 100.00
1A/31   as above but unframed, purple, 1783-84 .... *
1A/32   as above but framed and without 'D', red, 1785-94 .... 30.00

1A/33   1A/34   1A/35

1A/33 Double circle, with date and 'DUB', several varieties, black or
       purple, 1787-1807 .... 50.00
1A/34 "Mermaid", single or double frame, several varieties, brown,
       orange, red or yellow, 1808-14 .... 150.00
1A/35 "Mermaid" removed, single or double frame, several varieties,
       red or yellow, 1813-31 .... 15.00

| 1A/36 | 1A/37 | 1A/41 | 1A/45 |

1A/36	"Shield", several varieties, red or yellow, 1815-32	15.00
1A/37	Double circle with crown on top, red, 1832-35	30.00
	Single circle with crown breaking top of circle, time code letter below year, red, 1835-39 :	
1A/38	code A - Afternoon	15.00
1A/39	code E - Evening	10.00
1A/40	code F - Forenoon	75.00
1A/41	code M - Morning	15.00
1A/42	code * - Noon	30.00
1A/43	as above, but no code, red, 1839	75.00
1A/44	Any of the above, but January 1840	double values
1A/45	Double rim oval with SUNDAY, red, 1820-31	100.00

Notes :

1. The use of FREE handstamps by the Foreign Branch, other Government Departments and Charities, is not covered in this chapter.

2. During the mid- and late-1830s there developed a craze for collecting autographs by sticking the fronts (address panels) from letters into scrap albums. This has resulted in large numbers of inexpensive FREE FRANK fronts being available for collectors.

3. A detailed, scholarly account, with many illustrations and listings of all known marks is in "Herewith my Frank ...." by J W Lovegrove. See Bibliography later in this volume.

4. Entry 1A/11 is known with letter "O" below date. It may be counterfeit or may have been used for the "Secret Office of the Post Office".

2.   London Local Posts to 1839

Dockwra's Post, 1680-82

2/1

A private Penny Post organised by William Dockwra for letters within London and its suburbs. Triangular stamps show abbreviations for offices: L for Lime Street, B for Bishopsgate, W for Westminster, P for St Paul's and T for Temple. Only about twenty-five examples are known, the majority being in archives. In March 1988 an example from the Temple Office sold at auction for £15,400.

Government Penny Post, 1682-1794.

Dockwra's post was declared illegal (breach of the Royal monopoly), taken over by the Government and continued until 1794.

2/2 (two)   2/3

2/2   Dockwra-type marks, several types, with office abbreviation and day:

B/CH	Bishopsgate	see note	P	St. Paul's	100.00
B	Bishopsgate	150.00	S	Southwark	150.00
G	General Office (ie Chief Office)	75.00	T	Temple	100.00
H	Hermitage	150.00	W	Westminster	75.00

Note : B/CH Bishopsgate valuation "several thousand pounds"

2/3   Circular time markings .... additional   20.00
2/4   As above but in other shapes (e.g. heart-shaped)   additional   50.00

Reorganised Penny Post, 1794-1801:   Twopenny Post 1801-1839

2/5   2/6   2/10   2/11

2/5	Experimental circular datestamps, several similar, 1794	400.00
2/6	Indented sides types, 1794-1822, red	4.00
2/7	As above but in black, 1794-1822	10.00
2/8	Oval, 1795-1822, red....................................	2.00
2/9	Small oval with double frame, 1824-33, red	2.00
2/10	As above but single frame, 1834-35, red	2.00
2/11	Small stamp with indented sides, 1836-43, red	2.00
2/12	As above but with oval frame, 1836-43, red or black	3.50
2/13	Paid types, red	2.50

Receiving House and Country Sorting Offices

2/14   A   (with 1,2,3 or 4)

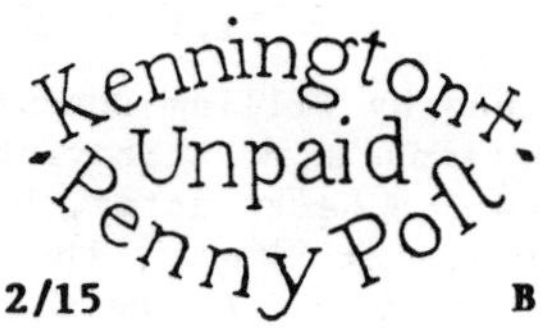

2/15   B

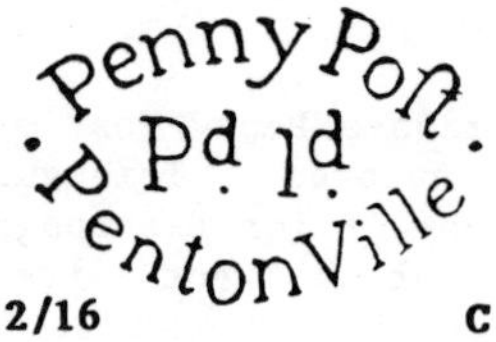

2/16   C

2/17   D

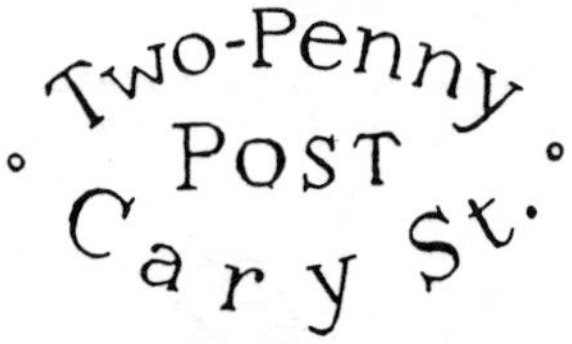

2/18   E

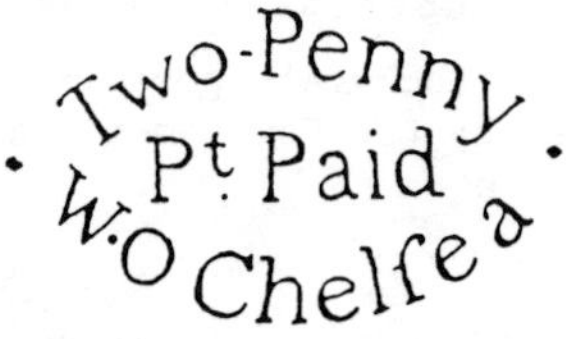

2/19   F

2/20   G

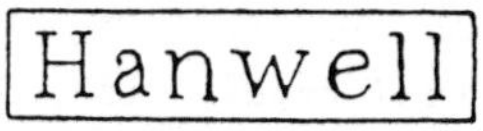

2/21   H

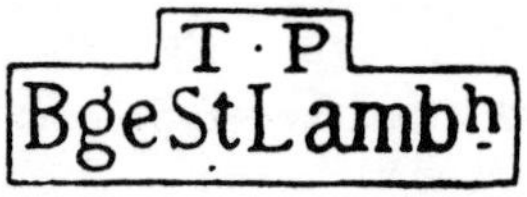

2/22   J

2/23   K

2/24   L

2/25   M

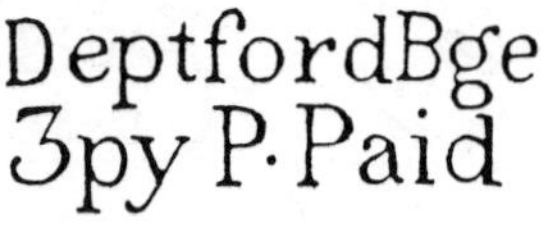

2/26   N

2/27   O

2/28   P

Cornhill
3ᴰ·PAID
2/29   Q

Devonshire St.
2/30   R

2/31   S

In this basic listing, one entry is given for each district and only major variations in wording are included (eg 8 different offices operated in Oxford Street). Black is the most common colour, thus blue and green are always worth more, red sometimes more. Full details are to be found in Willcocks and Jay.

Many Receiving Houses continued to use their handstamps after 1839. For most examples, values should be reduced to one third.

Acton A	£75	Barking K	£7	Bermondsey St. B	£30
C	£20	N	£10	G	£10
G	£10	Barkingside L	£8	J	£5
H	£10	Barnes G	£8	R	£5
J	£5	J	£5	Berners St. G	£10
K	£4	K	£5	J	£5
M	£10	M	£10	L	£9
O	£5	N	£8	M	£10
R	£5	O	£5	P	£5
S	£6	Barnesbury O	£7	Berwick St. O	£10
T	£6	R	£7	R	£10
Albany Road J	£7	Barnesbury Park R	£7	Bethnal Green A	£80
N	£20	Barnet J	£5	E	£20
Albany St. J	£5	M	£7	J	£5
L	£5	R	£7	K	£8
M	£12	T	£8	O	£5
R	£7	Battersea J	£7	P	£5
Aldersgate St. A	£75	K	£7	Bexley J	£5
E	£25	M	£10	R	£5
F	£80	Battersea Rise R	£10	T	£8
G	£15	Battle Bridge H	£15	Bexley Heath K	£5
J	£5	J	£10	Bishopsgate A	£75
M	£12	L	£12	C	£25
N	£15	M	£10	E	£20
Aldgate J	£5	O	£10	G	£10
L	£7	R	£10	J	£7
M	£10	Bayswater J	£6	K	£5
N	£12	K	£5	L	£5
O	£10	M	£6	M	£10
R	£7	N	£6	N	£10
Amwell St. J	£7	O	£5	O	£5
L	£10	P	£5	P	£5
M	£15	Q	£30	R	£5
O	£10	R	£7	Blackfriars Rd J	£5
Aylesbury St. J	£7	Beckenham G	£15	K	£5
M	£15	J	£10	L	£5
R	£7	M	£12	N	£5
Bagnigge Wells J	£7	N	£12	R	£5
O	£10	Beddington G	£15	Blackheath D	£60
R	£7	J	£7	G	£15
Balham G	£7	R	£10	J	£10
J	£5	Belvedere Place G	£20	L	£5
L	£5	J	£10	M	£5
M	£7	L	£9	N	£10
R	£10	M	£12	R	£10
Balls Pond O	£7	O	£10	Blackheath Hill O	£10
R	£10	P	£8	R	£15
Barbican J	£7	R	£7	Blackman St. G	£10
K	£5	Berkeley St. West K	£5	J	£5
L	£5	R	£10	K	£10
M	£10	Berkley Sq. A	£100	L	£10
O	£5	B	£35	M	£15
R	£5	C	£25	N	£15

O	£10	Bridge St.,		M	£10
P	£10	Westminster E	£20	O	£5
Q	£50	G	£20	R	£10
R	£10	J	£10	Cable St. J	£5
Blackmoor St. A	£125	K	£5	O	£5
B	£25	L	£5	P	£7
G	£10	M	£20	Caledonian Rd O	£10
J	£5	O	£5	R	£10
L	£10	R	£5	Camberwell A	£75
O	£10	Brixton J	£5	G	£10
Black St. A	£100	K	£5	J	£10
Blackwell B	£25	N	£10	N	£20
E	£25	O	£10	S	£18
G	£10	R	£5	Camberwell Gr. B	£16
J	£5	Brixton Hill G	£6	C	£25
K	£5	J	£5	D	£50
M	£10	K	£5	G	£20
N	£10	L	£5	J	£10
O	£10	M	£10	K	£20
R	£5	N	£10	M	£18
Blandford St. B	£25	Brixton New Rd J	£7	N	£10
J	£10	Brixton Rd J	£5	O	£7
R	£5	M	£10	P	£7
Bloomsbury A	£80	N	£5	R	£7
N	£10	Broad St.,		Camberwell New Rd J	£5
Bond St. E	£20	Bloomsbury E	£50	K	£5
G	£15	G	£10	L	£5
J	£10	J	£10	O	£5
K	£5	K	£10	Camberwell Rd K	£5
M	£12	O	£5	O	£5
N	£12	R	£5	R	£5
O	£10	Broad St.,		Camberwell,	
P	£10	Golden Sq. G	£10	Southampton St. K	£10
R	£5	J	£5	O	£5
Borough B	£40	Q	£10	R	£6
E	£40	Broadway,		Camden Town G	£10
G	£20	Stratford G	£15	H	£10
J	£10	Broadway,		L	£5
K	£10	Westminster J	£5	N	£10
O	£10	K	£10	O	£5
R	£10	O	£5	R	£5
Bow O	£10	R	£5	S	£10
R	£5	Bromley Kent J	£5	Canon St. East E	£20
S	£15	K	£5	G	£10
T	£15	N	£10	M	£10
Brentford A	£75	O	£10	Canon St. Rd J	£7
C	£20	R	£10	Carey St. B	£30
M	£10	T	£7	E	£25
S	£8	Bromley Middx. R	£5	F	£100
T	£7	Brompton B	£25	G	£10
Brentford End H	£15	G	£7	J	£5
J	£8	H	£10	M	£10
O	£10	K	£5	Carshalton G	£10
R	£10	N	£10	J	£5
Brewer St. E	£25	R	£5	N	£10
G	£10	S	£20	S	£8
J	£5	T	£15	Castle St.,	
M	£15	Brompton Row J	£10	Leicester Sq. G	£10
Brick Lane C	£20	L	£10	J	£5
E	£25	O	£10	M	£10
J	£5	R	£10	R	£5
L	£5	Brook St.,		Cateaton St. A	£100
M	£8	Grosvenor Sq. E	£30	Chadwell H	£15
N	£8	G	£10	Chancery Lane B	£30
O	£10	J	£5	E	£20
Bridge Rd, Lambeth		L	£5	G	£10
J	£10	M	£10	J	£5
R	£10	O	£5	K	£5
Bridge St., Lambeth		R	£5	L	£10
G	£10	Bruton St. O	£10	M	£10
J	£5	R	£10	N	£10
L	£10	Bunhill Row B	£30	O	£5
M	£10	G	£20	P	£5
N	£20	J	£10	Q	£30
		L	£10	R	£5

Chapel St., Belgrave Sq. J	£10	
K	£5	
Chapel St., Grosvenor Pl. J	£5	
M	£15	
R	£5	
Charing Cross B	£18	
C	£18	
D	£50	
G	£6	
J	£5	
K	£5	
M	£6	
N	£6	
O	£5	
P	£5	
R	£5	
Charles St., Manchester Sq. J	£10	
Charles St., Middlesex Hos. O	£10	
R	£10	
Charles St., Soho E	£30	
G	£10	
J	£5	
K	£10	
M	£10	
O	£10	
P	£10	
Charles St., Westminster G	£10	
J	£5	
K	£10	
L	£5	
M	£10	
N	£10	
O	£10	
P	£10	
Charlton J	£5	
L	£5	
O	£5	
R	£5	
Cheam J	£5	
R	£5	
Cheapside G	£10	
J	£5	
K	£5	
M	£8	
O	£5	
P	£5	
R	£7	
Chelsea A	£75	
D	£50	
E	£17	
F	£80	
G	£6	
H	£6	
J	£7	
K	£6	
L	£6	
M	£6	
N	£10	
Q	£30	
R	£10	
Chelsea Church St. N	£5	
Chelsea Common R	£10	
Chigwell G	£10	
H	£10	
J	£5	
N	£5	
S	£8	
T	£18	
Chigwell Row G	£10	
H	£10	
J	£5	
L	£5	
N	£10	
R	£10	
Chingford H	£15	
M	£15	
Chislehurst N	£15	
Chiswell St. A	£75	
C	£25	
E	£30	
G	£15	
J	£5	
Chiswick G	£10	
H	£10	
L	£5	
M	£7	
N	£10	
O	£10	
Circus G	£10	
J	£5	
M	£10	
City Road H	£5	
J	£5	
M	£10	
N	£5	
R	£5	
Clapham A	£75	
H	£5	
N	£10	
S	£20	
T	£8	
Clapham Comm. B	£35	
C	£30	
G	£10	
J	£5	
L	£5	
M	£8	
N	£10	
R	£5	
Clapham Lower Road J	£8	
N	£10	
R	£5	
Clapham Rise J	£10	
N	£15	
R	£5	
Clapham Rd J	£5	
N	£15	
O	£10	
Clapton C	£25	
G	£6	
N	£6	
O	£10	
R	£8	
Clarendon Sq. G	£10	
K	£5	
N	£12	
P	£10	
R	£5	
Clerkenwell Green C	£65	
G	£6	
J	£5	
L	£5	
O	£8	
R	£8	
Clifton St., Finsbury J	£10	
K	£10	
Cockspur St. G	£6	
M	£6	
N	£6	
Cold Harbour Lane R	£10	
Coleman St. G	£6	
J	£5	
M	£10	
N	£10	
College St., Westminster G	£10	
J	£5	
M	£10	
Collett Place, Commercial Rd J	£10	
L	£8	
M	£12	
O	£10	
Colney Hatch H	£10	
K	£5	
Commercial Rd K	£10	
O	£10	
R	£5	
Commercial Rd East J	£5	
K	£10	
L	£5	
O	£10	
Commercial Rd West J	£10	
K	£10	
L	£10	
O	£5	
Commercial Rd, Lambeth J	£5	
R	£8	
Conduit St., Paddington J	£5	
R	£5	
Connaught Terrace J	£10	
K	£5	
M	£15	
O	£10	
Coram St. J	£5	
K	£5	
N	£10	
R	£5	
Cornhill J	£5	
K	£5	
M	£7	
N	£7	
O	£10	
P	£5	
Q	£35	
R	£5	
Covent Gdn. A	£85	
B	£20	
Coventry St. B	£20	
E	£25	
G	£10	
J	£10	
K	£10	
L	£5	
M	£12	
N	£10	
O	£8	
Q	£35	
R	£8	
Crawford St. G	£10	
J	£5	
K	£5	
L	£5	
M	£10	
N	£10	
O	£5	
P	£5	
R	£5	

Crawley St. N	£7	Drury Lane B	£25	Edmonton C	£25
R	£5	G	£10	H	£10
Crayford K	£10	J	£5	J	£5
L	£5	L	£5	S	£10
N	£10	M	£10	T	£10
O	£5	O	£5	Elstree J	£5
Cromer St. J	£10	Duke St.,		M	£10
R	£10	Manchester Sq. B	£40	O	£5
Crouch End K	£5	G	£6	R	£5
Croydon G	£7	J	£5	Eltham C	£25
K	£7	K	£5	G	£15
M	£10	M	£12	J	£5
O	£7	R	£10	K	£5
R	£5	Dulwich S	£6	M	£15
S	£8	T	£6	N	£15
T	£8	Ealing A	£75	R	£5
Croydon Common J	£6	G	£6	S	£20
K	£6	J	£5	Enfield A	£75
N	£10	M	£6	B	£20
Croydon High St. G	£7	N	£6	D	£18
J	£5	R	£8	G	£15
K	£5	Ealing Common G	£10	H	£6
N	£6	J	£6	K	£5
R	£6	K	£5	M	£6
Curzon St. K	£5	Ealing Town B	£20	N	£6
N	£5	C	£20	R	£5
R	£5	H	£8	Enfield Highway G	£6
Dalston R	£6	J	£5	H	£6
Denmark Hill J	£6	Earl St.,		L	£5
K	£5	Blackfriars O	£5	Erith J	£5
L	£5	R	£5	L	£5
M	£10	East Acton J	£5	Euston Sq. O	£10
Deptford A	£75	N	£10	R	£5
G	£6	East Barnet G	£15	Euston St. J	£10
J	£5	H	£15	Exeter St. G	£10
K	£5	J	£10	Exmouth St. J	£5
M	£6	K	£5	M	£10
O	£8	R	£5	O	£10
R	£5	East Ham H	£15	R	£8
S	£17	J	£10	Farringdon St. K	£10
T	£10	East India Rd O	£5	M	£10
Deptford Bridge C	£35	R	£5	Q	£50
E	£25	East Place, Lambeth		R	£5
G	£15	K	£7	Fenchurch St. B	£25
M	£15	R	£5	E	£25
N	£10	East Sheen C	£25	G	£10
Deptford Broadway J	£5	G	£10	J	£5
K	£5	K	£10	L	£5
N	£15	L	£5	M	£7
O	£10	M	£10	N	£15
R	£5	East Smithfield G	£10	O	£5
Deptford High Street		J	£5	R	£5
O	£10	K	£5	Fetter Lane E	£25
Devonshire St.,		L	£5	F	£80
Marylebone B	£25	Ebury St. J	£5	G	£10
E	£20	K	£5	J	£5
G	£6	L	£5	K	£5
J	£5	R	£8	L	£5
N	£10	Edgeware K	£7	M	£8
R	£8	M	£10	O	£5
Dockhead E	£25	N	£10	R	£10
G	£10	R	£5	Finchley G	£8
J	£5	T	£20	G	£5
K	£5	Edgeware Rd G	£15	N	£6
M	£6	H	£15	O	£5
N	£10	J	£7	T	£8
O	£10	K	£7	Finchley Common J	£8
R	£8	M	£10	K	£5
Dover Rd K	£7	N	£10	R	£8
R	£7	O	£5	Finsbury Place E	£20
Drummond St. K	£10	P	£7	G	£10
O	£10	R	£7	J	£5
R	£8			M	£10

Finsbury Sq. A	£80	
O	£6	
R	£6	
Fish St. Hill B	£30	
E	£30	
F	£85	
G	£15	
J	£5	
M	£15	
Fleet Market G	£15	
Fleet St. A	£75	
G	£6	
J	£5	
K	£5	
L	£5	
M	£6	
N	£6	
O	£5	
P	£5	
R	£6	
Foots Cray J	£6	
Fore St. J	£8	
K	£8	
L	£8	
M	£10	
N	£10	
O	£5	
R	£8	
Fulham A	£75	
B	£25	
C	£25	
D	£50	
G	£10	
H	£10	
K	£5	
L	£5	
M	£10	
N	£8	
R	£5	
Gerrard St. B	£35	
C	£35	
D	£80	
F	£80	
G	£6	
J	£5	
M	£10	
N	£10	
Golden Hill A	£95	
Golden Sq. A	£85	
Goswell Rd O	£6	
Goswell St. G	£10	
K	£5	
M	£15	
N	£5	
O	£10	
Q	£60	
Goswell St. Rd G	£10	
H	£10	
Graces Alley E	£50	
Grange Rd K	£5	
O	£5	
R	£6	
Grays Inn K	£5	
O	£5	
R	£6	
Great Baker St. K	£7	
Great Coram St. O	£7	
Great Dover Rd J	£10	
M	£10	
R	£5	
Great Eastcheap K	£5	
P	£5	
Q	£35	
Great James St. B	£30	
Great Knightrider St.		
G	£10	
M	£15	
Great Marylebone St.		
B	£25	
C	£25	
E	£20	
F	£75	
G	£6	
J	£5	
K	£5	
L	£5	
M	£6	
O	£5	
P	£5	
R	£5	
Great Newport St. L	£6	
R	£5	
Great Portland St C	£25	
E	£25	
F	£75	
G	£8	
J	£5	
M	£6	
N	£8	
R	£5	
Great Russell St., Bloomsbury B	£25	
C	£25	
D	£60	
E	£25	
G	£10	
J	£5	
K	£5	
L	£5	
M	£6	
N	£8	
O	£5	
R	£8	
Great Russell St., Covent Garden G	£6	
J	£5	
K	£5	
L	£5	
M	£12	
O	£10	
P	£5	
R	£8	
Great Surrey St. E	£25	
F	£80	
G	£15	
J	£5	
L	£8	
M	£6	
N	£6	
O	£8	
R	£8	
Gt. Tower St. B	£30	
Greek St. K	£5	
R	£5	
Greenford J	£5	
O	£7	
R	£5	
Greenwich A	£75	
B	£35	
E	£30	
G	£15	
J	£10	
K	£5	
L	£5	
M	£10	
N	£15	
O	£5	
R	£5	
S	£8	
T	£18	
Greenwich Limekilns G	£17	
J	£10	
M	£10	
N	£10	
R	£7	
Grenville St. G	£15	
J	£10	
K	£5	
M	£10	
N	£10	
O	£5	
P	£5	
R	£5	
Grosvenor Sq. C	£25	
D	£60	
Grove St., Deptford G	£15	
Guildford St. J	£5	
K	£5	
L	£5	
M	£8	
O	£5	
P	£5	
Hackney B	£18	
G	£6	
M	£6	
J	£5	
K	£7	
L	£6	
M	£6	
R	£5	
S	£8	
Hackney Rd E	£20	
F	£75	
G	£6	
J	£5	
K	£5	
M	£6	
N	£6	
O	£5	
R	£8	
Ham C	£20	
G	£8	
J	£8	
M	£12	
N	£7	
R	£8	
Hammersmith A	£75	
B	£20	
C	£20	
D	£50	
G	£6	
H	£6	
J	£10	
K	£5	
M	£12	
O	£5	
Q	£4	
R	£7	
S	£8	
T	£8	
Hammersmith Broadway		
K	£5	
R	£5	
Hampstead A	£75	
B	£20	
D	£55	
G	£6	
J	£5	
K	£5	
L	£5	

M	£6
N	£6
O	£5
P	£5
Q	£30
R	£8
Hampstead Rd L	£10
O	£5
P	£8
R	£8
Hampton F	£6
J	£5
K	£5
M	£6
O	£5
S	£8
T	£8
Hampton Court G	£15
J	£5
K	£5
L	£5
N	£6
R	£8
Hampton Wick J	£10
N	£12
R	£7
Hanwell G	£7
H	£7
K	£5
L	£5
N	£10
O	£10
Harrow J	£5
K	£5
N	£8
O	£5
R	£5
Harrow Rd R	£8
Hayes (Kent) J	£7
Hendon A	£75
G	£6
H	£6
M	£8
N	£8
S	£10
Heston J	£8
Highbury O	£7
Highgate G	£6
K	£5
L	£5
M	£6
N	£6
O	£5
R	£6
S	£8
High Holborn B	£20
E	£20
G	£6
J	£5
K	£5
M	£6
N	£6
P	£5
Q	£35
High St., Borough J	£10
M	£10
N	£10
High St., Lambeth J	£5
O	£5
High St., Marylebone	
B	£25
E	£20
High St., St. Giles	
K	£5
O	£5
Holborn K	£5
O	£5
P	£5
R	£5
Holborn Bars B	£25
E	£25
F	£85
G	£6
J	£5
K	£5
M	£6
N	£12
O	£5
P	£5
Q	£35
R	£8
Holborn Hill A	£75
B	£25
C	£25
G	£6
J	£5
K	£5
L	£5
M	£6
N	£6
O	£5
P	£5
R	£5
Holloway H	£6
K	£5
Holloway Rd J	£5
K	£5
L	£5
O	£5
P	£5
R	£5
Homerton G	£7
H	£15
L	£8
M	£6
O	£8
R	£7
Hope Town H	£5
L	£5
N	£6
O	£5
R	£5
Hornsey G	£6
H	£6
L	£5
Hornsey Down O	£5
R	£5
Hornsey Rd K	£5
Hounslow J	£5
N	£6
O	£5
T	£10
Hoxton E	£30
F	£85
G	£10
J	£5
K	£10
O	£10
Hoxton New Town J	£5
O	£10
Ilford G	£6
H	£6
J	£5
K	£5
M	£6
Isleworth E	£25
G	£6
H	£6
J	£5
K	£5
M	£6
R	£8
Islington B	£35
C	£35
G	£6
H	£6
J	£5
K	£5
L	£5
M	£6
N	£6
O	£5
R	£5
S	£8
Islington, Back Rd J	£6
K	£6
L	£6
O	£5
R	£5
Islington, Boundary Rd K	£6
O	£5
R	£8
Islington, Lower Rd	
J	£5
L	£5
O	£5
Jermyn St. G	£6
J	£5
M	£6
N	£8
O	£5
R	£5
Jews Row B	£30
Judd Place, New Rd	
K	£8
O	£8
R	£5
Kennington B	£25
G	£6
J	£8
M	£7
Kennington "+" B	£25
Kennington, Clapham Rd J	£9
Kennington Common K	£8
R	£5
Kennington Cross G	£6
J	£5
K	£5
L	£5
N	£10
O	£10
P	£10
R	£7
Kensington A	£75
B	£25
C	£25
F	£80
G	£10
H	£10
J	£5
K	£5
M	£6
N	£6
O	£5
R	£5
S	£20
T	£8
Kensington Gravel Pits G	£12
H	£15
K	£10

N	£15	King St.,		Leytonstone C	£25
O	£10	Westminster B	£25	H	£6
Q	£50	E	£25	N	£10
R	£10	G	£10	S	£10
Kensington		King William St. K	£5	Lime Grove O	£8
New Town D	£6	O	£5	Limehouse G	£10
Kent Rd G	£7	P	£5	K	£5
J	£6	Q	£35	M	£7
K	£5	R	£5	N	£7
L	£5	Knightrider St. G	£10	O	£5
M	£8	J	£5	R	£10
N	£6	K	£5	Limehouse Causeway	
O	£5	L	£5	M	£15
R	£8	M	£8	Lincolns Inn A	£75
S	£10	N	£7	G	£10
Kent Street Rd G	£6	O	£8	M	£10
J	£5	P	£5	Lisson Grove H	£10
K	£5	R	£7	J	£5
N	£10	Knightsbridge B	£35	K	£5
P	£6	G	£10	N	£10
Kentish Town B	£20	K	£5	O	£5
D	£80	M	£10	P	£5
G	£6	N	£10	R	£5
H	£6	O	£5	Little Chelsea H	£10
J	£5	R	£5	K	£5
M	£6	Lambeth A	£75	L	£5
N	£6	Lambs Conduit St. E	£25	M	£7
O	£5	G	£6	N	£10
R	£5	J	£5	R	£10
Kew B	£25	K	£5	Little Ealing H	£12
C	£25	L	£5	M	£15
G	£6	M	£6	Little Earl St. G	£10
H	£6	N	£10	J	£5
J	£5	O	£5	Little	
K	£5	P	£5	Knightrider St. J	£5
Kilburn H	£6	Q	£40	Little Newport St. J	£5
J	£5	R	£8	L	£5
K	£5	Leadenhall St. B	£25	O	£5
R	£5	E	£25	R	£10
Kingsland B	£15	F	£80	Lombard St. B	£20
K	£5	G	£6	C	£30
L	£8	J	£5	D	£75
O	£8	K	£5	E	£20
P	£8	L	£8	F	£75
R	£8	M	£6	G	£10
Kingsland Rd J	£10	O	£5	J	£5
K	£8	P	£10	M	£10
L	£5	R	£8	N	£10
M	£9	Leather Lane G	£15	London Rd J	£5
O	£5	J	£5	K	£5
R	£8	K	£5	L	£5
Kings Rd K	£5	L	£5	M	£15
Kings Rd, Chelsea H	£6	M	£6	N	£17
K	£5	O	£5	O	£8
L	£5	P	£5	R	£10
M	£6	R	£5	Long Acre J	£5
N	£6	Lee K	£5	K	£5
O	£5	R	£5	Lothbury B	£25
S	£5	Leigh St., Burton		E	£25
Kingston J	£5	Crescent K	£5	F	£85
K	£5	O	£5	G	£10
L	£5	P	£5	Loughton H	£20
M	£10	R	£5	Lower Brook St. K	£10
N	£10	Leman St. O	£7	Lower Edmonton K	£5
O	£8	Lewisham A	£75	L	£5
T	£15	G	£6	O	£5
King St.,		J	£5	Lower Tooting G	£10
Covent Garden O	£5	L	£8	K	£5
P	£5	M	£15	L	£5
Q	£35	N	£8	M	£5
R	£5	R	£8	O	£5
		Leyton H	£6	P	£5
		J	£5	R	£5

Ludgate Hill C	£20	Minories E	£30	Newington Butts A	£85
E	£15	F	£80	G	£10
F	£80	G	£18	J	£5
G	£6	J	£8	K	£7
J	£5	K	£8	M	£12
M	£6	L	£5	R	£5
N	£7	M	£12	S	£5
P	£5	O	£7	Newington Causeway	
Ludgate St. E	£20	P	£7	G	£10
F	£75	Mitcham S	£10	J	£5
G	£10	T	£10	L	£5
J	£5	Mitcham, Lower F	£10	R	£5
M	£10	J	£7	Newington Green D	£60
N	£12	O	£6	H	£10
P	£5	Mitcham, Upper L	£5	J	£5
Lyall Place,		M	£10	M	£10
Eaton Sq. O	£10	N	£12	N	£12
R	£8	Mitre Court,		New Kent Rd J	£5
Maddox St. B	£25	Fleet St. B	£25	K	£5
G	£10	E	£25	L	£5
J	£5	Moorgate St. K	£5	New North Rd R	£5
L	£5	O	£5	New Park St.,	
M	£10	P	£5	Southwark O	£5
O	£5	R	£5	R	£5
R	£8	Morden J	£5	New Road E	£25
Maida Hill J	£5	Mortlake A	£75	G	£10
K	£5	C	£80	J	£5
O	£5	G	£10	M	£10
Manswell St. J	£5	J	£5	New St.,	
L	£5	M	£10	Covent Garden E	£25
O	£5	N	£12	G	£10
Marchmont St. G	£15	O	£5	J	£5
J	£5	S	£10	L	£5
Marylebone St.,		T	£10	M	£10
Golden Sq. K	£10	Mount St.,		New St.,	
O	£10	Grosvenor Sq. E	£25	Vincent Sq. K	£7
May Fair E	£30	G	£10	North Brixton J	£8
G	£15	J	£5	O	£7
J	£7	K	£5	North End (Fulham Rd)	
K	£7	L	£5	H	£10
L	£5	M	£5	N	£12
M	£10	Mount St.,		O	£5
Merton J	£5	Lambeth G	£10	Norton Folgate O	£5
O	£5	J	£5	R	£5
Mile End G	£15	M	£12	Norwood J	£5
J	£10	Muswell Hill J	£5	K	£5
K	£5	R	£8	L	£5
L	£5	New Bond St. J	£5	R	£5
M	£10	New Brentford B	£25	Notting Hill O	£5
O	£5	C	£25	R	£5
R	£5	E	£25	Old Brentford E	£25
Milk St. E	£25	G	£10	G	£10
F	£75	H	£10	H	£10
G	£12	K	£5	J	£5
J	£5	L	£5	K	£5
M	£10	M	£10	R	£5
N	£15	N	£12	Old Broad St. J	£5
Millbank St. B	£25	O	£8	K	£5
C	£25	R	£8	L	£5
D	£55	New Cross J	£7	M	£10
E	£25	M	£10	P	£5
G	£15	N	£12	Old Brompton J	£5
J	£5	R	£5	O	£5
M	£5	New Cut, Lambeth J	£7	R	£5
O	£5	K	£5	Old St. J	£5
R	£5	Newgate St. G	£10	O	£5
Mill Hill B	£20	J	£5	R	£5
G	£15	K	£5	Orford Place J	£5
H	£10	Newington J	£5	K	£5
R	£5	M	£10	Osnaburgh St. J	£5
Millwall O	£5	S	£25	K	£5
R	£5			N	£10
				Q	£45
				R	£5

Oxford St. B	£25
E	£15
F	£75
G	£6
J	£4
K	£4
L	£5
M	£6
N	£7
O	£5
P	£5
R	£5
Oxford & Vere St.	
B	£30
C	£30
Paddington A	£85
B	£25
G	£10
J	£5
L	£5
M	£6
N	£6
O	£5
R	£5
S	£20
T	£7
Pall Mall B	£20
C	£20
G	£8
H	£10
J	£5
K	£5
L	£5
M	£8
N	£8
O	£5
P	£5
Q	£30
Pancras H	£10
L	£5
O	£5
R	£5
Park St.,	
Camden Town O	£7
R	£5
Park St.,	
Grosvenor Sq. B	£25
G	£15
J	£5
M	£10
R	£5
Park Terrace J	£5
K	£5
O	£5
R	£7
Parson's Green B	£25
D	£60
J	£10
M	£10
R	£5
Paternoster Row J	£5
M	£5
Peckham A	£75
C	£25
D	£60
F	£10
J	£5
K	£5
M	£10
N	£12
O	£5
R	£5
S	£20
T	£20

Peckham New Town K	£7
O	£5
R	£5
Peckham Rye J	£5
N	£10
O	£5
R	£5
Pentonville C	£25
D	£60
G	£10
H	£10
J	£5
O	£5
R	£5
Petersham G	£17
J	£7
K	£5
Piccadilly B	£30
C	£20
D	£75
E	£25
G	£10
J	£5
K	£5
L	£5
M	£10
N	£10
O	£5
P	£5
R	£5
Pimlico B	£20
E	£25
F	£75
G	£10
J	£5
K	£5
L	£5
M	£7
O	£5
P	£5
R	£5
Pitfield St. E	£25
F	£85
Plaistow G	£8
J	£5
M	£10
Plumstead K	£5
R	£10
Poplar J	£5
K	£5
M	£10
N	£12
O	£5
P	£7
R	£7
Portland Sq. A	£75
Portland St. A	£75
B	£25
Portland Town J	£5
K	£5
M	£10
N	£12
O	£5
Portugal St. J	£5
K	£5
L	£5
M	£8
N	£10
O	£5
P	£5
R	£5
Potters Bar J	£5
M	£5

Pratt St.,	
Lambeth E	£30
G	£12
Princes St.,	
Leicester Sq. O	£5
R	£5
Putney A	£75
G	£15
J	£5
K	£5
L	£5
M	£8
N	£12
O	£5
R	£5
S	£20
T	£20
Queens Elm H	£10
J	£5
K	£5
L	£5
M	£7
O	£5
R	£7
Queen St.,	
Cheapside B	£30
G	£10
J	£5
K	£5
L	£5
M	£8
O	£5
P	£5
Rainham J	£7
Ratcliff J	£5
R	£7
Ratcliff Cross E	£30
L	£5
M	£7
Red Lion Sq. B	£40
Red Lion St. (Holborn)	
K	£5
O	£5
P	£5
R	£5
Regent St. J	£5
K	£5
L	£5
O	£7
P	£5
R	£5
Regent St.,	
Westminster J	£7
M	£7
Richmond A	£75
B	£25
C	£25
D	£50
E	£25
G	£10
H	£6
M	£7
O	£5
P	£5
S	£10
T	£8
Richmond Hill J	£5
Roehampton J	£5
K	£5
O	£5
Romford J	£5
N	£10
T	£20

Rotherhithe G	£10	O	£5	Stockwell Green K	£5
J	£7	P	£5	P	£5
K	£7	R	£5	Q	£35
L	£5	Skinner St. O	£5	R	£5
R	£8	R	£5	Stoke Newington A	£75
Royal Arcade J	£5	Sloane Sq. B	£35	B	£20
M	£12	Sloane St. B	£35	K	£5
N	£10	G	£7	M	£6
St. Agnes Place G	£10	H	£7	O	£5
J	£5	J	£5	R	£5
St. George's Fields		K	£5	S	£8
J	£10	M	£7	T	£7
St. James' St. A	£75	N	£10	Store St. J	£5
J	£10	R	£5	L	£5
K	£10	Smithfield Bars O	£6	M	£10
L	£7	R	£5	O	£5
M	£8	Snaresbrook C	£25	R	£5
N	£8	Snow Hill B	£25	Strand B	£15
O	£5	Somers Town G	£10	C	£15
P	£7	H	£8	D	£50
R	£5	J	£5	E	£20
St. John St. E	£25	M	£10	F	£50
G	£10	S	£15	G	£5
J	£5	Southall J	£5	H	£5
M	£7	M	£6	J	£4
N	£10	Southampton Court G	£6	K	£8
O	£5	J	£5	L	£4
P	£7	K	£5	M	£5
R	£5	L	£5	N	£8
St. John's Wood O	£5	N	£7	O	£4
R	£5	P	£5	P	£5
St. Martins Lane J	£5	Q	£35	Q	£25
N	£15	R	£5	R	£4
St. Martins le Grand		Southampton Row O	£10	Stratford B	£20
B	£25	R	£8	H	£10
E	£25	South Audley St. E	£35	L	£5
F	£75	G	£15	M	£6
G	£10	J	£5	N	£8
St. Mary at Hill K	£6	K	£5	O	£8
St. Mary Cray J	£5	L	£5	S	£8
O	£5	O	£5	T	£17
St. Paul's		R	£8	Stratford S.O. G	£15
Churchyard B	£25	South End, Lewisham		Streatham B	£25
E	£25	E	£25	G	£10
G	£10	G	£10	J	£5
N	£10	J	£5	M	£8
Saville Place,		R	£5	N	£10
Lambeth J	£5	Southgate B	£25	R	£5
L	£5	G	£10	Sunbury E	£25
M	£7	J	£5	J	£5
O	£5	K	£5	K	£5
Shackelwell J	£5	N	£10	N	£8
L	£5	South Lambeth J	£5	O	£5
O	£5	O	£5	R	£8
P	£10	S	£10	Sussex Place K	£6
Shadwell G	£10	Stamford Hill J	£5	O	£5
J	£5	K	£5	R	£5
L	£5	M	£10	Sutton K	£6
R	£7	R	£10	O	£5
Shepherds Bush J	£5	Stanmore J	£7	Swan St. B	£25
R	£5	K	£5	E	£25
Shooters Hill B	£25	R	£10	G	£6
G	£6	Stepney G	£10	Sydenham G	£6
J	£5	J	£7	N	£7
M	£6	L	£7	S	£20
N	£10	O	£5	T	£10
R	£5	R	£8	Tabernacle Sq. K	£8
Shoreditch A	£75	Stockwell G	£6	Tavistock Place J	£5
B	£25	J	£5	K	£5
E	£25	K	£5	M	£12
G	£8	M	£6	Teddington E	£25
J	£5	O	£5	G	£7
L	£5	R	£5	J	£5
M	£6			K	£5
N	£10			M	£7

O	£5	K	£5	Walthamstow G	£10
R	£6	L	£5	H	£10
Temple K	£5	M	£6	Walworth B	£25
O	£5	O	£5	G	£10
Thames St. A	£85	P	£5	J	£5
G	£10	R	£5	K	£5
J	£5	Tulse Hill O	£5	M	£10
M	£10	R	£5	N	£12
O	£5	Turnham Green C	£25	O	£5
Thayer St. J	£5	D	£60	R	£5
L	£7	G	£10	S	£18
M	£10	H	£10	T	£18
O	£7	K	£5	Wandsworth A	£75
R	£5	M	£6	C	£50
Theobalds Rd B	£30	N	£7	G	£10
Throgmorton St. O	£6	O	£5	J	£5
R	£5	R	£5	K	£5
Titchfield Pl. A	£100	Twickenham E	£20	M	£10
Tooley St. A	£75	G	£6	N	£12
E	£25	J	£5	Q	£60
G	£10	K	£5	R	£7
J	£5	M	£6	S	£18
K	£5	N	£7	Wanstead O	£5
L	£5	O	£5	Wapping A	£75
M	£10	R	£5	B	£20
O	£5	Union St.,		E	£25
R	£5	Southwark G	£6	G	£10
Tooting H	£10	O	£5	J	£5
J	£5	R	£5	L	£5
S	£15	Upper Baker St. J	£5	M	£8
T	£15	K	£5	N	£10
Tooting, Upper M	£10	P	£7	O	£5
N	£13	R	£5	R	£5
O	£5	Upper Berkeley St. G	£6	Wapping Dock G	£10
Torrington Place J	£7	J	£5	J	£5
L	£7	K	£5	L	£5
M	£10	M	£6	Wardour St. G	£10
N	£5	R	£5	Watling St. A	£90
Tottenham G	£6	Upper Clapton O	£7	E	£30
H	£6	R	£5	O	£7
J	£5	Upper Edmonton G	£10	R	£5
K	£5	L	£5	Wellclose Sq. G	£10
L	£5	N	£12	M	£10
M	£6	O	£5	Welling J	£5
N	£7	Upper Holloway J	£5	L	£5
R	£8	M	£6	R	£7
S	£18	R	£7	West Ham C	£25
T	£18	Upper Seymour St. B	£25	G	£10
Tottenham Court E	£25	E	£25	J	£5
F	£75	F	£75	L	£5
G	£6	M	£12	West Wickham R	£7
J	£5	Upper St., Islington		Whetstone G	£15
M	£6	H	£12	R	£7
Tottenham Court Rd		Vauxhall B	£25	S	£20
A	£75	G	£10	T	£18
D	£80	J	£5	Whips Cross G	£10
E	£20	K	£5	H	£10
F	£75	O	£5	J	£5
G	£6	R	£5	L	£5
J	£5	Vigo Lane O	£5	O	£5
L	£5	P	£6	Whitechapel A	£75
M	£6	R	£5	E	£35
O	£5	Vigo St. P	£6	G	£10
R	£5	Waddon J	£5	J	£5
Tottenham Court		Walcot Place, Lambeth		M	£10
Terrace E	£25	G	£10	N	£10
G	£10	J	£5	O	£5
Totteridge B	£60	K	£5	R	£5
G	£6	Walham Green H	£6	Whitechapel Rd G	£10
H	£7	J	£5	J	£5
K	£5	K	£5	L	£5
M	£6	L	£5	M	£10
N	£7	N	£10	N	£12
Tower St. E	£25	O	£5	Whitecross St. J	£5
J	£5	Waltham Abbey J	£5	L	£5
				R	£5

Whitehall A	£100
B	£25
C	£25
D	£50
Whitton H	£10
R	£5
Willisdon J	£5
R	£5
Wimbledon B	£40
G	£10
J	£5
K	£5
M	£10
N	£15
R	£5
Winchmore Hill J	£5
K	£5
Wood St. F	£75
G	£12
J	£7
Woodford G	£10
H	£10
M	£10
N	£12
O	£5
P	£5
S	£12
Woodford Bridge G	£10
M	£10
R	£10
Woolwich A	£75
B	£20
C	£35
E	£20
F	£75
G	£6
J	£5
K	£5
L	£5
M	£6
N	£7
O	£5
R	£5
S	£20
T	£10
Woolwich Common R	£7
Worton H	£10

Instructional Markings

| 2/32 | 2/37 | 2/39 |

2/32	Charge Mark 2	....	3.00
2/33	As above but 3	....	7.50
2/34	As above but 4	....	35.00
2/35	As above but 5	....	50.00
2/36	As above but 6	....	75.00
2/37	Erasure stamps, stars, spirals etc., overcharge marks	....	10.00
2/38	TP rate 2, boxed or unboxed	....	5.00
2/39	Too late for Morning Post (various types)	....	70.00
2/40	To be delivered by 10 o'clock on Sunday morning (various types)		40.00

3. Marks of the Provincial Post to 1839 - England & Wales

Handstamps were struck on letters despatched from or arriving at post towns.

<u>Marks introduced after 1839 are not included</u>. The number of post offices increased dramatically in the 1840s, largely using the sans serif version of type O. Listing of these marks is beyond the scope of this chapter. Towns and counties shown in brackets are given for identification: they do not form part of the postmark. Cross Post marks are excluded.

Values shown in this chapter are not easy to determine. We have examined lists of relative rarity (especially in the County Catalogues of Willcocks and Jay - see Bibliography), dealers' lists and material in Exchange Packets (especially those of the British Postmark Society). Many covers for sale are well below the quality standards which are defined in this volume and for which the prices here apply. We have made efforts to check all the data including archaic spellings, and we show the spellings as they appear in the postmark.

Key to types: (note not all are illustrated)

A	Distinctive town marks, many variations	S	Mileage before name, 1784-95
B	Abbreviated types	T	Mileage after name, 1784-95
C	One straight line, upper or lower case	U	Mileage in horseshoe
D	Divided words, two or three lines	V	Mileage boxed beneath, 1801-30
E	Undivided words, two or three lines	W	Mileage in bars beneath, 1804-40
F	One straight line, framed by bars, 1720-65	X	Circular dated mileage types, with or without small circles, stars or arcs, 1804-40
G	Convex or concave arc, 1789-1810	Y	Circular undated mileage types, 1809-28
H	Horseshoe, 1789-1801		
J	Reversed horseshoe	Z	Penny Post, unframed
K	Undulating town name	AA	Py Post, boxed
L	Name & date in two straight lines, 1798-1804	BB	Penny Post, boxed
		CC	Penny Post, italic letters, unframed or boxed
M	Circular undated, with stop		
N	Circular undated, with fleurons	FF	Fifth Clause Post, several types
O	Circular undated, with single or double arcs and seriffed letters, from 1820	HH	Paid At, several types
		JJ	Too Late, several types
		MM	Missent to, several types
P	Circular dated, double arcs, from 1829	NN	Returned to, several types
Q	Circular dated, single arc	OO	Addl ½d, on letters to Scotland, several types
R	Straight line, mileage below, 1784-95		

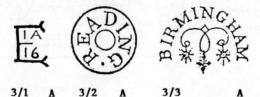

3/1 A	3/2 A	3/3 A	3/4 B

ALCESTER

3/5   C
One straight line,
upper or lower case

NOTTING HAM

3/6   D
Divided words,
two or three lines

BOLTON LEMOORS

3/7   E
Undivided words,
two or three lines

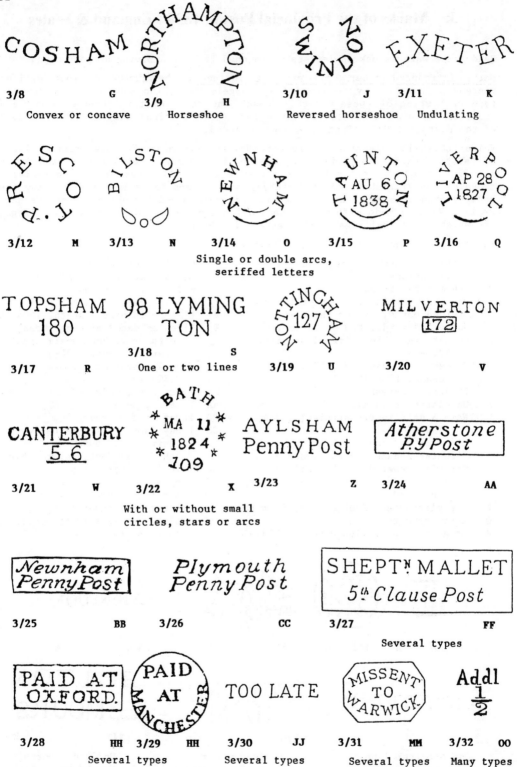

COSHAM

NORTHAMPTON

SWINDON

EXETER

3/8	G	3/9	H	3/10	J	3/11	K
Convex or concave		Horseshoe		Reversed horseshoe		Undulating	

PRESCOT.

BILSTON

NEWNHAM

TAUNTON AU 6 1838

LIVERPOOL AP 28 1827

3/12	M	3/13	N	3/14	O	3/15	P	3/16	Q

Single or double arcs,
seriffed letters

TOPSHAM
180

98 LYMING
TON

NOTTINGHAM 127

MILVERTON
172

3/17	R	3/18	S	3/19	U	3/20	V
		One or two lines					

CANTERBURY
5 6

BATH
* MA 11 *
* 1824 *
109

AYLSHAM
Penny Post

Atherstone
P.y Post

3/21	W	3/22	X	3/23	Z	3/24	AA

With or without small
circles, stars or arcs

Newnham
Penny Post

Plymouth
Penny Post

SHEPT.N MALLET
5.th Clause Post

3/25	BB	3/26	CC	3/27	FF
				Several types	

PAID AT
OXFORD.

PAID AT MANCHESTER

TOO LATE

MISSENT
TO
WARWICK

Addl
1/2

3/28	HH	3/29	HH	3/30	JJ	3/31	MM	3/32	OO
Several types		Several types		Several types		Several types		Many types	

Abbots Bromley O	£30
Abbotts Ann O	£50
CC	£75
Aberayon W erased	£10
Aberayron O	£10
W	£30
Abercarne CC	£15
Aberdovey C	£30
Aberford O	£30
Abergaveney D	£75
Abergavenney D	£50
Abergavenny D	£75
H	£50
P	£4
S	£50
V	£15
W	£10
Y	£10
Y erased	£15
Z	£50
BB	£30
JJ	£30
Abergele C	£50
O	£10
V	£15
V erased	£15
Aberistwith V	£10
W	£10
W erased	£15
JJ	£50
Aberystwyth D	£50
P	£2
Abingdon C	£30
D	£75
G	£30
O	£10
P	£2
S	£75
V	£15
Y	£15
Y erased	£15
BB	£50
HH	£50
Ab.n.don B	£200
Accrington P	£4
Acle R	£30
W	£50
Adderbury FF	£150
Addingham C boxed	£50
O	£30
Addington Place (Ramsgate) C	£50
Addlestone CC	£30
Aigburth (L'pool) O	£30
Albrighton O	£30
Alcester C	£30
Aldborough (Durham) CC	£30
Aldborough (Suffolk) D	£100
O	£15
V	£75
Aldborough (Yorks) CC	£50
Aldbourn C	£50
W	£30
W erased	£30
Aldbourne O	£30
Aldeburgh (Suffolk) O	£15
P	£6
W	£30
Alford C	£30
O	£30
W	£15
Alfreton P	£4
V	£15
W	£5
W erased	£5
Allendale CC	£50
Allesley O	£50
Allonby O	£15
CC	£75
Alnewick C	£75
Alnmouth CC	£50
Alnwick C	£30
H	£30
M	£50
O	£10
P	£4
V	£15
W	£15
W erased	£15
Y	£15
Y erased	£10
BB	£75
CC	£75
Alphington CC	£75
Alresford (Hants) C	£30
D	£75
O	£30
P	£4
S	£75
V	£15
W	£15
Y	£15
Y erased	£10
Alrewas C	£50
Alston O	£15
Z	£75
Z distinctive	£75
HH	£75
Althorn (Essex) CC	£150
Althorne CC	£150
Alton (Hants) C	£50
G	£30
O	£30
P	£4
S	£75
V	£15
Y	£30
Y erased	£30
Z	£50
AA	£75
Altrincham C	£30
G	£50
O	£30
P	£4
BB	£50
Altringham C	£30
Ambleside P	£2
CC	£75
Amersham C	£50
P	£4
S	£100
V	£15
W	£15
Y	£50
Y erased	£30
Amesbury C	£30
P	£4
S	£75
V	£30
V erased	£15
CC	£50
MM	£100
Amlwch CC	£50
Ampthill C	£75
C	£50
O	£20
P	£4
V	£15
Ancoats/Manchester E	£30
Ancoats/Manchr A	£75
Andover C	£50
G	£50
P	£2
R	£100
V	£15
W	£10
W erased	£15
CC	£50
Andover Road O	£30
P	£4
Andoversford O	£15
Y	£30
Appleby C	£30
H	£75
P	£2
R	£100
V	£30
W	£15
W erased	£15
BB	£75
Appleshaw O	£50
CC	£75
Ardwick/Manchester E	£30
Ardwick/Manchr A	£30
Arrington O	£30
W	£50
Arundel C	£50
G	£50
P	£4
S	£75
W	£15
Y	£10
Z	£30
AA	£15
Ashborn S	£100
V	£30
Ashborne C	£75
D	£50
Ashbourn D	£15
O	£10
P	£4
V	£15
W	£10
JJ	£75
Ashbourne W	£10
Z	£100
Ashburton D boxed	£100
H	£75
P	£4
R	£50
W	£30
Y	£15
Y erased	£15
Z	£30
AA distinctive	£30
Ashby O	£30
O	£15
P	£4
V	£30
W	£15
BB	£50
Ashby de la Zouch C	£30
Ashby/Z D	£100
Ashcott C	£15
Ashford (Kent) D	£75
G	£50
P	£2
V	£15
W	£15
W erased	£10
Z	£30
Ashford Kent S	£100
Ashford Kt C	£100
Ashtead Row (B'ham) C	£15
Ashton CC	£30
Ashton under Line P	£15
BB	£30
Askrigg CC	£50
Aston under L BB	£100
Athenaeum/Upper Parade (Leamington Spa) E two line	£30
Atherstone C	£30
D	£75
O	£10
P	£2
V	£30
W	£10
Y	£10
Z	£50
AA	£30
BB	£30
Attleboro C	£75
W	£15
Attleborough D	£75
O	£10
P	£2
S	£100
V	£15
Z	£75
BB	£75
JJ	£50
Attlebro Z	£75
Auckland C	£30
H	£30
O	£15
BB	£50
Aulcester D	£50
O	£10
Austerlands PP. AA distinctive	£75
Aversham D	£30
Axbridge C	£15
V	£15
Axminster D	£75
P	£4
W	£30
Y	£15
Z	£30
AA	£15
Aycliffe CC	£75
Aye C	£150
Aylesbury D	£50
G	£30
P	£4
S	£75
V	£15
W	£15
W erased	£30
AA	£30
Aylesham D	£150
Aylsham C	£50
D	£150
O	£10
P	£2
S	£100
V	£15
W	£10
Z	£75
JJ	£30
Ayton CC	£50
Backbarrow O	£15
Bacup O	£15
Bagshot C	£30
D	£50
P	£4
V	£30
V erased	£30
Z	£30
AA	£30
BB	£30
CC	£75
Bakewell C	£75
D	£50
O	£15
P	£2
V	£30
V erased	£15
Bala A (circular)	£50
C	£15
P	£2
R	£50
V	£10
Y	£15

Baldock O	£30		
P	£4		
V	£50		
W	£30		
Bamborough CC	£50		
Bampton (Oxon) CC	£50		
Bampton D (Devon) O	£15		
P	£4		
V	£50		
Banbury D	£50		
F	£75		
G	£30		
P	£2		
S	£75		
V	£10		
W	£10		
X	£10		
Y	£10		
Z	£50		
JJ	£50		
Bangor C	£30		
P	£2		
R	£100		
V	£30		
W	£10		
X	£10		
X erased	£30		
Z	£30		
AA	£15		
BB	£30		
CC	£50		
HH	£100		
JJ	£30		
MM	£75		
Banstead O	£75		
Barford (Wks) CC	£75		
Barham O	£50		
Barkhamsted D	£50		
F	£100		
Barkley C	£100		
Barmouth C	£50		
O	£15		
P	£2		
V	£30		
V erased	£50		
Z	£30		
BB	£30		
Barnard Castle D	£50		
W	£10		
W erased	£10		
Barnards Castle D	£50		
O	£10		
V	£15		
Barnard's Castle P	£2		
Barnby Z	£75		
Barnd Castle V	£30		
Barnds Castle H	£50		
Barnesly D	£100		
W	£15		
Barnet C	£50		
K	£75		
S	£75		
W	£15		
W erased	£30		
Z	£50		
AA	£75		
BB	£75		
CC	£75		
JJ	£50		
MM	£75		
Barnsley (Yorks) C	£30		
G	£50		
H	£50		
P	£2		
V	£10		
W	£10		
Y	£10		
JJ	£15		
MM	£50		

Barnstable C	£100		
D	£100		
AA	£30		
Barnstaple C	£250		
D	£75		
H	£75		
P	£30		
V	£75		
W	£30		
X	£50		
AA	£50		
BB	£50		
CC	£50		
Barrow (Lincs) CC	£75		
Barrow (Yorks) CC	£75		
Barrow on Humber C	£50		
Barrow upon Humber O	£50		
Bartley CC	£50		
Barton (Lincs) C	£50		
C framed	£75		
O	£50		
V	£30		
W	£30		
Barton (Staffs) C	£50		
Barton (Yorks) D	£30		
V	£15		
W	£15		
Barton on Humber O	£30		
Barwick C	£100		
D	£100		
Baschurch CC	£30		
Basingstoke C	£50		
D	£30		
G	£50		
G two lines	£60		
O	£50		
P	£2		
V	£15		
W	£10		
JJ	£50		
Bath C	£15		
P	£2		
R	£75		
S	£75		
V	£50		
X	£15		
X erased	£15		
Z	£30		
Z dated	£15		
AA	£30		
AA unframed	˜30		
JJ	£15		
MM	£50		
Returned from	£75		
Batley O	£15		
P	£4		
Battel C	£100		
S	£100		
Battle O	£15		
P	£4		
V	£50		
W	£30		
Z	£75		
AA	£75		
CC	£100		
MM	£100		
Bautry			
C distinctive	£150		
Bawtry C	£30		
P	£2		
R	£75		
V	£15		
W	£10		
W erased	£15		
Z	£50		
B Bridge (Boroughbridge)			
C	£150		

Beaconsfield C	£75		
D	£50		
P	£4		
W	£30		
W erased	£30		
Z	£75		
Beaford CC	£30		
Beaminster C	£30		
O	£50		
Beaulieu CC	£50		
Beaumaris C	£15		
O	£5		
P	£2		
V	£15		
W	£10		
HH	£150		
MM	£150		
Beccles C	£50		
O	£10		
V	£30		
Beckington O	£30		
Beckington-S (Som)			
O distinctive	£150		
Beconsfield V	£30		
Bedal C	£50		
V	£15		
Bedale C	£30		
H	£30		
O	£30		
P	£2		
V	£30		
W	£10		
Y	£30		
Z	£30		
AA	£15		
CC	£75		
Bedall C	£100		
D	£50		
Bedfont O	£100		
CC	£100		
Bedford C	£50		
G	£50		
O	£15		
P	£4		
S	£75		
V	£15		
W	£15		
JJ	£30		
MM	£75		
Bedford Place (S'ton)			
C	£50		
O	£50		
Bedlington CC	£50		
Bedwin C	£50		
O	£30		
Bedwin-Gt V	£30		
Bedworth O	£30		
Beer CC	£75		
Beeston O	£30		
BB	£30		
Belford C	£30		
D	£50		
H	£30		
O	£15		
P	£4		
V	£30		
W	£15		
Y	£15		
JJ	£50		
MM	£75		
Belper O	£50		
P	£6		
Beminster V	£30		
Benenden CC	£50		
Bensington V	£30		
Benson P	£4		
CC	£50		

Berkeley C	£75		
O	£10		
V	£15		
Berkhempstead S	£75		
S erased	£75		
V	£15		
W	£30		
Y	£50		
Y erased	£50		
JJ	£75		
Berkhemstead G	£75		
P	£4		
Bermingam (error) E	£150		
Bernard Castle D	£50		
Berriew O	£15		
Berstead Kent (error)			
O	£30		
Berwick C	£30		
D	£50		
F in circle	£30		
M in doub circle	£30		
P	£4		
Q	£4		
R	£75		
R framed	£15		
V	£15		
W distinctive			
Scottish type	£30		
X	£10		
X erased	£10		
Z	£30		
JJ	£30		
MM	£50		
OO	£12		
Besthorpe O	£75		
Beverley C	£30		
D	£50		
P	£2		
V	£15		
W	£15		
Y	£30		
Y erased	£15		
JJ	£15		
Beverly C	£50		
H	£30		
Bevois CC	£75		
Bewdley C	£15		
F	£75		
G	£100		
J	£50		
P	£2		
S	£75		
V	£30		
W	£15		
X	£15		
X erased	£10		
Y	£15		
Z	£30		
AA	£15		
BB	£50		
CC	£75		
MM	£75		
Bexhill O	£10		
V	£50		
Bexley O	£50		
Bicester C	£50		
P	£2		
S	£75		
V	£15		
W	£10		
X	£10		
Y	£10		
Biddeford H	£75		
V	£50		
Biddenden C	£75		
O	£50		
V	£30		
V erased	£15		

Bideford C	£50	Bishops Waltham Y	£30	Boroughbridge D	£30	Z	£30
P	£4	Y erased	£10	H	£30	AA	£75
W	£15	Bishops Waltm V	£30	V	£15	BB	£75
W erased	£30	Bissiter F	£150	W	£10	Braintrie D	£150
Z	£75	Bittern CC	£50	Borrough Bridg D	£100	Braintry C	£150
Bidford O	£30	Blackburn C	£50	Boscastle O	£50	Bramfordspeke CC	£75
Biggleswade D	£75	D	£50	Boston C	£50	Bramham O	£30
O	£15	G	£50	P	£4	Brampton (Cumbd) P	£2
P	£4	M	£30	R	£15	W	£15
S	£75	P	£4	S	£75	W erased	£15
V	£15	V	£50	W	£15	Brancaster CC	£30
W	£10	W	£15	X	£15	Brandon C	£50
Billericay P	£2	W erased	£30	Z	£75	P	£6
W	£75	AA	£50	Botesdale BB	£75	V	£30
W erased	£15	BB	£50	Botley CC	£30	W	£15
Billingshurst		CC	£50	Bourn C	£50	W erased	£30
O (red)	£50	HH	£100	S	£30	Brannston C	£75
CC	£100	JJ	£30	V	£30	Brasted O	£30
Bilston C	£50	MM	£75	W	£30	Brecknock C	£15
N	£150	Blackpool V	£50	Bourne O	£30	D	£50
Bilstone O	£30	CC	£30	Y	£30	V	£15
P	£6	Blackwater O	£50	Y erased	£30	W	£15
Bingham C	£30	CC	£50	Bournmouth CC	£50	Brecknock.L	
C dated	£100	Blackwood CC	£15	Bowes O	£30	M (double circ)	£75
O	£50	Blakeney O	£15	Bowness CC	£50	Brecon C	£10
Bingley C	£75	Blandford C	£30	Boxford C	£75	O	£5
O	£30	D	£30	D	£100	P	£2
P	£2	J	£50	V	£50	Y	£15
R	£30	P	£2	W	£30	CC	£50
V	£30	S	£75	Bozeat C	£50	JJ	£50
Birch CC	£50	V	£15	V	£75	Breewood C	£50
Birchington CC	£30	W	£10	Bps Auckland V	£15	O	£50
Birkenhead C	£75	Z	£30	Bps Stortford Z	£30	Brenchley O	£50
P	£6	Z dated	£15	AA	£50	CC	£50
Birmingham		JJ	£30	MM	£100	Brentwood C	£75
A (chandelier)	£500	MM	£75	Bp Stortford D	£100	G	£50
A (3 lines inside		Bletchingley W	£50	Brackley C	£75	P	£4
21mm circle)	£250	Bletchingly C	£30	F	£150	S	£100
B	£250	Blockley O	£15	O	£15	V	£50
C	£30	Blofield CC	£30	Q	£2	W	£50
D	£30	Bloxwich O	£50	S	£100	Y	£30
J	£30	Blyth CC	£50	V	£30	Y erased	£15
P	£2	Bocking G	£100	W	£15	Brereton C	£150
R	£100	Bodedern CC	£30	W erased	£5	Bridgend H	£100
S	£100	Bodmin C	£30	Bracknell G	£50	O	£15
V	£15	O	£50	O	£15	P	£2
W	£50	P	£2	P	£6	V	£30
X	£10	V	£30	W	£15	W	£10
AA	£50	W	£30	Bradford-W (Wilts) C	£50	Bridgenorth D	£30
HH	£10	Y	£15	D	£50	O	£30
JJ	£10	Bognor C	£50	Q	£6	P	£2
MM	£50	P	£6	S	£75	S	£50
Birstal O	£30	Bolingbroke V	£50	V	£30	Bri.water B	£150
BB	£50	V erased	£50	Y	£15	Bridgewater C	£50
Bishop Auckland P	£2	Bollington CC	£75	BB	£50	D	£30
Bishop Castle M	£10	Bolton C	£75	Bradford-Wilts P	£4	P	£2
Bishops Auckd V	£15	P	£4	Bradford (Yorks) C	£30	S	£75
Bishops Auckland D	£50	V	£15	D	£100	V	£30
Bishop's Auckland O	£10	X	£15	W	£10	W	£30
Bishops Castle D	£50	Z	£50	HH	£15	Y	£30
H	£30	JJ	£50	MM	£75	Y erased	£30
V	£15	Bolton-Le-Moors E	£30	Bradford Y C	£30	Z	£30
W	£10	O distinctive	£150	D	£30	AA	£30
Bishops-Cleeve O	£15	Bolton-Le-Sands CC	£50	P	£2	BB	£30
Bishops Stortd V	£30	Bookend CC	£75	V	£15	CC	£30
Bishop's Stortford P	£2	Bootle (Cumberland)		W	£10	JJ	£50
S	£75	C	£30	Bradford Yorks P	£2	MM	£50
Bishops Stortford		O	£15	AA	£50	Bridgnorth C	£50
G	£75	CC	£50	BB	£50	D	£50
Y	£50	Bootle (L'pool) N	£150	JJ	£15	O	£30
Y erased	£30	O	£15	MM	£150	V	£10
CC	£75	CC	£50	Bradwell V	£75	W	£10
(see also Bishops Torford				CC	£75	Y	£15
below, also Bps Stortford)				Brailes O	£15	Y erased	£15
Bishopsthorpe O	£30	Boreham (Sussex) C	£75	Braintree C	£75	Bridgwater D	£75
Bishopstoke CC	£50	O	£30	P	£6	Bridlington D	£50
Bishops Torford D	£150	Borobridge P	£2	V	£75	M	£30
Bishop Stortford D	£75	W	£10	W	£30	O	£30
W	£30			Y	£50	Q	£2

V	£15
W	£15
W erased	£15
Bridport C	£30
D	£75
P	£2
R (lower case)	£100
S	£75
V	£15
W	£15
Z	£30
Brierley Hill (Birm'ham)	
E	£15
Brigg C	£50
O	£15
P	£4
V	£30
W	£15
W erased	£30
BB	£50
Brighouse O	£30
BB	£30
Brighthelmstone D	£75
G	£75
S	£100
Brighton C	£75
G	£50
P	£2
Q	£2
V	£30
W	£15
X	£10
Z	£50
BB	£15
CC	£50
JJ	£50
MM	£100
NN	£100
Bristol	
A (capital 'B')	£75
A (double circle)	£500
A (dotted circle)	£75
C	£30
J	£75
K	£50
L	£30
P	£2
Q	£2
S	£100
V	£50
X	£10
Z	£50
Z dated	£15
AA	£50
FF	£75
HH	£15
JJ	£15
MM	£50
OO	£100
Bristol St (Birmingham)	
C	£30
Brittell Lane CC	£50
Brixham H	£75
M	£50
P	£6
V	£50
W	£50
Y	£30
Broadclist CC	£50
Broadstairs N	£150
Broadwas O	£10
Broadway C	£50
O	£10
P	£2
S	£100
V	£30
W	£15
X undated	£15
Brockley	
(Bristol) CC	£50

Bromley D	£150
G	£50
K	£50
O	£15
R	£100
V	£15
W	£15
W erased	£30
BB	£75
Bromley K (Kent) S	£100
Bromsgrove D	£30
Bromyard C	£75
D	£100
J	£75
O	£15
P	£4
V	£30
Y	£30
Brooke CC	£75
Brookland O	£50
Broomsgrove D	£30
O	£10
P	£2
S	£75
W	£30
Y	£15
Z	£100
CC	£75
Broomyard C	£75
Broseley C	£50
O	£15
Brough (W'morland) C	£30
O	£10
V	£15
W	£15
W erased	£10
Broughton (Cumberland)	
C	£30
Broughton (Hants) O	£50
P	£6
CC	£30
Broughton in Furness	
O	£15
Broyntliss O	£30
Bruton C	£50
O	£30
V	£30
W	£30
Brynmaur O	£30
Brynnllis O	£50
Bubwith O	£30
Buckden V	£30
W	£50
Buckingham D	£75
F	£150
P	£2
S	£75
V	£15
W	£15
W erased	£30
CC	£75
Builth H	£50
O	£10
P	£4
V	£15
W	£15
Bungay C	£50
P	£4
S	£100
V	£50
W	£30
W erased	£15
Bungey C	£100
Buntingford G	£75
P	£6
W	£30
W erased	£50
Burford C	£15
D	£50
P	£2

V	£10
V erased	£30
HH	£150
Burley CC	£50
Burnham (Berks) CC	£50
Burnham (Nfk) C	£75
D	£50
O	£30
V	£30
W	£50
BB	£75
Burnham-Somst O	£30
Burnley C	£50
H	£50
P	£4
V	£30
W	£30
Y	£30
JJ	£150
Burntwood (Essex) D	£150
Bursledon CC	£50
Burslem O	£30
Burton (Staffs) C	£50
Z	£50
Burton-K (Westm'd) H	£30
Burton-L C	£75
Burton on T (Staffs)	
V	£30
W	£15
Burton on Trent D	£50
P one arc	£2
S	£75
W	£15
W erased	£15
JJ	£30
Burton-OT (Staffs) V	£50
Burton-W (Westm'd) M	£30
O	£15
P	£4
Y	£15
Y erased	£10
Burwarton CC	£50
Burwash CC	£50
Burwaston	
CC (error)	£100
Bury (Lancs) C	£50
Bury.L. (Lancs)	
R distinctive	£50
V	£30
W	£30
W (erased)	£15
Z	£75
Bury Lanc Q	£4
Bury Lancashire Z	£50
Bury Lancr AA	£75
Bury.S H	£50
Bury (Suffolk) C	£75
G	£50
H	£50
Bury St E V	£50
Bury St.Edmds Z	£50
Bury St Edmonds Q	£6
V	£50
W	£30
Bury St.Edms W	£30
Bury St Edmunds D	£75
Q	£2
S	£100
W	£30
BB three line	£75
CC	£75
MM	£75
Bushey CC	£75
Buxted CC	£100
Buxton C	£50
O	£15
P	£4
V	£15
W	£50
MM	£100

Caemarthen D	£15
Caernarvon P	£2
Caerphilly C	£30
CC	£75
Caistor-L (Lincs) O	£50
V	£30
Y inside circle	£50
Calderbridge CC	£50
Callington C	£30
P	£2
V	£15
Y	£15
Y erased	£15
CC	£50
Calne C	£30
O	£30
P	£15
S	£75
V	£15
V erased	£15
Calverly (T.Wells) O	£30
Cambourn C	£50
Cambourne C	£15
P	£2
AA	£50
CC	£30
Cambridg C	£150
Cambridge C	£30
D	£30
G	£15
P	£2
Q	£2
R	£30
S	£70
V	£30
W	£5
X	£5
Y	£5
BB	£5
Cambridge Gloucr CC	£50
Camden (Glos) C	£100
P	£4
X undated	£30
X erased	£15
CC	£75
JJ	£30
Camelford C	£50
D	£50
O	£10
P	£2
W	£30
Y	£15
Y erased	£30
Cannock O	£50
Can Office (Mont)	
Q undated	£50
Canterbury C	£50
D	£30
G	£30
H	£30
P	£4
S	£50
V	£15
W	£10
X	£10
X erased	£10
AA	£30
CC	£50
Cardif C	£100
Cardiff C	£15
D	£75
H	£30
K	£30
P	£2
V	£10
W	£15
X	£10
AA	£15
JJ	£30
MM	£75

Cardigan C	£30	P	£5	X erased	£10	CC	£30
P	£4	S	£100	AA	£30	MM	£50
V	£10	V	£50	BB	£15	Chipping Norton D	£50
Y	£15	V erased	£75	JJ	£15	G	£50
Y erased	£10	Cefn Bedd C	£50	MM	£50	O	£10
Carleon O	£10	Cefn Bychan C	£75	Chepstow C	£15	P	£2
W	£30	Cemmes C	£30	J	£75	V	£30
W erased	£30	Chaddesley C	£75	P	£2	W	£10
Carlisle C	£30	Chagford CC	£50	V	£10	Chipping Ongar O	£30
D	£50	Chalford (Glos) O	£30	W	£10	P	£6
H	£30	P	£6	Y	£35	Chipping Sodbury O	£15
M	£50	AA	£30	BB	£30	Chirk C	£30
P	£2	CC	£75	Chertsey P	£4	C boxed	£30
R	£50	Chapel in Frith D	£30	V	£15	AA	£30
U distinctive		Chapel in Le Frith O	£50	CC	£75	Chobham O	£50
Scottish type	£50	Chapel Le Frith C	£15	MM	£100	CC	£75
V	£30	Chard C	£50	Chesham C	£50	Chorley C	£50
W	£15	O	£15	G	£50	G	£50
X	£10	P	£2	V	£30	O	£30
X erased	£10	S	£75	V erased	£30	P	£4
JJ	£100	W	£15	Chester		V	£50
MM	£75	Y	£15	A (capital 'C')	£150	JJ	£75
OO	£12	Y erased	£15	C	£30	Christchurch D	£30
Carlisle St (Hull) C	£30	AA	£50	D	£75	O	£30
Carlton on Trent O	£30	CC	£50	H	£30	P	£8
Carmarthen C	£15	JJ	£30	L	£50	V	£30
D	£15	Charing C	£30	P	£2	V erased	£30
H	£30	O	£30	R	£75	CC three line	£75
P	£2	V	£30	V	£50	Chudleigh C	£75
Q	£4	W	£30	X	£10	D	£75
V	£15	Charlton Kings O	£15	BB	£30	K	£75
W	£15	Charmouth C	£30	CC	£50	P	£4
X	£10	O	£30	JJ	£15	V	£50
BB	£30	P	£2	MM	£50	W	£30
MM	£150	Chartham CC	£50	Chesterfeild (error)		W erased	£30
Carnarvon C	£30	Chatham C	£30	D	£150	Z	£50
D	£50	G	£30	Chesterfield C	£50	AA	£75
P	£2	P	£2	D	£50	CC	£50
V	£15	V	£10	G	£50	Chumleigh P	£8
W	£10	W	£10	P	£2	V	£30
W erased	£15	Chatteris C	£100	V	£15	Y	£50
AA	£30	O	£30	W	£30	Y erased	£50
HH	£150	P	£4	X	£30	Church Stoke O	£50
JJ	£30	V	£75	X erased	£30	Church Stretton D	£50
Carnforth CC	£50	W	£30	Chester le Street C	£50	V	£10
Carrig-y-Druidion C	£30	W erased	£30	M	£10	Cirencester D	£30
Castle Ashby D	£150	Cheadle (Cheshire) O	£50	P	£2	V	£15
Castle Bromwich (Birm'ham)		BB	£75	Chichester C	£50	W	£15
E	£30	Cheadle (Staffs) C	£50	D	£50	Y	£15
Castle Cary C	£50	H	£75	F	£150	Y erased	£10
D	£50	P	£4	G	£50	BB	£50
O	£30	R	£75	P	£2	Clare G	£75
S	£100	V	£30	S	£100	P	£6
V	£50	V erased	£30	V	£50	W	£30
AA	£30	W	£15	W	£75	W erased	£75
AA erased	£75	Cheetham Hill PP (M'ter)		X	£10	Clay O	£30
Castle Eden C	£50	(distinctive)	£75	Z	£30	W	£50
O	£10	Chelmsford C	£50	AA	£75	Claydon CC	£75
Castle Rising C	£15	D	£50	BB	£30	Cleckheaton O	£30
CC	£30	G	£50	CC	£30	BB	£50
Castleton C	£50	H	£50	JJ	£50	Clenchwarton CC	£75
Castleton-Derbysh O	£50	P	£2	MM	£75	Cleobury CC	£30
Castletown (IOM) D	£500	S	£75	NN	£100	Cleveland Inn W	£50
Castletown Isle of Man		V	£30	Chilbolton CC	£50	W erased	£50
A boxed	£500	W	£15	Chilham CC	£50	Clifton (Bristol) O	£10
Catterick C	£50	Y	£50	Chimley		Clithero H	£50
D	£50	Y erased	£15	D (distinctive)	£75	P	£8
P	£2	Z	£75	Chip-Norton W	£75	V	£50
W	£30	CC	£75	Chip.nham B	£150	W	£30
Y	£15	HH	£150	Chippenham C	£30	W erased	15
Y erased	£15	MM	£75	D	£30	Clitheroe P	£6
Catterick V	£30	NN	£100	P	£4	Clynnog N	£75
Catton CC	£75	Chelmsford/D29 V	£100	S	£50	Coatham Mundeville CC	£75
Cave N/224 V	£30	Cheltenham D	£30	V	£15	Cobham (Surrey) C	£75
Cave S/224 V	£30	P	£2	W	£10	O	£50
Cavendish Bridge V	£50	S	£75	Y	£15	V	£50
Caxton B	£150	V	£15	Y erased	£15	W	£50
C	£100	W	£30	Z	£50	Cobridge Staffs O	£30
O	£30	X	£10	AA	£50		

Cockermouth C	£30			
D	£50			
H	£30			
M	£30			
O	£15			
P	£2			
S	£75			
V	£15			
W	£10			
Y	£10			
Y erased	£30			
Coddenham C	£75			
Colchester C	£30			
D	£75			
G	£50			
H	£75			
P	£2			
S	£100			
V	£30			
W	£15			
X	£5			
X erased	£5			
Z	£15			
AA	£15			
CC	£15			
NN	£75			
Cold Blow Y	£50			
Colebrooke D	£50			
Coleford AA	£30			
BB	£30			
HH	£50			
MM	£50			
Coleshill C	£15			
P	£4			
S	£75			
V	£50			
Collingham O	£30			
Collumpton C	£75			
H	£50			
Colnbrook O	£30			
P	£6			
S	£150			
V	£50			
Z	£30			
AA	£50			
BB	£30			
Colne C	£30			
O	£30			
P	£8			
V	£30			
Colsterworth D	£75			
G	£75			
O	£50			
P	£15			
V	£30			
W	£30			
Y	£15			
Coltishall V	£50			
CC	£75			
Columpton V	£30			
Y	£15			
Y erased	£15			
Colyton CC	£75			
Compton (Devon) CC	£75			
Congleton C	£30			
D	£50			
M	£30			
O	£15			
P	£4			
W	£15			
Y	£15			
HH	£75			
Conway C	£15			
O	£10			
P	£2			
V	£10			
Y	£15			
Copplestone CC	£50			

Corbridge (North'd)	
C framed	£50
Corfe Castle C	£15
D	£50
V	£30
Corsham N	£50
Corwen C	£15
C inside oval	£100
O	£10
P	£2
Y	£30
Cosham G	£30
O	£30
V	£50
Cotherstone CC	£75
Cottingham CC	£75
Coventry C	£30
D	£50
P	£2
S	£75
V	£15
X	£10
X erased	£15
Z	£50
AA	£30
CC	£50
JJ	£30
MM	£75
Cowbridge H	£50
O	£5
P	£2
V	£15
W	£10
Y	£10
Y erased	£10
Cowes (IOW)	
O distinctive	£30
P	£4
W	£15
W erased	£15
Cowfold CC	£75
Cowley Bridge CC	£75
Crabtree CC	£75
Cranbourn C	£50
P	£6
W	£30
Y	£30
Y erased	£15
Cranbrook G	£50
P	£4
S	£75
V	£15
V erased	£15
W	£15
W erased	£15
CC	£50
Crawley P	£6
W	£15
W erased	£30
Z	£50
Crediton C	£75
D	£50
V	£30
W	£15
W erased	£10
AA	£15
Crewkern D	£50
S	£50
W	£30
W erased	£30
Crewkerne C	£50
D	£50
P	£2
W	£30
AA	£30
FF	£100
Crickhowell C	£15
O	£10
P	£2

Z	£50
JJ	£50
Cricklade D	£75
V	£30
V erased	£30
Criklade C	£50
Crockernwell CC	£75
Crofe Castle E	£75
(Corfe Castle)	
Croft CC	£50
Cromer C	£75
O	£15
W	£75
AA	£50
CC	£75
Crookhorn D	£100
Crosby (L'pool) N	£150
O	£30
CC	£50
Cross O	£15
P	£6
BB	£30
CC	£30
Cross Hills C	£50
D	£75
O	£30
Cross In Hand CC	£75
Croyden C	£75
Croydon C	£50
K	£50
V	£15
V erased	£15
CC	£50
Cuckfield P	£6
V	£15
V erased	£30
W	£50
Z	£30
BB	£50
Cullercoats CC	£50
Culliton V	£15
Cullompton P	£4
CC	£30
Cullumpton Z	£50
Curdworth.P.P.	
(distinctive)	£100
Dagenham W	£50
Darking C	£50
D	£100
G	£50
S	£75
V	£30
W	£30
Darlaston O	£50
Darlington C	£50
D	£30
P	£2
R	£75
V	£10
W	£10
X	£10
CC	£100
Dartford C	£30
D	£50
K	£50
O	£15
P	£4
S	£75
V	£15
W	£10
W erased	£15
BB	£30
Dartmouth C	£75
D	£75
H	£100
P	£2
V	£15
Y	£15
BB	£15

Davenham N	£150
Daventry C	£50
D	£75
M	£50
P	£2
R	£15
R erased	£50
S	£75
V	£50
W	£30
Z	£50
AA	£50
CC	£30
MM	£75
Dawley Green CC	£75
Dawlish O	£30
P	£4
Deal C	£50
G	£50
H	£50
P	£2
S	£75
V	£15
X	£10
Z	£30
Deale C	£100
Debenham CC	£50
Deddington O	£15
V	£10
Y	£50
Y erased	£15
Dedham (Essex) O	£30
V	£50
Dedington D	£50
Deeping C	£75
Delph O	£30
AA distinctive	£50
Denbigh C	£15
D	£15
H	£30
O	£15
P	£2
V	£15
W	£10
Y	£10
Dent CC	£50
Denton (M'ter) BB	£100
Derby C	£15
P	£2
Q	£2
R	£75
S	£75
V	£15
W	£15
X	£10
Z	£30
AA	£30
HH	£100
MM	£75
Dereham C	£50
O	£10
P	£2
S	£100
V	£15
W	£30
Deritend (B'ham) C	£30
Devils Bridge C	£50
O	£15
Devizes C	£30
D	£75
P	£2
S	£75
V	£50
W	£10
Y	£10
Y erased	£10
Z	£50
AA	£30
BB	£50

CC	£50
HH	£50
MM	£75
Devonport P	£4
X	£15
X erased	£10
Z (dated)	£30
AA	£50
JJ	£30
MM	£50
Dewsbury O	£15
P	£2
Didsbury (M'ter) BB	£75
Disley C	£50
Diss C	£15
O	£10
V	£15
W	£15
Y	£30
Distington CC	£30
Dobcross	
AA distinctive	£50
Dobscross O	£30
Dolgelly C	£15
O	£10
V	£15
W	£10
W erased	£15
Y	£15
Y erased	£15
JJ	£50
Doncaster C	£30
C distinctive	£150
D	£30
G	£50
H	£30
M	£30
P	£2
S	£75
V	£10
W	£10
JJ	£30
Donnington Lincolns	
CC	£75
Dorchester C	£30
D	£30
F	£75
P	£2
S	£75
V	£15
W	£15
W erased	£15
X	£10
AA	£15
Dorking O	£15
P	£4
Douglas Isle of Man	
P distinctive	£15
CC	£1000
Down O	£30
Downham C	£75
D	£75
O	£10
P	£4
V	£15
W	£10
W erased	£50
CC	£75
Downton C	£50
Dover C	£30
F	£100
G	£30
P	£2
S	£50
V	£15
W	£10
X	£10
X erased	£15
AA	£30
Drayton (Shrops) C	£50
D	£50
Driffield C	£75
O	£15
P	£2
V	£15
W	£15
W erased	£15
Droitwich C	£30
P	£2
S	£50
S erased	£75
V	£15
W	£15
Y	£15
Y erased	£10
Dudeston Row (B'ham) C	£15
Dudley C	£30
O	£10
P	£2
R	£15
W	£15
X	£15
Y	£15
BB	£30
Duffield Derby O	£50
Dulverton O	£15
V	£15
Dunchurch W	£50
W erased	£50
Dunkirk C	£50
W	£50
Dunmow C	£75
O	£15
P	£4
V	£50
W	£30
W erased	£50
Dunstable C	£50
D	£75
O	£30
P	£4
V	£15
W	£15
MM	£75
Dunster G	£75
O	£30
W	£15
BB	£50
Durham C	£15
D	£50
H	£50
Q	£2
V	£10
W	£10
X	£10
CC	£100
Dursley C	£50
P	£4
V	£30
W	£30
Z	£30
AA	£30
BB	£15
Duxford O	£50
Dyffryn O	£30
E (for Exeter) A (cap 'E' dated)	£2000
Eardisley C	£75
Earsdon CC	£50
Easingwold P	£2
V	£15
W	£10
W erased	£10
Easingwould D	£50
V	£15
East Ayton O	£30
Eastbourn G	£50
V	£10
Z	£50
Eastbourne P	£4
V	£50
CC	£75
East Farleigh O	£30
East Grinstead A (+crown in circle)	£100
D	£50
P	£4
V	£10
V erased	£15
Z	£50
CC	£75
East Grinsted	
B distinctive	£150
S	£100
Eastham (L'pool) C	£75
East Hoathly CC	£75
East Moulsey CC	£50
East Strotten CC	£100
Eaton Socon CC	£75
Eccles PP (Manchester) distinctive	£50
Eccleshall C	£30
Eccleshill CC	£50
Edenbridge O	£50
Edgbaston BB	£75
Edgeware C	£75
S	£100
V	£15
Y	£30
Z	£50
Edgworth D	£100
Egham O	£50
V	£50
Eglwyswrw O	£50
*Egremont-Cumbrd O	£15
E-Griensted F	£150
Elland CC	£50
Ellesmere O	£30
P	£4
S	£100
W	£30
Y	£30
Y erased	£30
JJ	£75
Elmdon.P.P. distinctive	£50
Elmham C	£75
H	£50
Ely C	£75
O	£10
P	£2
V	£30
W	£30
W erased	£30
Emsworth H	£75
P	£8
V	£30
V erased	£30
Enfield D	£150
Ensham O	£30
S	£150
Enstone C	£75
O	£15
P	£4
S	£50
V	£30
Z	£75
BB	£50
Eping C	£150
Epping C	£30
G	£75
K	£150
O	£15
P	£4
V	£50
W	£30
W erased	£30
Epsom C	£30
K	£75
O	£30
P	£4
S	£75
V	£30
W	£15
W erased	£30
CC	£75
JJ	£30
Epworth O	£30
Erdington/PP (distinctive)	£50
Ermebridge O	£30
P	£6
BB	£75
Escrick C	£75
Esher H	£30
P	£4
V	£30
Etal crown (mail bag seal)	£150
Et Grinstead G	£75
Eton V	£50
Etruria O	£50
Everly (Beverley) C	£150
Eversham D	£75
Evesham C	£30
D	£30
P	£2
V	£15
W	£15
W erased	£10
Exeter C	£30
D	£100
F (boxed)	£175
H	£50
K	£75
M	£30
P	£2
R	£75
V	£15
W	£15
X	£10
X erased	£15
Z (dated)	£15
AA distinctive	£15
JJ	£10
MM	£75
OO	£100
Exmouth H	£50
P	£6
V	£15
W	£10
W erased	£10
Z	£50
Exon C	£200
Eye C	£50
O	£15
V	£30
W	£15
Eynsham O	£30
Fairford C	£50
O	£15
P	£4
S	£75
V	£50
W	£30
X undated	£30
Fakenham C	£50
D	£75
J	£50
O	£10
P	£2
S	£75
V	£30
W	£30
Y	£30
Falkingham C	£75
Falm O A	£100
Falmouth C	£15
D	£50
H	£15

L	£50
P	£2
V	£15
X	£10
X erased	£15
JJ	£15
MM	£75
OO	£75
Fareham C	£30
H	£50
O	£15
P	£6
S	£30
V	£15
W	£15
Z	£50
AA	£30
BB	£50
Farham C	£100
Faringdon C	£50
D	£75
W	£15
BB	£50
Farnborough (Hants)	
CC	£50
Farnborough (Kent)	
C	£50
O	£30
Farnham C	£30
V	£30
X	£15
X erased	£30
BB	£50
MM	£100
Farningham O	£30
Farringdon C	£30
D	£50
O	£10
P	£4
S	£75
V	£15
Y	£15
Y erased	£15
Faversham C	£50
BB	£50
Fawley CC	£50
Fazeley O	£30
Y	£30
Feckenham C	£15
V	£30
CC	£30
Felstead V	£75
V erased	£50
Feltham O	£50
Felton (North'd) O	£15
P	£6
Fenny Stratford D	£150
P	£6
S	£75
V	£30
W	£30
W erased	£30
Ferebridge D	£150
Feribridg C	£150
Ferrybridge C	£50
D	£30
P	£2
V	£15
V erased	£15
W	£10
Y	£15
Feversham C	£75
D	£50
G	£50
P	£4
S	£75
V	£15
W	£15
W erased	£15
Filby CC	£75
Fishergate	
(Preston) C	£50
Fishguard W	£15
CC	£50
Five Lanes C framed	£50
O	£30
BB	£75
Five Ways (B'ham) C	£15
Fleetwood O	£50
CC	£75
Fletchling CC	£50
Flint C	£50
O	£10
BB	£50
Flixton PP (Manch'r)	
distinctive	£50
Folkestone Z	£50
Folkingham C	£50
O	£30
P	£4
W	£30
Folkston F	£75
Folkstone H	£50
P	£4
S	£75
V	£15
W	£15
W erased	£30
Footscray D	£50
K	£75
P	£4
S	£75
V	£15
V erased	£10
Fordingbridge D	£50
O	£50
P	£6
V	£30
W	£30
Fore Street Hill	
(Exmouth) CC	£30
Forsbrook O	£50
Four Posts CC	£50
Fowey C	£15
O	£30
P	£2
V	£15
Y	£10
Framfield CC	£50
Framlingham D	£50
V	£50
Z	£30
BB	£15
Frampton on Seveon	
(error) CC	£50
Frimley O	£30
Frodsham C	£50
H	£50
· W	£30
Y	£30
Frogmill V	£50
Frome J	£75
O	£15
P	£2
R	£50
W	£15
Y	£15
HH	£50
Froom C	£50
V	£30
Froome C	£50
V	£30
Gaddesden V	£75
Gainford CC	£30
Gainsborough C	£50
D	£30
M dated	£10
S	£75
W	£15
Gainsbro V	£30
Gardner Street	
(Sussex) M	£50
Gargrave C	£15
D	£30
O	£15
V	£15
W	£10
Y erased	£15
Garreds Cross D	£150
Garstang D	£75
G	£50
P	£2
V	£30
W	£30
W erased	£15
Gateshead C	£75
D	£50
H	£30
O	£30
P	£2
R	£100
W	£10
Y	£10
Y erased	£15
BB	£15
CC	£75
JJ	£50
Gateshead High Fell	
CC	£50
Gedney CC	£75
Gee Cross BB	£100
Gerrards Cr V	£50
Gerrards Cross D	£75
G	£75
P	£4
W	£30
Y	£50
Y erased	£30
BB	£50
Gilling O	£30
Gilsland O	£30
Gisburne CC	£50
Glasbury O	£10
Glastonbury D	£50
P	£2
W	£15
AA	£50
Glocester C	£15
J	£50
V	£15
Glossop O	£30
Z	£50
BB	£75
Gloster C	£30
Gloucester C	£30
D	£30
P	£2
S	£50
W	£30
X	£10
X erased	£10
Z	£30
AA	£30
HH	£30
JJ	£15
MM	£50
:Eastgate Gloucester	
F	£15
:Northgate Gloucester	
F	£15
:Southgate Gloucester	
F	£15
:Westgate Gloucester	
F	£15
Glouster D	£75
Glyn Neath O	£15
Godalmin D	£75
P	£4
S	£75
V	£30
W	£15
W erased	£15
Godalming C	£50
Godmersham CC	£50
Godshill (IOW) O	£15
Godstone C	£50
P	£6
S	£100
V	£30
W	£30
W erased	£30
Z	£30
BB	£30
Goldhanger CC	£75
Gomersal O	£15
BB	£50
Gooch St (B'ham) C	£50
Gooderich CC	£50
Goodhurst O	£50
CC	£50
Goole C (boxed)	£75
O	£15
P	£2
Goring CC	£50
Gorlestone BB	£75
Gornal O	£50
Gorton (Manchester)	
BB	£100
Gosberton Z	£75
CC	£75
Gosforth CC	£30
Gosport C	£30
D	£75
P	£4
S	£50
V	£30
W	£30
X	£15
X erased	£30
BB	£50
Goudhurst CC	£50
Grampound C	£30
O	£15
V	£15
Grantham C	£30
D	£50
G	£30
O	£30
P	£15
S	£100
V	£30
W	£15
Y	£15
Z	£30
BB	£30
Gravesend C	£30
G	£30
Q	£2
V	£15
W	£15
X	£10
AA	£30
Grayes C	£150
H	£100
Grays C	£75
G	£100
S	£100
V	£50
Greabridge C	£150
Greatabridge V	£15
W	£10
Great Barr.P.P.	
(distinctive)	£50
Great Heywood M	£50
Great Malvern P	£4
Great Smeaton C	£50
Greenacres (M'ter)	
BB	£30
Green Hammerton O	£30
Greenhythe O	£50

Green Street CC	£50	CC	£50	Hartley Pans CC	£50	V	£15
Gretabridge D	£75	HH	£30	Harwich C	£75	W	£15
O	£15	JJ	£30	D	£100	Haydon Bge C framed	£50
P	£2	MM	£100	F	£150	Haydon Bridge	
W erased	£15	Halstead (Essex) C	£75	G	£50	E distinctive	£50
Gretna Z	£30	G	£75	P	£4	P	£4
Grimsby C	£15	P	£4	R	£100	Hayes Kent O	£50
O	£15	V	£50	V	£50	Hayle (Cornwall) O	£15
V	£30	W	£30	W	£50	P	£2
W	£30	W erased	£30	X	£30	Hayling Island O	£50
Z	£30	Z	£50	X erased	£15	CC	£75
Groombridge O	£50	AA	£30	Z	£50	Haylsham V	£30
Gt Malvern BB	£30	BB	£30	Haselbury (Som) CC	£50	V erased	£30
MM	£75	Halstead (Kent) O	£50	Haslemere F	£100	Hazel Grove C	£100
Gt Missenden G	£75	Halstow CC	£50	P	£4	Heacham CC	£75
Guernsey A (scroll)	£250	Haltwhistle C	£15	S	£100	Heathersett C	£100
G	£275	O	£15	V	£50	D framed	£150
P	£20	W	£30	W	£30	Heathfield CC	£50
Guildford C	£50	BB	£50	W erased	£30	Heavitree CC	£50
D	£75	Hamble CC	£75	Haslingden P	£4	Hebden Bridge CC	£50
G	£50	Hambledon O	£50	BB	£15	Heckmondwicke O	£30
P	£2	CC	£50	Haslingdon H	£50	Heckmondwike BB	£50
S	£100	Hambrook (Bristol) O	£15	Hastings C	£75	Heddon on the Wall O	£30
V	£30	Handcross O	£50	G	£50	Hedingham V	£75
W	£15	CC	£75	P	£2	Hedon O	£30
W erased	£15	Handley O	£30	S	£100	V	£30
Z	£30	Handsworth (B'ham) C	£15	V	£15	V erased	£30
BB	£30	Hanley Staffs O	£30	V erased	£30	Heighington CC	£50
JJ	£75	Harborough C	£50	W	£10	Helmesley D	£75
Guilsfield O	£15	D	£100	BB	£50	W	£30
Guisboro BB	£50	S	£50	Hatfield C	£75	Helmsley G	£75
Guisborough D	£50	Harbour St		G	£75	W	£30
O	£15	(Ramsgate) C	£50	P	£4	Y	£30
P	£2	Harewood O	£30	V	£50	Y erased	£30
V	£15	CC	£50	W	£30	Helston P	£2
W	£10	Harewood End (Heref)		Z	£75	R	£15
Y	£15	CC	£50	Hatherley V	£10	V	£50
CC	£75	Harleston C	£75	Hathersage C	£40	W	£50
Guiseley O	£30	D	£50	BB	£75	Y	£30
BB	£75	P	£2	CC	£50	Y erased	£15
Guist C	£30	V	£15	Havant G	£75	Helstone C	£50
C framed	£75	W	£15	H	£75	H	£75
G	£30	HH	£100	O	£50	P	£4
Gwindee V	£30	Harling C	£15	P	£4	Hemel Hempstead D	£100
Gwyndee H	£50	D	£75	R	£100	G	£75
Gwyndu S	£100	O	£15	V	£30	P	£4
H (for Hatherley) A	£200	P	£2	V erased	£30	V	£30
Hadleigh (Essex) CC	£100	W	£15	W	£30	W	£50
Hadleigh (Suf'k) G	£50	Harlington O	£50	CC	£75	Hemel Hemsted S	£75
O	£15	Harlow C	£15	albino bagseal	£100	Henbury (Bristol) O	£15
P	£4	H	£75	Haverf.dwest		Henfield O	£15
V	£50	P	£4	AA no frame	£50	V	£50
W	£30	S	£100	Haverfordwest C	£50	Henley (Oxon) C	£75
W erased	£30	V	£30	D	£15	G	£50
Z	£50	Harrietsham O	£30	H	£50	K	£75
AA	£30	Harrogate P	£2	M	£50	S	£100
CC	£50	W	£10	P	£2	Y	£15
Hagley (Worcs) C	£50	Z	£50	V	£30	Y erased	£75
O	£15	HH	£75	Y	£15	CC	£75
Hailsham O	£15	JJ	£30	Y erased	£10	Henley-A V	£30
Hales Owen C	£75	Harrowgate D	£30	Z	£30	Henley in A W	£30
Halesowen V	£50	V	£15	CC	£50	Henley in Arden D	£30
Halesworth C	£75	Y	£15	FF	£150	M	£10
D	£75	Y erased	£15	JJ	£30	KK	
O	£10	AA	£50	Haverhill C	£50	Henley on Thames M	£10
P	£4	CC	£75	Hawarden C	£15	P	£4
W	£50	Hartford (Herts) C	£50	O	£10	Henly in Arden E	£30
Y	£50	E	£150	Hawes O	£30	Henly.T V	£50
Y erased	£15	Hartfordbridge		P	£2	Henly-T W	£15
Halfway House O	£50	D three line	£75	BB	£50	Hereford C	£30
Halifax C	£30	G	£50	Hawkhurst O	£30	D	£50
D	£50	M	£15	V	£30	P	£4
M	£30	P	£4	Hawkshead C framed	£150	S	£75
P	£2	S	£75	V	£80	V	£30
R	£75	V	£30	V erased	£30	X	£15
V	£15	W	£15	CC	£75	BB	£30
W	£10	Harting CC	£50	Hay C	£15	JJ	£10
X	£10	Hartlebury CC	£30	O	£10	MM	£50
AA	£30	Hartlepool O	£10	P	£2	Herne Bay O	£30
		P	£2				

Hertford C	£50	W	£30
D	£75	Z (distinctive)	£100
G	£75	Hithe C	£150
P	£2	H	£50
V	£30	V	£15
W	£30	Hobbs Point P	£50
W erased	£50	Hockcliffe CC	£50
Z	£50	Hockley (Wks) CC	£30
CC	£75	Hockliffe CC	£50
JJ	£75	Hoddesdon P	£4
Hertfordbridge		W	£50
G two line	£50	W erased	£50
Hesket CC	£30	Holbeach P	£6
Hevingham CC	£30	W	£30
Hexham P	£4	Z	£75
V	£30	BB	£75
W	£15	Holdsworthy H	£50
X undated	£10	FF	£250
X erased	£10	Holkham C	£50
BB	£50	C framed	£50
Heytesbury P	£6	Hollingsgreen CC	£50
V	£50	Hollinwood (M'ter)	
Y	£50	BB	£75
Y erased	£30	V	£30
Heytsbury S	£50	Holmes Chapel O	£30
Heywood O	£30	V	£30
H.fordwest Z	£30	Holmfirth O	£30
H.Hempstead O	£15	Z	£30
Higham Ferrars V	£50	CC	£75
W	£75	Holms Chapell D	£150
W erased	£75	Holsworthy O	£30
Higham Ferrers C	£75	P	£6
O	£30	V	£30
P	£4	CC	£75
S	£150	Holt (Norfolk) C	£75
Higham Ferres W	£75	O	£10
Higham Ferris D	£150	P	£2
Highfield CC	£75	S	£100
High Street		W	£10
(Southampton) C	£50	W erased	£30
High St (Sunderland)		Holyhead C	£50
C	£30	H	£50
E	£50	P	£2
High Wickham D	£75	V	£30
High Wicomb S	£100	X	£10
Highworth C	£75	X erased	£15
D	£100	Holywell C	£30
G	£75	H	£75
P	£6	P	£2
S	£75	S	£50
V	£30	V	£15
W	£30	W	£10
W erased	£30	Y	£10
CC	£75	Honiton C	£50
High Wycomb D	£75	D	£75
W	£15	H	£15
W erased	£30	P	£4
High Wycombe		R	£100
G two line	£50	V	£50
O	£15	W	£10
P	£4	Z	£75
Hilborough CC	£75	Z (distinctive)	£75
Hinckley C	£50	CC	£15
P	£4	JJ	£15
V	£30	Honiton Clist CC	£75
V erased	£30	Hood Hill C	£30
Z	£50	Hoo Green CC	£50
BB	£50	Hook CC	£75
Hinden CC	£50	Horncastle C	£100
Hindon C	£50	D	£30
O	£30	O	£15
P	£8	S	£75
CC	£50	V	£30
Hingham CC	£30	Y	£15
Hitchen C	£75	Hornchurch W	£50
G	£75	Horndean H	£50
P	£2	P	£6
V	£30	V	£30
Hitchin C	£50	W	£30
G	£75	X	£15
O	£10	Y erased	£15
		CC	£30

Hornsea O	£30	H	£30
Horsforth O	£30	O	£15
BB	£50	P	£4
Horsham C	£50	S	£75
O	£30	V	£30
P	£4	W	£15
S	£100	X	£15
V	£10	Y	£30
W	£10	AA	£30
W erased	£15	CC	£50
Z	£30	Hunton Kent O	£50
BB	£30	Hursley CC	£50
CC	£50	Hurst CC	£75
Hot-Wells (Bristol)		Hurstbourne CC	£75
O	£30	Hurstbourne Tarrant	
Houghton-le-Spring		O	£50
CC	£30	CC	£75
Houlsworthy S	£75	Hurst Green C	£75
Hounslow K	£75	D	£75
O	£30	P	£4
P	£4	S	£100
V	£50	V	£30
W	£50	Hurstperpoint H	£75
Y	£30	O	£50
Y erased	£30	Hurworth CC	£50
AA	£30	H Wycombe Z	£30
CC	£50	Hyde (Manchester) CC	£75
MM	£100	Hythe (Hants) CC	£50
Hove CC	£50	Hythe (Kent) C	£30
Howden D	£100	O	£30
P	£2	P	£4
V	£15	W	£15
Y	£15	W erased	£10
Y erased	£15	Z	£50
CC	£100	Ide CC	£30
HH	£75	Idle CC	£50
MM	£100	Ightham O	£50
Howden Pans C	£50	CC	£50
Hubberstone H	£50	Ilchester C	£50
Huddersfield D	£50	O	£15
H	£50	P	£2
Q	£2	V	£30
V	£10	W	£15
W	£10	Ilfracombe O	£10
X	£10	P	£6
Y	£30	V	£15
Z	£50	CC	£30
AA	£50	Ilkley CC	£50
BB	£50	Ilminster D	£100
CC	£50	Q undated	£15
HH	£30	S	£30
JJ	£15	V	£30
MM	£150	W	£30
Hull A (circular		Y	£15
with star)	£100	Y erased	£15
C	£30	BB	£50
H	£15	FF	£100
L	£50	JJ	£30
P	£2	MM	£75
X	£15	Ilsley O	£15
X erased	£15	Ingatestone D	£75
X distinctive	£150	G	£50
BB	£75	O	£30
JJ	£30	P	£4
MM	£100	S	£100
Hungerford C	£30	V	£50
D	£30	W	£30
O	£15	W erased	£30
P	£6	Y	£30
S	£50	Y erased	£30
V	£15	Ipswich C	£30
W	£15	D	£75
Y	£15	G	£30
Y erased	£15	R	£75
Hunmanby O	£6	S	£75
Hunsdon CC	£75	V	£30
Hunstanton CC	£30	X	£15
Huntingdon B	£150	X erased	£10
C	£50	Y	£30
D	£50	Z	£50
G	£30	BB	£30
		NN	£75

Ironbridge C	£50
O	£10
BB	£30
CC	£30
Isle of Man C	£150
D	£500
H	£150
O	£100
P	£15
CC	£1000
Isle of Wight C	£75
D	£100
S	£100
Isle of Wight.N. C	£75
Isleworth C	£75
D	£50
G	£50
S	£100
Itchen CC	£50
Ivinghoe O	£30
Ivybridge D	£100
H	£75
P	£6
W	£15
W erased	£50
Ixworth BB	£30
Jarrow CC	£50
Jersey A (scroll)	£250
C	£250
G	£300
P	£20
BB	£250
JJ	£100
Jvybridge (error)	
AA	£50
K (for Kingsbridge)	
A	£300
Kegworth O	£30
V	£50
Keighley C	£50
H	£50
O	£15
P	£2
W	£15
W erased	£15
Keinton C	£50
F	£100
V	£50
W	£50
W erased	£30
Kelvedon C	£75
F	£150
G	£75
O	£30
P	£6
V	£30
Y	£30
Z	£50
BB	£50
Kempsey O	£5
Kemp Town O	£30
BB	£100
Kemsing-Kent O	£50
Kendal C	£30
P	£2
V	£15
W	£15
X	£15
X erased	£30
Z	£30
AA	£30
JJ	£75
Kenford CC	£50
Kenilworth O	£30
CC	£75
Kentchurch CC	£50
Kenyon PP (L'pool)	
(distinctive)	£75
O	£15
Kenyon PP (Manch'r)	
(distinctive)	£75

Kessingland R	£100
Keswick H	£30
P	£2
R	£50
V	£15
W	£15
W erased	£15
Kettaring D	£150
Kettering C	£75
D	£75
G	£50
P	£2
S	£100
V	£50
W	£30
W erased	£5
CC	£75
Keynsham (Som) O	£15
Key Street CC	£50
Kidderminster C	£30
D	£30
P	£2
S	£50
V	£30
W	£15
X	£15
X erased	£15
JJ	£30
MM	£75
Kidwelly C	£30
H	£30
O	£10
Kighley C	£75
Kildwick V	£30
V erased	£30
Kilsby CC	£50
Kilvedon AA	£100
Kimbolton C	£75
G	£50
O	£15
P	£4
S	£75
V	£30
W	£30
W erased	£50
Kineton Z	£75
Kingsbridge D	£75
P	£4
V	£15
W	£15
Y	£10
Y erased	£15
Z	£30
CC	£30
Kingscote Y	£30
Kings Langley W	£50
King's Norton.P.P.	
(distinctive)	£50
Kingston (Surrey) C	£30
K	£75
P	£4
Y	£30
Z	£50
CC	£50
MM	£75
Kingston on Tham S	£100
Kingston on Thames M	£15
W	£30
Kingston T V	£30
Kingswinford O	£30
Kington O	£15
P	£4
V	£50
W	£15
Kington-H (Heref) C	£30
Kinvar CC	£75
Kippax O	£30
Kirby Lonsdale P	£4
V	£15
Y	£15
Y erased	£10
BB	£50

Kirby Moorside O	£30
Kirkby Lonsdale C	£50
Kirkby Moorside C	£30
Kirkby Stephen O	£15
Kirkgate (Wakefield)	
C	£30
Kirkham V	£75
CC	£30
Kirk Oswald CC	£50
Kirkstall O	£30
BB	£50
Kirton Lindsey O	£50
Knaresborough D	£75
H	£50
M	£30
P	£2
W	£10
Y	£15
CC three line	£100
Knighton H	£30
O	£30
V	£15
Knot Mill/Manchr A	£100
Knott Mill/Manchester	
E	£50
Knowle (B'ham) C	£30
Knowle (Som) CC	£50
Knutsford B	£200
C	£75
D	£75
H	£75
P	£4
V	£30
W	£10
Y	£10
Y erased	£10
Laleham CC	£75
Lamberhurst C	£50
D	£75
P	£2
V	£10
Z	£50
CC	£50
Lambourn V	£15
Lambourne O	£15
Lampeter C	£30
D	£30
H	£10
P	£4
V	£15
W	£10
W erased	£15
BB	£50
Lancaster	
C (lower case)	£100
C	£30
D	£50
G	£50
H	£50
M	£50
P	£4
R	£75
V	£30
X	£10
X erased	£30
BB	£50
HH	£50
JJ	£30
MM	£75
Lancaster St (B'ham)	
C	£50
Lanceston D	£30
Landillo C	£15
Landovery D	£30
H	£50
Landrake CC	£50
Lanfair C	£30
Langadock H	£30
Langollen C	£50
Langport C	£30
V	£15

Lantwitt CC	£30
Lapford CC	£50
Larlingford W	£30
W erased	£15
Latchingdon CC	£75
Laugharne C	£75
D	£50
V	£75
CC	£75
Launceston C	£50
D	£50
P	£2
V	£15
Y	£10
AA	£50
BB	£30
HH	£50
Lavenham C	£50
Lawton C	£30
O	£15
V	£15
W	£15
Lea C framed	£75
O	£15
BB	£75
Leachlade D	£75
Leamington N	£75
O	£15
P	£4
BB	£30
CC	£30
JJ	£15
MM	£75
Leatherhead C	£30
D	£75
P	£4
S	£100
V	£30
BB	£75
Lechlade O	£10
P	£2
V	£15
Y	£15
Lechmere Heath CC	£75
Ledbury C	£50
D	£50
O	£15
P	£4
V	£30
W	£30
X	£15
X erased	£30
CC	£75
Leedes C	£175
Leeds C	£30
G	£50
H	£50
M	£30
P	£2
Q	£2
R	£75
V	£15
W	£10
X	£10
BB	£50
CC	£50
HH	£10
JJ	£15
MM	£100
: Holbeck/Leeds E	£30
: Hunslet/Leeds E	£30
: Marsh Lane/Leeds E	£30
: North St/Leeds E	£30
: West St/Leeds E	£30
Leek A (unframed	
circular)	£30
C	£30
H	£30
O	£15
P	£4
R	£30

44

R boxed	£30
Y	£15
JJ	£50
Leeke V	£15
Lees (Manch'r) BB	£50
Leicester C	£30
D	£75
G	£50
P	£4
R	£75
S	£75
V	£30
W	£30
X	£15
X erased	£5
CC	£75
HH	£50
JJ	£15
MM	£50
Leigh (Essex) CC	£75
Leigh (Kent) CC	£50
Leigh PP (Manch'r) distinctive	£50
Leighn Buzzard V	£15
Leighton-Buz F	£100
Leighton Buzzard D	£50
P	£4
W	£15
W erased	£15
Leintwardine Y	£30
Lenham O	£30
Leominster C	£30
D	£50
P	£4
S	£75
V	£30
W	£30
X	£15
X erased	£15
BB	£30
CC	£50
MM	£50
Leskeard V	£30
V erased	£15
Lestwithiel D	£100
Letherhead D	£100
Letton CC	£50
Leverport D	£100
Leverpoole C	£100
D	£150
Lewes (Sussex) C	£30
G	£50
P	£2
Q	£2
S	£100
V	£15
W	£15
X	£10
X erased	£15
AA	£50
MM	£100
Lewis (Sussex) C	£75
S	£100
Leyburn CC	£75
Leyland O	£50
Lg Stratton C	£75
Lichfield C	£30
D	£75
J	£30
P	£4
X	£10
CC	£30
JJ	£30
MM	£100
Limber C boxed	£75
O	£50
Lime C	£150
Limington C	£50
D	£75

Lincoln C	£50
P	£4
S	£75
V	£30
W	£30
X	£15
X erased	£10
Lindal CC	£50
Linton (Cambs) G	£100
O	£15
P	£4
V	£75
W	£50
Linton (Devon) O	£50
Linton-Kent O	£50
Liphook O	£50
V	£50
W	£50
Liscard (Cornwall) D	£75
Liskeard (Cornwall)	
H	£75
P	£2
Z	£30
Litchfield C	£50
D	£75
S	£50
V	£15
X	£10
Littlebourne O	£50
Little Gaddesden G	£100
Littlehampton O	£15
W	£50
Liverpool C	£30
D	£30
H	£15
L	£15
P	£2
Q	£2
R	£75
S	£100
X	£10
AA	£15
CC	£30
HH	£10
JJ	£10
MM	£50
OO	£30
: Berry St E	£50
: Church St E	£10
: Edge Hill E	£30
: Everton E	£15
: Falkner St E	£50
: Kirkdale E	£10
: London Rd E	£15
: Low Hill E	£15
: Oldhall St E	£30
: Oxford St E	£10
: Park Rd O	£15
: Regent Rd E	£50
: St James's E	£15
: Scotland Rd E	£50
: Vauxhall Rd E	£50
Liverpoole C	£150
Llanbedr O	£30
Llandillo V	£10
Llandilo H	£15
O	£10
P	£2
W	£10
Y	£10
Y erased	£15
Llandissyl CC	£50
Llandovery D	£50
O	£5
P	£2
V	£50
W	£15
Y	£15
Y erased	£15

Llandudno CC	£50
Llanelly O	£10
P	£2
BB	£30
Llanerchymedd CC	£30
Llanfair C	£15
O	£15
Llanfihangel Crucorny CC	£30
Llanfyllin O	£10
Llangaddock W	£30
Llangadock O	£30
P	£6
Llangefni CC	£30
Llangollen P	£4
Y	£15
Llanidloes P	£4
V	£10
Llannelly W	£15
Llanrhaiadr O	£30
Llanrwst C	£10
O	£5
Llansaintfraid O	£30
Llansantfraid O	£15
Llanyblodwell O	£30
Llanydlos C	£30
Llanymynech O	£15
Llaugharne FF	£150
Loddon O	£30
Lodsworth CC	£75
Loe C	£100
F	£150
Loftus CC	£75
London Colney CC	£50
London Rd.Worcester O	£15
Long Benton CC	£30
Long Buckly C	£50
Long Ditton CC	£75
Longdon C	£50
Long Melford C	£50
Longparish CC	£50
Longport Staffs O	£30
Long Stratton C	£75
O	£30
P	£4
JJ	£50
Long Sutton CC	£50.
Longtown C	£15
M double circle	£50
R framed	£15
R framed, mileage etc erased	£15
U distinctive Scottish type	£15
V	£30
Loo C	£75
BB	£100
Looe C	£75
V	£75
W	£15
Loose O	£50
Lostwithiel O	£15
P	£2
W	£30
W erased	£30
Z	£50
CC	£50
Lougharne C	£50
Loughborough A	£150
C	£50
D	£50
F	£150
G	£50
P	£2
S	£75
V	£30
W	£15
W erased	£15
MM	£75

Loughborow D	£150
Loughor CC	£15
Louth C	£30
P	£4
V	£30
W	£30
Lower Wallop O	£50
CC	£75
Lowestoff P	£4
Lowestoffe S	£75
Lowestoft D	£75
O	£15
V	£30
Low Harrogate O	£30
Luddenden C	£30
Ludlow C	£50
P	£2
S	£75
V	£15
W	£10
X	£10
JJ	£75
Lugershall O	£20
Luterworth D	£75
Luton C	£50
G	£50
O	£15
P	£4
S	£50
V	£15
W	£15
W erased	£15
MM	£75
Lutterworth D	£15
O	£30
P	£4
V	£30
W	£30
CC	£75
Lydd O	£50
V	£15
Lydney O	£15
CC	£75
Lyme C	£30
G	£50
O	£30
P	£4
V	£15
W	£15
Lymington C	£30
D	£50
O	£30
P	£4
S	£75
V	£30
W	£15
Y	£15
Y erased	£15
AA	£30
JJ	£50
Lympston H	£50
CC	£15
Lyndhurst C	£50
P	£4
S	£75
V	£30
V erased	£15
W	£15
Lynn C	£15
L	£100
P	£2
S	£75
X	£10
X erased	£10
Z	£15
BB	£30
CC	£75
JJ	£30
MM	£75

Lynn Regis D	£100	MM	£50	W	£30	Midwich C	£175
Lynton (Devon) O	£50	OO	£30	Y	£15	Milbrook CC	£50
Lytchett CC	£75	Manningtree C	£100	Y erased	£30	Mildenhall (Suffk) C	£75
Macclesfield D	£50	O	£15	CC	£50	P	£4
H	£30	P	£4	HH	£75	V	£50
P	£2	V	£30	Marlow C	£30	W	£15
V	£30	V erased	£30	P	£4	W erased	£15
W	£15	Mansfield C	£50	V	£15	AA	£15
X	£10	P	£4	W	£30	Milford (Wales) C	£30
JJ	£30	V	£50	W erased	£30	P	£4
Machell St (Hull) C	£30	W	£30	Marsden (Yorks) O	£30	X	£30
Machynleth C	£50	Y	£15	Marsefield CC	£50	Y	£30
D	£30	Y erased	£15	Marsk CC	£75	Milford Haven V	£50
Machynlleth O	£5	Marazion C	£75	Marske O	£30	Millbridge O	£30
P	£2	D	£75	Martock C	£50	BB	£50
Y	£10	O	£30	Y	£15	Milnthorp Y	£30
Y erased	£10	P	£2	Marton CC	£50	Y erased	£30
CC	£75	V	£15	Maryport P	£2	Milnthorpe H	£50
Madeley O	£30	V erased	£15	W	£15	V	£30
Madeley Wood D	£50	March C	£100	W erased	£15	W	£30
Maghull (Liverpool)		O	£50	Masham CC	£50	BB	£30
C framed	£75	P	£6	Matlock C	£50	Milverton C	£15
O	£10	V	£50	Matlock Bath O	£15	V	£15
Maidenhead D	£50	Marden O	£50	P	£2	Minchinhampton D	£50
G	£30	Margate A oval		Matton C	£150	O	£15
P	£6	with crown	£200	Mavagissey C	£75	S	£75
S	£50	C	£50	Mayfield CC	£50	V	£30
V	£15	G	£50	M.dean (Mitcheldean)		W	£30
V erased	£15	H	£30	AA	£75	Y	£30
BB	£50	P	£2	Meifod O	£15	AA	£30
Maidston D	£100	V	£15	Melbourne O	£50	BB	£50
F	£75	W	£15	Melksham C	£30	Minehead C	£50
Maidstone C	£50	X	£10	D	£50	D	£30
D	£50	Market Deeping P	£6	P	£4	W	£15
G	£30	V	£30	V	£30	CC	£30
P	£2	Y	£30	W	£15	Minster CC	£50
S	£50	Y erased	£30	Y	£15	Mirfield C boxed	£50
V	£10	BB	£75	Y erased	£15	O	£30
W	£10	Market Drayton O	£10	Z	£75	Missenden O	£15
W erased	£15	P	£2	AA	£50	V	£50
Z	£30	V	£15	Melton Mowbray D	£50	W erased	£50
BB	£15	W	£10	M	£15	Mitcheldean O	£15
Malden C	£100	W erased	£10	V	£30	Mitcheldever CC	£50
Maldon C	£50	MM	£100	W	£30	Mitford (North'd) CC	£50
H	£75	Market Harborough D	£50	Y	£15	Mk Weighton W	£15
P	£4	P	£2	CC	£100	M.Lavington O	£50
V	£50	W	£15	Melton.S G	£30	Mochdrai O	£50
W	£30	Y	£15	Menai Bridge O	£15	Modbury C	£15
Z	£50	Market Raisen M	£15	Mere C	£50	W	£15
BB	£30	Market Raisin D	£50	O	£15	W erased	£15
Malmesbury V	£50	H	£75	V	£15	Mold C	£50
Malmsbury C	£30	P	£4	V erased	£30	P	£2
D	£100	V	£30	Merthyr Tidvil V	£15	V	£10
O	£6	W	£30	W	£10	V erased	£15
Malpas C	£50	Y	£30	Merthyr Tydfil P	£2	W	£10
Malten C	£75	Market St (Beds) Y	£50	BB	£30	Monksheath O	£30
Malton C	£30	Market St (Herts) V	£50	Merthyr Tydvill M	£10	Monk Wearmouth CC	£50
P	£2	Y	£75	Mevagissey C	£15	Monmouth C	£30
R	£15	Market Street (Beds)		Michldean C	£100	D	£30
V	£15	C	£75	Middleham CC	£50	P	£2
W	£10	G	£75	Middlesborough O	£30	S	£75
X	£10	P	£15	MiddlesBro CC	£50	V	£10
CC	£75	V	£50	Middleton (M'ter) C	£75	W	£10
JJ	£15	Market Street (Herts)		K	£75	Y	£10
Malvern C	£15	C	£75	BB	£30	Y erased	£30
Z	£30	G	£100	Middleton One Row CC	£75	Z	£30
Malvern Wells Z	£50	P	£6	Middle Wallop O	£15	BB	£30
Manchester C	£50	Market Weighton P	£2	CC	£75	JJ	£15
D	£15	V	£15	Middlewich D	£50	Montgomery D	£30
G	£50	W	£15	O	£30	P	£4
H	£15	Y	£15	P	£4	V	£15
L	£15	Y erased	£15	V	£30	Y	£30
P	£2	Marlboro MM	£75	W	£30	Y erased	£30
Q	£5	Marlborough C	£150	FF	£200	Moreton Hampstead K	£100
X	£5	D	£75	Midhurst C	£30	CC	£15
X inverted	£50	K	£75	D	£50	Moreton in Marsh O	£10
BB	£150	O	£50	O	£50	W	£15
HH	£15	P	£2	P	£4	Y	£15
JJ	£50	S	£75	S	£75	Y erased	£15
		V	£30	V	£30	CC	£50

North Walsham D	£20
W	£10
Y	£10
JJ	£50
Northwich D	£50
H	£30
O	£15
P	£4
V	£30
W	£15
BB	£75
JJ	£50
Norton CC	£50
Norton Sheffield O	£30
Nortwich B	£200
Norwich C	£20
D	£50
J	£50
P	£2
Q	£4
S	£50
V	£15
W	£30
X	£10
X erased	£5
Z	£75
BB	£30
CC	£15
JJ	£10
MM	£75
Nottingham C	£75
D	£50
P	£2
Q	£4
S	£100
U	£75
V	£30
W	£10
W erased	£15
X	£15
JJ	£15
N.Shields C	£30
V	£30
Z	£50
BB	£50
CC	£30
Nursling CC	£50
Nuthurst CC	£75
Oakham C	£100
O	£15
P	£4
V	£50
W	£50
W erased	£50
Y	£50
Oakhampton D	£75
V	£50
Odiam C	£50
F	£100
O	£30
P	£6
V	£15
W	£15
Okehampton O	£10
P	£4
Y	£30
Y erased	£15
AA	£15
FF	£50
Old Buckenham CC	£75
Oldbury (Birm'ham) C	£15
Oldbury (Shrops) C	£30
Old-Down C framed	£15
P	£4
Old Hall Green CC	£75
Oldham A (in double circle)	£75
BB	£10
Old Swan (L'pool) C	£100
O	£30

Ollerton O	£15
Q	£4
V	£30
W	£30
Ombersley O	£30
Ongar C	£75
G	£75
V	£30
W	£50
Y	£50
Orford V	£30
W	£30
Z	£50
Ormskirk C	£30
D	£50
P	£6
V	£50
W	£15
Y	£50
Z	£50
BB	£50
Orpington O	£50
Ossett BB	£50
Oswaldkirk CC	£75
Oswestry C	£50
D	£50
P	£2
R	£75
V	£50
W	£30
X	£10
Z	£50
AA	£15
JJ	£30
Otford O	£50
Otley G	£50
O	£15
P	£2
V	£15
W	£15
BB	£100
CC	£100
JJ	£30
Otterbourne CC	£50
Otterton C	£30
D	£75
AA	£30
BB	£30
CC	£50
JJ	£75
Ottery C	£50
W	£50
Ottery St Mary CC	£50
Oulney C	£100
G	£75
O	£10
V	£30
Oundle C	£75
O	£15
P	£2
V	£50
W	£30
Y	£30
Y erased	£30
Over Darwen C	£75
Overseal C	£50
CC	£75
Overton (Hants) C	£50
V	£30
V erased	£30
Overton F (Flint) Y	£10
Overton-Hants P	£6
Oxford C	£30
G	£2
P	£2
S	£50
V	£10
W	£10
X	£10
X erased	£10

BB	£100
HH	£50
MM	£75
Oxford Street/Manchester	
E	£15
Oxted O	£50
Padiham O	£30
Padstow C	£50
O	£15
Y	£30
Y erased	£50
Painswick C	£50
O	£10
V	£30
V erased	£10
BB	£75
Panswick C	£75
Parkgate Kent O	£30
Parkstone CC	£50
Pateley Bridge O	£30
Patrington O	£30
Peacock Inn H	£100
Pearsmarsh W	£30
Peasmarsh O	£50
CC	£75
Peeltown Isle of Man	
A boxed	£250
Pembrey (Wales) O	£15
Pembrock D	£150
Pembrok D	£100
Pembroke C	£30
D	£15
K	£50
P	£2
V	£15
W	£10
Y	£10
FF	£150
JJ	£15
Pembroke Dock O	£15
Pembrook C	£100
D	£100
Pembury CC	£50
Pencraig CC	£50
Penkridge C	£30
O	£30
P	£6
Penny Bridge CC	£50
Penrin C	£150
Penrith C	£30
D	£50
G	£30
H	£15
P	£2
R	£50
V	£15
W	£15
X	£10
X erased	£10
Z	£30
Z distinctive framed	£75
JJ	£30
Penryn C	£30
H	£50
P	£2
R	£30
V	£50
W	£15
X no date	£10
X no mileage	£10
Penshurst CC	£50
Pentrevoelas V	£30
Penybont D	£30
W erased	£15
Penzance C	£50
P	£2
V	£30
X no circles	£10
BB	£75
CC	£50
JJ	£50

Pershore C	£30
O	£15
P	£2
V	£30
W	£30
JJ	£15
Peterboro W	£50
Peterborough C	£100
D	£50
G	£75
O	£15
P	£2
S	£75
V	£50
W	£30
Z	£75
BB three lines	£75
Peterchurch CC	£50
Petersfield C	£50
D	£75
G	£50
O	£50
P	£6
S	£50
W	£30
BB	£50
Petworth C	£15
D	£50
P	£4
S	£100
V	£15
W	£15
Y	£50
Y erased	£15
Pewsey C	£75
O	£50
P	£4
V	£50
Y	£50
Y erased	£50
CC	£50
Pickering C	£30
O	£15
P	£2
Q	£2
CC	£100
Pierce Bridge CC	£30
Pinner O	£30
Plimpton R	£100
Plym Dock X	£15
Plymouth C	£30
D	£75
F	£200
H	£15
M	£15
P	£2
R	£150
S	£100
V	£30
W	£15
X	£10
X erased	£30
Z	£15
AA	£15
CC	£30
JJ	£15
Plymouth Dk V	£50
X	£15
Plymouth Dock C	£75
D	£15
H	£75
M	£75
V	£50
W	£30
Z	£50
Plympton M	£50
P	£4
V	£50
W	£50
Plymton W	£50
W erased	£15

Pmouth (Portsmouth)	
B	£175
Pocklington D	£50
H	£50
P	£2
W	£15
W erased	£15
Polpero C	£50
Polperro N	£75
Pontefract C	£50
D	£30
G	£30
O	£15
P	£2
W	£10
Y	£15
Ponterdulais M	£10
O	£30
Ponterfract C	£75
Pontfract C	£150
Pontypool O	£5
Pool C	£30
W	£15
X	£15
X erased	£15
Pool.D. S	£75
Poole P	£2
V	£15
CC	£30
Portchester O	£50
Port Madoc O	£30
Portsea C	£50
O	£30
Portsmouth C	£30
D	£50
G	£50
H	£50
P	£2
Q	£4
S	£75
V	£30
X	£15
X inside circle	£75
Z	£75
AA	£30
JJ	£50
MM	£75
Post Witham (Lincs)	
D	£150
Potton BB	£30
Poulton CC	£30
Powick O	£10
Prescot C	£50
C lower case	£150
M	£50
O	£50
P	£6
S	£100
V	£50
W	£30
Y	£50
Y erased	£30
Z	£75
BB	£50
CC	£75
JJ	£30
Prestbury (Glos) O	£15
Presteign C	£15
D	£30
H	£15
O	£10
P	£2
V	£15
Y	£15
Y erased	£30
Prestein C	£100
Preston C	£30
D	£50
G	£30
H	£30
P	£4
Q	£2
R	£100
R distinctive	£150
V	£30
W	£15
X	£15
Z	£30
HH	£50
JJ	£50
MM	£100
Preston Brook P	£6
BB distinctive	£75
Princes Risborough O	£15
Prittlewell O	£20
CC	£75
Puckeridge CC	£75
Pudsey O	£30
BB	£50
Pulborough O	£15
Pulhely C	£30
Purbrook O	£50
Pwllheli O	£15
P	£2
Pyle O	£10
Queenboro G	£50
Queenborough D	£50
G	£75
H	£50
P	£4
S	£50
V	£15
V erased	£15
W	£15
Radcliffe BB	£100
Radnor H	£50
V	£30
W	£15
W erased	£10
Ragland O	£30
Rainham CC	£50
Raisen (Lincs) W	£50
Ramsbury (Wilts) O	£50
S	£50
V	£30
V erased	£15
Ramsey Isle of Man	
A boxed	£200
C	£1000
Ramsgate C	£50
G	£50
P	£2
S	£75
V	£10
W	£10
BB	£30
CC	£50
MM	£75
Ravenglass H	£30
O	£30
P	£2
Y	£30
Y erased	£30
BB	£50
CC	£50
Rawclife D	£75
Rawcliffe C	£30
D	£75
H	£75
Rawden O	£30
BB	£50
Rawtenstall BB	£75
Rayleigh C	£75
O	£30
W	£50
Reading A (in double circle)	£200
C	£50
D	£75
F	£100
G	£30
P	£2
R	£50
V	£15
X	£15
Z	£30
BB	£30
JJ	£15
: London St/Reading	
E	£30
: Russell St/Reading	
E	£30
Redbridge CC	£50
Redburn G	£100
Redcar CC	£50
Redditch C	£50
O	£10
V	£30
Y	£15
Redland (Bristol) CC	£15
Redruth C	£50
O	£15
P	£2
Y	£15
Y erased	£30
JJ	£50
Reepham O	£30
Reeth O	£30
Reigate C	£50
O	£15
P	£4
W	£30
Y	£50
Y erased	£30
Retford C	£30
D	£100
O	£10
P	£4
V	£30
W	£15
W erased	£30
Rewe CC	£75
Rhayader D	£75
H	£30
O	£10
P	£4
V	£30
W	£30
Rhuabon C	£10
O	£10
BB	£75
Richmond C	£50
D	£75
H	£50
O	£15
P	£2
V	£15
W	£10
BB	£50
Richmond Y C	£30
H	£50
Richmond YE C	£50
Richmond Yorkshe D	£50
Rickmansworth P	£4
V	£50
W	£30
W erased	£50
BB	£75
Ridge CC	£75
Ringwood C	£30
D	£50
O	£30
P	£4
S	£75
V	£30
W	£15
CC	£50
Ripley (Surrey) C	£100
G	£75
O	£30
P	£4
S	£100
V	£50
W	£30
W erased	£30
Z	£30
Ripley Yorks O	£30
Ripon H	£30
P	£2
R	£15
V	£15
W	£10
X	£10
BB	£30
Rippon C	£50
G	£30
R	£75
V	£15
Risca CC	£15
R.Isle of Wight D	£100
R distinctive	£200
Robertsbridge C	£30
O	£15
P	£6
Rochdale C	£30
D	£50
M	£50
P	£4
V	£50
W	£30
X	£50
Z	£50
CC	£50
MM	£100
Rochester C	£30
D	£50
F	£100
G	£30
P	£2
Q	£2
S three line	£75
V	£15
W	£15
W erased	£15
Rochford C	£50
O	£15
P	£4
V	£30
W	£15
Z	£50
AA	£50
CC	£50
Rockbeare CC	£75
Rockingham D	£100
W	£50
W erased	£50
Rolvenden C	£15
O	£50
Romford	
PP distinctive	£50
P	£2
X	£15
X erased	£15
Z	£30
AA	£30
BB	£30
CC	£30
Romney BB	£50
Romsey P	£4
X	£15
X erased	£15
Ross C	£30
P	£4
V	£30
W	£15
W erased	£15
Z	£15
CC	£30
HH	£75
JJ	£10
Rotherfield CC	£75
Rotherham C	£30
D	£75
P	£2

S	£100
V	£15
W	£10
JJ	£15
MM	£100
Rothersbridge G	£100
Rothwell O	£30
Rougham C	£100
O	£10
P	£2
V	£15
Z	£15
CC	£75
Royston C	£75
D	£75
O	£10
P	£2
V	£30
V erased	£30
CC	£75
Rudgeley C	£30
Rudgwick CC	£75
Rugby C	£30
O	£10
P	£2
V	£15
Y	£30
Y erased	£10
JJ	£50
MM	£75
Rugeley C	£30
O	£30
P	£6
JJ	£75
Rumford C	£50
D	£100
K	£75
R	£30
V	£30
W	£30
Rumney F	£75
G	£50
Rumsey C	£30
G	£50
R	£75
V	£30
W	£15
Rumsy C	£75
Runcorn C	£30
P	£4
Rushyford C	£50
D	£50
O	£30
P	£2
W	£15
BB	£50
Ruthin C	£15
P	£2
V	£15
W	£10
X	£15
X erased	£10
JJ	£50
Ruyton CC	£30
Ryde (IOW) C	£50
O	£30
Q	£2
W	£15
BB	£150
JJ	£50
MM	£100
Ryde IW W	£30
Rye C	£30
G	£75
P	£4
S	£100
V	£30
W	£30
W erased	£15
Z	£50
AA	£75
Ryegate C	£50
D	£100
S	£100
V	£30
W	£30
Ryton CC	£50
Saffron Walden D	£75
G	£100
O	£30
P	£4
S	£100
V	£50
W	£30
Y	£50
St Albans C	£75
D	£100
G	£50
P	£2
S	£100
V	£30
W	£30
Y	£15
Y erased	£30
Z	£50
CC	£75
JJ	£75
MM	£75
St Asaph C	£30
D	£50
H	£30
O	£10
P	£2
V	£15
W	£10
W erased	£10
BB	£50
CC	£75
HH	£100
St Austell O	£15
P	£2
CC	£30
JJ	£50
St Austle C	£50
H	£100
V	£50
W	£15
W erased	£30
Y	£15
St Clairs FF	£100
St Clears C	£75
O	£15
MM	£75
St Colmbes C	£175
St Colombe C	£150
St Columb C	£30
D	£100
P	£2
V	£15
V erased	£15
Y	£15
Y erased	£30
CC	£75
St Cross CC	£30
St Davids CC	£50
St Davids Hill CC	£30
St Faiths CC	£75
St Germains H	£50
St Germans D	£15
CC	£75
St Helens O	£50
St Ives (Hunts) A	£150
C	£50
P	£2
R	£100
V	£30
W	£15
W erased	£50
St Ives C(Cornw'l) C	£30
K	£75
St John's Common CC	£75
St John's Worcester	
O	£10
St Lawrence (Kent) O	£50
St Leonards D	£75
P	£4
St Mary Bourne CC	£50
St Mawes C	£15
O	£15
St Maws C	£50
St Neots C	£30
O	£15
P	£4
V	£75
W	£30
St Noets (error) O	£100
St Peters (Kent) N	£100
O	£30
St Sidwell CC	£15
St Thomas CC	£15
Salesbury D	£100
Salford/Manchester E	£15
Salford/Manchr A	£100
Salisbury C	£30
D	£50
D boxed	£150
P	£2
Q	£2
S	£50
V	£15
X	£10
Z	£30
JJ	£10
MM	£30
Salop C	£75
Saltersgate D	£100
Salterton AA	£75
Sandbach O	£15
P	£4
V	£30
W	£15
Sandgate O	£30
Sandhurst W	£15
Sandhurst-Kent O	£50
Sandling O	£50
Sandpits (B'ham) C	£50
Sandwich C	£15
D	£50
G	£50
O	£15
P	£4
S	£75
V	£15
W	£10
Sarre CC	£75
Sawbridgeworth O	£30
P	£4
W	£50
Sawston O	£50
Saxmundham D	£50
P	£4
W	£15
W erased	£30
Scarboro W	£15
Scarboroug J	£50
Scarborough C	£50
D	£50
H	£50
P	£2
V	£15
W	£15
X	£10
CC	£100
JJ	£30
Scilly C	£150
P	£100
Scole C	£75
P	£2
V	£15
JJ	£50
Scottou Y	£75
Seacomb (L'pool) CC	£30
Seacombe (L'pool) N	£150
O	£15
CC	£50
Seaford G	£50
O	£30
W	£50
Seaham O	£50
Sea Houses (Sussex)	
CC	£50
Seal O	£50
Seaton (Devon) A	
(in circle with no.2)	£75
C	£75
C (with no.2)	£30
Seaton (Durham) CC	£50
Sedberg CC	£50
Sedbergh C	£30
O	£30
Seddlescomb CC	£30
Sedgefield O	£50
Selby C	£50
M	£30
O	£15
P	£2
Y	£30
MM	£150
Settle C	£50
H	£30
O	£15
P	£2
V	£15
W	£10
X	£15
Y	£15
BB	£50
Sevenoaks Z	£30
Seven Oaks	
A (inside circle)	£100
G	£50
P	£2
V	£10
V erased	£10
AA	£30
Sevenoaks C	£30
D	£50
G	£50
S	£75
Shaftesbury D	£50
P	£2
V	£30
W	£10
Y	£10
Y erased	£10
Z	£50
AA	£15
BB	£15
FF	£75
MM	£50
Shaftsbury C	£30
S	£75
Z	£75
FF	£150
Shaldon O	£15
Shap C	£100
O	£30
Shardelow V	£50
Sheerness C	£50
P	£4
V	£15
W	£15
W erased	£15
Sheffeild D	£100
Sheffield C	£30
D	£50
G	£50
P	£2
S	£100
U	£100
V	£15
W	£10
X	£10
X erased	£15
Z	£50
Z small boxed	£75
AA	£75

JJ	£15
MM	£75
: Duke St/Sheffield D	£30
: Gibralter St/ Sheffield E	£30
: Glossop Rd/ Sheffield E	£30
: South St/ Sheffield E	£30
: The Wicker/ Sheffield E	£30
Shefford V	£30
W	£30
Z	£50
BB	£50
CC	£50
Shefield C	£150
Shefnal C	£50
Shefnall C	£100
Shelton Staffs O	£50
Shenley CC	£75
Sheptn Mallet FF	£150
Shepton Mallet P	£2
V	£30
W	£30
JJ	£50
Shepton Mallett W	£30
Sherbone D	£100
Sherborn D	£75
Sherborne A (in circle with Post Office)	£200
D	£30
P	£2
S	£75
V	£15
W	£15
W erased	£15
Z	£30
JJ	£30
Sherbourne C	£150
Shields-N V	£15
Shields.S V	£15
Shiere O	£50
BB	£50
Shiffnal C	£50
P	£2
S	£75
V	£30
W	£10
W erased	£10
X	£10
AA	£15
BB	£75
MM	£75
Shiffnall D	£50
Z	£30
Shifnal C	£75
Shifnall C	£30
D	£75
Shildon O	£10
CC	£30
Shipdam C	£50
D	£150
Shipdham C	£15
Shipston C	£30
W	£30
Shipstone on Stour M	£15
P	£6
BB	£50
Shipton V (another spelling of Shipston)	£50
Shipton Mallet D	£100
J	£50
Shirley CC	£50
Shirley Street/PP distinctive	£30
Shirleywich C	£50
Shooters Hill CC	£15
Shoreham D	£100
H	£75
P	£4
V	£30
Y	£30
Y erased	£15
Z	£75
BB	£75
Shoreham S D	£100
Shrewsbury C	£30
D	£15
H	£15
P	£2
V	£30
X	£10
X erased	£10
BB	£30
JJ	£10
MM	£30
Sidmouth C	£50
D	£50
O	£15
P	£2
V	£15
W	£15
Silsoe G	£50
O	£50
Silverton CC	£30
Sittingbourn D	£30
V	£15
Sittingbourne D	£75
M dated	£10
S	£75
W	£10
W erased	£10
Z	£50
CC	£50
Skelton O	£30
CC	£50
Skipton C	£30
D	£75
O	£15
P	£2
V	£15
W	£15
Y	£30
Y erased	£15
BB	£75
Skirlaugh O	£30
Slaithwaite O	£30
Sleaford C	£150
D	£75
J	£75
P	£4
S	£75
V	£30
Y	£15
Y erased	£15
Sledmere C	£30
C boxed	£30
O	£30
Slough (Bucks) P	£2
Smarden CC	£50
Smethwick P.P (distinctive)	£30
Snaith M	£30
O	£30
Snettisham CC	£30
Sodbury (Glos) C	£75
Solva CC	£30
Somersham C	£75
O	£30
Somerton C	£50
D	£75
P	£2
S	£75
V	£30
W	£30
BB	£50
Sonning O	£30
So.Shields BB	£75
Southall C	£75
D	£75
O	£30
P	£4
S	£100
V	£30
W	£30
BB	£75
Southam C	£75
P	£2
V	£30
Southampton C	£50
D	£30
G	£30
P	£2
S	£50
V	£30
W	£10
X	£10
X erased	£10
Z	£30
Z dated	£15
AA	£30
BB	£30
MM	£75
Southbourne CC	£50
South Cave C	£50
D	£50
O	£30
Southend O	£20
P	£2
CC	£75
Southminster G	£150
CC	£75
South Molton C	£15
M	£10
P	£4
South Moulton D	£20
South Parade (Leamington,Wks) E	£30
South Petherton D	£50
E	£50
P	£2
Southport C	£100
P	£10
CC	£75
South Shields D	£75
P	£2
Q	£2
X	£10
JJ	£30
South Teal CC (error for South Zeal)	£50
Southwell C	£50
O	£15
P	£4
W	£15
Southwold C	£50
Z	£50
BB	£15
CC	£15
Spalding C	£30
D	£75
H	£75
O	£10
P	£4
R	£15
S	£75
V	£30
W	£15
Y	£15
BB	£50
CC	£50
Spennithorpe CC	£50
S.Petherton O	£30
Spilsby C	£30
O	£10
P	£4
S	£75
W	£30
W erased	£30
BB	£75
Spittal O	£50
Spittal-Durham O	£30
S.Shields C	£75
R	£100
S Strat B	£150
S Stratford D	£100
Stafford C	£50
D	£50
O	£30
P	£6
S	£75
W	£15
W erased	£15
Z	£50
MM	£75
Staford C	£150
Staindrop O	£15
Staines C	£75
G	£50
P	£4
R	£100
V	£15
W	£30
X	£15
X erased	£15
Z	£50
MM	£75
Staleybridge C	£30
Staley Bridge BB	£75
Stalham CC	£75
Stalybridge C	£30
Stamford C	£50
D	£75
P	£4
S	£75
V	£15
W	£15
Y	£15
JJ	£75
Stampford D	£75
Standish O	£30
Stanes C	£100
Stanhope C framed	£100
O	£30
Stanmore P	£10
Stanstead (Herts) CC	£75
Stapleford Cambridge O	£50
Staplehurst O	£50
P	£6
Starcross CC	£30
Staying E	£150
Stevenage D	£100
G	£100
P	£6
V	£50
V erased	£30
Stewkeley CC	£75
Steyning C	£75
H	£75
O	£30
P	£4
S	£100
V	£50
W	£30
Z	£75
AA	£50
Stillington CC	£50
Stilton C	£75
D	£100
G	£100
O	£30
P	£6
V	£30
Y	£50
MM	£150
Stockbridge G	£50
P	£4
V	£30
V erased	£30
CC	£30
Stockenchurch C	£75

Stockport A	£50	Y erased	£10
(8 varieties, 1784-1813)		Z	£50
C	£30	CC	£50
D	£50	MM	£75
P	£2	Stourport C	£30
V	£30	D	£30
W	£15	E inside oval	£50
X	£15	O	£10
X erased	£15	P	£2
Y	£50	W	£30
Z distinctive	£75	MM	£75
JJ	£50	Stow X undated	£50
MM	£75	Stowerbridg D	£100
Stockton C	£30	Stowerbridge C	£150
D	£75	D	£50
H	£30	D inside circle	£150
M	£30	Stow in the Wold M	£15
P	£2	Stowmarket O	£15
V	£10	P	£4
W	£10	V	£50
X	£10	W	£30
BB	£75	Y	£50
CC	£100	Y erased	£30
Stockton on T V	£15	Stratfd on Avon AA	£50
Stoke (Norfolk) C	£30	BB	£30
Stoke-Bucks O	£15	Stratford V	£50
Stoke Canon CC	£75	Z	£75
Stoke Climsland CC	£50	HH	£50
Stoke Ferry C	£20	JJ	£50
O	£5	Stratford on A Y	£10
CC	£75	AA	£50
Stoke-N (Norfolk) V	£30	BB	£50
Stokenchurch O	£30	Stratford on Avon E	£50
P	£6	M dated	£15
V	£30	P	£2
Y	£50	S	£75
Y erased	£30	W	£10
Stokesley C	£50	BB	£50
P	£2	CC	£75
V	£15	JJ	£50
W erased	£15	MM	£75
Y	£15	Stratford Upon Avon	
BB	£50	E	£100
Stoke under Ham (Som)		Strathfield Turgis M	£30
C	£50	Stratton (Cornwall)	
Stoke upon Trent O	£30	H	£30
Stone C	£30	O	£10
P	£4	CC	£50
S	£75	Stratton (Norfolk)	
V	£30	V	£30
W	£10	W	£50
MM	£75	Stretford PP (Manch'r)	
Stonecrouch C	£150	(distinctive)	£50
D	£50	Stretton CC	£50
S	£75	Stretton on Dunsmore	
Stoneham O	£30	O	£30
P	£4	Stroud C	£30
Stoney Cross C boxed	£75	P	£2
Stoney Middleton H	£50	V	£30
Stoney Stratford M	£10	W	£15
P	£4	X undated	£15
V	£30	X erased	£15
W	£30	CC	£75
W erased	£30	HH	£75
Stonham C	£75	Studley C	£15
O	£30	O	£30
V	£50	Sturminster Marshall	
W	£50	O	£30
Stony Stratford D	£75	Sudbury (Suffolk) C	£75
G	£75	D	£50
S	£100	F	£150
Storington O	£15	P	£4
Storrington C	£50	V	£50
Stouerbridg D	£75	W	£15
Stourbridge C	£15	Z	£50
D	£30	BB	£30
P	£2	CC	£30
S	£50	Sudbury-D (Derbysh)C	£50
V	£15	Sudbury-S (Suffk) C	£75
W	£15		
Y	£15		

Sunderland C	£75	R	£50
D	£50	V	£30
H	£50	W	£15
P	£2	W erased	£15
V	£10	X	£15
W	£10	Z	£30
X	£10	Z dated	£10
BB	£15	FF	£150
JJ	£30	JJ	£10
Sunng Hill B framed	£75	MM	£75
Sunninghill C	£50	Tavistock C	£75
O	£30	H	£75
CC	£50	O	£15
Sutterton Z	£75	P	£4
CC	£50	V	£50
Crown bag seal	£150	W	£10
Sutton (Yorks) CC	£75	Y	£10
Sutton Coldfield E	£15	Z	£75
Sutton-in-Ashfield		AA	£75
CC	£75	HH (scroll)	£50
Sutton Scotney CC	£50	MM	£100
Swaffham C	£10	Tean O	£50
D	£150	Tedbury (Glos) C	£50
P	£2	Teignmouth C	£75
S	£100	P	£4
V	£30	V	£50
W	£15	Y	£10
BB	£50	Y erased	£10
CC	£50	BB	£50
Swanage C	£30	CC	£50
H	£30	Temple Sowerby CC	£50
Swansea C	£15	Tempsford CC	£50
Q	£2	Tenbury C	£30
V	£10	O	£10
X	£10	P	£2
X erased	£10	S	£75
JJ	£10	V	£30
Swanton C	£75	Tenby C	£30
Swanwick CC	£30	P	£2
Swanzey (Swansea) C	£15	V	£30
D	£30	W	£10
Swathling CC	£50	Y	£30
Swinden C	£50	Y erased	£10
Swindon C	£50	Tenterden C	£30
D	£50	D	£75
J	£50	P	£4
O	£30	R	£75
P	£4	V	£15
MM	£50	W	£10
Swineshead (Lincs)		Y	£15
C distinctive	£100	Y erased	£15
Swineshead Lincolns		Terrington (Nfk) CC	£50
CC	£75	Tetbury C	£50
Tadcaster C	£30	O	£10
D	£50	P	£2
O	£15	V	£30
P	£2	W	£15
V	£10	Tetsworth C	£30
W	£10	D	£50
Taibach O	£30	O	£50
P	£4	V	£10
JJ	£50	W	£10
Tamworth C	£50	Z	£50
D	£75	BB	£75
O	£30	Tettenhall O	£50
P	£4	Tewkesbury C	£30
V	£30	D	£50
W	£15	P	£2
Y	£15	R	£75
Y erased	£15	X	£15
Tanybwlch M	£30	BB	£30
Taplow O	£30	CC	£30
CC	£50	JJ	£15
Tarleton CC	£50	Tewksbury C	£30
Tarporley O	£30	D	£50
P	£6	V	£15
W	£30	Thame C	£100
Taunton C	£50	F	£150
H	£50	P	£2
P	£2	R	£10

Item	Price	Item	Price	Item	Price	Item	Price
S	£100	Topsham Road CC	£75	Circular mileage	£30	Ventnor (IOW) O	£15
V	£30	Torquay C	£50	Circ mileage erased	£15	Wadebridge C	£30
W	£15	P	£6	Tunb-Wells A framed	£75	M	£10
CC	£50	CC	£30	V	£15	Wadesmill CC	£75
Thames Ditton CC	£50	JJ	£75	W	£15	Wadhurst BB	£50
Thaxted BB	£75	Torrington D	£100	Tunstall O	£30	CC	£50
Thetford C	£20	H	£50	Tutbury O	£50	Wailingford (error)	
D	£50	O	£30	Tuxford C	£150	D	£100
R mileage above	£150	P	£6	D	£100	Wakefield C	£30
S	£100	Totnes C	£75	P	£10	D	£50
V	£10	D	£75	V	£30	H	£30
W	£10	O	£10	W erased	£30	P	£2
Y	£10	BB	£75	Twycross CC	£75	R	£75
Y erased	£15	Totness C	£50	Twyford (Hants) CC	£50	V	£15
Thirsk C	£50	H	£50	Twyford-Berks O	£30	W	£10
G	£30	P	£4	Tynemouth C	£30	X	£10
H	£30	V	£50	O	£15	X erased	£30
O	£15	W	£50	Uckfield C	£50	BB	£75
P	£2	Y	£50	G	£50	HH	£50
V	£15	Y erased	£50	O	£15	JJ	£15
W	£10	CC	£50	P	£4	Wakering CC	£50
Y	£15	Totton CC	£30	V	£30	Wallingford D	£50
Thornbury (Som) O	£15	Towcester C	£50	V erased	£30	M	£15
Thorne C	£50	D	£100	Z	£50	P	£6
H	£50	G	£50	AA	£30	V	£15
O	£15	O	£15	Uley (Glos) C	£30	W	£15
P	£2	P	£4	O	£15	Z	£30
V	£15	S	£100	Y	£30	BB	£50
W	£10	V	£30	Ullesthorpe O	£50	CC	£50
Thorney O	£50	V erased	£15	Ulverston C	£50	Wallsend CC	£30
Thornham CC	£50	Town Malling D	£100	W	£15	Walmer O	£50
Thorp-Arch O	£30	S	£100	Ulverstone M	£15	Walsall C	£30
Thorpe (Essex) C	£50	Towyn C	£30	P	£4	O	£30
Thorpe (Norfolk) CC	£75	Trecastle O	£50	V	£30	P	£6
Thrapston C	£75	Tredegar C	£15	W	£30	V	£30
Thrapstone D	£75	Tregony C	£50	BB	£50	W	£15
O	£30	Y	£30	Upper Mill O	£30	Z	£75
P	£4	Y erased	£15	BB	£50	Walsingham C	£15
V	£50	Tring C	£100	Upper Parade/Leamington		D	£50
W	£30	G	£75	E	£30	O	£15
Z	£75	O	£15	Uppingham C	£75	Y	£15
BB	£75	P	£4	D	£150	Waltham Cross D	£75
Thropston D	£100	S	£75	O	£15	P	£4
Thwaite C	£100	V	£30	P	£4	R	£100
V	£75	W	£30	W	£30	V	£50
Ticehurst O	£15	W erased	£50	Y	£15	W	£30
CC	£50	Trowbridge C	£50	Upton (Liverpool) N	£150	W erased	£50
Tickhill O	£15	D	£50	O	£50	Z	£50
Tid CC	£50	O	£30	Upton (Worcs) O	£10	AA	£75
Tiddeswell D	£100	P	£6	V	£50	BB	£75
Tideswell C	£75	S	£50	Y	£30	CC	£75
D	£75	V	£50	Upton.C (Liv'pl) CC	£60	Walton (Liv) C framed	£50
O	£50	W	£15	Upton on S. C	£30	Wandesford D	£150
V	£75	W erased	£30	Upton on Severn D	£30	Wandsford O	£15
W	£75	MM	£100	Usk C	£15	P	£4
Tillingham CC	£75	Truro C	£15	P	£4	Wangford D	£75
Tintern Abbey O	£50	P	£2	S	£50	P	£6
Tipton C	£50	V	£30	V	£10	W	£50
Titchfield O	£75	W	£15	W	£10	Z	£50
Tiverton C	£50	AA	£15	W erased	£15	Wansford V	£75
D	£100	HH	£30	CC	£50	W	£75
H	£75	JJ	£50	JJ	£30	W erased	£50
K	£75	MM	£75	Usworth CC	£75	Wantage C	£30
P	£4	Truroe C	£150	Utoxeter D	£100	D	£75
V	£50	Trysall CC	£75	Uttoxeter C	£30	G	£30
W	£10	Tunbridge C	£50	D	£50	P	£4
Y	£10	D	£50	P	£4	S	£75
Y erased	£15	G	£30	V	£30	W	£15
Z	£50	O	£50	W	£15	W erased	£15
CC	£75	P	£2	W erased	£10	Ware C	£50
Tocester D	£150	S	£50	Z	£50	O	£15
Todmorden CC	£30	V	£15	Uxbridge C	£75	P	£2
Tolleshurst D'Arcy		W	£10	D	£75	V	£30
CC	£75	BB	£50	K	£75	W	£30
Tonbridge Wells P	£4	CC	£50	O	£50	Y	£50
JJ	£50	MM	£75	P	£4	Y erased	£50
Topsham C	£75	Tunbridge Wells D	£50	S	£100	Z	£75
H	£75	G	£75	V	£50	AA	£50
P	£6	S	£75	W	£30	BB	£50
V	£50	Y	£15	W erased	£50	Wareham C	£30
V erased	£50			CC	£75	D	£50

Name	Price
P	£2
W	£15
W erased	£15
Wareham-D D	£75
Wargrave O	£15
CC	£50
Warminster C	£50
D	£50
P	£8
S	£100
V	£30
Y	£15
Y erased	£30
Warrington B	£150
C	£30
D	£50
H	£50
P	£6
V	£50
X	£30
X erased	£50
Z	£50
BB	£50
CC	£50
Crown bag seal	£150
Warwick C	£15
D	£30
F	£100
P	£2
S	£75
V	£15
X	£10
X erased	£30
Y	£10
Z	£30
AA	£50
BB	£30
JJ	£30
MM	£50
Watchet CC	£50
Wateringbury O	£30
Waterloo St (Brighton)	
C	£15
Watford C	£75
G	£100
P	£4
S	£100
V	£30
W	£30
W erased	£50
Z	£75
Wath C dated	£100
Watton (Herts) CC	£75
Watton (Norfolk) C	£15
W	£15
Watton-Herts O	£50
Watton Norfolk O	£15
Waverley St.(Hull) C	£30
Wavertree (L'pool) O	£15
CC	£50
Wednesbury C	£30
P	£4
Weedon C	£75
P	£6
MM	£100
Weely C	£75
Welchpool C	£30
D	£30
H	£30
V	£15
W	£10
AA	£50
BB	£30
Weldon Bridge CC	£50
Welford O	£50
P	£6
Wellesbourne O	£30
Wellingboro W	£30
Wellingborough D	£75
G	£100
H	£75
P	£2
S	£100
V	£50
W	£30
Y	£15
JJ	£75
Wellington (Salop) C	£75
D	£50
V	£50
Y	£15
Y (erased)	£15
Wellington (Som) D	£50
V	£15
V erased	£30
Wellington Com	
(error for Som) CC	£75
Wellington Rd. (B'ham)	
C	£30
Wellington-S (Salop)	
W	£30
Y	£30
Wellington.S (Som) D	£50
Wellington-Salop D	£75
P	£4
Wellington Somst M	£30
Wellington Somerset P	£2
Wells (Norfolk) C	£75
R	£75
Wells (Som) C	£50
W	£30
MM	£100
Wells-N R	£75
R erased	£15
V	£10
Wells Norfolk P	£2
Wells.S. C	£30
R	£50
V	£30
W	£30
Y	£30
Z	£30
AA	£30
HH	£100
MM	£75
Wells Som. Z	£30
Wells Somerset P	£2
Wel.n.borough B	£150
Welshpool C	£30
P	£2
Y	£10
Z	£50
CC	£30
Welwyn C	£100
G	£75
O	£10
P	£4
S	£100
V	£30
W	£50
Wem C	£30
O	£15
Y	£30
Y erased	£30
Wendover F	£150
G	£75
P	£4
S	£100
V	£50
W	£50
W erased	£50
Wenlock O	£10
W	£50
Weobley CC	£50
West Auckland O	£15
West Boldon CC	£50
West Bromwich E	£30
P	£2
West Burton CC	£50
Westbury C	£50
D	£75
P	£4
S	£75
V	£50
W	£30
W erased	£15
Westbury on Trym	
(Bristol) CC	£15
Westbury Salop CC	£50
West Derby (L'pool)	
C framed	£50
O	£30
West Drayton O	£50
West End (Hants) CC	£30
Westerham O	£30
Westfield CC	£75
Westgate C	£50
West Grinstead CC	£50
West Haddon C	£80
West Malling O	£30
West Moulsey CC	£50
Weston super Mare P	£2
West Tarring CC	£75
West Wycombe O	£15
Wetherby C	£50
D	£50
G	£50
M	£30
P	£2
R	£50
V	£15
W	£10
W erased	£10
BB	£50
Weyhill O	£50
CC	£50
Weymouth C	£30
D	£50
G	£50
Q	£2
S	£100
V	£30
W	£15
X	£10
JJ	£50
MM	£75
Whalton CC	£75
Wheatley G	£100
O	£30
P	£4
R	£30
V	£50
Y erased	£50
Whickham CC	£50
Whiddon Down CC	£75
Whimple CC	£30
Whitby C	£30
H	£30
P	£2
R	£100
V	£15
W	£15
X	£10
X erased	£15
Whitchurch (Hants) G	£75
V	£30
W	£15
Whitchurch (Shrop) D	£50
G	£50
Whitchurch H.(Hants)	
D three line	£100
G	£75
Whitchurch Hants M	£10
BB three line	£75
Whitchurch Herefords	
CC	£50
Whitchurch - Oxon O	£15
Whitchurch S (Shrops)	
D	£30
H	£30
O	£15
V	£15
BB	£50
Whitchurch.Salop P	£4
Whitechurch (Shrops)	
D	£75
Whitehaven D	£30
G	£30
M	£30
P	£2
S	£100
V	£15
X	£15
X erased	£15
BB	£50
CC	£75
JJ	£30
Whitfield CC	£50
Whitminster CC	£50
Whittingham O	£15
Y	£15
Y erased	£15
Whittington CC	£75
Whittlesea O	£75
Whitwell (Yorks) O	£30
Whitworth O	£30
Wichnor (Staffs) C	£50
Wickford C	£30
Wickham O	£50
Wickham.Mk C	£15
Wickham Market D	£50
Wickwar C	£75
Widford CC	£75
Wigan C	£50
C in oval	£150
H	£50
P	£6
R	£100
V	£50
X	£30
X erased	£30
Z distinctive	£100
BB distinctive	£100
JJ	£50
MM	£100
Wiggan C	£100
Wigton C	£50
G	£15
P	£2
W	£15
MM	£75
Wiley (Warwicks) C	£50
Wiley (Wilts) C	£30
P	£8
CC	£75
Willenhall O	£30
BB	£50
Willingdon CC	£50
Wilmslow (Manch'r) Z	£50
BB	£50
Wilton C	£30
P	£4
Wily (Wilts) MM	£75
Wimborn D	£75
K	£75
S	£75
V	£30
W	£15
Wimborne O	£15
P	£2
CC	£100
Wimbourn C	£50
Wincanton C	£50
D	£75
P	£2
W	£30
FF	£150

HH	£75
MM	£75
Wincaunton D	£75
Winchcomb O	£10
Y	£30
Y erased	£15
Wincheap (Kent) C	£50
Winchelsea O	£50
Winchester C	£50
D	£30
G	£50
P	£2
Q	£4
S	£50
V	£30
W	£15
X	£10
X erased	£15
CC	£75
Windham C	£100
F	£100
S	£100
V	£30
Windlesham O	£50
CC	£75
Windsor (Berks) C	£30
D	£50
G	£30
P	£4
S	£50
V	£15
W	£15
X	£15
Y	£15
BB	£50
JJ	£15
MM	£75
NN	£75
Windsor/Manchester E	£50
Wingham C	£50
H	£50
P	£6
S	£75
V	£15
W	£15
W erased	£15
CC	£50
Winkleigh CC	£75
Winlaton CC	£50
Winsford C	£30
O	£50
Winslow C	£75
P	£4
V	£50
W	£50
W erased	£30
CC	£100
Winwick CC	£50
Wirksworth C	£50
D	£75
P	£10
V	£50
W	£50
Z	£50
Wisbeach C	£75
O	£10
P	£2
V	£75
W	£30
Y	£15
CC	£75
Wisbich C	£100
D	£150
Witham C	£50
F	£150
G	£50
O	£15
P	£2
R	£100
V	£50
W	£30
W erased	£30
Witham-Hull C	£30
Witney C	£50
D	£50
O	£50
P	£4
V	£30
W	£10
Z	£50
BB	£50
Wittersham CC	£50
Witton Le Wear O	£30
Wiveliscomb O	£15
Wiveliscombe P	£2
Wivelscombe V	£15
W. Malling C	£75
Woburn C	£50
G	£50
O	£30
P	£4
V	£30
W	£15
W erased	£30
Woking CC	£75
Wokingham C	£30
O	£15
P	£4
V	£15
Wolseley Bridge D	£50
M	£30
O	£50
Wolsingham O	£30
Wolston O	£30
CC	£50
Wolverhampton D	£30
G	£50
J	£50
P	£2
R	£75
V	£30
X	£10
X erased	£15
Z	£50
AA	£50
CC	£50
MM	£75
Wolviston O	£50
Woodbridge C	£15
D	£50
P	£4
V	£50
W	£15
CC	£30
NN	£100
Woodbury CC	£75
Woodhouse Lane (Leeds)	
C	£30
Woodside (L'pool) C	£50
N	£150
CC	£50
Woodstock D	£100
K	£50
O	£10
P	£2
S	£75
V	£10
W	£10
AA	£50
CC	£50
Woodyates O	£30
P	£8
CC	£50
Wooler O	£15
X undated	£15
X erased	£10
Woolpit C	£50
O	£30
W	£50
Woolton (L'pool) CC	£75
Woolverhampton D	£175
Woolviston O	£15
Woore N	£150
Wooten under Edge D	£50
S	£75
V	£15
W	£15
W erased	£15
Wootten Bassett D	£150
Wootten Bridge (IOW)	
(spelling error)	
CC	£100
Worcester C	£15
D	£30
H	£15
Q	£2
S	£50
V	£30
X	£15
X erased	£10
Z	£30
BB	£30
JJ	£30
MM	£30
Wordesley CC	£30
Workington C	£100
D	£30
H	£30
P	£2
V	£15
W	£15
Y	£15
Y erased	£15
BB	£50
CC	£50
Worksop C	£50
G	£50
O	£15
P	£6
S	£75
V	£30
W	£30
Z	£75
Worstead C	£50
O	£15
Worthing C	£75
P	£4
W	£30
W erased	£30
NN	£100
Wotten Bassett D	£75
V	£50
Wotton.G (Glos)	
C distinctive	£100
Wotton under Edge D	£50
O	£10
P	£2
CC	£100
JJ	£30
Wotton un.r.Edge AA	£100
Wragby C	£50
O	£30
V	£30
W	£30
Wray O	£30
Wrentham V	£30
W	£30
CC	£30
Wrexham C	£15
D	£50
O	£10
P	£2
V	£15
W	£10
Y	£10
BB	£50
JJ	£50
MM	£100
Wrington C	£30
Wrotham O	£30
Wroughton O	£50
WTR (Warrington) A	£200
Wycombe-H V	£30
Wye O	£50
Wykeham CC	£75
Wykeham-Yorks O	£30
Wymondham C	£50
O	£10
P	£2
W	£10
Wyndham C	£75
X Church (Christchurch)	
D	£100
Yalding O	£50
Yarm C	£75
O	£15
P	£2
V	£15
W	£15
Yarmouth (Nfk) C	£100
D	£75
J	£50
P	£4
V	£15
W	£15
X	£10
CC	£75
JJ	£50
Yarmouth I.W. W	£50
Y	£30
Y erased	£80
Yarmouth-N C	£75
S	£75
V	£15
Yarmouth Norfk P	£2
Yarmouth Norfolk P	£2
Yeaden BB	£50
Yeadon O	£30
Yealmpton O	£50
P	£6
Yeovil C	£30
P	£2
S	£30
V	£15
W	£15
BB	£50
York C	£15
D	£100
H	£30
P	£2
Q	£2
R	£75
V	£15
W	£10
X	£10
CC	£100
JJ	£15
MM	£50
: Micklegate/York C	£30
: Walmgate/York C	£30
Yoxford C	£30
H	£50
O	£15
W	£30

4.   Early Scottish Marks to 1839

The General Post (G.P.O. Edinburgh)

From the 16th century the Scottish burghs (chartered towns and boroughs) gradually developed Posts within their own areas. In addition, messengers were employed to carry mail between burghs and the seat of government in Edinburgh.

In 1616 the Master of Posts, William Seton, set up a General Post which could be used by the public. In 1657 the English North Post Road (cf. chapter 1) was extended to Edinburgh. Surviving examples of items from this period are rare and bear only manuscript indications of charges to be paid.

In 1693 the Postmaster General of the General Letter Office, Edinburgh, decreed that :
  (i)   a dated handstamp should be struck on letters to and from London
  (ii) letters to other parts of England should receive a name stamp
  (iii) letters to other parts of Scotland should <u>not</u> be handstamped at all.

From 1730 only mail going out from Edinburgh was handstamped. From 1758 <u>all</u> mail was handstamped.

Bishop Marks

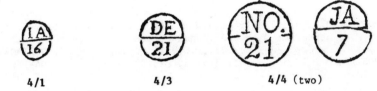

4/1	4/3	4/4 (two)

4/1	Small oval, 13x10mm, in two segments, black	1693-1714	150.00
4/2	As above but in red	1714-1725	150.00
4/3	Single circle, slightly irregular, approx 15mm, red	1725-1757	50.00
4/4	Larger single circle, various sizes and styles, red	1758-1806	5.00
	(15.00 prior to 1785)		

Later datestamps

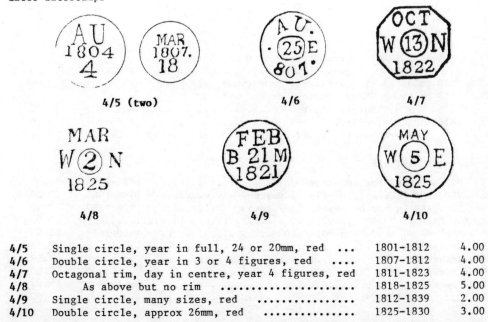

4/5 (two)	4/6	4/7
4/8	4/9	4/10

4/5	Single circle, year in full, 24 or 20mm, red ...	1801-1812	4.00
4/6	Double circle, year in 3 or 4 figures, red	1807-1812	4.00
4/7	Octagonal rim, day in centre, year 4 figures, red	1811-1823	4.00
4/8	As above but no rim	1818-1825	5.00
4/9	Single circle, many sizes, red	1812-1839	2.00
4/10	Double circle, approx 26mm, red	1825-1830	3.00

EDING
BURGH

4/11

EDIN=
BURGH

4/12

4/11	EDING/BURGH, 2 lines, black or red	....	1723-1732	150.00
4/12	EDIN=/BURGH, 2 lines, black or red	....	1732-1756	150.00
4/13	As above but without =, red	....	-1757	150.00

Paid Marks

4/14

4/15

4/16

4/17

4/14	POST/PAID in single circle, 20mm, red	....	1790-1796	20.00
4/15	As above but with additional curved lines, 26mm, red	....	1796-1808	15.00
4/16	POST/PAID in fancy scroll design, red or black	.	1804-1807	50.00
4/17	PAID in upright dated oval, red	....	1807-1813	10.00

4/18

4/19

4/20

4/21

4/18	PAID at EDINBURGH, many types, with or without frame, black or red	....	1808-1839	2.00
4/19	PAID in dated single circle, many types, red	..	1814-1821	2.00
4/20	PAID in the COUNTRY, various types, with or without frame, red	....	1818-1823	12.00
4/21	PAID and date, unframed, red	....	1824-1831	4.00
4/22	As above but in framed single or double circle		1832-1839	2.00

Instructional Markings

4/23	MISSENT/TO/EDINBURGH (various)	....	1813-1839	30.00
4/24	TOO/LATE in single circle, 20mm, red	....	1796-1805	12.00
4/25	TOO LATE in various varieties/frames	....	1806-1839	7.50
4/26	TO PAY/ONE PENNY	....		30.00
4/27	POSTAGE TO EDINBURGH NOT PAID	....	1810-1839	12.00
4/28	Handstruck "1"	....		2.00
4/29	Handstruck "2"	....		7.50
4/30	Crown Inspector's marks, many varieties	....		10.00
4/31	Time stamps	....	to 1808	15.00
4/32	Time plus date stamps	....		2.00

Edinburgh Local Posts (Penny Posts)

Williamson's Post 1773-1793

A private Penny Post organised by Peter Williamson for letters within Edinburgh and Leith. It was taken over by the Post Office and a compensation pension paid.

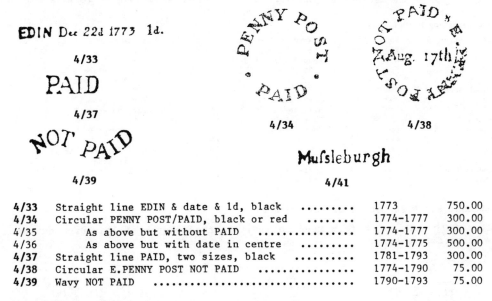

EDIN Dec 22d 1773 1d.

4/33

PAID

4/37

NOT PAID

4/39

4/34

4/38

Mufsleburgh

4/41

4/33	Straight line EDIN & date & 1d, black	....	1773	750.00
4/34	Circular PENNY POST/PAID, black or red	....	1774-1777	300.00
4/35	As above but without PAID	....	1774-1777	300.00
4/36	As above but with date in centre	....	1774-1775	500.00
4/37	Straight line PAID, two sizes, black	....	1781-1793	300.00
4/38	Circular E.PENNY POST NOT PAID	....	1774-1790	75.00
4/39	Wavy NOT PAID	....	1790-1793	75.00

Semi Official Posts

Postmasters were officially appointed to handle General Post in three nearby towns, but in addition organised Penny Posts as private ventures.

4/40	Small straight line **Dalkeith**, black	....	1776-1797	30.00
4/41	As above but **Mufsleburgh**	....	1776-1797	30.00
4/42	As above but **PreftonPans**	....	1776-1797	50.00

City Receiving Houses

A   4/43   B   4/44   C   4/45

Double circle with P.P.O   Double circle with PAID   Double circle with UNPAID

CROSS

DUNDAS STREET

DUKE STREET P.P.O.

D   4/46   E   4/47   F   4/48

One line, with or without frame   Two lines, with or without frame   With or without frame, P.P.O., or other abbreviations

```
┌─────────────────────┐
│  HOWE STREET        │
│ PENNY POST PAID     │
└─────────────────────┘
```

┌─────────────────────────┐
│ HOWE STREET   │
│ PENNY POST UNPAID   │
└─────────────────────────┘

G   4/49
With or without frame,
PP abbreviations or in full

H   4/50
With or without frame,
PP abbreviations or in full

City Receiving Houses

Castle Street A	£50	Grassmarket D	£4	Leith Walk E	£4
B	£50	E	£4	G	£20
C	£30	Hanover Street B	£50	H	£12
E	£4	C	£30	Leopold Place D	£4
F	£8	E	£4	Nicolson Street E	£4
Chapel Street A	£30	F	£4	F	£8
B	£50	High Street E	£4	Port Hopeton E	£20
C	£30	Hillhousefield D	£8	Port Hopetoun D	£50
Cross D	£4	Holyrood D	£4	E	£20
Duke Street B	£50	Howe Street D	£4	Portsburgh D	£20
C	£30	E	£4	F	£20
E	£4	G	£20	West Nicolson Street	
F	£4	H	£20	F (3 lines)	£8
Dundas Street E	£4	India Street E	£4	William Street E	£4
bag seal	£300	Lauriston Place E	£4		

Outbounds and District Receiving Houses

Note : Outbounds was a term used to indicate the suburbs of Edinburgh outside
the legal city area.

J   4/51
With or without frame

┌──────────────────┐
│ RATHO. P.P.O   │
│ 396 — E   │
└──────────────────┘

K   4/52
With or without frame

┌──────────────────┐
│ CURRIE P. P.O   │
│   UNPAID   │
│ 400 →   E   │
└──────────────────┘

L   4/53

┌──────────────────┐
│ CURRIE P. P.O   │
│   PAID   │
│ 400 →   E   │
└──────────────────┘

M   4/54

┌──────────────┐
│ DALKEITH   │
│ JY 14   │
│ 1837   │
└──────────────┘

N   4/55
With or without duty
code letter/time

Outbounds Receiving Houses

Burrowmuirhead	
K (3 lines)	£12
W	£12
AA	£12
Newhaven G	£20
H	£12
Handstruck "2"	£4
Newington AA	£20
AA erased	£4
Handstruck "2"	£4
Stockbridge D	£20
AA	£20
Handstruck "2"	£4
Warriston D	£4
AA	£20

(PERTH)

O   4/56
With lines: place name in
straight line(s) or curved

(MUSSLE BURGH)

P   4/57
Without lines: place name in
straight line(s) or curved

(PENNICUIK PAID PENNYPOST)

Q   4/58
Paid or Unpaid,
abbreviations or in full

District Receiving Offices

Balerno AA	£20	Hermenston J	£12	N with PPO	£8
Broxburn AA	£20	Hermiston AA	£12	AA	£12
Colington H	£100	Kirkliston D	£8	Handstruck "2"	£4
Colinton B	£20	J	£12	Mussleburgh P	£20
D with PP	£12	L	£20	Pennicuik Q	£50
K	£12	M	£30	Q Unpaid	£30
Corstorphin D	£12	AA	£12	Pennycuik H	£8
H	£20	Kirknewton K	£12	J	£12
Corstorphine B	£20	AA	£12	L	£8
K	£20	Lasswade B	£30	M	£20
K erased	£8	C	£20	AA	£12
Cramond D	£150	D	£8	Portobello H	£20
D curved	£8	H	£8	J	£12
H	£20	J	£12	K	£8
K	£12	K	£12	AA	£12
AA	£12	O	£30	AA (fancy)	£300
Currie H	£20	AA	£12	Prestonpans A	£30
K	£12	Handstruck "2"	£8	B	£20
L	£12	Leith B	£12	C	£12
L erased	£8	C	£8	G (variety)	£30
M	£20	D	£20	H	£12
Dalkeith B	£30	H	£12	H (variety)	£8
C	£20	J	£12	J	£12
D	£8	T	£2	K	£8
H	£12	U with PPO	£12	N	£2
J	£8	Y	£2	BB	£30
K	£8	BB	£4	Handstruck "2"	£8
N	£2	CC	£50	Ratho J	£12
AA	£12	DD	£30	K	£8
BB	£8	octagonal d/s	£4	AA	£12
CC	£75	circular d/s	£2	Roslin N	£2
EE	£20	Handstruck "1"	£4	AA	£12
Handstruck "2"	£8	Handstruck "2"	£12	Slateford F	£20
Duddingston N	£8	Libberton B	£20	Tranent B	£20
AA	£50	J	£12	C	£12
CC	£75	K	£12	D	£8
Fisherrow D	£12	AA	£12	G	£12
Ford H	£20	Loanhead AA	£12	H	£8
J	£12	Musselburgh A	£30	J	£12
K	£12	B	£20	N	£2
L	£12	C	£20	P	£30
M	£20	H	£12	AA	£12
N	£2	J	£12	Uphall AA	£20
AA	£12	K	£8	Winchburgh AA	£30

The Provincial Post

R   4/59
Many varieties
(with or without 1 or 2 arcs)

S   4/60
Many varieties
(with or without frame)

GLASGOW
12 MAY 1806

T   4/61

STIRLING
26 APR 1823
431—E

JEDBURGH
374——B

KINGUSSIE
- - - ⚊ E

U   4/62
with or without frame
(see note below)

V   4/63
with or without frame
(see note below)

V erased   4/64
(see note below)

W 4/65 (see note below) **X** 4/66 with or without double circle frame (see note below) **Y** 4/67 double or single arcs **Z** 4/68 with or without arcs

LEVEN PENNY POST

PAID at DUNDEE

GLASGOW PAID N DE 16 1839

AA 4/69 many types **BB** 4/70 (two) many types

MISSENT TO DUNFERMLINE

DUNDEE TOO LATE

TOO LATE

CC 4/71 many varieties **DD** 4/72 **EE** 4/73 many varieties/frames

Notes concerning above illustrations:
a) Route letters shown in types **U,V,W** and **X**:
   B (Berwick), C(Carlisle), D(Dumfries), E(Edinburgh), G(Glasgow), L(Leith)
b) The example shown of **V erased** shows traces of mileage and route letter, but others show no such traces at all

Abercherder D	£8	Air D	£12	Anstruther D	£20	Arocher P	£20
Aberdeen D	£12	D curved	£15	D curved	£12	Aros D	£20
E	£12	Airdrie D	£8	N	£2	N	£4
N	£2	N	£2	V	£8	AA	£30
O	£8	O	£12	V erased	£8	V	£20
T	£4	V	£8	W	£20	V erased	£20
U	£4	W	£12	Anwith D	£50	AA	£30
U (day mth/year)	£8	Alexandria D	£12	Appin D	£8	Arran D	£25
Y	£2	Alford D	£20	N	£4	Arrochar D	£8
AA	£20	V	£8	V	£8	V	£8
BB	£4	W	£12	V erased	£8	W	£12
CC	£50	Alloa D	£12	W	£12	Assynt D	£20
Handstruck "1"	£4	O	£12	AA	£20	Auchenblae SO E	£12
Aberdour D	£12	V	£8	Arbroath D	£12	Auchnacraig D	£30
D curved	£20	W	£12	E	£12	E	£20
V	£8	Y inverted	£12	N	£2	V	£20
V erased	£8	AA	£12	R	£20	V erased	£20
W	£20	Alness AA	£20	V	£8	Auchterarder N	£2
Aberfeldy D	£20	Alyth O	£12	V erased	£8	O	£20
N	£2	V	£8	W	£12	V	£8
P	£12	W	£12	CC	£50	V erased	£8
V	£8	Anderston (Glasgow)		EE	£12	W	£20
V erased	£8	D	£4	Ardersier D	£8	Auchertermuchty D	£8
W	£20	Anderston Walk (Glasgow)		Ardrie (Airdrie) AA	£20	E	£8
AA	£20	E	£12	Argyle Street (Glasgow)		AA	£20
Aboyne D	£8	Annan D	£8	E	£8	Avemore D	£50
N	£2	W	£12	Arisaig D	£12	Aviemore D	£50
V	£20	V	£8	V	£8		
V erased	£12	V erased	£8	V erased	£8		
Achterarder E	£20	Y	£2	W	£12		

Ayr D	£30
N	£2
U	£8
U erased	£8
V	£8
W	£8
Y	£2
AA	£12
CC	£50
EE	£20
Ayton D	£8
N	£2
P	£12
V	£8
W	£12
Balfron V	£12
AA	£30
Balichulish D	£20
Ballantrae E	£12
V	£8
V erased	£8
W	£20
AA	£20
Ballater D	£12
Ballindalloch D	£8
N	£2
V	£8
V erased	£8
Banchory N	£2
O	£12
V	£8
V erased	£8
W	£12
W erased	£20
Banff D	£8
N	£2
O	£12
V	£8
V erased	£12
W	£12
AA	£12
Barrhead AA	£30
Barrowfield (Glasgow)	
D	£20
Bathgate P	£20
V	£8
V erased	£8
W	£12
Beauly D	£8
N	£2
V	£8
AA	£20
Beild D	£12
W	£20
bag seal	£150
Beith D	£12
N	£2
V	£8
V erased	£8
W	£12
AA	£20
Bellshill bag seal	£75
Bervie D	£12
V	£8
V erased	£8
W	£12
Biggar D	£8
V	£8
W	£12
Blackburn D	£12
Blackhillock D	£8
Blackshiells D	£8
Blackshiels O	£12
P	£30
W	£8
Blairadam V	£8
V erased	£8
Blair Athole V	£8
Blairgowrie N	£2
O	£12
V	£8
V erased	£8
W	£20
Boat of Forbes W	£20
Bogroy D	£12
Bonar Bridge V	£8
V erased	£8
Bonaw D	£8
V	£12
W	£12
Bo'ness (various spellings incl Borrowstowness)	
D	£8
D curved	£20
N	£2
V	£8
V erased	£8
W	£12
Bowholm V	£12
V erased	£12
Bowmore E	£20
V	£12
V erased	£12
AA	£50
Braco D	£12
Braemar V	£10
Brechin D	£8
V	£8
W	£12
Bridgend of Halkirk	
E	£20
Bridge of Earn D	£8
V	£8
W	£12
Bridge of Erne E	£20
Bridge of Halkirk O	£20
S	£20
Broadford (Skye) E	£12
V	£12
V erased	£12
Brodick D	£12
Broomielaw (Glasgow)	
D	£8
Broughton V	£12
W	£12
Broughton/Tweed E	£12
Brucklaw D	£12
Buckie V	£12
V erased	£8
Bunessan D	£30
Burghead AA	£20
Burntisland D	£8
E	£12
V	£8
W	£12
Cairndow D	£8
O	£12
V	£12
W	£20
Y	£4
AA	£20
Cairnish V	£12
W	£12
Callander N	£2
R	£20
V	£8
V erased	£8
W	£12
Cambuslang AA	£30
Campbellton (Argyll)	
E	£12
Campbelton (Argyll)	
E	£12
N	£2
V	£8
V erased	£8
W	£12
Y	£2
Campbeltown (Argyll)	
E	£12
Canonbie D	£12
N	£2
EE	£20
Carinish D	£20
Carlinwark D	£20
Carluke D	£8
Carmoustie AA	£30
(error for Carnoustie)	
Carnwath D	£12
V	£12
V erased	£12
W	£12
Carrbridge D	£12
Castle Douglas E	£12
N	£2
S	£20
V	£8
V erased	£8
W	£12
Y	£2
AA	£12
Cathcart H	£30
Catrine AA	£30
Cawdor AA	£20
Chance Inn D	£12
O	£12
V	£8
V erased	£8
W	£12
Chapel of Seggat P	£75
Clachan D	£8
Cluny D	£8
Cockburnspath N	£2
Coldingham D	£12
V	£12
V erased	£12
W	£12
Coldstream D	£8
E	£20
N	£2
R	£20
V	£8
W	£12
AA	£20
Colinsburgh E	£12
N	£2
O	£12
V	£8
V erased	£8
Coll V	£30
W	£30
Comrie D	£8
W	£20
Cornhill AA	£20
Coupar Angus E	£12
V	£8
W	£12
Coupar Fife E	£12
V	£8
V erased	£8
W	£12
Cowcaddens (Glasgow)	
D	£12
Cowdenburn D	£12
V	£12
W	£12
Cowpar Angus E	£12
Cowpar Fife E	£12
Craigellachie N	£2
V	£8
V erased	£8
Crail D	£8
V	£8
W	£12
Creetown D	£20
O	£20
V	£8
V erased	£8
W	£12
Crieff D	£8
N	£2
O	£12
V	£8
V erased	£8
W	£12
Crinan D	£12
Crinan SO D	£8
W	£12
Cromarty D	£8
V	£8
V erased	£8
W	£12
Crook V erased	£12
Crook on Tweed V	£12
Cruden D	£12
Cullen D	£8
W	£12
Culross D	£12
N	£2
V	£8
V erased	£8
W	£12
Cumbernauld AA	£20
Cumnock D	£12
N	£2
V	£12
V erased	£12
W	£12
AA	£30
Cupar Fife E	£30
N	£2
O	£12
W	£12
Y	£2
AA	£12
CC	£50
EE	£12
Daljarrock bag seal	£300
Dalmally P	£12
V	£8
W	£12
Dalmellington V	£8
Dalry (Ayrshire) V	£4
V erased	£4
W	£12
Denny D	£8
N	£2
V	£8
V erased	£8
W	£12
Dingwal D	£20
Dingwall D	£8
O	£12
V	£8
W	£12
Y	£2
AA	£20
Dornoch D	£12
O	£12
V	£8
V erased	£8
W	£12
Douglas D	£8
D curved	£20
V	£8
V erased	£8
AA	£20
Douglas Milln E	£12
Doune N	£2
P	£12
V	£8
V erased	£8

W	£12
AA	£20
Drumlanrig E	£20
Drumnadrochit D	£12
E	£12
Drymen P	£20
V	£20
W	£12
Duke Street (Glasgow)	
D	£20
Dumbarton D	£8
E	£20
N	£2
V	£8
V erased	£8
W	£12
AA	£12
CC	£50
Dumfermline D	£12
E	£12
V	£8
V erased	£12
Dumfries D	£12
D with mileage 341 boxed below	£20
N	£2
O	£12
P	£12
T	£4
U	£4
U erased	£8
V	£8
W	£12
Y	£2
AA	£12
BB	£8
CC	£50
EE	£12
Dunbar D	£8
E	£75
N	£2
V	£8
V erased	£8
W	£12
Dunbeath D curved	£12
O	£12
V	£8
W	£12
Dunblane D	£8
N	£2
R	£20
V	£8
V erased	£8
W	£12
Dundee D	£8
E	£12
N	£2
P	£12
T	£4
U	£4
Y	£2
AA	£12
BB	£4
CC	£50
EE	£20
Handstruck "2"	£8
TO PAY/ONE PENNY	£30
Dunfermline D	£12
E	£12
P	£8
W	£12
Y	£2
AA	£12
CC	£50
Dunkeld D	£12
D curved	£12
N	£2
V	£8
V erased	£8
W	£12
Dunnet SO E	£12
Dunning D	£8
Dunoon D (1806 only)	£20
N	£2
V	£8
V erased	£8
W	£12
Y	£4
Duns D	£30
Dunse D	£8
N	£2
O	£12
V	£8
V erased	£8
W	£12
Y	£4
AA	£12
Dunvegan D	£12
V	£12
W	£20
Dysart D	£12
V	£8
V erased	£8
W	£12
Eaglesham D	£12
Earlston D	£8
V	£8
V erased	£8
W	£12
Handstruck "2"	£12
Easdale AA	£30
Ecclefechan D	£8
E	£12
V	£8
V erased	£8
W	£12
Echt F	£30
Eddleston V	£12
W	£12
Eddlestone D	£20
Elgin D	£12
O	£12
V	£8
V erased	£8
W	£12
Y	£2
AA	£12
Elie N	£2
Elie Fife O	£12
Ellon D	£8
N	£2
W	£12
Ely Fife O	£20
V	£8
W	£12
Errol D	£8
O	£12
W	£12
Evanton V	£8
Exchange (Glasgow) D	£8
Eyemouth R	£20
V	£8
V erased	£8
Eyemouth SO V	£12
W	£20
Falkirk D	£8
E	£12
O	£12
V	£8
W	£12
Y	£2
AA	£12
BB	£8
EE	£12
Falkland D	£8
AA	£20
Farr SO E	£12
Fearn AA	£30
Fenwick D	£12
Fettercairn D	£8
V	£8
Findhorn AA	£20
Finhaven SO E	£20
Focabus D	£12
E	£12
O	£20
S	£20
V erased	£8
W	£12
Fordoun D	£30
Forfar D	£12
N	£2
V	£8
V erased	£8
W	£12
BB	£12
EE	£20
Bag seal	£300
Forres D	£8
N	£2
O	£12
V	£8
W	£12
Fort Augustus	
D curved	£30
E	£8
R	£20
V	£12
AA	£20
Fort George D	£12
D curved	£12
S	£20
V	£8
V erased	£8
W	£12
Fortingal AA	£20
Fortrose D	£8
V	£8
W	£12
Fort William D	£8
E	£12
N	£2
S	£20
V	£8
V erased	£8
W	£20
AA	£20
"Thistle" (fancy)	£500
Fraserburgh E	£8
N	£4
V	£8
V erased	£8
W	£12
AA	£30
Fushiebridge E	£8
N	£2
W	£8
Fyvie D	£8
BB	£50
G (Glasgow)	
3 lines dated	£2
Galashiels D	£8
N	£2
R	£20
V	£8
V erased	£8
W	£12
CC	£50
Handstruck "1"	£12
Handstruck "2"	£20
Gallowgate (Glasgow)	
D	£8
Galston AA	£20
Garlieston D	£12
N	£4
Garmouth AA	£20
Gartmore AA	£20
Garve SO E	£20
Gatehouse D	£8
S	£30
V	£8
V erased	£8
W	£12
Gatehouse of Fleet	
E	£12
Girvan D	£8
N	£2
V	£8
V erased	£8
W	£12
AA	£20
CC	£50
Handstruck "2"	£50
Glammis D	£12
V	£8
V erased	£8
W	£12
Glasgow E	£50
N	£2
P	£4
P (fancy frame)	£75
T	£2
U	£2
X	£2
X erased	£2
Y	£2
Y with EX	£4
Z	£2
AA	£8
BB	£2
CC	£50
DD	£30
EE	£12
Handstruck "1"	£4
Handstruck "2"	£4
MORE TO PAY	£50
Glenlivat D	£8
W	£12
Glenluce D	£8
E	£12
N	£2
V	£8
W	£12
AA	£30
Glenmoreston E	£50
Golspie D	£8
N	£2
V	£30
W	£12
Gorbals (Glasgow) D	£20
Grangemouth N	£2
R	£30
V	£12
V erased	£8
W	£30
Grantown D	£12
V	£8
W	£12
Greenlaw D	£8
P	£12
V	£8
W	£12
Greenock D	£12
E (fancy)	£150
O	£12
P	£12
T	£8
U	£4
Y	£2
AA	£12

BB	£4
CC	£50
Handstruck "1"	£20
Handstruck "2"	£30
Gretna AA	£20
Haddington D	£20
E	£20
V	£4
V erased	£8
W	£8
Y	£2
AA	£12
EE	£12
Handstruck "1"	£8
Hamilton D	£8
E	£12
N	£2
R	£20
V	£8
W	£12
Y	£2
Y undated	£12
AA	£12
CC	£50
Hauick D	£20
Hawick D	£8
V	£8
V erased	£8
W	£12
Y	£2
AA	£12
CC	£50
EE	£20
Helensburgh D	£8
N	£2
V	£8
V erased	£8
W	£12
AA	£20
Helmsdale V	£12
V erased	£8
Holytown D	£12
N	£2
V	£8
V erased	£8
W	£12
Hope Street (Glasgow) D	£4
Howgate D	£20
Huna D	£12
V	£12
V erased	£12
W	£20
Huntley D	£8
N	£2
V	£8
W	£12
Inchture P	£8
Inveerkithing E	£12
Inverary D	£8
E	£12
R	£20
V	£8
V erased	£8
W	£12
Y	£2
AA	£20
CC	£50
Invergordon E	£8
R	£20
V	£12
V erased	£8
W	£30
Inverkeithing D	£8
N	£2
R	£20
V	£8
V erased	£8
W	£12
AA	£20
CC	£50
Inverkip AA	£20
Inverness D	£12
D curved	£30
E	£20
N	£2
P	£12
V	£8
W	£12
X	£8
X erased	£8
Y	£2
BB	£50
EE	£12
Irvine D	£8
N	£8
V	£8
V erased	£8
W	£12
AA	£12
CC	£50
Jedburgh D	£8
E	£20
V	£8
W	£12
Y	£2
Handstruck "1"	£20
Johnstone D	£8
AA	£20
Jura V	£30
V erased	£30
Keith D	£8
V	£8
W	£12
Keith Hall N	£4
V	£12
V erased	£12
Kelso D	£12
N	£2
O	£12
P	£12
V	£8
W	£12
Y	£2
AA	£12
BB	£30
EE	£12
Kelty Bridge E	£20
W	£20
Kenmore V	£8
V erased	£8
Kennoway S	£20
V	£8
V erased	£8
W	£20
Kerriemuir E	£12
Kettle N	£2
AA	£20
CC	£75
EE	£12
Bag seal	£150
Kilbride AA	£30
Killearn AA	£30
Killin D	£8
O	£12
W	£12
Kilmarnock D	£12
E	£12
N	£2
R (no frame)	£12
S	£12
V	£8
W	£12
Y	£2
AA	£12
BB	£4
CC	£50
Kilmaurs AA	£30
Kilpatrick H	£20
AA	£20
Kilsyth D	£8
D curved	£20
O	£30
V	£8
W	£12
Kincardine D	£8
V	£12
V erased	£8
W	£12
AA	£12
Kincardine O'Niel R	£20
V	£8
V erased	£8
W	£12
Kinghorn D	£12
N	£2
V	£12
V erased	£8
W	£12
CC	£75
Kingorn D	£12
Kingussie D	£12
V	£12
V erased	£8
Kinross D	£8
O	£12
V	£8
V erased	£8
W	£12
Y	£2
AA	£12
Kintail D	£12
Kintore D	£12
V	£12
V erased	£8
W	£12
Kintra D	£150
Kippen V	£12
V erased	£8
W	£12
AA	£20
Kippin P	£30
Kircaldy Y	£4
Kirkaldy D	£30
Kirkcaldie W	£12
Kirkcaldy D	£12
N	£2
P	£12
V	£8
Y	£2
AA	£12
BB	£12
CC	£50
EE	£12
UNPAID TO	£50
Kirkcudbright D	£12
E	£12
R	£20
V	£8
V erased	£8
W	£12
Y	£2
Kirkintulloch D	£8
E	£12
V	£8
W	£12
Kirkmichael AA	£20
AA erased	£20
Kirkwall D	£12
E	£20
N	£2
P	£12
V	£12
V erased	£20
W	£12
Kirriemuir N	£2
V	£12
V erased	£8
W	£12
Laggan D	£12
Lairg D	£12
Lamlash D	£8
Lanark D	£8
N	£2
V	£8
V erased	£8
W	£12
Langholm D	£8
E	£20
V	£8
V erased	£8
W	£12
Y	£2
Largs D	£8
N	£2
P	£12
V	£8
V erased	£8
W	£12
AA	£12
Lauder D	£8
E	£12
W	£8
Laurencekirk E	£8
N	£2
W	£12
Leadhills D	£8
W	£12
Leith Lumsden D	£20
Leitholm AA	£20
Lennoxtown AA	£30
Lerwick E curved	£30
N	£2
V	£12
W	£20
AA	£30
Lesmahagow N	£2
V	£8
V erased	£8
Leven D	£8
V	£8
W	£12
Y	£2
AA	£12
CC	£50
Handstruck "2"	£20
Linlithgow D	£8
E	£20
N	£2
V	£8
W	£20
Linton D	£20
V	£12
W	£12
Lismahago CC	£50
Lithgow AA	£12
Lochalch V	£12
Lochalsh D	£8
V	£12
AA	£20
Lochcarron D	£8
S	£75
V	£20
W	£30
Lochearnhead R	£30
W	£12
Lochgilphead D	£8
N	£2
R	£20
V	£12
V erased	£8
W	£12
AA	£20
Lochgylphead V	£12

Lochinver D	£12
Lochmaben E	£12
W	£12
V	£8
V erased	£8
Lochwinnoch D	£20
Lockerby D	£8
N	£2
P	£12
V	£8
V erased	£8
W	£12
EE	£12
Longhope D	£30
Lossiemouth AA	£12
Luib V	£20
Luss D	£8
O	£12
V	£12
W	£12
Lybster D	£12
Lynwilg SO V	£12
Markinch N	£2
AA	£12
CC	£50
EE	£12
Maryhill F	£20
Muchlin D	£8
AA	£20
Mauchline D	£12
N	£2
V	£8
V erased	£8
W	£12
Maybole D	£8
N	£2
V	£8
V erased	£8
W	£12
Meigle D	£12
V	£8
V erased	£8
W	£12
Melrose D	£12
V	£8
V erased	£8
W	£12
Y	£2
Handstruck "1"	£12
Handstruck "2"	£20
Melvich SO E	£12
Methlic D	£12
Mey SO V	£20
Mid Calder D	£8
N	£2
P	£12
V	£8
W	£12
AA	£30
Middleton D	£12
W	£30
Millgavie F	£20
Minnhyve D	£20
Mintlaw N	£2
V	£8
V erased	£8
AA	£20
Moffat D	£8
N	£2
V	£8
V erased	£8
W	£12
AA	£20
CC	£50
Moneymusk E	£12
Moniaive D	£8
O	£20
V	£12
W	£30
Monnigaff E	£30
Montrose D	£12
V	£8
W	£12
Y	£2
Y (inverted)	£50
AA	£20
EE	£20
Mortlach O	£12
W	£12
Morvern D	£12
N	£4
W	£30
Mossat D	£12
Mount Stewart P	£50
Moy D	£30
Muirdrum D	£12
N	£4
O	£12
V	£8
W	£12
Muirkirk D	£8
V	£8
V erased	£8
W	£20
Munlochy D	£8
V	£12
V erased	£8
W	£30
Nairn D	£8
N	£2
O	£12
V	£8
W	£12
Neilston P	£30
V	£30
W	£30
AA	£20
Newburgh D	£8
N	£2
AA	£20
EE	£12
Newburgh Fife E	£12
W	£12
New Deer D	£12
New Galloway E	£8
V	£8
W	£12
Newmills AA	£20
New Pitsligo D	£12
Newport V	£8
V erased	£8
Newton Douglas E	£20
R	£20
Newton Stewart E	£12
N	£4
V	£8
W	£12
AA	£20
Noblehouse E	£12
N	£2
V	£12
V erased	£8
AA	£20
North Berwick S	£20
V	£12
W	£8
North Queensferry D	£12
V	£8
V erased	£8
W	£12
Novar O	£20
V	£12
Oban D	£8
N	£2
V	£8
W	£12
AA	£12
Old Deer D	£12
V	£8
W	£12
Old Meldrum D	£12
E	£8
E (step frame)	£75
V	£12
W	£12
Old Rain D	£12
V	£8
V erased	£8
W	£12
Paisley D	£8
N	£2
O	£12
T	£4
U	£4
V	£4
W	£8
Y	£2
AA	£12
BB	£4
CC	£50
Handstruck "2"	£30
Paisly D	£12
Parkhead H	£20
AA	£20
Parkhill D	£8
Peebles D	£12
V	£8
W	£12
Y	£2
AA	£12
Perth D	£12
D curved	£12
O	£12
T	£8
U	£4
W	£50
Y	£4
AA	£12
BB	£4
CC	£50
EE	£12
"Lamb" (fancy)	£400
Peterhead D	£8
N	£2
V	£8
V erased	£8
W	£12
Y	£2
Pitcaple D	£8
Pitlochry N	£2
V	£8
AA	£20
Pitmain D	£30
Pittenweem D	£8
E	£12
W	£12
Pollockshaws F	£30
AA	£30
Polmont AA	£30
Poolewe V	£12
Portaskaig D	£12
S	£50
W	£20
Port Askeg E	£75
Port Dundas RH (Glasgow)	
Z	£12
Port Glasgow D	£8
E	£12
R	£20
S	£20
V	£4
W	£12
Y	£2
CC	£50
Portland Street (Glasgow)	
E	£12
Portmahomac AA	£30
Portnacroich E	£50
Port Patrick E	£12
W	£12
Y	£2
Portree D	£8
V	£12
Portsoy D	£8
W	£12
Port William E	£8
N	£4
V	£12
Poyntzfield D	£12
Press D	£12
W	£20
Prestonkirk D	£8
N	£2
R	£20
V	£8
V erased	£8
W	£12
Rachanmill V	£12
V erased	£12
Rannoch AA	£20
Reay AA	£30
Renfrew D	£8
V	£8
W	£12
Rhynie D	£8
W	£12
W erased	£30
Rothes D	£20
V	£8
W	£12
Rothesay D	£8
E	£12
V	£8
W	£12
Y	£2
AA	£20
Rothiemay AA	£20
Ruthven D	£20
St Andrews D	£12
V	£8
V erased	£8
W	£12
Y	£2
CC	£50
EE	£12
St Boswells Green E	£8
N	£2
V	£12
W	£12
St Margts Hope D	£12
St Rollox (Glasgow)	
D	£30
Saltcoats D	£8
N	£2
V	£8
V erased	£8
W	£12
AA	£12
Sanday AA	£30
Sanquhar D	£8
D curved	£12
V	£8
V erased	£8
W	£12
AA	£20
Sauchiehall (Glasgow)	
D	£12
Sconser D	£20
W	£20
Selkirk D	£8
N	£2
V	£8
W	£12
Y	£4
Handstruck "2"	£20
Skene D	£12
V	£8
W	£12

South Ferry R	£20	V	£8	Tayinloane V	£12	Tyndrum V	£20
South Queensferry V	£8	V erased	£8	V erased	£12	V erased	£8
V erased	£8	W	£12	Tayn D	£30	W	£20
W	£12	Y	£2	Thornhill D	£8	Tyree V	£30
Stage Hall D	£12	AA	£20	N	£2	W	£50
E	£12	Strathaven V	£12	R	£12	Udney D	£12
O	£12	V erased	£8	V	£8	Uist to/Dunvegan	
V	£12	W	£30	W	£12	E (see chap 14)	£200
W	£12	Strathblane V	£20	Thornton AA	£20	Ullapool D	£20
Stanley AA	£12	AA	£30	Thurso D	£12	V	£12
Stewarton D	£8	Strathdon D	£12	N	£2	W	£12
N	£2	W	£12	O	£12	Watten D	£20
V	£8	Strathpeffer E	£12	P	£20	W Kilbride V	£20
V erased	£8	Strichen D	£10	V	£8	V erased	£8
W	£12	W	£10	V erased	£8	Westray AA	£30
Stewartton E	£20	Stromness O	£20	W	£12	West Salton V	£20
Stirling D	£8	V	£12	Tiry D	£50	Whitburn D	£8
N	£2	W	£20	Tobermoray D	£12	E	£8
O	£8	Stronsay AA	£30	Tobermorry D	£30	N	£2
P	£12	Strontian D	£8	Tobermory N	£4	W	£8
U	£4	N	£4	V	£12	Whitehouse D	£12
V	£8	V	£12	W	£20	Whithorn D	£8
W	£12	W	£20	AA	£30	E	£12
Y	£2	AA	£20	Tomintoul V	£8	N	£2
AA	£12	Strontien E	£20	Tomintoul SO W	£12	V	£8
BB	£8	Swinton AA	£20	Tongue D	£30	V erased	£8
CC	£50	Tain D	£8	R	£30	Wick D	£12
Stonehaven D	£8	N	£2	V	£12	V	£8
N	£2	V	£8	W	£12	V erased	£8
V	£8	W	£12	Tradestown (Glasgow)		W	£12
V erased	£8	Tamnavoulen SO E	£12	D	£20	Y	£2
W	£12	Tarbert D	£8	Troon N	£2	BB	£12
EE	£30	D curved	£12	V	£12	Wigtown D	£8
Stornaway D curved	£12	P	£12	V erased	£8	V	£8
V	£12	V	£8	Tullick D	£12	W	£12
V erased	£8	V erased	£8	W	£12	Y	£2
W	£12	W	£12	Turriff D	£8	AA	£12
Stow D	£8	Y	£2	N	£2	Wilsontown D	£20
W	£8	Tarland D	£12	V	£8	V	£12
Stranraer D	£12	O	£12	V erased	£8	W	£20
E	£20	W	£12	W	£8	Windygates V	£8
O	£20			AA	£12	Wishaw D	£8
				BB	£30		

The Additional Halfpenny

For the 26 years from 1813 to 1839 letters carried by 4-wheeled coaches on roads in Scotland <u>for any part of the journey</u> were charged a tax of ½d in addition to the postage. Letters inside a Penny Post area were exempt as were those re-directed within Scotland and Free Franks.

If the tax was paid by the sender a red manuscript "½" was noted next to the postage amount. When tax was due from the receiver a black manuscript "½" or a special handstamp was appropriate. Instructions were issued that, should a mark be noticed as indistinct at a transit or arrival office, a second mark must be applied. Hence the existence of letters bearing two different "½" marks.

At first only a few main offices had special handstamps, but their use (with colour variations) was gradually extended to many towns in Scotland, plus some in England and Dublin. Note : the Wales/Ireland manuscript additional halfpenny charge (1836-39) is an unrelated matter.

Further reading : The Additional Halfpenny Mail Tax by W G Stitt Dibden (1963). The Scottish Additional Halfpenny Mail Tax by K Hodgson and W A Sedgewick, second edition 1984.

The main types are illustrated below, but there are very many different sizes and variations.

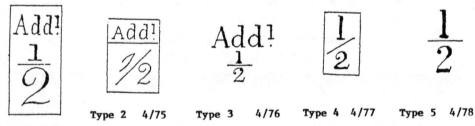

Type 1 4/74   Type 2 4/75   Type 3 4/76   Type 4 4/77   Type 5 4/78

In the listing that follows each town is followed by the types used (see illustrations) ans the colours are shown in brackets. The colours are : b=black, bl=blue, g=green, r=red. Note : Ballantrae has weak/missing left frame line.

Aberdeen 5 (b,bl)	£4
Annan 3 (b)	£10
Arbroath 4 (b)	£10
Ayr 4 (b,bl)	£10
Ayton 4 (b)	£20
Ballantrae 4 (b)	£20
Blackshiels 4 (b)	£50
Bonaw 4 (b)	£35
Bo'ness/Borrowstouness 5 (b)	£20
Bridge of Earn 4 (b)	£20
Campbellton 4 (b)	£20
Canonbie 4 (b)	£20
Castle Douglas 4 (b)	£20
Coldstream 3,5 (b,bl,r)	£10
Culross 4 (b)	£50
Cumnock 4 (bl)	£35
Cupar 4 (b,bl,g)	£10
Denny 4 (bl)	£50
Dumbarton 4 (b)	£20
Dumfries 1,4 (b,r)	£4
Dunbar 4 (b,bl)	£20
Dundee 3,5 (b,bl,g,r)	£4
Dunfermline 4 (b,bl)	£10
Duns 4 (b,bl)	£10
Edinburgh 1,2,3 (b,r)	£4
Falkirk 4,5 (b,bl)	£4
Fort William 4 (b)	£50
Fraserburgh 4 (b)	£20
Galashiels 4 (b)	£20
Garlieston 4 (b)	£20
Girvan 4 (b)	£20
Glasgow 1,2,3,4 (b,bl,r)	£4
Golspie 4 (r)	£75
Greenock 3,4 (b,bl)	£4
Hamilton 4 (b)	£20
Hawick 3,4 (b)	£10
Inverary 4 (b)	£20
Inverkeithing 4 (b)	£20
Inverness 3,5 (b)	£4
Irvine 4 (b)	£50
Jedburgh 4 (b)	£10
Kelso 3 (b)	£4
Kettle 4 (b)	£20
Kilmarnock 4,5 (b,bl)	£10
Kinghorn 4 (b)	£50
Kinross 4 (b)	£50
Kircaldy 4 (b,bl,g)	£10
Kirkcudbright 4 (b)	£20
Leadhills 4 (b)	£30
Leith 1,3 (b,bl,g)	£10
Lesmahago 4 (b)	£35
Leven 4 (b,bl,g)	£20
Linlithgow 4 (b)	£10
Lochalsh 4 (b)	£20
Lockerby 4 (b,r)	£20
Markinch 4 (b)	£20
Mauchline 1 (b)	£50
Maybole 4 (b)	£20
Moffat 4 (b)	£20
Montrose 5 (b)	£4
Newburgh 4 (b,bl)	£10
New Galloway 4 (g)	£50
Newton Stewart 4 (r)	£75
Oban 4 (b)	£20
Paisley 1,2,3,4 (b)	£4
Perth 5 (b)	£4
Peterhead 4 (b)	£20
Port Glasgow 3 (b)	£10
Port Patrick 4 (b)	£20
Portree 4 (b)	£35
Rothsay 1 (b)	£20
St Andrews 4 (bl)	£20
Saltcoates 4 (b)	£20
Stewarton 4 (b)	£50
Stirling 3 (b,bl,g)	£10
Stranraer 4 (b)	£10
Whitburn 4 (b)	£20
Wigtown 4 (b)	£20

5. Early Irish Marks

Bishop Marks were used at Dublin for the General Post in Ireland from 1670. The straight line provincial town name stamps were first used in 1698.

Our planned major new Early Irish chapter is under development and is planned as a major feature of the Eighth Edition.

5/1

5/2

5/3

5/5

5/6

5/7

5/1	Small Dublin Bishop marks, 1670–1746	100.00
5/2	Larger Dublin Bishop marks, 1746–95	30.00
5/3	Circular year marks, 1796–1807	10.00
5/4	'Mermaids', 1808–14 .... (average quality)	60.00
5/5	'Mermaid' paid marks, in red, 1808–15 .... (average. quality)	100.00
5/6	Octagonals, 1811–31	2.50
5/7	Diamonds, in red, 1815–36	1.00
5/8	Octagonal or rectangular paid marks, in red, 1814–46	2.50

WATERFORD   BELFAST   DERRY 118

5/9

5/10

5/13

5/9	Town stamps, straight line with large first letter, 1698–1736.......	250.00
5/10	As above but uniform height, 1700–1839	20.00
5/11	As above but contracted names 1712–63	150.00
5/12	Undated double arc town names, black, green, blue or red, 1829–39 ..	20.00
5/13	Mileage marks, straight line, unboxed, various colours, 1808–39 ...	20.00
5/14	as above, but boxed, 1820–32	40.00
5/15	Single circle mileage marks, 1818–29	30.00
5/16	Single circle date stamps, 1829–31	30.00
5/17	Single or double arc date stamps from 1832	2.00
5/18	Provincial paid stamps	25.00

6. The Great Post Office Reforms, 1839 - 1844

Uniform 4d Post, 5 Dec 1839 - 9 Jan 1840

Despite very heavy postal charges, for years the Post Office was run at a loss. From 5 December 1839, as an experiment, a flat rate of 4d per ½ ounce was introduced on all letters formerly charged at 4d or more, regardless of distance. Most towns marked letters with a black manuscript '4' (unpaid) or in red for those paid in advance. Some towns used handstamps but these are scarce.

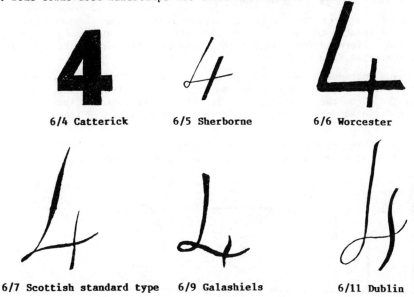

6/4 Catterick   6/5 Sherborne   6/6 Worcester

6/7 Scottish standard type   6/9 Galashiels   6/11 Dublin

6/1 Manuscript '4', 'P4', 'Pd 4' or 'Paid 4', black for unpaid letters   35.00
6/2   As above but in red for paid letters 60.00

6/3 Handstruck '4' from English or Welsh towns (several in some cases): from 500.00

	Arundel	Dorchester	Ipswich	Scarborough
	Ashburton	Grimsby	Kington	6/5 Sherborne
	Ashby	Guildford	Leominster	Stockton
	Baldock	Halifax	Manchester	Wakefield
	Blackburn	Hawes	Norwich	Welshpool
	Carlisle	Hertford	Nottingham	Whitchurch
6/4	Catterick	Hoddesdon	Oxford	Woodbridge
	Chester	Horsham	Rushyford	6/6 Worcester
	Cullompton			

Note : a cover from Nottingham sold for £1430 at auction in 1992

6/7   Handstruck '4' from Scottish towns (standard type):

Aberdeen	£85	Glasgow	£80	Leith (blue)	£100
Dundee	£100	Haddington	£85	Perth	£80
Edinburgh	£50	Inverness	£100	Stonehaven	£100

6/8   As above but individual Scottish types:

Ayr	£100	Golspie	£250	Lochgilphead	£600
Coldstream	£250	Hawick	£400	Port Glasgow	£200
Galashiels 6/9	£300	Kirkwall	£300	Wigtown	£250

6/10 Handstruck '4' from Irish towns:

Armagh (blue)	£750	Drogheda	£750	Galway	£750
Ballymena	£750	Dublin **6/11**	£350	Newry	£750
Belfast	£750	Dundalk	£750	Roscrea	£750
Derry	£750	Dungannon	£750	Rosscarberry	£1000
Down	£750	Enniskillen	£750		

Further reading : "Charge Marks of The 4d Post" (1990) by P.J. Chadwick.

Uniform 1d Post, from 10 Jan 1840

The Uniform 4d Post was such a great success that it soon became clear the charge could be reduced to 1d for a pre-paid letter and 2d when paid by the recipient. The Uniform 1d Post started on 10 January 1840 and the Free Frank system was abolished from that date.

Many post towns introduced handstamps, usually in red, to show that 1d postage had been pre-paid. Similarly there were handstamps, usually in black, to show that 2d was due, from the recipient, for letters not pre-paid. This system continued in diminishing use after the introduction of adhesive stamps and until the 1850s.

Many towns used thick or thin straight lines sometimes appearing like a red handwritten line without serifs. Some towns used more than one type.

6/13	6/14 6/15	6/16	6/17	6/18
Standard types of England and Wales		**Aberystwyth**	**Burnley**	**Chester**

6/12 Manuscript '1' in red, paid letters 1.50
Handstruck '1' (see **6/13-15**), 'pd 1', 'Paid 1d', 'P1', etc. from English or Welsh towns (usually in red) :

Abergavenny	£30	Bawtry	£50	Bungay	£150
Aberystwyth **6/16**	£50	Beaconsfield	£75	Buntingford	£100
Addingham	£100	Beaumaris	£250	Burford	£250
Amlwch	£75	Bedale	£75	Burnley **6/17**	£250
Andover	£150	Berwick	£30	Bury St. Edmunds	£30
Arundel	£100	Beverley	£50	Carlisle	£30
Attleborough	£75	Biddenden	£100	Carnarvon	£150
Aylsham	£30	Bingham	£100	Catterick	£100
Baldock	£150	Bishop Auckland	£75	Cawood	£150
Bangor	£50	Bishop's Stortford	£75	Chelmsford	£50
Banstead	£250	Blackburn	£75	Chertsey	£50
Barford	£75	Bognor	£100	Chester **6/18**	£30
Barnet	£75	Bolton	£100	Chichester	£100
Barrow in Furness	£250	Bradford	£30	Colchester	£50
Barrow on Humber	£100	Braintree	£100	Coleford	£75
Basingstoke	£15	Brentford	£150	Colne	£250
Battle	£150	Bridgend	£75	Conisborough	£50
		Brighton	£15	Cranbrook	£50

Crawley	£75	Long Stratton	£100	Sevenoaks	£75
Croydon	£75	Lyndhurst	£50	Shaftesbury	£75
Darlington	£50	Maidstone	£30	Sheffield	£100
Dorking	£100	Margate	£75	Skipton	£100
Douglas IOM	£200	Marlborough	£75	Slough	£100
Edgware	£75	Merthyr Tydfil	£100	Southampton	£15
Englefield Green	£100	Middleham	£100	Staplehurst	£100
Epsom	£75	Montgomery	£100	Stevenage	£150
Esher	£100	Nantwich	£75	Swindon	£75
Falmouth	£50	Newbury	£75	Tadcaster	£100
Folkestone	£100	Newcastle on Tyne	£15	Thetford	£100
Gateshead	£50	Newcastle-u-Lyme	£50	Thrapston	£100
Goole	£75	New Cross (Manchester)	£150	Ticehurst	£100
Gravesend	£50	Newmarket	£75	Todmorden	£100
Guernsey	£275	Newport Pagnell	£100	Tunbridge	£30
Guildford	£30	New Romney	£75	Tunbridge Wells	£50
Halifax	£15	Northampton	£30	Ulverstone	£150
Harleston	£100	Nottingham	£75	Uxbridge	£50
Hastings	£75	Oldham	£150	Wadhurst	£100
Havant	£100	Otley	£50	Waltham Cross	£75
Haverfordwest	£150	Oulney (Olney)	£75	Warwick	£75
Hawes	£75	Petworth	£75	Watton	£75
Henfield	£100	Poole	£75	Wednesbury	£75
Hertford	£75	Port Madoc	£75	Weedon	£150
High Wycombe	£75	Portsmouth	£150	Welwyn	£75
Hoddesdon	£100	Presteign	£100	West Bromwich	£30
Horsham	£50	Pyle	£100	West Drayton	£100
Horwich	£250	Ramsgate	£75	West Haddon	£250
Huddersfield	£30	Rickmansworth	£100	Whitchurch	£75
Hull	£15	Ripley	£100	Whitehaven	£30
Hurst Green	£100	Robertsbridge	£100	Wigan	£150
Ipswich	£30	Rochford	£75	Wigton	£50
Ixworth	£100	Romford	£75	Windsor	£50
Jersey	£275	Romsey	£75	Wokingham	£75
Kingston	£100	Rushyford	£100	Wolverhampton	£50
Lamberhurst	£75	St.Leonards-on-Sea	£150	Workington	£75
Ledbury	£50	Salisbury	£5	Worthing	£75
Leeds	£5	Sawbridgeworth	£75	Wrexham	£75
Liverpool	£5	Scarborough	£50	York	£50
London	£5	Selby	£150		

| 6/20 | 6/21 | 6/22 | 6/23 | 6/24 | 6/26 | 6/27 |

| Standard types of Scotland | Ballater | Ballymena | Dundalk |

6/19 Handstruck '1', etc., from Scottish towns (usually in red):

Aberdeen	£4	Ballantrae	£7.50	Cockburnspath	£20
Aberdour	£7.50	Ballater 6/24	£150	Coldstream	£12
Alloa	£7.50	Banff	£4	Collinsburgh	£7.50
Annan	£7.50	Bathgate	£7.50	Crail	£7.50
Anstruther	£7.50	Beith	£12	Crieff	£20
Appin	£7.50	Biggar	£7.50	Culross	£12
Arbroath	£12	Boness	£12	Cumnock	£7.50
Auchinblae	£30	Braco	£20	Cupar	£7.50
Auchterarder	£12	Bridge of Earne	£7.50	Dalkeith	£12
Auchtermuchty	£7.50	Callander	£7.50	Denny	£12
Ayr	£7.50	Campbelton	£12	Douglas	£12
Ayton	£12	Canonbie	£7.50	Dumbarton	£7.50

Dumfries	£4	Jedburgh	£7.50	Newport	£12		
Dunbar	£7.50	Kelso	£7.50	Newton Stewart	£12		
Dundee	£4	Kettle	£12	North Queensferry	£12		
Dunfermline	£12	Kilmarnock	£4	Paisley	£4		
Dunoon	£7.50	Kincardine	£7.50	Peebles	£7.50		
Dunse	£12	Kinghorn	£7.50	Perth	£7.50		
Ecclefechan	£7.50	Kirkcaldy	£12	Peterhead	£7.50		
Edinburgh	£2	Kirkcudbright	£7.50	Pittenweem	£7.50		
Elgin	£7.50	Kirkwall	£300	Port Patrick	£12		
Falkirk	£4	Lanark	£7.50	Port William	£12		
Fisherrow	£20	Langholme	£7.50	Prestonkirk	£12		
Forfar	£4	Largs	£7.50	Rhynie	£30		
Forres	£7.50	Lauder	£7.50	St Andrews	£7.50		
Fort William	£7.50	Laurencekirk	£30	St Boswells	£12		
Fraserburgh	£7.50	Leith	£4	Sanquhar	£12		
Galashiels	£7.50	Lerwick	£30	Selkirk	£7.50		
Garliestone	£20	Lesmahago	£12	Stewarton	£7.50		
Girvan	£12	Leven	£12	Stirling	£7.50		
Glasgow	£4	Linlithgow	£12	Stonehaven	£50		
Glenluce	£20	Lochgilphead	£7.50	Stow	£12		
Golspie	£12	Lockerby	£4	Stranraer	£7.50		
Greenock	£4	Mauchline	£7.50	Tarbert	£20		
Haddington	£7.50	Maybole	£7.50	Thornhill (Doune)	£20		
Hamilton	£7.50	Melrose	£12	Tobermory	£12		
Hawick	£7.50	Midcalder	£12	Whithorn	£12		
Holytown	£20	Moffatt	£7.50	Wick	£7.50		
Huntly	£7.50	Montrose	£7.50	Wigtown	£12		
Inverkeithing	£12	Musselburgh	£7.50				
Inverness	£12	Newburgh	£7.50				

6/25 Handstruck '1d', etc., from Irish towns (usually in red):

Town	Price	Town	Price	Town	Price
Abbeyleix	£40	Cookstown	£75	Maryborough	£70
Armagh	£30	Derry	£25	Navan	£40
Athlone	£30	Donaghadee	£50	Parsonstown	£30
Athy	£75	Down	£30	Portarlington	£100
Ballymena 6/26	£30	Drogheda	£20	Portglenone	£35
Ballymoney	£45	Dublin	£15	Roscrea	£20
Borrisakane	£40	Dundalk 6/27	£25	Tallow	£45
Carrickfergus	£50	Dungarvan	£60	Verner's Bridge	£55
Castleburn	£40	Maghera	£50		

6/30	6/31	6/33	6/35
Blackburn	Colchester	Kirkcaldy	Castlebar

6/28 Manuscript '2' or '2d', black, for unpaid letters 4.00
6/29 Handstruck '2' or '2d' from English and Welsh towns (usually
    black, sometimes blue or green):

Town	Price	Town	Price	Town	Price
Aberayron	£75	Gilsland	£75	Portsmouth	£50
Abingdon	£75	Guernsey	£275	Preston	£75
Attleborough	£75	Halifax	£75	Reading	£100
Bangor	£100	Harwich	£100	Richmond (Yks)	£75
Basingstoke	£75	Hastings	£100	Rochford	£75
Bawtry	£75	Haverfordwest	£50	Romford	£75
Beaumaris	£150	Hawes	£100	Romsey	£75
Bedale	£75	Haydon Bridge	£50	Ryde	£50
Belford	£75	Hertford	£75	Salisbury	£30
Beverley	£75	Holyhead	£100	Selby	£50
Birmingham	£50	Hounslow	£100	Sleaford	£50
Bishop Auckland	£75	Huddersfield	£75	Southampton	£50
Blackburn 6/30	£75	Ipswich	£50	Stafford	£75
Bolton	£100	Isle of Man	£250	Stockport	£75
Bradford	£50	Jersey	£275	Stoneham	£75
Braintree	£75	Leeds	£50	Sunderland	£30
Bridgewater	£100	Litchfield	£50	Todmorden	£150
Burnley	£100	Liverpool	£15	Wakefield	£75
Bury (Lancs)	£100	London	£5	Waltham Cross	£75
Canterbury	£50	Loughborough	£75	Warwick	£75
Carlisle	£100	Market Deeping	£50	Wellington (Salop)	£100
Carnarvon	£150	Marlborough	£150	Weymouth	£75
Catterick	£75	Middlesborough	£100	Whitehaven	£50
Chester	£50	Newbury	£75	Wigan	£100
Cockermouth	£50	Newcastle on Tyne	£15	Wigton	£50
Colchester 6/31	£50	Newcastle-u-Lyme	£50	Winchester	£50
Darlington	£50	Newport (Mon)	£150	Windsor	£75
Derby	£50	Northampton	£100	Wolverhampton	£50
Dorchester	£50	North Shields	£50	Woodbridge	£75
Douglas	£200	Nottingham	£50	Workington	£50
Durham	£100	Otley	£75	Wrexham	£50
				York	£50

6/32 Handstruck '2' from Scottish towns (usually black, sometimes blue or green):

Town	Price	Town	Price	Town	Price
Aberdeen	£75	Falkirk	£20	Linlithgow	£12
Alloa	£20	Galashiels	£20	Lochgilphead	£20
Annan	£50	Glasgow	£20	Maybole	£12
Auchtermuchty	£12	Glenluce	£30	Melrose	£20
Ayr	£50	Greenock	£7.50	Moffatt	£12
Ayton	£30	Haddington	£12	Newburgh	£12
Ballantrae	£20	Hamilton	£50	Newport	£20
Beith	£20	Hawick	£12	Paisley	£50
Bridge of Earn	£50	Inverkeithing	£20	Peebles	£30
Cairnryan	£30	Irvine	£20	Perth	£12
Canonbie	£20	Jedburgh	£50	Pittenweem	£20
Carsphairn	£12	Kelso	£20	Portobello	£20
Cockburnspath	£30	Kettle	£30	St Boswells	£20
Creetown	£20	Kilmarnock	£12	Sanday	£50
Crieff	£20	Kinross	£20	Selkirk	£20
Dumbarton	£20	Kirkcaldy 6/33	£50	Stirling	£20
Dunbar	£12	Kirkwall	£30	Stonehaven	£75
Dunblane	£20	Langholme	£30	Stow	£20
Dundee	£7.50	Largs	£20	Stranraer	£12
Dunfermline	£12	Leith	£12	Tranent	£50
Dunse	£20	Lerwick	£30	Whithorn	£50
Edinburgh	£7.50	Leven	£20		

6/34 Handstruck '2' from Irish towns (usually black, sometimes blue or green):

Town	Price	Town	Price	Town	Price
Abbeyleix	£25	Donegal	£25	Maryborough	£20
Armagh	£20	Drogheda	£20	Monaghan	£20
Athlone	£20	Dublin	£15	Moneymore	£20
Ballyboro	£25	Dungannon	£20	Mullingar	£20
Ballyjamesduff	£25	Dundalk	£20	Newry	£20
Ballymena	£20	Enniskillen	£25	Newtownlimavady	£30
Ballymote	£20	Kells	£20	Portadown	£25
Banbridge	£20	Kilbeggan	£35	Roscrea	£25
Belfast	£20	Killucan	£30	Tipperary	£25
Castlebar 6/35	£20	Lisnaskea	£30	Tralee	£30
Cookstown	£20	Longford	£25	Tuam	£30
Derry	£20	Lurgan	£20	Warren Point	£30
Donaghadee	£20	Magherafelt	£25		

Maltese Cross Cancellations, 1840 - 1844

These were introduced in May 1840 to obliterate the new adhesive stamps and prevent their fraudulent re-use. They appear also on postal stationery - centrally on Mulready sheets, but over the Queen's head on other items.

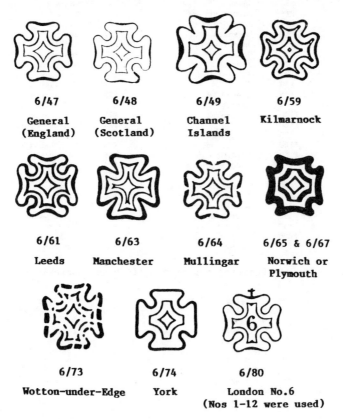

6/47	6/48	6/49	6/59
General (England)	General (Scotland)	Channel Islands	Kilmarnock

6/61	6/63	6/64	6/65 & 6/67
Leeds	Manchester	Mullingar	Norwich or Plymouth

6/73	6/74	6/80
Wotton-under-Edge	York	London No.6 (Nos 1-12 were used)

The value of an imperf stamp, on and off cover, varies considerably with the number and width of its margins. The following values are based on a 3 clear-margins stamp of good appearance at our regular 85% (3 star) quality. A 4 wide-margins stamp of fine appearance would be at least double.

		One Penny Imperf				Two Penny Blue Imperf			
		1840 Black		1841 Red		1840 No Lines		1841 White Lines	
	Colours:	⊠	○	⊠	○	⊠	○	⊠	○
6/36	Red	£100	£50	+	£300	£300	£150	–	++
6/37	Black	£100	£50	£10	£3	£300	£150	£75	£15
6/38	Blue	++	£500	£110	£35	++	+	+	£400
6/39	Brown	£450	£200	–	–	–	–	–	–
6/40	Green	–	–	+	£500	–	–	–	–
6/41	Magenta	£800	£200	–	–	++	+	–	–
6/42	Orange	£450	£150	–	–	–	–	–	–
6/43	Ruby	£350	£200	–	–	++	+	–	–
6/44	Vermilion	£300	£125	–	–	–	–	–	–
6/45	Violet	+	£500	–	–	–	–	–	–
6/46	Yellow	–	+	–	–	–	–	–	–

Values :   + = more than £1000
           ++ = more than £2000

Types:	One Penny Imperf				Two Penny Blue Imperf			
	1840 Black		1841 Red		1840 No Lines		1841 White Lines	
	⊠	○	⊠	○	⊠	○	⊠	○
6/47 General	£100	£50	£10	£3	£300	£150	£75	£25
6/48 Scottish	£125	£50	£15	£8	£300	£150	£85	£35
6/49 Ch Isles	–	–	+++	£375	–	–	–	–
6/50 Belfast	–	–	£75	£30	–	–	£140	£75
6/51 Brighton	–	–	£125	£40	–	–	–	–
6/52 Cork	–	–	£150	£60	–	–	£140	£75
6/53 Coventry	–	–	£200	£55	–	–	–	–
6/54 Dublin	£350	£150	£40	£12	£600	£300	£100	£50
6/55 Dursley	–	–	£100	£45	–	–	–	–
6/56 Greenock	£400	£125	£35	£12	£850	£375	–	–
6/57 Hollymount	–	–	£900	£140	–	–	–	–
6/58 Kelso	–	–	£125	£35	£700	£335	£300	£125
6/59 Kilmarnock	–	£500	£500	£75	+	£750	£400	£150
6/60 Leamington	–	–	£50	£20	–	–	–	–
6/61 Leeds	£450	£200	£250	£75	+	£500	£350	£150
6/62 Limerick	–	–	£75	£30	–	–	–	–
6/63 Manchester	£175	£75	£20	£10	+	£300	–	–
6/64 Mullingar	+	£500	£750	£175	+	£875	–	–
6/65 Norwich	–	–	£65	£25	+	£475	£400	£125
6/66 Perth	–	–	£50	£18	–	–	–	–
6/67 Plymouth	£400	£200	–	–	+	£475	–	–
6/68 Settle	–	–	£700	£150	–	–	–	–
6/69 Stirling	–	–	£45	£15	–	–	–	–
6/70 Stonehaven	+	£200	£300	£100	£900	£375	–	–
6/71 Welshpool	–	£200	£250	£60	–	–	–	–
6/72 Whitehaven	–	–	£700	£100	–	–	–	–
6/73 Wotton	+	£400	£1500	£400	++	£950	–	–
6/74 York	–	–	£200	£60	+	£650	£300	£125
6/75 London 1	–	+	£60	£15	–	++	£200	£75
6/76 London 2	+	£750	£50	£12	–	++	£200	£75
6/77 London 3	+	£750	£60	£15	–	–	£200	£75
6/78 London 4	+	£750	£150	£40	–	++	£200	£75
6/79 London 5	+	£750	£50	£12	–	++	£350	£100
6/80 London 6	+	£750	£40	£10	–	++	£200	£75
6/81 London 7	+	£750	£40	£10	–	++	£375	£150
6/82 London 8	+	£750	£40	£10	+++	++	£300	£100
6/83 London 9	+	£750	£50	£12	–	++	£450	£150
6/84 London 10	+	£750	£60	£15	–	++	£550	£175
6/85 London 11	–	–	£100	£25	–	–	£400	£100
6/86 London 12	+	£750	£100	£25	–	++	£100	£50

Maltese Crosses on piece are worth about 50% above the price for loose stamps.

Values :   + = more than £1000
          ++ = more than £2000
         +++ = more than £4000

7. Numeral, Spoon and Duplex Postmarks

Numeral handstamps replaced the Maltese Crosses in 1844, but it was still necessary to place an additional dated postmark on the reverse of each cover. From 1853 the first double, or duplex, handstamps started to appear. Thus the place of origin and the date could be combined into one strike.

Basic Prices for London, England and Wales:

		Numeral	Duplex
Queen Victoria:	Penny Red Imperf.	7.00	-
Queen Victoria:	Penny Red Perf.	1.50	1.50
Queen Victoria:	Penny Lilac	2.00	1.00
King Edward VII:	½d or 1d	2.00	1.00
King George V:	½d or 1d	3.50	1.00
King George VI period		5.00	-
Queen Elizabeth II period		10.00	-

London: Inland Section

7/1

7/4

7/5

7/1	Horizontal oval with number in diamond, single, 1-37, 39-44 and 52-75, from 1844	1.50
7/2	As above but twin, 45, 46 or 47	25.00
7/3	As above but triple, 48 or 49	100.00
7/4	Duplex, square datestamp with indented corners, from 1853	10.00
7/5	Duplex, circular datestamp, number in diamond, vertical oval, 1-107	2.00
7/6	As above but double circle datestamp	8.50
7/7	Single obliterators with number with or without diamond, vertical oval or circular	3.00

London: District Post and Suburban Offices

7/8

7/9

7/10

7/11

7/13

7/8 Horizontal oval with number in circle, 1-98, from 1844 .... 5.00
7/9 Duplex, circular datestamp with vertical oval, 1853-57 .... 3.50
7/10 Single obliterators with District initials, vertical oval or circular 3.00
7/11 Duplex with vertical oval, several series, from 1858 .... 2.00
7/12 Sideways duplexes of London W or SE, 1857-62 .... 4.00
7/13 Duplex with hexagonal datestamps, for late fees 10.00

Numbers used in London District Post cancellations
(note – the datestamps sometimes include the "handstamp number" and/or the code for the London District as shown below) :

				B and C Series, issued from 1861
1	Highgate	41	Brentford	
2	Finchley		Barnes	1B Ponders End
	E. Finchley	42	Paddington	2B Colney Hatch
3	Whetstone		Walworth	3B Hornsey
4	Hampstead	43	Charing Cross	4B Southgate
5	Hendon		Sutton	5B Holloway
6	Edgware		Aldgate	6B Clapton
	Churton St	44	North Row	7B Loughton
7	Stoke Newington		Wimbledon	8B Hackney
8	Tottenham		Manor Park	9B Canning Town
	W. Brompton	45	Portland St	10B Chadwell
9	Kentish Town		Tottenham	11B Poplar
10	Edmonton		North Woolwich	12B Charlton
	S. Kensington	46	Stepney	13B Chislehurst
11	Enfield	47	Southwark	14B Erith
	Chelsea	48	Shoreditch	15B Foots Cray
12	Bow	49	Sidmouth St	16B Lessness Heath
13	Stratford		Royal Hill Greenwich	17B Lewisham
14	Leyton	50	Victoria Docks	18B Peckham
	St. Martin's Place	53	Woodford Green	19B Penge
15	Woodford		Homerton	20B Plumstead
	Highbury	54	Norwood	21B Rotherhithe
16	Chigwell	55	Leyton St	22B Welling
	Victoria St, EC	56	Isleworth	23B Brixton Hill
17	Ilford	57	Sutton	Brixton
	Leytonstone	58	Wimbledon	24B Camberwell
18	Deptford	60	Kilburn	25B Merton
19	Halfway St	61	Willesden	26B South Lambeth
	Finsbury Pk.	62	Harrow	27B Stockwell
20	Greenwich	63	Elstree	28B Streatham
21	Woolwich	64	Cheshunt	29B Thornton Heath
	Wanstead		W. Ealing	30B Walworth
22	Eltham	65	Camberwell	Maida Hill
	Plaistow	66	Lewisham	31A New Wandsworth
23	Bexley	67	Peckham	31B Battersea
	Brockley	68	Kennington	32B Petersham
24	Dulwich	69	Blackheath	33B Teddington
25	Sydenham	70	Anerley	34B Acton
26	Beckenham	71	Catford	35B Ealing
	Kensal Town	72	Lower Norwood	36B Hanwell
27	Clapham	73	Shooter's Hill	37B Notting Hill
28	Tooting		WC District Office	37C Notting Hill
29	Mitcham	74	Tottenham	38B Paddington
	Forest Gate	75	Edmonton	38C Paddington
30	Carshalton		Paddington DO	39B Shepherds Bush
	Lee	76	New Cross	40B Southall
31	Wandsworth	77	E Dulwich	41B St. John's Wood
32	Putney	78	SE District Office	42B Stanmore
33	Mortlake	79	SW District Office	43B Sudbury
34	Richmond	80	Tottenham	44B The Hyde
	Earl's Court	81	Lower Edmonton	45B Barking
35	Twickenham	82	Leyton	46B Walham Green
	Bethnal Green	83	Upper Edmonton	Fulham
36	Hampton	84	Chingford	47B Sunbury
	Walthamstow	85	Walthamstow	48B Forest Hill
	Balham	86	NW District Office	49B Sth Norwood
37	Brompton	87	N District Office	51B Winchmore Hill
38	Kensington	88	E District Office	52B Wood Green
39	Hammersmith	89	W District Office	53B Upper Holloway
40	Acton	90	Muswell Hill	Junction Rd.,
	House of Commons	91	Cricklewood	Upper Holloway

England and Wales

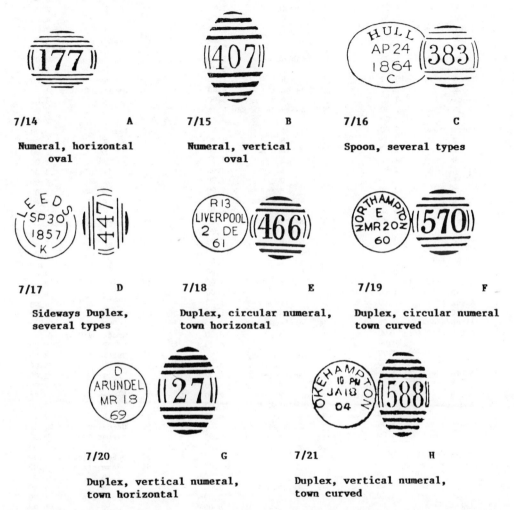

7/14   A   7/15   B   7/16   C

Numeral, horizontal oval   Numeral, vertical oval   Spoon, several types

7/17   D   7/18   E   7/19   F

Sideways Duplex, several types   Duplex, circular numeral, town horizontal   Duplex, circular numeral town curved

7/20   G   7/21   H

Duplex, vertical numeral, town horizontal   Duplex, vertical numeral, town curved

Notes :

(a) The numbers and thickness of bars vary
(b) Some vertical types have numbers/letters in top and/or bottom bars
(c) Many minor variations in placenames are not listed
(d) Marks for which a value is not at present established (noted as "?" in Fifth Edition) have been omitted
(e) Marks which did not relate to a specific geographical location, eg Railway Sorting Tenders and TPOs, are not listed - see chapter 13 for these
(f) Some numbers and periods of non-geographical use eg in London Chief Office; such additional usages are not listed in this edition.

We are indebted to John Parmenter for permission to use information from his 6-volume work "Barred Numeral Cancellations" in this chapter. See Bibliography for details.

1	Abergavenny A	3.00
	B	7.00
	F	4.00
	H	2.00
2	Aberystwith A	3.00
	F	2.00
	H	2.00
	Aberystwyth H	1.00
3	Abingdon A	3.00
	D	10.00
	H	2.00
4	Wantage A	3.00
	G	2.00
	H	2.00
5	Accrington A	5.00
	B	8.00
	F	2.00
	H	1.00
6	Alfreton A	3.00
	F	2.00
	H	2.00
7	Crich A	20.00
	Longhope B	15.00
8	Alnwick A	3.00
	E	2.00
	G	3.00
	H	2.00
10	Alresford A	3.00
	H	2.00
	Alresford/Hants	
	H	1.00
11	Alton A	2.00
	G	2.00
	Alton/Hants H	2.00
12	Altrincham A	3.00
	B	10.00
	F	2.00
	H	2.00
13	Ambleside A	3.00
	B	8.00
	H	2.00
14	Amersham A	3.00
	H	1.00
15	Chesham A	3.00
	B	8.00
	H	5.00
	Chesham/Bucks H	1.00
16	Great Missenden	
	A	3.00
	B	8.00
	H	1.00
17	Amesbury A	15.00
	B	15.00
	H	2.00
18	Ampthill A	3.00
	F	4.00
	H	2.00
20	Silsoe A	20.00
21	Andover A	3.00
	B	10.00
	G	2.00
	H	2.00
22	Andover Rd. A	15.00
	Micheldever	
	Station A	15.00
	F	10.00
	H	4.00
23	Whitchurch A	5.00
	Senny Bridge B	20.00
	H	8.00
24	Overton A	7.00
	B	5.00
25	Appleby A	3.00
	H	1.00

26	Arrington A	15.00
	Cray B	20.00
27	Arundel A	3.00
	B	6.00
	E	2.00
	G	2.00
	H	2.00
28	Ashbourne A	3.00
	F	2.00
	H	1.00
29	Ashburton A	3.00
	B	5.00
30	Ashby de la Zouch	
	A	3.00
	B	8.00
	H	2.00
31	Ashford A	4.00
	B	8.00
	E	3.00
	G	3.00
	H	2.00
	Ashford/Station	
	Office H	4.00
32	Ashton Under	
	Lyne A	3.00
	B	8.00
	D	10.00
	F	2.00
	H	1.00
33	Atherstone A	3.00
	B	10.00
	F	3.00
	H	1.00
34	Attleborough	
	A	10.00
	B	6.00
	Attleborough/	
	Norfolk H	2.00
35	Axminster A	4.00
	B	5.00
	H	2.00
36	Colyton A	10.00
37	Seaton A	10.00
	Buckfastleigh	
	B	4.00
38	Aylesbury A	3.00
	B	8.00
	F	2.00
	H	2.00
39	Aylsham A	3.00
	B	8.00
	H	8.00
40	Bagshot A	3.00
	E	200.00
	Newtown/	
	Monmouthshire	
	H	4.00
	Chapel Town/Mon	
	H	3.00
41	Bakewell A	2.00
	F	8.00
	H	2.00
42	Baslow A	10.00
	Chiswick H	6.00
	Login B	20.00
43	Turnham Green	
	B	40.00
	Docking B	8.00
44	Tideswell A	30.00
45	Baldock A	3.00
	B	7.00
	E	12.00
	H	2.00

46	Banbury A	3.00
	B	10.00
	E	2.00
	G	4.00
	H	2.00
47	Bangor A	5.00
	D	15.00
	E	2.00
	G	2.00
	H	1.00
48	Barnard Castle	
	A	3.00
	F	2.00
	H	2.00
49	Barnsley A	3.00
	B	5.00
	F	2.00
	H	1.00
50	Barnstaple A	3.00
	B	5.00
	D	12.00
	F	2.00
	H	1.00
51	Barton-on-Humber	
	A	6.00
	F	12.00
	H	2.00
52	Basingstoke A	3.00
	H	2.00
53	Bath A	2.00
	B	8.00
	D	4.00
	E	2.00
	H	2.00
	Woodford Green	
	H	100.00
54	Battle A	3.00
	D	75.00
	G	2.00
	H	2.00
55	Bawtry A	8.00
	E	2.00
	H	2.00
56	Gringley A	20.00
	Forest Row B	8.00
	H	3.00
57	Beaconsfield A	4.00
58	Beaumaris A	5.00
	B	10.00
	H	1.00
59	Beccles A	5.00
	B	8.00
	G	2.00
	H	2.00
60	Bedale A	3.00
	B	15.00
	E	2.00
	G	2.00
	H	2.00
61	Bedford A	3.00
	B	8.00
	D	12.00
	E	2.00
	H	2.00
62	Belford A	4.00
	G	8.00
	H	2.00
63	Wooler A	12.00
	H	2.00
64	Belper A	3.00
	E	2.00
	H	5.00

No.	Place	Code	Value		No.	Place	Code	Value		No.	Place	Code	Value
65	Berkhemstead	A	3.00		81	Stanhope	A	6.00		102	Woolpit	A	10.00
		B	8.00				B	8.00			Leyton/S.O.	B	7.00
		H	2.00		82	Bishops Castle						H	6.00
	Berkhampstead	H	2.00				A	3.00			Winfrith	B	7.00
66	Berwick	A	2.00				B	10.00		103	Bourn	A	6.00
		B	6.00				H	1.00				B	6.00
		E	2.00		83	Bishops Stortford						E	4.00
		G	2.00				A	6.00			Bourne	H	2.00
		H	2.00				B	8.00		104	Brackley	A	3.00
	Berwick Station						F	2.00				F	2.00
		B	25.00				H	2.00				H	1.00
		F	20.00		84	Canterbury	A	3.00		105	Bracknell	A	4.00
67	Beverley	A	3.00				B	6.00				H	2.00
		B	12.00				D	10.00		106	Bradford on Avon		
		F	2.00				F	2.00				A	12.00
		H	2.00				H	2.00				H	2.00
68	Bewdley	A	3.00		85	Bishops Waltham				107	Bradford Yks	A	2.00
		E	3.00				A	5.00				B	8.00
		G	6.00				B	7.00				D	5.00
		H	2.00				H	1.00				H	5.00
69	Bicester	A	3.00		86	Blackburn	A	6.00			Bradford/Yks	H	2.00
		F	4.00				B	8.00			Bradford Yorks		
		H	2.00				E	2.00				F	2.00
70	Bideford	A	2.00				H	1.00				H	2.00
		B	5.00		87	Blandford	A	3.00			Bradford/Yorks		
		F	2.00				B	7.00				H	2.00
		H	1.00				F	2.00			Bradford		
71	Biggleswade	A	4.00				H	1.00			(Yorks)	H	5.00
		B	8.00		88	Bodmin	A	2.00		108	Carnarvon	A	3.00
		F	4.00				G	2.00				B	20.00
		H	1.00				H	4.00				D	10.00
72	Billericay	A	3.00		89	Wadebridge	A	5.00				F	2.00
		B	10.00		90	Padstow	A	5.00				H	2.00
		H	1.00		91	Bognor	A	3.00		109	Walthamstow	B	3.00
73	Bilston	A	4.00				G	2.00				H	3.00
		E	2.00				H	2.00			Walthamstow S.O.		
		G	4.00		92	Bolton	A	3.00				H	8.00
		H	2.00				B	6.00			Walthamstow/		
74	Birkenhead	A	5.00				D	10.00			Orford Rd	H	30.00
		C	85.00				E	2.00		110	Keighley	A	3.00
		D	3.00				H	1.00				B	12.00
		F	2.00		93	Boroughbridge						H	2.00
		H	1.00				A	6.00			Ingrow/Keighley		
75	Birmingham	A	2.00				B	15.00				H	25.00
		A (roller)	100.00		94	Boston	A	6.00		111	Bingley	A	3.00
		B	3.00				B	8.00				B	12.00
		C	10.00				D	20.00				H	2.00
		D	4.00				E	2.00		112	Braintree	A	3.00
		F	2.00				G	2.00				F	2.00
		H	2.00				H	2.00				H	2.00
		H (5 bars)	75.00		95	Alford	A	3.00		113	Brampton	A	10.00
	Five Ways/						E	2.00				H	5.00
	Birmingham	H	2.00				G	2.00			Brampton/		
	Gt. Hampton St./						H	2.00			Carlisle	H	1.00
	Birmingham	H	2.00			Alford Linc.	H	2.00		114	Brandon	A	4.00
	Smethwick/				96	Stickney	A	12.00				E	2.00
	Birmingham	H	2.00			Aldershot Camp						H	2.00
76	Campden	A	3.00				B	20.00		115	Stoke Ferry	A	8.00
		H	1.00				H	10.00				B	8.00
77	Halesowen	A	12.00		97	Bury St.Edmunds				116	Brecon	A	2.00
78	Henley-in-Arden						A	3.00				B	15.00
		A	12.00				B	8.00				G	3.00
	Aldershot	B	7.00				D	20.00				H	1.00
		H	2.00				F	2.00		117	Trecastle	A	20.00
79	Knowle	A	10.00				H	2.00			Tottenham	B	15.00
80	Bishop Auckland					Bury St.Edmonds						H	10.00
		A	3.00				D	15.00			Tottenham S.O.		
		F	2.00		98	Blackburn	A	8.00				H	4.00
		H	2.00				B	10.00		118	Brentwood	A	3.00
	South Rd./					Dinas Mawddwy	B	4.00				B	8.00
	Bishop Auckland				100	Botesdale	A	15.00				D	10.00
		H	25.00		101	Ixworth	A	8.00				F	5.00
	Bishops Auckland					Alnmouth	B	7.00				H	2.00
		H	6.00				H	1.00					

119	Edmonton H	25.00
	Trebanos B	15.00
120	Bridgend A	3.00
	F	2.00
	H	2.00
	Ringwood	
	(error) A	40.00
	Bridgend/Glam H	2.00
121	Pyle A	10.00
	Morpeth	
	(error) A	80.00
	West Cross B	15.00
122	Bridgenorth A	3.00
	B	6.00
	C	40.00
	H	1.00
123	Bridgewater A	2.00
	B	8.00
	F	2.00
	H	2.00
124	Bridlington A	3.00
	H	6.00
125	Bridlington Quay	
	A	5.00
	B	4.00
	H	4.00
126	Hunmanby A	15.00
	Spennymoor H	4.00
127	Bridport A	4.00
	B	5.00
	F	3.00
	H	1.00
128	Beaminster A	100.00
129	Brigg A	10.00
	E	2.00
	G	6.00
	H	6.00
130	Caister A	7.00
	E	10.00
	H	10.00
131	Limber A	15.00
132	Brighton A	2.00
	B	6.00
	D	4.00
	F	2.00
	G (diamond)	150.00
	H	2.00
	Brighton/A H	2.00
	Brighton/A1 F	2.00
	H	2.00
	Brighton/B H	2.00
	Brighton/B2 F	2.00
	H	4.00
	Brighton/C H	3.00
	Brighton/D H	2.00
	Brighton/E H	2.00
	Brighton/I H	6.00
	Brighton/2 H	2.00
	Brighton/	
	H.P.O. H	20.00
	Alma Terr/	
	Hove Brighton	
	H	15.00
	Bedford St./	
	Brighton H	30.00
	Dyke Rd./	
	Brighton H	20.00
	Hove B.O./	
	Brighton H	3.00
	Kemptown B.O./	
	Brighton H	12.00
	Lewes Rd./	
	Brighton H	10.00
	Preston Rd./	
	Brighton H	10.00
	St. Georges Rd./	
	Brighton H	40.00
	St. James's St./	
	Brighton H	20.00
	Victoria Rd./	
	Brighton H	15.00
	Western Rd./	
	Brighton H	2.00
	Western Rd. B.O./	
	Brighton H	2.00
	West Pier B.O./	
	Brighton H	12.00
133	Catterick A	3.00
	B	10.00
	H	2.00
134	Bristol A	2.00
	C	10.00
	D	3.00
	E	2.00
	G	2.00
	H	1.00
	Clifton/Bristol	
	F	2.00
	H	1.00
	North St./	
	Bristol F	3.00
	H	3.00
	Redcliffe/	
	Bristol F	2.00
	H	3.00
135	Caxton A	20.00
	Corbridge H	1.00
136	Brixham A	5.00
	H	1.00
137	Broadway A	2.00
	H	15.00
138	Bromyard A	5.00
	F	3.00
	H	4.00
139	Bromsgrove A	3.00
	B	10.00
	F	2.00
	H	2.00
140	Redditch A	4.00
	H	2.00
141	Studley A	15.00
142	Brough A	3.00
	Brough/	
	Penrith H	10.00
	Brough/	
	Westd. H	8.00
143	Temple Sowerby	
	A	10.00
	Pontardawe H	2.00
144	Bromley/Kent A	5.00
	B	8.00
	H	1.00
	Shortlands/	
	Kent H	2.00
145	Buckingham A	3.00
	H	1.00
146	Builth A	8.00
	B	9.00
	H	5.00
147	Bungay A	7.00
	B	10.00
	D	25.00
	E	4.00
	G	5.00
	H	3.00
148	Buntingford A	3.00
	B	7.00
	H	1.00
149	Burford A	5.00
	G	2.00
	H	2.00
150	Burnley A	3.00
	D	10.00
	E	2.00
	H	2.00
151	Colne A	3.00
	B	8.00
	E	5.00
	G	4.00
	H	4.00
	Colne/Lanc H	3.00
152	Burton upon Trent	
	C	35.00
	Burton-on-Trent	
	A	3.00
	B	8.00
	F	3.00
	H	2.00
153	Burton/	
	Westmoreland A	3.00
	H	4.00
154	Bury Lanc A	3.00
	B	6.00
	D	6.00
	E	2.00
	H	2.00
	Bury/	
	Lancashire H	2.00
155	Buxton A	4.00
	E	2.00
	G	4.00
	H	3.00
156	Chapel en le Frith	
	A	20.00
	Maesycwmmer B	15.00
	H	1.00
	Ilfracombe B	60.00
157	Calne A	2.00
	B	8.00
	G	2.00
	H	5.00
	Calne/Wilts H	2.00
158	Cambridge A	2.00
	B	6.00
	D	4.00
	F	2.00
	H	1.00
159	Chard A	3.00
	B	8.00
	G	5.00
	H	2.00
160	Camelford A	2.00
	H	7.00
161	Five Lanes A	12.00
	Bardney B	10.00
162	Cardiff A	4.00
	B	10.00
	D	5.00
	E	2.00
	G	2.00
	H	2.00
	Barry Dock B.O./	
	Cardiff H	25.00
	Bute Docks/	
	Cardiff H	20.00
	Cardiff/	
	Ship Letter	
	H	250.00

163	Pontypridd A	2.00	182	Hawarden A	20.00	208	Cobham/Surrey A	3.00
	H	2.00		Betchworth H	2.00		B	10.00
	Haford/		183	Mochdrai A	25.00		H	1.00
	Pontypridd A	15.00	184	Neston A	15.00	209	Cockermouth A	4.00
164	Cardigan A	3.00		Shipley/Yorks H	2.00		B	5.00
	B	15.00		Windhill/			F	5.00
	H	1.00		Shipley Yks H	20.00		H	1.00
165	Carlisle A	3.00	185	Northop A	15.00	210	Colchester A	3.00
	D	8.00		B	10.00		B	7.00
	E	5.00		H	2.00		D	15.00
	F	2.00	186	Chesterfield A	3.00		F	2.00
	H	2.00		D	8.00		H	1.00
166	Haltwhistle A	15.00		F	2.00	211	Boxford A	15.00
167	Carmarthen A	5.00		H	2.00	212	Coleford A	5.00
	B	15.00	187	Staveley A	20.00		H	2.00
	D	5.00		Consett B	10.00		Coleford/Glos H	2.00
	F	2.00		H	1.00	213	Coleshill A	10.00
	H	1.00	188	Chester le Street			Woodville H	2.00
	Stockton A			A	8.00	214	Cullompton A	3.00
	(error)	100.00		B	10.00		H	1.00
168	Kidwelly A	7.00		H	1.00	215	Colsterworth A	12.00
	B	20.00	189	Leadgate B	10.00		Repton H	1.00
	H	2.00	190	Chichester A	3.00	216	Congleton A	3.00
169	Chelmsford H			D	5.00		F	6.00
	(error)	75.00		F	2.00		H	1.00
170	Newcastle Emlyn			H	2.00	217	Monksheath A	15.00
	A	5.00		Chichester/			Barton-under-	
	H	2.00		Station Office			Needwood H	2.00
171	Chalford A	20.00		H	12.00	218	Conway A	3.00
	Campsea Ash B	10.00	191	Chippenham A	2.00		E	2.00
172	Minchinhampton			B	8.00		H	1.00
	A	12.00		F	2.00	219	Corwen A	3.00
173	Chatham A	3.00		H	2.00		B	10.00
	B	8.00	192	Malmesbury A	6.00		G	4.00
	D	8.00		H	2.00		H	2.00
	E	2.00	193	Chipping Sodbury		220	Bala A	2.00
	G	5.00		A	15.00		H	1.00
	H	2.00		Worthing (error)		221	Barmouth A	5.00
174	Chatteris A	15.00		A	120.00		H	1.00
	West Felton B	7.00	194	Charmouth A	3.00	222	Dolgelly A	5.00
175	Cheadle/			B	10.00		B	15.00
	Staff A	3.00	195	Chipping Norton			H	1.00
	B	8.00		A	3.00	223	Coventry A	3.00
	H	2.00		B	10.00		D	7.00
176	Chelmsford A	5.00		F	8.00		F	2.00
	B	7.00		H	2.00		H	1.00
	D	15.00	196	Chirk A	10.00	224	Cowbridge A	3.00
	F	2.00	197	Ruabon A	5.00		H	3.00
	H	2.00		G	5.00	225	Cowes A	5.00
177	Cheltenham A	2.00		H	2.00		B	5.00
	B	3.00	198	Chorley Lanc A	3.00		G	4.00
	C	1000.00		F	5.00		H	3.00
	D	5.00		H	3.00	226	Cranbrook A	10.00
	F	2.00	200	Christchurch A	2.00		Tutbury H	2.00
	H	1.00		B	8.00	227	Swadlincote H	1.00
178	Chepstow A	3.00		H	2.00	228	Crawley A	3.00
	F	7.00		Christchurch/			G	2.00
	H	2.00		Hants H	1.00		H	2.00
179	Chertsey A	4.00	202	Chudleigh A	4.00	229	Crediton A	2.00
	B	10.00		B	8.00		H	2.00
	D	12.00	203	Chumleigh A	15.00	230	Crewkerne A	2.00
	E	2.00		Bwlch B	15.00		B	5.00
	H	2.00		H	1.00		H	1.00
180	Chester A	3.00	204	Cirencester A	3.00	231	Crickhowell A	3.00
	B	10.00		D	12.00		B	12.00
	C	10.00		F	2.00		H	8.00
	D	4.00		H	2.00	232	Cuckfield A	3.00
	E	2.00	205	Worcester Park			B	15.00
	G	2.00		H	2.00	233	Darlington A	3.00
	H	1.00	206	Clare A	10.00		B	10.00
	Chester/R.O. H	25.00		Bream B	10.00		D	8.00
181	Abergele A	5.00	207	Clitheroe A	3.00		F	2.00
	H	2.00		H	2.00		H	1.00

234	Smeaton A	15.00	255	Doncaster A	2.00	271	Eastbourne A	3.00
	Llansamlet B	15.00		B	10.00		B	8.00
235	Staindrop A	15.00		D	8.00		F	2.00
236	Dartford A	3.00		F	2.00		H	2.00
	D	80.00		H	2.00	272	East Grinstead	
	F	2.00	256	Dorchester A	3.00		A	2.00
	H	2.00		B	10.00		H	2.00
237	Dartmouth A	2.00		D	5.00	273	Eccleshall A	6.00
	H	2.00		F	2.00		B	8.00
238	Daventry A	3.00		H	1.00		H	2.00
	H	2.00	257	Dorking A	6.00	274	Ellesmere A	4.00
239	Dawlish A	2.00		D	35.00		H	2.00
	B	3.00		E	2.00	275	Ely A	3.00
	H	1.00		G	8.00		E	2.00
240	Deal A	2.00		H	1.00		G	2.00
	B	8.00	258	Dover A	4.00		H	2.00
	G	2.00		D	12.00	276	Much Wenlock B	8.00
	H	2.00		E	2.00		H	2.00
241	Denbigh A	5.00		G	2.00	277	Emsworth A	3.00
	B	10.00		H	2.00		B	12.00
	G	4.00		Dover/Station			H	1.00
	H	2.00		Office H	4.00	278	Enstone A	3.00
242	Derby A	2.00	259	Walmer A	15.00		G	8.00
	B	10.00		New Walsingham			H	5.00
	D	4.00		B	10.00	279	Epping A	7.00
	E	2.00		H	10.00		E	5.00
	G	2.00		Walsingham/			H	1.00
	H	1.00		Norfolk H	4.00	280	Epsom A	3.00
	Duffield Rd/Derby		260	Downham A	6.00		G	2.00
	H	25.00		B	8.00		H	2.00
243	Melbourne/Derby			G	8.00	281	Ermebridge A	15.00
	A	5.00		H	2.00		Madeley/Salop B	8.00
	H	10.00	261	Driffield A	3.00		H	2.00
	Melbourne/			B	12.00	282	Modbury A	6.00
	Derbyshire H	1.00		F	5.00		Dawley B	10.00
244	Ticknall A	15.00		H	2.00		H	8.00
	Talley B	15.00	262	Droitwich A	3.00	283	Esher A	3.00
245	Dereham A	10.00		B	8.00		H	2.00
	B	8.00		F	8.00	284	Evesham A	3.00
	G	8.00		H	2.00		G	2.00
	H	2.00	263	Dudley A	3.00		H	2.00
	East Dereham F	4.00		C	80.00	285	Exeter A	2.00
246	Briningham A	15.00		D	8.00		B	6.00
	Mountain Ash H	2.00		E	2.00		D	6.00
247	Elmham A	12.00		G	6.00		E	2.00
248	Guist A	12.00		H	2.00		G	2.00
	Felstead B	10.00	264	Dunchurch A	25.00		H	1.00
249	Devizes A	4.00		Woolwich B	8.00		Exeter Station	
	B	10.00		H	1.00		B - see chapter 13	
	D	10.00	265	Dunmow A	6.00	286	Exmouth A	3.00
	E	2.00		B	8.00		B	6.00
	G	2.00		H	2.00		H	6.00
	H	2.00	266	Dunstable A	2.00	287	Eye A	3.00
250	Devonport A	2.00		H	2.00		B	8.00
	D	6.00	267	Durham A	3.00		G	7.00
	F	2.00		B	10.00		H	7.00
	H	2.00		D	10.00	288	Fakenham A	4.00
	Devonport/			E	2.00		D	40.00
	H.M.S. H	150.00		G	2.00		F	6.00
251	St. Germans A	8.00		H	2.00		H	2.00
252	Torpoint A	10.00	268	Seaham A	5.00	289	Walsingham A	12.00
	Seascale H	1.00		Broseley H	1.00		Coalbrookdale	
253	Dewsbury A	2.00	269	Dursley A	5.00		B	5.00
	B	12.00		B	8.00		H	2.00
	F	2.00		G	2.00	290	Falmouth A	3.00
	H	2.00		H	2.00		D	10.00
254	Diss A	5.00	270	Berkeley A	3.00		F	2.00
	B	10.00		B	8.00		H	1.00
	G	5.00		H	2.00			
	H	2.00						

291	Fareham A	2.00	312	Gloucester A	2.00	329	Halesworth A	6.00
	E	2.00		B	8.00		B	6.00
	G	2.00		C	12.00		H	4.00
	H	2.00		D	4.00	330	Halifax A	3.00
	Faversham A			H	1.00		B	12.00
	(error)	80.00		Gloster F	2.00		D	5.00
292	Farnham A	3.00		G	1.00		E	2.00
	B	6.00		H	2.00		G	2.00
	E	2.00		Gloster Station			H	2.00
	H	2.00		H	6.00	331	Sowerby Bridge	
293	Faringdon A	3.00		Gloucester Station			A	8.00
	B	8.00		B	25.00	332	Todmorden A	8.00
	F	2.00		H	6.00		E	8.00
	H	2.00	313	Lea A	20.00		H	2.00
	Dudley A			Cromford H	5.00	333	Northowram A	15.00
	(error)	50.00	314	Painswick A	15.00	334	Halstead A	3.00
294	Fairford A	8.00	315	Thornbury A	4.00		B	8.00
	H	1.00		B	10.00		F	2.00
295	Highworth A	2.00		H	2.00		H	2.00
	H	2.00	316	Godalming A	3.00		Halstead/Essex	
296	Lechlade A	3.00		B	8.00		H	2.00
	H	2.00		H	2.00	335	Haverhill A	15.00
297	Fazeley A	12.00	317	Godstone A	12.00	336	Harleston A	3.00
298	Felton A	12.00		Chelford H	1.00		B	8.00
	B	8.00	318	Bletchingley A	15.00		D	150.00
	H	4.00		Llanfyrnach B	6.00		H	2.00
299	Fenny Stratford		319	Goole A	5.00	337	Harlow A	6.00
	A	8.00		E	2.00		B	6.00
	Horsehay B	4.00		G	10.00		E	5.00
300	Ferrybridge A	10.00		H	2.00		H	5.00
	H	2.00		Booth Ferry Rd/		338	Harrogate A	3.00
301	Faversham A	3.00		Goole H	25.00		B	6.00
	H	2.00		Old Goole/Goole			D	15.00
302	Folkingham A	7.00		H	25.00		F	2.00
	B	10.00	320	Gosport A	2.00		H	2.00
	F	2.00		B	4.00	339	Hartfordbridge	
	H	2.00		D	25.00		A	8.00
303	Folkestone A	3.00		E	2.00	340	Harwich A	6.00
	B	8.00		H	2.00		B	6.00
	D	4.00	321	Grantham A	5.00		G	3.00
	F	2.00		B	10.00		H	4.00
	H	2.00		D	8.00	341	Haslemere A	12.00
304	Fordingbridge A	6.00		F	2.00	342	Hastings A	3.00
	B	8.00		H	2.00		B	6.00
	H	1.00	322	Gravesend A	3.00		D	6.00
305	Fowey A	4.00		B	8.00		F	2.00
	B	6.00		D	15.00		H	2.00
306	Frome A	3.00		F	2.00		Hastings/Station	
	E	2.00		H	2.00		Office H	8.00
	G	2.00	323	Grimsby A	7.00		High St/	
	H	1.00		B	8.00		Hastings H	8.00
307	Gainsborough A	7.00		E	2.00		White Rock/	
	F	3.00		H	2.00		Hastings H	12.00
	H	2.00	324	Guernsey A	30.00		Kings Rd/	
308	Garstang A	3.00		B	40.00		St. Leonards-on-	
	H	2.00		F	25.00		Sea H	10.00
309	Gateshead A	3.00		H	20.00		St. Leonards-on-Sea/	
	D	8.00	325	Guildford A	3.00		Kings Rd B.O.	
	F	2.00		B	8.00		H	2.00
	H	2.00		D	12.00		St. Leonards	
310	Gerrards Cross			F	2.00		on Sea/Marina	
	A	10.00		H	2.00		H	7.00
	Malpas B	8.00	326	Guisborough A	3.00		St. Leonards-on-	
	Malpas/Ches H	10.00		B	10.00		Sea/Station	
	Malpas/			H	4.00		Office H	8.00
	Cheshire H	4.00	327	Greta Bridge A	15.00	343	Hatfield/Herts	
311	Glastonbury A	3.00		Shrewton B	12.00		A	3.00
	B	6.00	328	Hadleigh A	7.00		B	8.00
	H	1.00		Edgware H	1.00		H	1.00

344	Havant A	5.00
	D	60.00
	G	4.00
	H	1.00
345	Haverfordwest A	3.00
	B	8.00
	D	5.00
	F	2.00
	H	2.00
346	Hawes A	10.00
	H	2.00
347	Hay A	5.00
	B	6.00
348	Bruntless A	20.00
349	Glasbury A	20.00
	B	12.00
350	Haydon Bridge	
	A	20.00
351	Helston A	2.00
	B	10.00
	D	60.00
	G	2.00
	H	6.00
352	Hayle A	2.00
	B	10.00
	G	10.00
	H	2.00
353	Hemel Hempstead	
	A	3.00
	B	7.00
	F	2.00
	H	1.00
354	Kings Langley	
	A	15.00
	H	1.00
355	Henley-on-Thames	
	A	3.00
	B	8.00
	H	2.00
356	Nettlebed A	20.00
	Charing H	2.00
357	Hereford A	3.00
	B	8.00
	D	8.00
	F	2.00
	H	1.00
358	Eardisley A	12.00
	Radstock B	10.00
	H	2.00
359	Hertford A	3.00
	B	5.00
	D	20.00
	F	2.00
	H	2.00
360	Hexham A	2.00
	B	10.00
	G	2.00
	H	2.00
361	Heytesbury A	5.00
	B	8.00
	Loughor B	20.00
362	Deptford Inn A	50.00
	Brize Norton B	15.00
363	Higham Ferrers	
	A	4.00
	B	6.00
364	High Wycombe A	3.00
	B	8.00
	F	2.00
	H	2.00
365	Hinckley A	7.00
	F	2.00
	H	2.00

366	Hindon A	5.00
	B	12.00
367	Hitchin A	2.00
	E	2.00
	G	5.00
	H	2.00
368	Pembroke Dock A	4.00
	D	20.00
	F	5.00
	H	5.00
369	Hoddesdon A	2.00
	H	2.00
370	Holbeach A	10.00
	B	7.00
	H	7.00
371	Holt A	6.00
	B	8.00
372	Blakeney A	12.00
374	Holyhead A	3.00
	H	2.00
375	Holywell A	7.00
	B	10.00
	H	5.00
	Holywell/Flints	
	H	2.00
376	Honiton A	3.00
	B	8.00
	D	8.00
	G	2.00
	H	2.00
377	Ottery St. Mary	
	A	3.00
	B	6.00
	H	1.00
378	Horncastle A	3.00
	F	2.00
	H	2.00
379	Old Bolingbroke	
	A	10.00
	Charlton B	10.00
	H	15.00
	Church Lane/	
	Charlton Kent	
	H	15.00
	Lower Rd/	
	Charlton Kent	
	H	15.00
	Old Charlton H	8.00
380	Horndean A	5.00
	H	5.00
381	Horsham A	3.00
	E	2.00
	G	2.00
	H	2.00
	Horsham/Station	
	Office H	10.00
382	Howden A	6.00
	E	2.00
	H	2.00
383	Hull A	2.00
	B	8.00
	C	12.00
	D	5.00
	E	2.00
	G	2.00
	H	2.00
	H (5 bars)	100.00
	Hull S.T.- see chap 13	
384	Filey A	5.00
	E	4.00
385	Hedon A	8.00
	Shooters Hill	
	B	15.00

386	Barrow-on-Humber	
	A	15.00
	Welling B	15.00
	H	1.00
387	Huddersfield A	2.00
	B	10.00
	D	6.00
	F	2.00
	G	2.00
	H	1.00
388	Marsden A	12.00
	Bexley Heath B	15.00
	H	4.00
389	Bexley B	15.00
390	Hungerford A	3.00
	B	6.00
	F	6.00
	H	2.00
391	Aldbourne A	20.00
	Holt B (error)	80.00
392	Lambourne A	12.00
	B	12.00
	Dudley A	
	(error)	50.00
393	Ramsbury A	5.00
	B	4.00
	H	12.00
394	Hounslow A	4.00
	B	10.00
	F	10.00
	H	2.00
395	Southall A	15.00
	H	2.00
396	Huntingdon A	10.00
	B	8.00
	D	70.00
	F	2.00
	H	2.00
397	Buckden A	15.00
	Crayford B	15.00
	H	2.00
398	Hythe/Kent A	4.00
	H	2.00
399	Ilchester A	3.00
	B	5.00
	H	5.00
400	Ilfracombe A	7.00
	B	12.00
	H	1.00
401	Ilminster A	2.00
	B	7.00
	H	3.00
402	Ingatestone A	3.00
	B	8.00
	H	8.00
403	Rayleigh A	15.00
	Erith B	6.00
	H	1.00
404	Wickford A	20.00
	Belvedere B	8.00
	H	15.00
	Ironbridge	
	(error) H	60.00
405	Ipswich A	3.00
	D	8.00
	E	2.00
	G	2.00
	H	2.00
406	Ironbridge A	3.00
	B	10.00
	H	1.00

407	Isle of Man A	30.00
	D	100.00
	Douglas Isle of Man	
	F	20.00
	Douglas/Isle of Man	
	H	6.00
408	Ivybridge A	3.00
	B	8.00
	F	3.00
	H	2.00
409	Jersey A	25.00
	B	30.00
	E	25.00
	G	25.00
	H	20.00
410	Kelvedon A	3.00
	B	8.00
	H	2.00
411	Kendal A	3.00
	B	6.00
	D	4.00
	E	2.00
	G	2.00
	H	2.00
412	Bowness A	6.00
	Lessness Heath	
	B	15.00
	H	25.00
	Picardy Belvedere	
	H	12.00
413	Keswick A	3.00
	B	5.00
	G	2.00
	H	1.00
414	Kettering A	3.00
	B	8.00
	H	2.00
415	Kidderminster A	3.00
	B	10.00
	C	90.00
	D	25.00
	F	2.00
	H	2.00
416	Kimbolton A	8.00
	B	6.00
	H	1.00
417	Kineton A	12.00
	Hucknall Torkard	
	H	1.00
418	Kingsbridge A	3.00
	B	8.00
	H	2.00
419	Kington A	3.00
	B	10.00
	G	2.00
	H	1.00
420	Pen Y Bont A	8.00
	B	8.00
421	Radnor A	20.00
	Long Eaton H	1.00
422	Kingston A	3.00
	D	50.00
	Kingston on Thames	
	F	2.00
	H	2.00
	Norbiton/	
	Kingston on	
	Thames H	15.00
423	Kirkby Lonsdale	
	A	3.00
	New Charlton B	8.00
	C	12.00

424	Knaresborough A	3.00
	B	6.00
	H	2.00
425	Knutsford A	4.00
	H	2.00
426	Lamberhurst A	15.00
427	Hawkhurst A	10.00
	H	2.00
428	Hurst Green A	3.00
	D	6.00
	F	2.00
	H	2.00
429	Newenden A	15.00
	Broxbourne B	10.00
430	Northiam A	8.00
	Headcorn H	2.00
431	Peasmarsh A	10.00
	Wye H	2.00
432	Rolvenden A	15.00
	Croesgoch B	15.00
433	Sandhurst A	15.00
	Maesteg H	2.00
434	Lampeter A	5.00
	H	1.00
435	Aberayron A	20.00
436	Lancaster A	3.00
	B	8.00
	D	5.00
	F	2.00
	H	2.00
437	Kirkby Stephen	
	A	6.00
	H	3.00
438	Sedbergh A	4.00
	H	4.00
	Sedbergh R.S.O.	
	H	8.00
439	Launceston A	3.00
	B	10.00
	D	100.00
	H	2.00
440	Holsworthy A	7.00
	B	8.00
	H	1.00
441	Stratton A	5.00
	B	4.00
442	Bude A	10.00
443	Lawton A	12.00
	Aberkenfig B	10.00
444	Leamington A	2.00
	C	40.00
	D	25.00
	F	2.00
	H	2.00
	Leamington Spa	
	H	2.00
445	Leatherhead A	4.00
	H	1.00
	Ledbury H	
	(error)	20.00
446	Ledbury A	2.00
	B	8.00
	E	2.00
	H	1.00
447	Leeds A	2.00
	B	6.00
	C	40.00
	D	5.00
	E	2.00
	F (double circle	
	datestamp)	150.00
	G	2.00
	H	2.00

	Chapeltown Rd.	
	B.O./Leeds H	3.00
	Hunslet B.O./	
	Leeds H	3.00
	Hyde Park B.O./	
	Leeds H	3.00
	Hyde Park	
	Corner B.O./	
	Leeds H	1.00
	Market St.	
	B.O./Leeds H	25.00
448	Leek A	6.00
	B	8.00
	E	2.00
	H	2.00
449	Leicester A	3.00
	B	6.00
	D	5.00
	F	2.00
	H	1.00
450	Leighton Buzzard	
	A	4.00
	F	1.00
	H	1.00
451	Lewes A	3.00
	B	12.00
	D	8.00
	E	2.00
	G	2.00
	H	2.00
	Lewes/Station	
	Office H	12.00
452	Newhaven A	10.00
	Porthcawl B	15.00
	H	4.00
453	Seaford A	12.00
	Llanfairfechan	
	H	2.00
454	Leominster A	6.00
	F	4.00
	H	1.00
455	Pembridge A	8.00
	B	10.00
	H	2.00
456	Shobden A	15.00
	B	20.00
457	Lichfield A	6.00
	B	6.00
	F	2.00
	H	2.00
458	Lincoln A	4.00
	B	8.00
	D	12.00
	E	2.00
	G	2.00
	H	2.00
	Lincoln Sorting	
	Tender - see chap 13	
459	Kirton	
	Lindsey A	10.00
	F	4.00
	H	2.00
460	Wragby A	10.00
	E	5.00
	G	10.00
	H	1.00
461	Linton A	15.00
	Upper Bangor H	6.00
462	Liphook A	8.00
	H	1.00
463	Liskeard A	3.00
	B	12.00
	H	2.00

464	Looe A	15.00
	Hessle H	2.00
465	Polperro A	20.00
	Llangennech B	20.00
466	Liverpool A	2.00
	A (roller)	200.00
	B	6.00
	C	5.00
	C Reg	100.00
	D (French)	1500.00
	E	2.00
	G	2.00
	H	8.00
	H (5 bars)	20.00
	E.D./Liverpool	
	G	3.00
	Liverpool E	
	H	6.00
	N.D./Liverpool	
	G	3.00
	Liverpool N	
	H	6.00
	S.D./Liverpool	
	G	3.00
	Liverpool S	
	H	3.00
	W.D./Liverpool	
	B	60.00
	G	2.00
	H	6.00
	Exchange	
	Liverpool H	5.00
	Bootle/	
	Liverpool H	8.00
	Bootle-cum-Linacre/	
	Liverpool H	9.00
467	Llandilo A	5.00
	H	2.00
468	Llandovery A	5.00
	H	2.00
469	Llanelly A	2.00
	F	2.00
	H	2.00
	Llanelly Dock	
	H	30.00
	Llanelly Docks	
	H	20.00
470	Pontardulais A	15.00
	H	3.00
471	Llangadock A	15.00
	B	15.00
	H	2.00
472	Llangollen A	3.00
	B	7.00
	H	1.00
473	Long Stratton	
	A	10.00
	H	6.00
474	Lostwithiel A	3.00
	B	5.00
	H	2.00
475	Loughborough A	5.00
	B	5.00
	F	2.00
	H	2.00
	Loughboro H	2.00
476	Mountsorrel A	50.00
477	Louth A	4.00
	E	3.00
	G	2.00
	H	2.00

478	Lowestoft A	3.00
	B	6.00
	D	10.00
	F	2.00
	H	2.00
479	Ludlow A	3.00
	B	12.00
	E	2.00
	G	2.00
	H	1.00
480	Knighton A	4.00
	B	8.00
	H	2.00
481	Leintwardine A	5.00
	Haslemere H	2.00
482	Luton A	7.00
	B	5.00
	E	2.00
	G	2.00
	H	1.00
483	Lutterworth A	3.00
	B	8.00
	H	1.00
484	Lyme A	4.00
	B	10.00
	G	2.00
	H	8.00
	Lyme Regis H	1.00
485	Lymington A	2.00
	F	2.00
	H	2.00
486	Yarmouth/Isle	
	of Wight A	15.00
	B	10.00
	H	5.00
	Yarmouth/	
	I.of Wight H	2.00
487	Lyndhurst A	6.00
	B	8.00
	H	2.00
488	Lynn A	3.00
	B	8.00
	D	25.00
	E	2.00
	G	2.00
	H	2.00
489	Burnham A	12.00
	Hildenborough	
	H	4.00
490	Holkham A	15.00
	Ham Street H	4.00
491	Macclesfield A	4.00
	F	2.00
	H	2.00
	Chestergate B.O./	
	Macclesfield	
	H	10.00
492	Maidenhead A	4.00
	D	20.00
	F	3.00
	H	2.00
493	Maidstone A	2.00
	B	4.00
	D	6.00
	F	2.00
	H	2.00
	Maidstone/Station	
	Office H	15.00
494	Maldon A	3.00
	B	8.00

	E	4.00
	G	2.00
	H	2.00
495	Malton A	2.00
	B	8.00
	E	2.00
	G	6.00
	H	2.00
	Norton/Malton	
	H	30.00
496	Sledmere A	15.00
	Kew H	4.00
497	Malvern A	3.00
	D	10.00
	E	2.00
	G	2.00
	H	2.00
498	Manchester A	2.00
	A (roller)	150.00
	B	3.00
	C	10.00
	D	4.00
	D (French)	1200.00
	E	2.00
	F	2.00
	F (Beard)	250.00
	G	2.00
	H	2.00
	Manchester/E	
	H	2.00
	Manchester/N	
	H	2.00
	Manchester/NW	
	H	3.00
	Manchester/S	
	H	2.00
	Manchester/S.D.O.	
	H	2.00
	Manchester/SE	
	H	2.00
	Manchester/SW	
	H	2.00
	Manchester/W	
	H	3.00
499	Glossop A	20.00
	G	10.00
	H	10.00
500	Haslingden A	15.00
	Keymer H	12.00
501	Rawtenstall A	10.00
	H	8.00
502	Stalybridge A	10.00
	H	2.00
503	Manningtree A	3.00
	H	3.00
504	Mansfield A	5.00
	F	2.00
	H	1.00
	Ipswich	
	(error) H	100.00
505	March A	3.00
	B	8.00
	G	4.00
	H	1.00
506	Margate A	3.00
	D	10.00
	E	2.00
	G	2.00
	H	2.00
	Northumberland Rd/	
	Margate H	35.00

507	Marazion A	4.00	
	B	5.00	
	H	1.00	
508	Market Deeping		
	A	15.00	
	H	1.00	
509	Market Drayton		
	A	3.00	
	B	8.00	
	H	1.00	
510	Woore A	20.00	
511	Market Harborough		
	A	3.00	
	F	2.00	
	H	2.00	
	Market Harboro		
	H	2.00	
512	Market Raisin		
	A	8.00	
	F	8.00	
	H	3.00	
513	Market Street		
	A	15.00	
	Merstham H	2.00	
514	Market Weighton		
	A	8.00	
	H	2.00	
515	South Cave A	10.00	
	Whyteleafe H	1.00	
516	Marlborough A	2.00	
	B	8.00	
	H	2.00	
	Marlboro F	2.00	
517	Great Bedwin A	10.00	
518	Marlow A	2.00	
	E	3.00	
	H	4.00	
519	Maryport A	3.00	
	H	1.00	
520	Matlock Bath A	4.00	
	F	2.00	
	H	1.00	
521	Melksham A	3.00	
	H	2.00	
522	Melton Mowbray		
	A	3.00	
	B	6.00	
	F	5.00	
	H	1.00	
523	Merthyr Tydfil		
	A	2.00	
	B	10.00	
	D	10.00	
	F	2.00	
	H	2.00	
524	Middlewich A	4.00	
	H	2.00	
525	Holmes Chapel		
	A	12.00	
	H	2.00	
526	Winsford A	20.00	
	Boston Spa H	2.00	
527	Midhurst A	5.00	
	B	7.00	
	H	8.00	
528	Mildenhall A	15.00	
529	Milford A	3.00	
	G	10.00	
	Milford Haven H	2.00	
530	Milnthorpe A	3.00	
	B	8.00	
	H	2.00	

531	Mold A	7.00	
	G	7.00	
	H	2.00	
	Morpeth (error)		
	E	30.00	
532	Monmouth A	3.00	
	B	6.00	
	F	2.00	
	H	1.00	
	Over Monnow/		
	Monmouth H	25.00	
533	Raglan A	15.00	
534	Moreton-in-Marsh		
	A	2.00	
	B	10.00	
	H	1.00	
535	Stow on the Wold		
	A	3.00	
	B	10.00	
	H	1.00	
536	Winchcombe A	4.00	
	H	1.00	
537	Morpeth A	8.00	
	E	4.00	
	G	3.00	
	H	1.00	
538	Nantwich A	8.00	
	F	2.00	
	H	2.00	
539	Narberth A	2.00	
	B	6.00	
	H	2.00	
540	Neath A	2.00	
	G	3.00	
	H	2.00	
541	Newark A	3.00	
	B	8.00	
	D	8.00	
	E	2.00	
	G	2.00	
	H	2.00	
542	Southwell A	10.00	
	F	8.00	
	H	1.00	
543	Carlton-on-Trent		
	A	20.00	
	Liss H	10.00	
544	Newbury A	3.00	
	D	10.00	
	E	2.00	
	G	2.00	
	H	1.00	
545	Newcastle on Tyne		
	A	2.00	
	B	8.00	
	D	4.00	
	F	2.00	
	H	2.00	
	H (Scottish)	5.00	
	Neville St/		
	Newcastle on Tyne		
	H	4.00	
	Quayside/		
	Newcastle on Tyne		
	H	4.00	
546	Newcastle-under-		
	Lyme A	3.00	
	F	3.00	
	Newcastle, Staff		
	F	2.00	
	H	2.00	
	Newcastle/Staff		
	H	2.00	

547	Stoke on Trent		
	A	5.00	
	B	10.00	
	C	150.00	
	F	2.00	
	H	2.00	
548	Tunstall A	8.00	
	F	5.00	
	H	2.00	
	Tunstall/Staff		
	H	2.00	
549	Hanley A	8.00	
	G	6.00	
	H	2.00	
	Hanley/Staff H	2.00	
	Hanley/Stoke		
	on Trent H	6.00	
550	Cobridge A	15.00	
	Kenley B	8.00	
	H	3.00	
551	Burslem A	10.00	
	E	6.00	
	H	2.00	
552	Lane Delph A	15.00	
	Sandgate H	2.00	
553	Longton Staff A	5.00	
	F	2.00	
	Longton/Staff H	2.00	
554	Etruria A	20.00	
555	Longport A	20.00	
556	Shelton A	20.00	
557	Newmarket A	3.00	
	B	8.00	
	D	15.00	
	F	3.00	
	H	2.00	
558	Newnham A	3.00	
	G	2.00	
	Newnham Glos H	2.00	
559	Lydney A	5.00	
	G	2.00	
	H	1.00	
560	Newport/I of Wight		
	A	4.00	
	B	10.00	
	F	3.00	
	H	1.00	
	Newport/I.W.		
	H	15.00	
	Newport/		
	Isle of Wight		
	H	1.00	
561	Newport/Mon A	3.00	
	B	7 00	
	D	6.00	
	F	2.00	
	H	1.00	
	Newport Mon. F	2.00	
	H	2.00	
	Newport Docks		
	H	15.00	
	Newport Docks/		
	Newport Mon		
	H	7.00	
562	Caerleon A	15.00	
	B	10.00	
563	Tredegar A	10.00	
	F	2.00	
	H	2.00	
564	Newport Pagnell		
	A	4.00	
	H	2.00	

565	Newport/Salop	
	A	4.00
	B	10.00
	H	1.00
566	New Romney A	7.00
	H	2.00
567	Newton Abbot A	3.00
	B	4.00
	D	10.00
	F	2.00
	H	1.00
568	Newtown Mont A	4.00
	B	10.00
	H	3.00
	Newtown/Mont H	2.00
569	Northallerton	
	A	3.00
	F	4.00
	H	2.00
570	Northampton A	3.00
	B	8.00
	C	15.00
	D	3.00
	F	2.00
	H	2.00
571	Northleach A	6.00
	H	1.00
572	Andoversford A	15.00
	Wighton B	12.00
573	North Shields A	4.00
	B	6.00
	D	8.00
	F	3.00
	H	1.00
574	Northwich A	8.00
	F	2.00
	H	1.00
575	Norwich A	2.00
	B	6.00
	D	5.00
	E	2.00
	G	2.00
	H	2.00
576	Acle A	15.00
	Rolvenden H	1.00
577	Cromer A	8.00
	B	8.00
	H	5.00
578	Loddon A	12.00
	Appledore/Kent	
	H	4.00
579	North Walsham	
	A	8.00
	B	8.00
	H	1.00
580	Reepham A	12.00
	Lamberhurst H	10.00
	Wednesbury	
	(error) A	60.00
581	Scottow A	15.00
	Burnham (Som)	
	B	20.00
582	Worstead A	15.00
583	Nottingham A	3.00
	D	5.00
	F	2.00
	H	2.00
584	Bingham A	10.00
	Woodchurch/Kent	
	H	5.00
585	Ilkeston A	20.00
	H	1.00
586	Stapleford A	15.00

587	Oakham A	8.00
	B	10.00
	E	2.00
	G	2.00
	H	2.00
588	Okehampton A	3.00
	B	7.00
	H	1.00
589	Hatherleigh A	15.00
	Grasmere B	6.00
	H	1.00
590	Odiham A	10.00
	Billingshurst H	2.00
591	Oldham A	5.00
	B	10.00
	E	2.00
	G	2.00
	H	2.00
592	Ollerton A	15.00
593	Ormskirk A	5.00
	B	8.00
	H	3.00
594	Southport A	5.00
	B	8.00
	F	3.00
	H	2.00
595	Oswestry A	3.00
	B	10.00
	C	50.00
	F	2.00
	H	2.00
596	Cerrig-y-druidion	
	A	20.00
	Fittleworth H	2.00
597	Llanrwst A	7.00
	B	20.00
	H	2.00
599	Otley A	2.00
	E	2.00
	H	4.00
600	Addingham A	15.00
601	Oundle A	3.00
	B	4.00
	G	8.00
	H	1.00
602	Ongar A	2.00
	B	8.00
	H	5.00
603	Oxford A	3.00
	B	8.00
	D	7.00
	E	2.00
	G	2.00
	H	2.00
604	Pembroke A	5.00
	H	2.00
605	Penkridge A	3.00
	B	8.00
	H	2.00
606	Penrith A	3.00
	B	5.00
	D	8.00
	E	2.00
	G	2.00
	H	2.00
607	Alston A	10.00
608	Penryn A	3.00
	G	10.00
	H	1.00
609	Penzance A	2.00
	H	1.00
610	Scilly A	120.00
	B	80.00

611	Pershore A	3.00
	H	2.00
612	Peterborough A	5.00
	B	6.00
	D	12.00
	F	2.00
	H	2.00
613	Petersfield A	3.00
	F	2.00
	H	2.00
	Oxford	
	(error) H	15.00
614	Petworth A	3.00
	H	2.00
615	Fittleworth A	15.00
616	Pulborough A	8.00
	H	2.00
617	Storrington A	8.00
618	Pewsey A	4.00
	B	6.00
619	Pickering A	3.00
	H	2.00
620	Plymouth A	3.00
	B	5.00
	C	12.00
	D	8.00
	F	2.00
	H	1.00
	Stonehouse/	
	Plymouth H	30.00
	Plymouth/H.M.S.	
	H	150.00
621	Plympton A	5.00
	B	5.00
	H	1.00
622	Pocklington A	8.00
623	Pontefract A	2.00
	B	10.00
	H	2.00
624	Poole A	4.00
	B	10.00
	D	15.00
	E	4.00
	G	4.00
	H	2.00
625	Portsmouth A	3.00
	B	6.00
	D	4.00
	F	2.00
	H	1.00
	Portsmouth/	
	H.P.O. H	12.00
	High St. BO/	
	Portsmouth H	3.00
	Landport/	
	Portsmouth H	5.00
	Portsea/	
	Portsmouth H	2.00
626	Prescot A	4.00
	G	3.00
	H	1.00
627	Presteign A	7.00
	B	10.00
	H	10.00
628	Preston A	3.00
	B	8.00
	D	4.00
	E	2.00
	G	2.00
	H	2.00
629	Fleetwood A	8.00
	H	2.00

630	Preston Brook	
	A	10.00
	B	10.00
	F	4.00
631	Frodsham A	15.00
632	Pwllheli A	8.00
	B	15.00
	H	2.00
633	Queenborough A	10.00
634	Ramsgate A	3.00
	B	8.00
	D	5.00
	F	2.00
	H	1.00
	Addington St/	
	Ramsgate H	35.00
635	Reading A	3.00
	B	8.00
	D	10.00
	D (biscuit)	40.00
	E	2.00
	G	2.00
	H	2.00
636	Redruth A	4.00
	B	8.00
	E	2.00
	G	10.00
	H	1.00
637	Reigate A	6.00
	B	8.00
	D	12.00
	E	2.00
	G	2.00
	H	2.00
638	Retford A	4.00
	B	10.00
	E	4.00
	G	2.00
	H	8.00
639	Rhayader A	4.00
	B	15.00
	H	4.00
640	Devils Bridge	
	A	20.00
641	Richmond Yorks	
	A	2.00
	H	2.00
	Richmond/Yorks	
	H	2.00
642	Ravenglass A	8.00
643	Rickmansworth	
	A	8.00
	F	3.00
	H	1.00
644	Ringwood A	6.00
	B	6.00
	H	6.00
645	Ripley A	10.00
646	Ripon A	2.00
	E	2.00
	H	2.00
647	Robertsbridge	
	A	10.00
648	Rochdale A	2.00
	B	6.00
	D	7.00
	F	2.00
	H	2.00
649	Snodland B	8.00
	H	10.00
650	Rochester A	3.00
	D	7.00
	F	2.00
	H	2.00

	Rochester/Kent	
	H	1.00
651	Rochford A	2.00
	B	5.00
652	Rockingham A	12.00
	Crymmych B	15.00
653	Romsey A	6.00
	G	2.00
	H	2.00
654	Ross A	3.00
	B	6.00
	E	2.00
	G	8.00
	H	1.00
	Ross/Herefordshire	
	H	2.00
655	Rotherham A	3.00
	D	6.00
	F	2.00
	H	2.00
656	Wath A	10.00
	Bingham/Notts H	2.00
657	Rougham A	12.00
	B	8.00
658	Royston A	3.00
	B	6.00
	D	25.00
	E	2.00
	G	2.00
	H	2.00
	Royston/Cam H	12.00
659	Rugby A	3.00
	B	4.00
	C (shoe)	80.00
	E	2.00
	G	2.00
	H	2.00
	Rugby Station	
	B	50.00
	H	8.00
660	Rugeley A	3.00
	E	3.00
	H	1.00
661	Great Heywood	
	A	10.00
	Rotherfield H	3.00
662	Shirleywich A	20.00
	Sowerby Bridge	
	B	8.00
	H	2.00
663	Wolseley Bridge	
	A	12.00
	Feltham H	1.00
664	Ilkley H	2.00
665	Ruthin A	3.00
	B	10.00
	G	8.00
	H	2.00
666	Ryde A	5.00
	B	10.00
	E	4.00
	G	3.00
	H	3.00
667	Rye A	3.00
	H	2.00
668	Romford A	2.00
	G	2.00
	H	2.00
669	Saffron Walden	
	A	3.00
	B	8.00
	H	1.00
670	St. Austell A	2.00
	B	5.00
	H	2.00

671	Grampound A	5.00
672	St. Mawes A	25.00
673	Mevagissey A	7.00
	B	10.00
674	Tregoney A	10.00
	Great Chesterford	
	B	15.00
675	St. Albans A	3.00
	B	5.00
	F	4.00
	H	2.00
676	St. Asaph A	7.00
	H	2.00
677	St. Clears A	3.00
	H	3.00
678	St. Columb A	3.00
	B	8.00
679	St. Helens A	3.00
	F	2.00
	H	1.00
	St. Helens/Lanc.	
	H	2.00
680	St. Ives Hunts.	
	A	6.00
	B	12.00
	F	2.00
	St. Ives/Hunts.	
	H	1.00
681	Somersham A	15.00
	Dukinfield H	1.00
682	St. Leonards A	3.00
	F	2.00
	H	2.00
	St. Leonards-	
	on-Sea H	2.00
	St. Leonards	
	on Sea/Hastings	
	H	2.00
	Borough Green/Kent	
	H	2.00
683	Salisbury A	2.00
	B	12.00
	D	10.00
	F	2.00
	H	2.00
684	Downton A	5.00
	B	7.00
	H	4.00
685	Wilton A	5.00
	Wilton/Wilts. H	2.00
686	St. Neots A	3.00
	B	8.00
	E	2.00
	G	8.00
	H	2.00
687	Sandbach A	8.00
	H	2.00
688	Sandwich A	3.00
	B	8.00
	H	2.00
689	Sawbridgeworth	
	A	6.00
	B	10.00
	H	3.00
690	Saxmundham A	3.00
	B	8.00
	F	2.00
	H	2.00
691	Aldeburgh A	8.00
	Eglwyswrw B	15.00
692	Yoxford A	15.00
	Velindre B	15.00

693	Scarborough A	2.00
	B	6.00
	D	8.00
	F	2.00
	H	2.00
	Scarbro' E	2.00
	South Cliff B.O./	
	Scarborough H	8.00
694	Scole A	12.00
	E	8.00
	H	2.00
695	Selby A	2.00
	E	7.00
	G	4.00
	H	2.00
696	Settle A	2.00
	B	5.00
	H	2.00
697	Sevenoaks A	2.00
	F	2.00
	H	2.00
	Eden Bridge	
	(error) H	60.00
698	Shaftesbury A	4.00
	B	7.00
	H	1.00
699	Sheerness A	10.00
	B	5.00
	D	75.00
	F	2.00
	H	2.00
	Saffron Walden	
	(error) H	30.00
700	Sheffield A	2.00
	D	5.00
	F	2.00
	G	2.00
	H	2.00
701	Shepton Mallet	
	A	3.00
	F	2.00
	H	2.00
702	Sherborne A	3.00
	B	7.00
	H	2.00
703	Queen Camel A	10.00
	Hatherleigh B	15.00
704	South Shields A	4.00
	F	2.00
	H	1.00
705	Shifnal A	3.00
	H	2.00
706	Shipston on Stour	
	A	3.00
	B	8.00
	H	2.00
707	Shoreham A	3.00
	B	6.00
	H	5.00
	Shoreham/Sussex	
	H	1.00
708	Shrewsbury A	3.00
	C	15.00
	D	5.00
	F	2.00
	H	2.00
709	Church Stretton	
	A	6.00
	B	10.00
	H	20.00
710	Llanidloes A	6.00
	H	2.00

711	Wem A	8.00
	H	1.00
712	Sidmouth A	3.00
	H	2.00
713	Sittingbourne A	4.00
	B	6.00
	H	2.00
714	Skipton A	3.00
	B	6.00
	E	2.00
	H	2.00
715	Cross Hills A	100.00
	H	2.00
716	Sleaford A	3.00
	F	2.00
	H	2.00
717	Slough A	3.00
	B	10.00
	D	15.00
	E	2.00
	G	2.00
	H	2.00
718	Colnbrook A	20.00
	Manorbier B	15.00
719	Solihull A	5.00
720	Somerton/Somerset	
	A	3.00
	B	5.00
	H	10.00
721	Langport A	3.00
	B	8.00
	H	2.00
722	Southam A	12.00
723	Southampton A	2.00
	B	6.00
	D	5.00
	F	2.00
	H	2.00
	H (5 bars)	20.00
	Southampton	
	H.P.O. H	5.00
	Oxford St. B.O./	
	Southampton	
	H	30.00
724	South Molton A	3.00
	B	7.00
	H	1.00
725	South Petherton	
	A	3.00
726	Martock A	6.00
727	Spalding A	5.00
	B	6.00
	D	8.00
	F	4.00
	H	2.00
728	Spilsby A	3.00
	E	2.00
	G	3.00
	H	2.00
729	Spittal A	15.00
730	Stafford A	6.00
	D	5.00
	F	2.00
	H	2.00
	Stafford Station	
	H	12.00
731	Stilton A	10.00
	Spelter Works	
	B	20.00
732	Stockbridge A	8.00
	Stafford (error)	
	C	250.00

	South Stockton	
	H	6.00
	Thornaby on Tees	
	H	2.00
733	Stockport A	3.00
	B	8.00
	D	25.00
	F	2.00
	H	2.00
734	Whalley B	10.00
	H	1.00
735	Hazelgrove A	40.00
	Trecastle H	2.00
736	Stockton A	3.00
	B	8.00
	F	2.00
	Stockton on Tees	
	H	2.00
	Cecil St./	
	Stockton on Tees	
	H	25.00
	Norton Rd./	
	Stockton on Tees	
	H	25.00
737	Castle Eden A	5.00
	Broadstairs B	12.00
	H	8.00
	Broadstairs/	
	Station Office	
	H	10.00
	Broadstairs/	
	Station Office	
	B.O. H	5.00
738	Stokenchurch A	15.00
	Byfield B	7.00
	H	2.00
739	Stokesley A	3.00
	H	2.00
740	Ingleby Cross	
	A	15.00
	Crawley Down B	10.00
741	Staines A	5.00
	B	8.00
	E	2.00
	G	2.00
	H	2.00
742	Stamford A	3.00
	B	6.00
	D	12.00
	F	2.00
	H	2.00
743	Stevenage A	3.00
	B	4.00
	H	2.00
744	Steyning A	8.00
	B	8.00
	H	5.00
745	Stone A	5.00
	G	4.00
	Stone/Staff H	2.00
746	Stonham A	8.00
	G	12.00
747	Thwaite A	15.00
748	Newton Heath H	5.00
749	Stoney Stratford	
	A	3.00
	B	10.00
	F	2.00
	H	10.00
	Stony Stratford	
	H	1.00

750	Stourbridge A	3.00
	D	12.00
	F	2.00
	H	2.00
	Stourbrigde (error)	
	H	25.00
751	Stourport A	3.00
	F	8.00
	H	2.00
752	Stowmarket A	3.00
	B	10.00
	H	2.00
753	Needham Market	
	A	3.00
	B	6.00
	H	1.00
754	Stratford on Avon	
	A	3.00
	F	2.00
	H	2.00
755	Alcester A	12.00
756	Budleigh Salterton	
	A	4.00
	B	5.00
	H	2.00
757	Stroud A	3.00
	B	8.00
	D	15.00
	E	2.00
	G	4.00
	H	1.00
	Stroud Glos F	2.00
	H	2.00
	Stroud/Glos H	2.00
759	Uley A	20.00
760	Sudbury A	3.00
	E	3.00
	G	3.00
	H	5.00
	Sudbury/Suffolk	
	H	5.00
761	Sunderland A	3.00
	B	8.00
	D	4.00
	F	2.00
	H	2.00
762	Swaffham A	5.00
	B	8.00
	F	4.00
	H	2.00
763	Swansea A	3.00
	B	10.00
	D	5.00
	E	2.00
	G	2.00
	H	2.00
	The Docks/ Swansea H	5.00
	The Docks BO/ Swansea H	6.00
	Swansea/ Mumbles H	15.00
	Swansea/ Walters Rd H	25.00
	Walters Rd./ Swansea H	25.00
764	Brynmawr A	10.00
	H	8.00
	Brynmawr/ Breconshire H	1.00
765	Reynoldstone A	25.00
	Partridge Green B	10.00
766	Swindon A	3.00
	B	10.00
	D	15.00
	E	2.00
	G	4.00
	H	2.00
	New Swindon/ Swindon H	2.00
767	Cricklade A	3.00
	H	2.00
768	Wootton Bassett	
	A	8.00
	B	10.00
	H	2.00
769	Wroughton A	10.00
	H	2.00
770	Stanmore A	12.00
	B	15.00
	H	2.00
771	Caerphilly B	15.00
772	Tadcaster A	3.00
	B	6.00
	F	2.00
	H	2.00
773	Taibach A	2.00
	G	2.00
	H	10.00
	Aberavon/ Port Talbot H	10.00
774	Tamworth A	6.00
	B	6.00
	F	2.00
	H	2.00
775	Tarporley A	3.00
	H	1.00
776	Taunton A	2.00
	B	7.00
	D	5.00
	E	2.00
	G	2.00
	H	2.00
777	Williton A	3.00
	B	3.00
778	Dunster A	4.00
	B	5.00
779	Minehead A	6.00
	B	6.00
780	Tavistock A	3.00
	D	12.00
	F	2.00
	H	2.00
	Stafford (error) A	60.00
781	Callington A	3.00
	B	3.00
782	Teignmouth A	3.00
	B	6.00
	H	2.00
783	Tenbury A	3.00
	G	5.00
	H	2.00
784	Tenby A	2.00
	D	6.00
	G	4.00
	H	1.00
785	Tenterden A	7.00
	H	2.00
786	Tetbury A	12.00
	E	2.00
	G	4.00
	H	1.00
787	Tetsworth A	4.00
	F	4.00
	H	2.00
788	Tewkesbury A	3.00
	F	2.00
	H	1.00
789	Thame A	3.00
	B	8.00
	E	2.00
	H	2.00
790	Thetford A	3.00
	B	10.00
	D	60.00
	F	2.00
	H	2.00
791	Harling A	5.00
	B	4.00
	H	10.00
	East Harling H	2.00
792	Larlingford A	15.00
	New Tredegar B	15.00
793	Shipdham A	8.00
	Sandringham B	8.00
794	Watton A	7.00
	B	8.00
	Watton/Norfolk	
	H	1.00
795	Thirsk A	2.00
	G	6.00
	H	2.00
796	Osmotherley A	15.00
797	Thorne A	12.00
	Kibworth Harcourt H	4.00
798	Thrapstone A	3.00
	B	4.00
	Thrapston H	5.00
799	Tipton A	8.00
	E	8.00
	G	2.00
	H	2.00
800	Tiverton A	3.00
	B	10.00
	D	60.00
	F	2.00
	H	2.00
801	Wimbledon B	20.00
	H	6.00
	Wimbledon Camp	
	H	35.00
	Tonyrefail H	10.00
802	Bampton A	6.00
	B	10.00
803	Dulverton A	6.00
	B	5.00
804	Topsham A	7.00
	B	7.00
805	Torquay A	3.00
	B	8.00
	D	6.00
	E	2.00
	G	2.00
	H	2.00
806	Torrington A	3.00
	B	8.00
	H	1.00
807	Totnes A	3.00
	B	7.00
	G	3.00
	H	1.00
808	Towcester A	3.00
	B	4.00
	F	8.00
	H	2.00
809	Merton H	5.00
	Eastgate B	10.00

810	Tring A	3.00
	B	6.00
	E	2.00
	G	3.00
	H	2.00
811	Montford Bridge	
	B	15.00
812	Princes	
	Risborough A	10.00
813	Trowbridge A	2.00
	B	8.00
	F	2.00
	H	2.00
814	Truro A	2.00
	B	8.00
	D	40.00
	E	2.00
	G	2.00
	H	1.00
815	Camborne A	3.00
	B	8.00
	H	2.00
816	Sunbury	
	Common H	3.00
817	St. Ives/Cornwall	
	A	3.00
	B	8.00
	H	1.00
818	Tunbridge A	5.00
	B	8.00
	F	2.00
	H	2.00
	Tunbridge/Station	
	Office H	8.00
	Tonbridge H	5.00
	Tonbridge/Station	
	Office B	25.00
	H	8.00
819	Aspatria H	2.00
820	Tunbridge Wells	
	A	3.00
	D	12.00
	F	2.00
	H	1.00
	High St. B.O./	
	Tunbridge Wells	
	H	2.00
	High St./	
	Tunbridge Wells	
	H	2.00
	Calverley/	
	Tunbridge Wells	
	H	15.00
821	Tuxford A	15.00
	Ashford/Middx	
	B	10.00
	H	3.00
822	Uckfield A	3.00
	B	6.00
	H	2.00
823	Hailsham A	6.00
	B	12.00
	H	1.00
824	Ulverstone A	2.00
	B	8.00
	F	2.00
	H	1.00
	Wrexham	
	(error) H	100.00
825	Uppingham A	3.00
	H	2.00

826	Usk A	5.00
	H	1.00
827	Uttoxeter A	3.00
	B	7.00
	H	2.00
828	Abbots Bromley	
	A	12.00
	Lanchester B	8.00
	H	2.00
829	Sudbury/Derby	
	A	10.00
	H	1.00
	Crowborough H	20.00
830	Uxbridge A	3.00
	B	10.00
	D	10.00
	F	2.00
	H	2.00
831	Wakefield A	2.00
	B	8.00
	D	6.00
	F	2.00
	H	2.00
832	Wallingford A	5.00
	B	10.00
	H	1.00
833	Benson A	15.00
	Chingford H	10.00
	Cowshill B	10.00
834	Walsall A	8.00
	C	100.00
	E	2.00
	G	2.00
	H	2.00
835	Waltham Cross	
	A	7.00
	H	2.00
836	Wangford A	3.00
	B	8.00
	F	3.00
	H	2.00
837	Wrentham A	15.00
	Reeth B	10.00
838	Southwold A	8.00
	H	2.00
839	Wansford A	6.00
	F	2.00
	H	1.00
840	Cannock H	1.00
841	Weldon A	15.00
	Hednesford H	1.00
842	Ware A	3.00
	B	3.00
	E	2.00
	G	2.00
	H	2.00
843	Wareham A	3.00
	B	7.00
	H	1.00
844	Corfe Castle A	7.00
	B	5.00
845	Swanage A	8.00
	B	8.00
	H	1.00
846	Warminster A	2.00
	B	5.00
	H	2.00
847	Warrington A	3.00
	C	50.00
	D	12.00
	F	2.00
	H	1.00

848	Warwick A	4.00
	E	2.00
	G	2.00
	H	1.00
849	Watford A	3.00
	E	2.00
	G	2.00
	H	2.00
850	Wednesbury A	4.00
	F	2.00
	H	2.00
851	Weedon A	2.00
	B	5.00
	H	2.00
852	Welshpool A	2.00
	B	10.00
	H	1.00
853	Machynlleth A	4.00
	B	12.00
	H	1.00
854	Montgomery A	10.00
	H	8.00
855	South Ferndale-	
	Tylorstown B	20.00
856	Churchstoke A	10.00
	Pumpsaint B	25.00
857	Welford A	3.00
	Silloth B	8.00
	H	2.00
858	Wellingboro' A	3.00
	B	10.00
	F	6.00
	H	12.00
	Wellingborough	
	H	2.00
859	Wellington/Salop	
	A	3.00
	B	8.00
	D	10.00
	F	3.00
	H	2.00
	Wellington Salop	
	H	2.00
860	Wellington Som.	
	A	2.00
	B	5.00
	D	6.00
	Wellington/Som.	
	H	1.00
862	Milverton A	4.00
	B	8.00
863	Wells/Norfolk	
	A	15.00
	B	8.00
	F	10.00
864	Wells, Somst A	3.00
	D	5.00
	H	2.00
	Wells/Somt H	2.00
	Wells/Som H	2.00
865	Welwyn A	3.00
	B	6.00
	H	2.00
867	Wendover A	10.00
868	West Bromwich	
	A	3.00
	F	15.00
	H	2.00
869	Port Dinorwic	
	H	2.00
870	Westbury/Wilts	
	A	4.00
	B	12.00
	H	1.00

871	Weston-super-Mare	
	A	4.00
	B	8.00
	D	5.00
	F	2.00
	H	2.00
872	Wetherby A	8.00
	B	8.00
	H	6.00
873	Weymouth A	3.00
	D	7.00
	F	2.00
	H	2.00
874	Wheatley A	6.00
	Godstone Station	
	H	30.00
	South Godstone	
	H	3.00
875	Whitby A	2.00
	E	2.00
	H	2.00
876	Whitchurch/Salop	
	A	6.00
	F	6.00
	H	2.00
	Whitchurch Salop	
	H	2.00
877	Whitehaven A	3.00
	B	8.00
	F	2.00
	H	1.00
878	Wigan A	3.00
	D	15.00
	E	2.00
	G	2.00
	H	1.00
879	Wigton A	3.00
	E	2.00
	H	2.00
880	Allonby A	10.00
	Didsbury H	4.00
881	Swindon Station	
	B	60.00
	H	6.00
882	Wimborne A	3.00
	B	6.00
	F	4.00
	H	2.00
883	Wincanton A	3.00
	B	2.00
	H	1.00
884	Henstridge A	15.00
	Aberbeeg B	15.00
885	Milborne Port	
	A	15.00
	Abertillery B	12.00
886	Crumlin B	15.00
887	Stalbridge A	15.00
	Cwmtillery B	15.00
888	Winchester A	3.00
	D	8.00
	F	2.00
	H	2.00
889	Elland B	8.00
	H	2.00
890	Windsor A	5.00
	B	8.00
	D	10.00
	E	2.00
	G	2.00
	H	2.00
891	Godstone H	2.00
892	Chatteris H	1.00

893	Wingham A	5.00
	H	15.00
894	Winslow A	7.00
	E	5.00
	H	1.00
895	Wirksworth A	3.00
	F	8.00
	H	2.00
897	Wisbeach A	3.00
	D	8.00
	F	2.00
	H	1.00
898	Brightlingsea	
	B	15.00
899	Hunstanton B	10.00
900	Witham A	2.00
	B	4.00
	Witham/Essex H	2.00
901	Pangbourne H	1.00
902	Witney A	3.00
	G	2.00
	H	2.00
903	Wiveliscombe A	3.00
	B	6.00
904	Wokingham A	2.00
	H	1.00
905	Wolverhampton	
	A	3.00
	B	8.00
	C	35.00
	D	5.00
	F	2.00
	H	2.00
906	Woburn A	6.00
	E	4.00
	H	2.00
907	Woodbridge A	3.00
	D	20.00
	F	2.00
	H	2.00
908	Wembley B	15.00
910	Woodstock A	2.00
	H	2.00
911	Elmham B	8.00
	H	2.00
912	Deddington A	15.00
	Hebron B	25.00
913	Woodyates A	20.00
	Crook Log/	
	Bexley Heath	
	B	12.00
	H	4.00
914	Cranborne A	5.00
	B	8.00
	H	1.00
915	Wotton-under-Edge	
	A	3.00
	B	8.00
	H	2.00
917	Wickwar A	15.00
	Askam B	12.00
	H	2.00
918	Worcester A	2.00
	B	6.00
	C	15.00
	D	6.00
	F	2.00
	H	2.00
919	Llanfallteg B	12.00
920	Upton-on-Severn	
	A	3.00
	H	2.00

921	Workington A	3.00
	B	9.00
	F	5.00
	H	1.00
922	Worksop A	8.00
	E	3.00
	G	8.00
	H	2.00
923	Worthing A	3.00
	B	10.00
	F	2.00
	H	2.00
	Brighton Rd/	
	Worthing H	30.00
	Brunswick Rd/	
	Worthing H	25.00
	Chapel Rd. North/	
	Worthing H	30.00
	Montague St./	
	Worthing H	20.00
	Worthing/Station	
	Office H	15.00
	Worthing Station	
	B.O./Worthing	
	H	15.00
924	Wrexham A	3.00
	B	10.00
	C	50.00
	D	10.00
	E	2.00
	G	5.00
	H	1.00
925	Wymondham A	3.00
	B	6.00
	F	5.00
	H	2.00
926	Yarm A	4.00
	B	10.00
	G	10.00
	H	2.00
927	Yarmouth Nfk A	3.00
	B	8.00
	D	10.00
	Yarmouth/Norfolk	
	F	2.00
	H	2.00
	Great Yarmouth	
	H	2.00
928	Yealmpton A	5.00
	Crowborough Cross	
	H	10.00
929	Yeovil A	3.00
	B	8.00
	G	2.00
	H	2.00
930	York A	2.00
	B	8.00
	• C	40.00
	D	6.00
	E	2.00
	G	2.00
	H	2.00
	Micklegate/York	
	H	10.00
	Strensall Camp/	
	York H	5.00
931	Easingwold A	6.00
	B	8.00
	H	2.00
	H (side bars)	75.00
932	Escrick A	15.00
	Barnetby B	12.00
933	Hammerton A	15.00

934	Helmsley A	15.00	953	Blackpool A	3.00	978	Littlehampton A	4.00
	Mundford H	1.00		F	2.00		B	10.00
935	Kirby Moorside			H	1.00		H	1.00
	A	15.00		South Shore/		979	Acklington A	6.00
	Castle Acre B	10.00		Blackpool H	1.00		F	7.00
936	Whitwell A	15.00	954	Longtown A	10.00		H	2.00
937	Barnet A	5.00		H	6.00	980	Rhymney A	10.00
	B	5.00		Longtown/Cumbd.			B	15.00
	G	2.00		H	2.00		G	10.00
	H	1.00	955	Budleigh Salterton			H	3.00
938	Croydon A	5.00		A	10.00	982	Dowlais A	7.00
	B	8.00		Southborough H	3.00	983	Soham A	7.00
	D	35.00	956	Hurstpierpoint			B	8.00
	E	2.00		A	6.00		H	2.00
	G	2.00		F	2.00	984	Mere A	8.00
	H	2.00		H	2.00		B	10.00
	Croydon/E H	6.00	957	Nuneaton A	3.00		H	2.00
	Croydon E H	6.00		B	8.00	985	Aberdare A	5.00
	Croydon/S H	6.00		F	5.00		F	2.00
	Croydon W H	6.00		H	2.00		H	2.00
	New Thornton		958	Leigh/Lanc. A	60.00		Churston Ferrers	
	Heath/Croydon			H	6.00		H (error)	8.00
	H	10.00		Leigh Lancashire		986	Treherbert B	10.00
	Thornton Heath			H	3.00		H	2.00
	H	4.00		Fence Houses A	75.00	987	Burbage A	25.00
	Thornton Heath/		959	Clifton A	4.00		Treorchy B	15.00
	High St. H	6.00		D	12.00		H	2.00
939	Staplehurst A	6.00		E	2.00	988	Ystrad Rhondda	
	B	8.00		Long Sutton H	4.00		B	15.00
	D	25.00		Long Sutton/Linc.			H	8.00
	F	2.00		H	2.00	989	Tonypandy B	15.00
	H	2.00	960	Crewe A	10.00		H	4.00
940	Alne A			B	8.00	990	Collingbourne	
	(side bars)	200.00		E	2.00		A	25.00
	Litcham B	10.00		H	1.00		Dinas B	15.00
941	Burton Agnes A		961	Sutton Bridge H	1.00	991	Porth H	10.00
	(side bars)	150.00	962	Middleham A	5.00		Porth/Glam B	10.00
	Three Cocks B	20.00		H	2.00		H	2.00
942	Sedgefield A	12.00	963	Winchfield A	10.00	992	Tidworth A	25.00
943	Beaminster A	3.00		B	8.00		Pen-y-graig B	15.00
	B	5.00		F	2.00	993	Blaenllecha B	20.00
	H	1.00		H	1.00		Ferndale H	2.00
944	Lynton A	5.00	964	Euston Square		994	Axbridge A	15.00
	B	7.00		Station A	60.00		Trealaw B	15.00
945	Runcorn A	10.00		B	50.00	995	Brierley Hill A	6.00
	G	2.00		Wearhead B	8.00		B	10.00
	H	2.00	965	Alderney A	75.00		F	3.00
946	Middlesborough		966	Hadlow H	3.00		H	2.00
	A	2.00	967	Edenbridge A	5.00	996	Sturminster A	10.00
	B	6.00		H	3.00		B	5.00
	F	2.00		Edenbridge/Kent		997	Shillingstone	
	H	8.00		H	2.00		A	20.00
	Middlesbrough H	2.00	968	Winchelsea H	1.00	998	Charfield H	1.00
947	Hartlepool A	3.00	970	Lynmouth A	20.00	999	Paulton B	10.00
	B	10.00	971	Ventnor A	5.00	001	Pensford B	15.00
	F	2.00		G	4.00	002	Ulceby A	12.00
	H	1.00		H	2.00		B	10.00
948	Bruton A	7.00	972	Flint A	10.00		E	12.00
	B	4.00		G	10.00		G	7.00
949	Castle Cary A	3.00		H	2.00		H	2.00
	B	2.00	973	Rhyl A	5.00	003	Weobley A	10.00
	H	1.00		D	7.00		B	6.00
950	Kenilworth A	4.00		G	1.00	004	Redcar A	4.00
	F	6.00		H	1.00		E	3.00
	H	2.00	974	Sedbergh A	6.00		H	2.00
951	Pontypool A	3.00	976	Windermere A	4.00	005	Corsham A	15.00
	B	8.00		B	8.00		B	15.00
	F	4.00		F	2.00		H	2.00
	H	2.00		H	2.00	006	Temple Cloud B	12.00
952	Hollytroyds A	20.00	977	Ferry Hill A	8.00	007	Brough A	15.00
	Greenhithe H	1.00		F	2.00		E	3.00
				H	1.00		Brough/Yorkshire	
							H	3.00

```
008   Clutton B        15.00
010   Copplestone A    10.00
011   Hallatrow B      15.00
012   Highampton A     15.00
013   North Tawton A   10.00
      B                10.00
      H                10.00
014   Witheridge A      6.00
      H                 4.00
015   Milford Junction
      A                30.00
      B                25.00
      South Milford
      H                 2.00
016   Brockenhurst B   10.00
      H                 2.00
017   Upper Clevedon
      A                15.00
      Rainham B        10.00
      Rainham/Kent H    2.00
018   Egham H           2.00
019   New Malden H      2.00
020   Clevedon A        3.00
      H                 1.00
021   St. Just A       10.00
      B                 8.00
022   Ripley Yorks A   15.00
      F                 8.00
      Ripley/Yorks
      H                 2.00
023   Farnboro'
      Station A        20.00
      B                20.00
      D                45.00
      F                10.00
      H                 6.00
      Farnborough
      Station H        10.00
      Farnborough/
      Hants H           2.00
024   Stonehouse A     10.00
      Stonehouse
      Glos. F           2.00
      Stonehouse/
      Glos. H           4.00
025   Bletchley
      Station A        30.00
      B                20.00
      H                 8.00
026   Southend A        5.00
      B                 8.00
      H                 3.00
      Southend/Essex
      H                 2.00
      Southend-on-Sea
      H                 2.00
028   Ramsey/Hunts A   10.00
      St. Keyne B      10.00
029   West Hartlepool
      A                 8.00
      B                 8.00
      F                 2.00
      H                 2.00
030   Tremadoc A       25.00
      B                15.00
031   Portmadoc A       8.00
      H                 2.00
032   Festiniog A      10.00
      B                10.00
      H                 2.00
033   Tanybwlch H       7.00

034   Smethwick F       8.00
      H                 3.00
      Oldbury A
      (error)          80.00
035   Oldbury E         3.00
      H                10.00
      Smethwick A
      (error)          75.00
036   Ramsey/I. of Man
      A                40.00
      H                10.00
037   Castletown/
      Isle of Man A    50.00
      B                70.00
      H                10.00
038   Chathill A        6.00
      F                 5.00
      H                 2.00
039   Willenhall H      2.00
040   Whittlesea A     15.00
      Duloe B          10.00
041   Kirkby Thore B   15.00
      H                15.00
042   Sandplace B      10.00
043   Yatton Keynell
      A                15.00
044   Lacock A         15.00
      Polperro B       10.00
045   Sutton Benger
      A                15.00
      Temple Sowerby
      B                15.00
046   Aldershot Camp
      A                40.00
      D                30.00
      F                10.00
      Trawsfynydd B    20.00
047   Crewe Station
      A                25.00
      B                25.00
      H                 2.00
048   Normanton D      15.00
      F                 2.00
      H                 2.00
      Normanton/
      Station Office
      H                12.00
      Normanton Station
      H                 8.00
049   St. John's Chapel
      B                 8.00
050   Bampton/Oxon A    3.00
      H                 2.00
052   Shotley Bridge
      A                12.00
      B                 8.00
      H                 1.00
053   Heckmondwike H    2.00
054   Farnworth H       4.00
      Farnworth/Bolton
      H                 2.00
055   Beaford A        10.00
      H                 3.00
056   Bow A            15.00
057   Brandis Corner
      A                15.00
      B                 8.00
058   Bridestowe A     15.00
      B                 6.00
059   Chulmleigh A      4.00
      H                 3.00
060   Newent B          8.00
061   Eynsford H        2.00
062   Dolton A         20.00
      B                 7.00

063   Exbourne A       15.00
064   Lewdown A         8.00
      B                10.00
065   Lifton A         15.00
      B                 8.00
066   Capel Bangor B   15.00
067   Morchard Bishop
      A                15.00
      B                 7.00
      H                 1.00
068   Ponterwydd B     20.00
069   Devils Bridge
      B                20.00
070   Sampford
      Courtenay A      20.00
071   Wembworthy A     10.00
      B                 8.00
072   Winkleigh A       8.00
      H                 2.00
073   Waltham A        15.00
074   Probus A          6.00
      H                 8.00
075   Newton in Cartmel
      A                 6.00
      Rhydyfelin B     15.00
076   Knottingley A     8.00
      B                10.00
      H                 2.00
077   Aston on Clun
      A                20.00
      H                 3.00
078   Brampton Brian
      A                 8.00
      B                16.00
079   Bromfield A      10.00
      H                 7.00
080   Clun A           20.00
      H                 3.00
081   Castletown B      8.00
082   Leintwardine A    8.00
      B                 6.00
084   Lydbury North
      A                20.00
      B                15.00
      H                 3.00
085   Craven Arms A    20.00
      B                15.00
      H                 2.00
086   Fortuneswell/
      Portland B       10.00
      H                 1.00
087   Onibury A        20.00
      Goginan B        15.00
088   Sunninghill H     5.00
089   Usk B            15.00
090   Wistanstow A     20.00
091   Kirkby Lonsdale
      B                10.00
      H                 2.00
092   Fence Houses A   12.00
      F                 2.00
      H                 2.00
093   Harwell A        20.00
      Crowthorne B     15.00
094   Steventon/Berks
      A                 8.00
      B                10.00
      H                 5.00
095   Drayton A        20.00
096   Colwyn Bay H      3.00
097   Shiplake A       60.00
      Twyford A        30.00
      B                10.00
      Mitcheldean H     2.00
```

099	Whitchurch/Hants			B20	Nailsea A	15.00	B60	Bournemouth A	8.00
	B	8.00			B	12.00		B	6.00
	H	2.00		B21	Yatton A	15.00		H	2.00
A16	Newcastle			B22	Congresbury A	6.00		Bournemouth/S.O.	
	Station A	150.00		B23	Wrington A	8.00		H	2.00
	B	150.00		B24	Langford A	15.00	B61	Gowerton H	2.00
A19	Appledore A	10.00		B25	Burrington A	15.00	B63	Blaydon-on-Tyne	
	B	10.00		B26	Blagdon A	15.00		A	10.00
A20	Wickham Market				B	10.00		F	3.00
	A	12.00		B28	Moreton Hampstead			H	2.00
	B	10.00			B	15.00	B66	Briton Ferry	
	F	3.00		B29	Chagford B	15.00		A	10.00
	H	2.00		B30	Petersham B	25.00		H	4.00
A21	Red Hill A	10.00		B33	Grampound Road			Kibworth	
	B	10.00			A	15.00		Harcourt F	30.00
	E	2.00			B	8.00	B67	Winsford F	5.00
	F	12.00			H	10.00		H	2.00
	H	4.00		B34	London-Holyhead TPO			Winsford/Cheshire	
	Red Hill/				- see chap 13			H	2.00
	Station Office			B35	Shrivenham A	5.00	B68	Lympstone A	20.00
	H	12.00			B	10.00		B	6.00
A22	Boxmoor B	15.00			H	1.00	B69	Paignton A	4.00
A23	Fremington A	10.00		B36	Stratton			B	8.00
	B	6.00			St. Margaret			H	1.00
A24	Instow A	8.00			A	15.00	B70	Dalton-in-Furness	
	B	6.00		B37	Longcot A	10.00		A	12.00
A84	Brasted H	1.00		B38	Pinner A	5.00		H	2.00
A86	Upper Cwmtwrch				B	8.00	B71	Barrow-in-Furness	
	B	15.00			H	1.00		A	12.00
A87	Forest Fach B	15.00		B39	Harpton A	20.00		B	8.00
A90	East Liss H	2.00			Herne Bay B	10.00		H	2.00
A91	Southsea B.O./				H	2.00	B72	Malvern Wells F	8.00
	Portsmouth H	2.00		B40	Hundred House			H	3.00
A92	Masham H	2.00			A	20.00	B73	Wylam A	15.00
A93	Llanfarian B	10.00		B41	Nantmel A	20.00		H	2.00
A94	Penarth B	15.00		B42	Walton (Radnor)		B74	Blyth A	15.00
	H	3.00			A	20.00		H	4.00
A95	Newport (Yorks)				Whitstable B	8.00		Blyth/Northumberland	
	B	10.00			H	1.00		H	2.00
A96	North Cave B	8.00		B43	Washington		B75	Bedlington A	15.00
A97	South Cave B	8.00			Station A	50.00		B	8.00
A98	South Bank H	4.00			H	12.00		H	3.00
A99	Chwilog B	15.00		B44	Flax Bourton A	10.00	B76	Cowpen A	10.00
	H	6.00			B	8.00		Emma Colliery	
B03	Northfleet B	12.00		B45	West Town A	15.00		B	10.00
	H	12.00			B	15.00	B77	Cowpen Lane A	8.00
B04	Par Station A	15.00		B46	Rhyddlan A	25.00		Bebside H	4.00
	B	15.00			Llandudno		B78	Nedderton A	15.00
B05	Scorrier A	7.00			(error) B	50.00	B79	Boscastle A	10.00
	H	6.00		B47	Llandudno A	10.00		B	4.00
B06	Hatt A	15.00			F	2.00		----------	
	B	8.00			H	1.00			
B07	St. Issey A	10.00		B48	Trefriw A	15.00			
B08	St. Mellion A	8.00			H	2.00			
	B	8.00		B49	Amlwch A	25.00			
B09	Washaway A	20.00			H	2.00			
	B	10.00		B50	Llangefni A	25.00			
B10	Perranarworthal				H	2.00			
	A	10.00		B51	Menai Bridge A	12.00			
B11	Devoran A	15.00			H	2.00			
	B	10.00		B52	Hatch End A	15.00			
B12	Bickley Station/				B	15.00			
	Kent B	25.00		B54	Cramlington A	15.00			
	H	35.00			F	5.00			
B13	Kingsland A	20.00			H	2.00			
	B	10.00		B55	Beal A	4.00			
B14	Staunton-on-Arrow				B	8.00			
	A	10.00			H	3.00			
B15	Titley A	15.00		B57	Bagshot B	12.00			
B16	Plymouth-Bristol TPO				H	8.00			
	- see chap 13			B58	Bucknell A	20.00			
B17	Bronwydd Arms				B	15.00			
	B	25.00		B59	Shap A	6.00			
B18	Mardy B	15.00			H	3.00			
B19	Wolverton A	8.00			Shap/Westmoreland				
	B	8.00			H	2.00			

Note: erratic use of B80-B84 in Totnes area, not in accordance with official regulations and lists.

B80	Blackawton (1890-		
	-1902) A	15.00	
	Harbertonford		
	(1868-93) A	30.00	
B81	Blackawton		
	(1863-66) A	30.00	
B82	Harbertonford (1899-		
	-1905) A	15.00	
	Mounts (1877-80)		
	A	15.00	
B83	Harberton		
	(1870-72) A	30.00	
	Halwell (1870)		
	A	30.00	
B84	Halwell (1869-92)		
	A	30.00	
	Mounts (1867-99)		
	A	30.00	

Ref	Place	Grade	Price		Ref	Place	Grade	Price		Ref	Place	Grade	Price
B85	Malvern Link	B	15.00		C24	Plymouth & Exeter/				C75	Newchurch	H	12.00
		F	6.00			N.M.T. - see chap 13					Newchurch/		
		H	3.00		C25	Mostyn	A	25.00			Manchester	H	8.00
B86	Matlock Bridge						H	5.00		C76	Prestwich	H	3.00
		A	8.00		C26	Darwen	B	8.00		C77	Radcliffe	H	4.00
		H	8.00				G	5.00		C78	Wilmslow	H	3.00
B87	Weybridge Station						H	3.00		C79	Purley/Surrey	H	3.00
		A	25.00		C27	Cleckheaton	H	5.00		C80	Helperby	B	15.00
		B	25.00		C29	Jarrow	A	15.00		C84	Aberayron	H	2.00
		H	15.00				G	7.00		C85	Enfield	B	10.00
	Weybridge	H	3.00				H	2.00				G	6.00
B88	Sandown	A	30.00		C31	Castleford	H	2.00				H	2.00
		B	8.00		C32	Aberdovey	A	15.00		C89	Dudley	B	8.00
B89	Shanklin	A	20.00				B	15.00			Dudley/		
		B	8.00				H	2.00			Northumberland		
B90	Starcross	A	15.00		C33	Towyn	A	15.00				H	2.00
		B	9.00				B	15.00			Dudley/Northd		
B91	Saltash	A	10.00				H	2.00				H	10.00
		B	6.00		C34	Pennal	A	15.00		C90	Burgess Hill	B	10.00
B92	Rainhill	A	12.00		C44	Fishguard	H	3.00				H	2.00
		B	8.00		C45	Mossley	G	12.00		C91	Harrow	G	30.00
		H	12.00				H	3.00			West Malling	H	1.00
B93	Lelant	A	15.00		C46	Hoyland	G	15.00		C92	Neyland	G	8.00
		B	8.00			Everthorpe	B	15.00			Neyland Pem.	H	6.00
B94	Saltburn-by-				C47	Mirfield	H	2.00		C93	Twickenham	H	2.00
	the-Sea	A	12.00		C48	Chipping Sodbury				C94	Teddington	B	15.00
		H	2.00				A	30.00				H	5.00
B95	Horrabridge						H	1.00		C95	Hampton	G	8.00
		A	6.00		C49	Stretford	H	2.00				H	2.00
		B	8.00		C50	Ashton on Mersey				C96	Sunbury	G	6.00
B96	Roborough	A	10.00				H	8.00				H	2.00
		B	8.00			Sale	G	4.00		C97	Elstree	B	8.00
B97	Skegness/Linc.						H	1.00				H	2.00
		H	2.00		C52	Godshill	A	15.00		C98	Newhaven	B	10.00
B98	Princetown						B	6.00		C99	Broughton-in-		
		A	15.00				H	2.00			Furness	B	8.00
		B	10.00		C53	Rookley	A	50.00				H	2.00
B99	Abermule	A	8.00		C54	Brading	A	20.00		D01	Holborn Hill	B	10.00
C01	Berriew	A	10.00				B	15.00			Millom	B	8.00
		B	8.00				H	3.00				H	2.00
C02	Borth	A	20.00		C55	Wootton Bridge				D02	Grange	B	12.00
		H	2.00				A	20.00				G	6.00
C03	Bow Street	A	10.00		C63	Heywood	H					H	7.00
C04	Caersws	A	8.00			(error)		15.00			Grange over Sands		
C05	Carno	A	8.00		C65	Heywood	G	12.00				H	2.00
C06	Cemmaes	A	12.00				H	5.00		D03	Seaford	B	15.00
C07	Chirbury	A	12.00		C66	Woking Station				D04	Dowlais	G	10.00
C08	Churchstoke	A	15.00				B	20.00				H	2.00
C09	Cemmaes	A	12.00				H	12.00		D05	Chislehurst	H	1.00
C10	Garthmyl	A	8.00			Woking	H	3.00			Chislehurst/		
C11	Glandovey	A	20.00		C67	Droylsden	H	8.00			Station Office		
		B	15.00		C68	London & Dover	TPO					H	10.00
		H	5.00			- see chap 13					Lower Camden/		
C12	Llanbrynmair	A	12.00		C69	Newton-le-					Chislehurst		
		B	12.00			Willows	H	3.00				H	6.00
C13	Llandinam	A	8.00			Newton-le-				D06	Erwood	B	6.00
C14	Taliesin	A	15.00			Willows/Lanc				D07	Llanuwchllyn	B	15.00
C15	Pateley Bridge						H	2.00			Yalding	H	1.00
		H	5.00		C70	Cosham	A	10.00		D08	Llyswen	B	15.00
C16	Chorley/Cheshire						B	10.00		D09	Rhydymain	B	15.00
		H	8.00				H	10.00		D10	Gretna	B	40.00
	East Cowes	A	35.00			Cosham/Hants	H	2.00		D11	Framlingham	B	8.00
C17	Brighouse	F	8.00		C71	Willington/						H	2.00
		H	5.00			Durham	B	10.00		D12	Burgh/Linc.	H	12.00
C18	Bilton	A	10.00				H	2.00			Burgh	H	10.00
C19	Holmfirth	H	2.00		C72	Cheetham Hill				D13	Beckenham	B	10.00
C21	St. Columb Minor						H	12.00				H	1.00
		A	15.00		C73	Eccles	G	12.00		D15	Aldeburgh	B	15.00
C22	Newquay/Cornwall						H	4.00				H	2.00
		A	15.00		C74	Middleton	H	8.00		D16	Leiston	B	10.00
		B	8.00			Middleton/Lanc						H	2.00
		H	2.00				H	8.00		D18	Newbridge-on-Wye		
C23	Tywyn	A	20.00									B	10.00
												H	2.00

100

Code	Location	Type	Price
D19	Burnopfield/Co.of Durham	H	4.00
D20	Black Hill/Co.of Durham	B	10.00
		H	2.00
D21	Richmond/Surrey	B	6.00
		H	2.00
D23	Sutton/Surrey	B	8.00
		H	2.00
D24	Mitcham	B	12.00
		G	4.00
		H	3.00
D25	Llandyssil	H	3.00
	Llandyssil/Sorting Tender - see chap 13		
D31	Carn Brea	H	2.00
D32	Llanfihangel-ar-Arth	B	20.00
D33	Newport (Essex)	B	15.00
D34	Waterfoot	H	8.00
D35	Talybont	B	15.00
D36	Hopkinstown	B	15.00
D37	Coggeshall	H	2.00
D38	Earls Colne	H	2.00
D39	Bourton-on-the-Water	H	1.00
D41	Padiham	B	12.00
		H	2.00
D42	Blaenllecha	B	15.00
D43	Llanarth	B	8.00
D44	Potters Bar	H	1.00
D46	Cockfield	B	8.00
D49	Treharris	B	15.00
D51	Peel/IOM	B	50.00
		H	10.00
D52	Figure Four	B	15.00
D53	Llanilar	B	10.00
D54	Crosswood	B	20.00
D55	Clydach Vale	B	15.00
D56	Olney	B	10.00
D57	Bute Docks	B	20.00
		H	8.00
	Bute Docks/Cardiff	H	6.00
	Bute Docks B.O./Cardiff	H	6.00
D58	Harrington	B	8.00
		H	2.00
D59	Marske-by-the-Sea	B	10.00
		H	2.00
D60	Valley	A	20.00
		H	3.00
	The Valley	H	10.00
D61	Barrasford	H	12.00
D62	Southwick/Sussex	H	15.00
D63	Nawton	B	15.00
D64	Kirby Moorside	B	8.00
		H	2.00
	Kirkby Moorside	H	8.00
D65	Helmsley	B	12.00
	Yoxford (error)	H	4.00
D66	Gillingham/Dorset	B	6.00
		H	2.00
D69	Wingate	B	30.00

Code	Location	Type	Price
D70	Castle Eden Station	B	15.00
		H	20.00
D71	Wingate	H	3.00
	Castle Eden Colliery	B	30.00
D72	Coxhoe	B	15.00
		H	5.00
D73	Trimdon Grange	B	15.00
		H	5.00
D75	Harrow	B	10.00
		G	6.00
		H	1.00
D76	Buckhurst Hill	B	8.00
		H	2.00
D77	Loughton	B	8.00
		H	3.00
D78	Brancepeth	B	8.00
D79	Sandy	B	15.00
	Twyford	B	10.00
D80	Potton	B	12.00
		H	3.00
D81	Bures	B	15.00
D82	Llwyngwril	B	15.00
D83	Blaina	G	4.00
D84	Beaufort	H	8.00
D85	Ebbw Vale	B	10.00
		H	2.00
D86	Nantyglo	H	3.00
D88	Linton	G	10.00
D89	Haverhill	H	8.00
D90	Long Melford	H	6.00
D91	Lavenham	H	8.00
D92	Clare	G	8.00
		H	2.00
D93	Shefford	B	15.00
		H	3.00
D94	Woodford Bridge	B	10.00
	Penarth Docks/Penarth (error)	H	75.00
D96	West Drayton	B	10.00
D97	Carshalton	B	10.00
		H	3.00
D98	Pentre	B	15.00
		H	4.00
E03	Letterstone	H	4.00
	Letterston	H	2.00
E04	Dinas Cross	H	2.00
E05	Solva	G	5.00
E07	Newport/Pem.	H	5.00
E08	St. Davids	H	5.00
E09	Tangiers	B	10.00
E10	Treffgarne	B	10.00
		H	8.00
E11	Wolfcastle	B	10.00
E12	Dwrbach	B	6.00
E13	Camrose	B	10.00
E14	Roch	B	10.00
E15	Penycwm	B	7.00
E18	Llanbyther	B	15.00
		H	2.00
E19	Llanwnen	B	20.00
E20	Talsarn	B	20.00
E21	Ciliau Aeron	B	15.00
E22	Aberarth	B	10.00
E23	Llanon	B	10.00
E24	Llanrhystyd	B	10.00
E25	Brimfield	B	10.00
		H	3.00
E27	Llechryd	B	4.00

Code	Location	Type	Price
E29	South Benfleet	B	8.00
E31	Little Haywood	B	10.00
E32	Pontlottyn	B	15.00
E33	New Barnet	H	1.00
E34	Landore	B	15.00
		H	2.00
E35	Morriston	B	15.00
		H	2.00
E36	Clydach	B	15.00
E37	Pontardine	B	15.00
E38	Ystalyfera	B	7.00
		H	4.00
E39	Ystradgynlais	B	15.00
		H	2.00
	Ystradgnlais	H	10.00
E40	Abergwilly	B	10.00
E41	Llanarthney	B	15.00
E42	Nantgaredig	B	15.00
E43	Manordilo	B	15.00
E44	Golden Grove	B	15.00
E46	Sketty	B	15.00
E48	Penclawdd	B	15.00
E49	Reynoldstone	B	10.00
E51	Greenhill	B	15.00
E52	Henfield	B	10.00
		H	2.00
E54	Cross Inn	H	8.00
	Ammanford	H	5.00
E55	Cwmamman	H	15.00
	Garnant	B	15.00
E56	Llandebie	B	25.00
	Treforest	B	15.00
		H	4.00
E57	Haughley	B	15.00
E59	Llanpumpsaint	B	12.00
E60	Llangunllo	B	10.00
E61	Dolau	B	10.00
E62	Llandrindod	B	10.00
		H	5.00
	Llandrindod Wells	H	2.00
E63	Llangammarch	B	5.00
E64	Beulah	B	15.00
E65	Llanwrtyd	B	10.00
		H	2.00
E66	Hovingham	B	15.00
E67	Slingsby	B	15.00
E68	New Quay/Car.	H	8.00
	New Quay/Cardiganshire	H	2.00
E69	Winforton	B	12.00
E70	Whitney	B	12.00
E71	Clifford	B	10.00
E72	Talgarth	B	8.00
		H	2.00
E73	Carnforth	H	1.00
E74	Penmaenmawr	B	15.00
		H	2.00
E75	Leamside	H	4.00
E76	Didcot	B	10.00
E77	Ferryside	B	8.00
		H	8.00
E78	Chigwell Rd	H	2.00
	Chigwell Road	H	6.00
E79	Burwash	B	15.00
E80	Mortimer	B	5.00
E81	Etchingham	B	15.00
		H	10.00
E82	Norham	B	10.00
		H	2.00

Code	Place	Type	Value
E83	Caterham Valley		
		B	15.00
		H	3.00
E84	Garth	B	15.00
E85	Begelly	B	8.00
E86	Saundersfoot	B	10.00
		H	2.00
E87	Crook/Co. Durham		
		H	2.00
E89	Tyne Docks	H	12.00
	Tyne Docks/ South Shields		
		H	5.00
E90	Pencader	B	15.00
E91	Conwyl Elfed	B	20.00
E92	Burry Port	B	20.00
		H	3.00
E93	Horley	B	20.00
E94	Gloucester Station	H	15.00
E95	Brentford	B	15.00
		H	5.00
E96	Pontrilas	B	12.00
E97	Isleworth	H	6.00
E98	Aberavon	B	7.00
E99	Cwm Avon	B	15.00
		H	4.00
F01	Haywards Heath		
		H	2.00
	Cuckfield	H	3.00
F02	Bethania	B	15.00
F03	Bagillt	B	20.00
F04	Four Crosses	H	12.00
	Blaenau Festiniog		
		H	2.00
F05	Rhiwbryfdir	B	15.00
F06	Tanygrissiau	B	15.00
F07	Ilford	B	8.00
		G	5.00
		H	7.00
F08	Barking	G	8.00
		H	2.00
F09	Holm Rook	B	10.00
		H	7.00
F10	Chadwell	B	15.00
		H	8.00
F11	Ramsbottom	H	8.00
F12	Batley	G	5.00
		H	2.00
F13	Wotton	B	25.00
F14	Askrigg	B	6.00
F15	Parkend	B	12.00
F16	Falfield	B	10.00
		H	2.00
F17	Alveston	B	10.00
F18	Rudgeway	B	10.00
F19	Almondsbury/Glos.		
		B	8.00
		H	3.00
F20	Woodford Green		
		H	5.00
F24	Whitland	B	20.00
		H	2.00
	Whitland R.S.O.		
		H	20.00
F25	Llanfair Pwllgwyngyll		
		B	15.00
		H	3.00
F26	Gaerwen	B	25.00
F27	Llanerchymedd		
		B	10.00
		H	4.00
F28	Rhosybol	B	12.00
F30	Charlbury	B	10.00
		H	2.00
F31	Maesycrugiau	B	20.00
F32	Bettwys-y-Coed		
		H	6.00
	Bettwsycoed	H	2.00
	Bettws Bledrws		
		B	25.00
	Derry Ormond	B	10.00
F33	Ystrad Meurig	B	6.00
F34	Llanddewi Brefi		
		B	20.00
F35	Tregaron	B	20.00
		H	3.00
F36	Surbiton	H	4.00
	Surbiton/ Kingston-on- Thames	H	6.00
F37	St. Leonards/ Gensing Station Rd.	H	5.00
	Gensing Station Rd./ Hastings	H	5.00
F38	Stanford-le-Hope		
		B	6.00
F39	Leigh	B	15.00
F40	Grays	H	1.00
F41	Purfleet/Essex		
		B	15.00
		H	1.00
F42	Rainham	B	10.00
F43	Hyde	H	2.00
F44	Denton	H	12.00
	Denton/Lanc.	H	4.00
F45	Patricroft	H	4.00
F46	Shorncliffe Camp		
		H	10.00
F47	St. Mellons	B	15.00
F48	Criccieth	B	10.00
F49	Dyffryn	B	15.00
		H	3.00
F50	Groeslon	H	5.00
F51	Harlech	H	3.00
F52	Llanbedr	H	7.00
F53	Penygroes	H	4.00
F54	Penrhyn Deudraeth		
		H	8.00
F55	Talysarn	H	5.00
F56	Alderley Edge	H	2.00
F57	Leyburn	B	25.00
		H	3.00
F58	Ponders End	H	2.00
F59	Talysarnau	B	15.00
F60	Llangranog	B	20.00
F61	Blaenyffos	B	10.00
F62	Kilgerran	B	5.00
F63	Boncath	B	10.00
		H	3.00
F64	Llanymynech	B	15.00
		H	3.00
F65	Llanfyllin	B	15.00
		H	3.00
F66	Sutton Benger		
		B	12.00
F67	Little Haven	B	10.00
F68	Rhydlewis	B	12.00
F74	Walton on the Naze		
		B	10.00
F77	Lintz Green Station	H	35.00
	Lintz Green	H	5.00
F78	Tebay	B	10.00
		H	3.00
F79	Sandy	H	1.00
F82	Warcop	B	15.00
		H	15.00
F89	Six Mile Bottom		
		H	2.00
F90	Sharpness Point	H	5.00
F92	Llantrissant	H	3.00
F93	Paddock Wood	B	8.00
		H	2.00
F94	Ripley, Derby	H	2.00
G01	London & Exeter T.P.O.- see chap 13		
G02	Walton-on-Thames		
		B	10.00
		H	2.00
G04	Rothbury	H	2.00
G05	Widnes	H	4.00
G07	Bacup	H	4.00
G08	Highbridge	B	15.00
G09	Stonehouse/Devon		
		B	10.00
	St. Mary Cray	H	2.00
G11	Llanio Road	B	12.00
G20	Much Marcle	B	10.00
G21	Narberth Road		
		B	10.00
G22	Eltham	B	15.00
		H	2.00
G23	Cleator	H	2.00
G24	Cark-in-Cartmel		
		H	4.00
G25	Egremont	H	6.00
	Egremont/Cumbᵈ		
		H	2.00
G26	St. Bees	H	3.00
G27	Cleator Moor	H	2.00
G28	Garn Dolbenmaen		
		B	8.00
G29	Eastwood/Notts		
		H	3.00
G30	Stantonbury	B	10.00
G31	Castle Donnington	H	12.00
G32	Duffield	H	2.00
G33	Kegworth	H	2.00
G35	Lesbury	H	2.00
G37	Grosmont/Yorks		
		H	15.00
G38	St. Peters/Kent		
		H	6.00
G39	Rhoshill	B	10.00
G40	Rhostryfan	H	6.00
G41	Fishponds	B	10.00
G42	Gorseinon	H	3.00
G43	Blaenavon	H	3.00
G44	Cookham	B	10.00
G45	Bourne End	B	10.00
G46	Wooburn	B	8.00
G47	Birchington	H	1.00
G48	Westgate-on-Sea		
		H	1.00
G50	Dolwyddelan	B	3.00
G51	Morecambe	B	10.00
		H	1.00
G52	Beckermet	B	8.00
		H	2.00
G53	Frizington	B	8.00
		H	2.00
G54	Tilbury/Essex	H	1.00
	Tilbury Docks/ Essex	H	35.00

Code	Name		Price
G55	Gorleston	B	10.00
G57	Hollinwood	H	3.00
G60	Hersham Road	H	2.00
G61	Cottingham	H	15.00
G62	Haltwhistle	H	2.00
G63	Snettisham	B	8.00
G64	Burnham Market	B	5.00
G65	Bankyfelin	B	15.00
G67	Clarbeston Road	H	8.00
G68	Marden/Kent	H	1.00
G69	Roche/Cornwall	H	8.00
G70	Skelton-in-Cleveland	B	12.00
		H	3.00
	Skelton R.S.O.	H	30.00
G71	Cleobury Mortimer	H	3.00
G72	Angmering	H	6.00
G73	Angmering Station	H	30.00
G74	New Hampton	H	15.00
	Hampton Hill	H	2.00
G75	Ascot	H	5.00
G76	Shillingstone	H	2.00
G77	Heytesbury	B	12.00
G78	Upper Edmonton S.O.	H	25.00
G79	Stalbridge	B	15.00
G80	Lower Edmonton	H	25.00
	Parton	B	8.00
G82	Ceinws	B	15.00
G84	Cranbrook	H	1.00
G87	Cemmaes Road	B	15.00
G88	Lytham	H	2.00
G89	Corris	H	2.00
	Pantperthog	B	12.00
G90	Tow Law	B	10.00
		H	2.00
G91	Wainfleet/Linc	H	6.00
G92	Portfield Gate	B	15.00
G93	Orpington	H	1.00
G94	Ebchester	B	10.00
		H	2.00
G95	Swalwell	H	2.00
G96	Wickham	H	5.00
G97	Sarnau	B	15.00
G98	Cross Inn	B	6.00
G99	Ffostrassol	B	25.00
H01	Cenarth	B	20.00
H02	Maesllyn	B	15.00
H03	Tunstall	B	15.00
H04	Orford	B	6.00
H05	Dymock	B	10.00
H06	School Green/Isle of Wight	H	20.00
	Freshwater Station/I. of Wight	H	5.00
H07	Ynysmudw	B	15.00
H08	Stanley/Co.Durham	H	3.00
H10	Tram Inn	H	3.00
H11	Birchgrove	B	15.00
H14	Llanbadarn Fawr	B	7.00
H16	Brotton	H	2.00
H17	Carlin How	B	12.00
H18	Easington	B	12.00
H19	Staithes	H	3.00
H20	Loftus	H	3.00
H21	Longfield/Kent	H	10.00
H22	Seaton	H	1.00
H23	Hassocks/Sussex	H	2.00
H26	Hinderwell	H	3.00
H27	Pensarn	B	25.00
H28	Abinger Hammer	H	2.00
H29	Bures	H	3.00
H30	Pocklington	H	2.00
H33	Llandderfel	B	10.00
H34	Waterlooville	H	2.00
H35	Mersham	H	10.00
H36	Lydd	H	3.00
H37	Horley Station/Surrey	H	20.00
	Horley Station Rd	H	12.00
H38	Shoeburyness	B	12.00
		H	1.00
H41	Willesborough	H	3.00
H43	Coalville	H	3.00
H44	Whitefield	H	8.00
	Whitefield/Lanc.	H	2.00
H45	Connah's Quay	H	4.00
H46	Carlton Iron Works	H	7.00
H47	Sedgefield	H	3.00
H48	West Cornforth	H	4.00
H49	Wingate Station	H	15.00
H50	Sidcup	H	3.00
H51	Heathfield	H	10.00
H52	Church	H	3.00
	Church/Lanc	H	8.00
H53	Nelson-in-Marsden	H	12.00
	Nelson	H	1.00
H54	Heathfield Station	H	30.00
H55	Ingleton	H	10.00
H56	Greenfield	B	15.00
H57	St.Dogmaels	H	3.00
H58	Northiam	H	3.00
H59	Wittersham	H	3.00
H60	Brandon Colliery	H	15.00
H62	Snaith	H	3.00
H64	Seaham Harbour	H	4.00
H65	Velindre	B	15.00
H66	Greatham	H	6.00
H67	Seaton Carew	H	3.00
H68	Purton	H	4.00
H69	Stratton St.Margaret	H	4.00
	Stratton St.Margarets	H	8.00
H70	Bramley/Yorks	H	2.00
H71	Harrow Weald	B	10.00
		H	5.00
H72	Llandebie	B	20.00
H73	Wealdstone	B	10.00
		H	4.00
H74	Parkstone	H	2.00
H75	Hotham	B	5.00
H76	North Newbald	B	8.00
H80	Nunthorpe	B	15.00
H81	Reedness	B	15.00
H84	Sancton	B	15.00
H85	Langwathby	H	2.00
H86	Kirkoswald, Cumb.	H	8.00
H87	Lazonby	H	2.00
H88	Dedham	B	15.00
H89	Llanfaelog	B	25.00
H91	Rhosgoch	B	25.00
H92	Baildon	H	6.00
H93	Saltaire	H	8.00
H94	Llanfihangel	B	30.00
H95	Hylton	B	8.00
H96	Talysarn	B	15.00
H97	Chelsfield	H	2.00
H98	Glanamman	H	8.00
H99	Thames Ditton	H	2.00
J01	Englefield Green	H	2.00
J02	Butterknowle	B	8.00
J03	Trefnant	B	15.00
		H	5.00
J04	Rhyddlan	H	15.00
J06	Upper Brynamman	H	10.00
J07	Oxted	H	12.00
J08	Limpsfield	H	2.00
J09	Wellington College Station	B	50.00
J10	Langley Park	B	8.00
J11	Armley	H	5.00
J12	Birstall	H	4.00
J13	Morley	H	8.00
	Morley/Yorks	H	2.00
J14	Pudsey	H	2.00
J15	Jackfield	H	3.00
J16	Farnborough/Kent	H	3.00
J17	Great Harwood	H	2.00
J18	Brierfield	H	2.00
J19	Stoke-under-Ham	H	3.00
J20	Hinstock	B	15.00
J21	Tycroes	B	25.00
J22	Westerham	H	2.00
J24	Greenstreet/Kent	H	5.00
J25	Addlestone/Surrey	H	2.00
J27	Bissoe	B	8.00
J28	Stamford Bridge	B	15.00
J29	Llandrillo	B	10.00
J31	Bethersden	H	3.00
J32	East Molesey	H	2.00
J33	Willingdon	H	3.00
J34	Cranleigh	H	2.00
J35	Burnopfield	H	3.00
J36	Takeley	B	15.00
J37	Bramley/Surrey	H	2.00

J38	Llanuwchllyn B	12.00
J39	East Cowton H	5.00
J40	Great Ayton H	2.00
J41	Great Smeaton	
	H	15.00
J42	Newby Wiske H	15.00
J43	South Otterington	
	H	6.00
J44	Thornton-le-Moor	
	H	4.00
J45	Newtown/	
	Southborough	
	H	3.00
J46	Virginia Water	
	H	3.00
J48	Wickford B	15.00
J49	Ripley/Surrey	
	H	10.00
J50	Ewell/Surrey H	5.00
J51	West Tanfield B	6.00
J52	Broadstone H	2.00
J53	Llangwyllog B	25.00
J54	Carnforth &	
	Whitehaven TPO	
	- see chap 13	
J55	Wrafton B	15.00
J56	Braunton B	10.00
J57	Morthoe B	15.00
J58	Abersychan B	15.00
J59	Wallsend H	3.00
J60	Bodorgan H	6.00
J61	Whitley H	3.00
J62	Bisley Camp/	
	Woking H	5.00
J63	Wallington H	7.00
	Upper Wallington	
	H	15.00
J65	Camberley B	10.00
	H	2.00
J66	Ramsey/Hunts H	2.00
J67	Chapel-en-le-	
	Frith B	7.00
J68	Wool H	3.00
J69	Boscombe B	12.00
J70	Shepperton H	2.00
J71	Hockley B	10.00
J72	Cambo H	3.00
J73	Eastleigh H	2.00
J74	Totton H	3.00
J75	Blackwater/Hants	
	H	10.00
J76	Horwich H	2.00
J77	Marton/Yorks H	3.00
J78	Medomsley H	4.00
J79	Thatcham H	10.00
J80	Beenham B	10.00
J81	Woolhampton B	10.00
J82	Wadhurst	
	Station H	30.00
J83	Datchet B	8.00
J84	Ossett H	3.00
J85	Church Lane/	
	Old Charlton	
	B	10.00
	H	6.00
J86	Woolwich Rd./	
	Old Charlton	
	H	15.00

J87	Cloughfold H	3.00
J88	Haslingden H	3.00
J89	Summerseat H	12.00
J90	Luddenden H	3.00
J91	Luddendenfoot	
	H	3.00
J92	Mytholmroyd H	3.00
J93	Yeadon H	3.00
J94	Ingleby Greenhow	
	H	3.00
J95	Bradford/Lanc	
	H	10.00
J96	Bodenham H	20.00
J97	Willington Quay	
	H	6.00
J98	Eston H	3.00
J99	Normanby/	
	Middlesborough	
	H	10.00
K01	Felling H	3.00
K02	Hebburn H	3.00
K03	Walker H	3.00
K04	Helmshore H	2.00
K05	Stacksteads H	8.00
K06	Little Hereford	
	H	2.00
K07	Shaw H	6.00
K08	Lymm H	3.00
K09	Woodborough B	10.00
K10	Howden-le-Wear	
	B	8.00
K11	Sinnington H	10.00
K13	Brenchley H	3.00
K14	Liversedge H	3.00
K15	Ryton H	3.00
K16	Brotherton B	15.00
K17	Purston B	15.00
K18	Melplash H	3.00
K19	Carlton/Yorks H	6.00
K20	Rawcliffe/Yorks	
	H	8.00
K21	Rawcliffe Bridge	
	H	10.00
K22	Whitley Bridge	
	H	4.00
K23	Ravenstonedale	
	B	8.00
K24	Llanwnda H	8.00
K25	Plasmarl B	15.00
K26	Bexhill H	10.00
K27	Bexhill Station	
	H	35.00
K31	Goudhurst H	3.00
K32	Gomshall H	4.00
K33	Coniston/Lanc.	
	H	2.00
K37	Mumbles H	2.00
K38	Brayton Station	
	H	35.00
K39	Dalston/Cumbd H	6.00
K40	Littlestone H	3.00
K41	Swinton/Lanc. H	3.00
K42	Northwood/Herts	
	H	15.00
K43	Collingbourne	
	Ducis B	10.00
K44	Mayfield/Sussex	
	H	2.00
K45	Saltford B	12.00
K48	London & Holyhead	
	TPO - see chap 13	

K49	Minster/Ramsgate	
	H	2.00
K50	Boot H	2.00
K51	Eskdale H	2.00
K52	Gosforth H	2.00
K53	Ravenglass H	2.00
K54	Arnside H	5.00
K55	Silverdale/Lanc.	
	H	3.00
K56	Bigrigg H	8.00
K57	Bootle/Cumbd H	2.00
K58	Bootle Station	
	H	12.00
K59	Silecroft H	3.00
K60	The Green H	8.00
K61	Kirkby-in-Furness	
	H	3.00
K62	Furness Abbey H	3.00
K63	New Oxted H	4.00
K64	Lindal H	6.00
K67	Goring B	15.00
K68	Littleport H	1.00
K71	Blockley B	15.00
K73	Newbiggin B	12.00
K76	Gwaun-cae-Gurwen	
	B	15.00
K78	Witton Park B	8.00
K79	Lakeside B	12.00
K80	Calderbridge B	8.00
K81	Danby B	5.00
K83	Aynho B	8.00
K84	Heyford B	15.00
K85	King's Sutton B	5.00
K86	Somerton B	15.00
K87	Souldern B	15.00
K88	Hook Norton B	5.00
K90	Haworth B	10.00
K91	Silsden B	15.00
K92	Pitsea B	8.00
K93	Waskerley B	8.00
K95	Shipton-under-	
	Wychwood B	7.00

T01-6	150.00

The precise use of these marks is not known. They are believed to have been used by PO-employed staff on Mail Boats.

Scotland

7/22   **7/24**

7/25   **7/26**

Basic Prices for Scottish marks

7/22	Numbered cancellations between horizontal bars, from 1844	2.50
7/23	Duplex cancellations, circular datestamp from 1857	2.00
7/24	Duplex cancellations, dotted circle types	6.00
7/25	Duplex cancellations, Edinburgh 'Brunswick Star' types	10.00
7/26	Glasgow 'Madeleine Smith' type	15.00

Numbers used in Scottish numeral and duplex marks:

1	Aberdeen	27	Ayr	51	Blackburn	77	Chance Inn	
2	Aberfeldy	28	Ayton		Buckhaven		Crossmichael	
3	Aberdour	29	Assynt	52	Borrowstouness	78	Colinsburgh	
	Achnacroish		Auchnasheen		Boness	79	Comrie	
4	Aboyne		Achnasheen		Bunchrew		Coll	
5	Aberchirdir	30	Alyth	53	Bowmore	80	Crail	
	Abernethy,	31	Ballater		Bridgend	81	Cromdale	
	Strathspey	32	Crathie	54	Braco	82	Craigellachie	
	Nethy Bridge		Bannockburn	55	Blackhillock	83	Creetown	
6	Alford	33	Ballantrae		Buchlyvie	84	Crieff	
	Advie	34	Ballindalloch	56	Braemar	85	Cromarty	
7	Alloa	35	Banchory		Bothwell	86	Craigellachie	
8	Aberlour	36	Banff	57	Brechin		Station	
9	Alexandria	37	Macduff	58	Edzell	87	Cullen	
10	Alness		Birnam		Brodick	88	Culross	
11	Annan	38	Bathgate	59	Broadford		Corstorphine	
12	Auchenblae	39	Bauly		Bridge of Earn	89	Crosshill	
	Ardgour	40	Beith	60	Bridge of Earn	90	Cumnock	
13	Arbroath	41	Biggar	61	Buckie	91	Cupar Angus	
14	Ardersier	42	Blackshiels	62	Burntisland		Coupar Angus	
	Fort George		Bogroy	63	Brucklaw	92	Cupar	
	Station		Blackridge		Burnbank	93	Cluny	
	Gollanfield	43	Bervie	64	Callander		Colintraive	
15	Ardrossan	44	Blair Athole	65	Campbelton	94	Castleton	
16	Abington		Blair Atholl		Campbeltown		Colinton	
17	Airdrie	45	Dalnacardoch	66	Canonbie	95	Crinan	
18	Arisaig		Bankfoot	67	Carluke		Crianlarich	
	Ardersier	46	Blairgowrie	68	Cairnryan	96	Cruden	
19	Aultbea	47	Blair Adam		Catrine		Cowdenbeath	
20	Arrochar	48	Bonaw	69	Carnwath	97	Cockburnspath	
	Avoch		Bunessan	70	Carsphairn	98	Dalkeith	
21	Auchnacraig	49	Bonar Bridge		Carstairs Junction	99	Delny	
22	Anstruther		Ardgay	71	Castle Douglas	100	Dalmally	
23	Aros	50	Bogroy	72	Cairndow	101	Dalry	
24	Appin		Ballachulish		Castle Kennedy	102	Denny	
25	Auchterarder		Ballachulish Ferry	73	Coldingham	103	Dingwall	
26	Auchtermuchty		Ballachulish	74	Coldstream	104	Dornoch	
			Quarries	75	Carrbridge	105	Dunbeath	
				76	Carnoustie			

106	Douglas	159	Glasgow	210	Kirkcaldy	260	Muirdrum
	Dalmellington		Glasgow Carlisle	211	Kirkintulloch		Munlochy
107	Doune		Sorting Tender		Kirkintilloch	261	Munlochy
108	Dumfries		Hope St. Glasgow	212	Kirriemuir		Minto
109	Drimnin	160	Glenluce	213	Kirkmichael	262	Muirkirk
110	Dumbarton	161	Grangemouth		Largs	263	Musselburgh
111	Dunbar	162	Greenlaw	214	Kincardine O'Neil	264	Nairn
112	Dunblane		Gairloch		Lamlash	265	Newburgh
113	Dunfermline	163	Greenock	215	Lanark	266	New Galloway
114	Dundee		Iona Steamer/	216	Langholm	267	New Deer
115	Broughty Ferry		Greenock	217	Largs		Newington
116	Lochee		Columba Steamer/		Upper Largo		Newington R.O./
	Drummore		Greenock	218	Lauder		Edinr.
117	Kincaldrum		Iona Steamer		Lochgelly	268	New Pitsligo
118	Dunkeld	164	Glenlivat	219	Laurencekirk		Newmilns
119	Dunphail		Garve	220	Leadhills	269	Newport
120	Dunning	165	Glamis		Larkhall		New Cumnock
121	Dunoon		Garlieston	221	Leith	270	Newton Stewart
122	Dunse	166	Grantown	222	Leithlumsden	271	Noblehouse
	Duns		Grantown on Spey		Lumsden		Nigg Station
123	Dunvegan	167	Golspie		Leuchars	272	North Queensferry
124	Durness	168	Brora	223	Lerwick		Noblehouse
	Dunalastair	169	Gartly	224	Lynwilg		Mountain Cross
125	Dunnett	170	Glenmorriston		Ledaig	273	Oban
	Dunragit	171	Haddington	225	Laggan	274	Old Meldrum
126	Drumnadrochit	172	Halkirk		Lentran	275	Old Rain
127	Dysart	173	Hamilton	226	Lochcarron		Old Aberdeen
128	Eaglesham	174	Hawick	227	Lochearnhead	276	Orton
	Ettrick	175	Helmsdale	228	Lesmahagow		Pencaitland
129	Earlston	176	Helensburgh		Lochgoilhead	277	Paisley
	Elvanfoot	177	Harris	229	Leven	278	Parkhill
130	Ecclefechan		Holytown	230	Linlithgow		Kildary
131	Edinburgh	178	Huntly	231	Lochalsh	279	Peebles
	Edin-Carlisle	179	Holytown		Balmacara	280	Perth
	Sorting Tender		Innellan	232	Lochgilphead	281	Peterhead
	Carstairs &	180	Huna	233	Lockerby	282	Pitcaple
	Edinr. Sorting		Innerleithen		Lockerbie	283	Pittenweem
	Tender	181	Inveraray	234	Lochmaddy	284	Pitlochry
132	Eddleston	182	Inverkeithing	235	Lochmaben	285	Poolewe
	Easdale	183	Inverness		Lossiemouth	286	Portaskaig
133	Elgin	184	Inchture	236	Lochinver		Parton
134	Ellon	185	Invergordon		Luib	287	Port Glasgow
135	Elie	186	Irvine	237	Lairg	288	Port Patrick
136	Errol	187	Jedburgh	238	Longhope		Port of Montieth
137	Evanton	188	Johnstone		Longniddry		Station
138	Eyemouth		Innerwick	239	Luss	289	Portree
	Fairlie	189	Invergarry	240	Lybster	290	Portsoy
139	Falkirk	190	Jura	241	Markinch	291	Port William
140	Falkland		Inverkip	242	Mauchline	292	Poyntzfield
	Fasnacloich	191	Kinaldie	243	Maybole		Port Patrick
141	Fenwick	192	Keith	244	Melrose	293	Prestonkirk
	Forgandenny	193	Kelso	245	Meigle	294	Rachan Mill
142	Fettercairn	194	Keith Hall	246	Melvich		Rannoch
143	Fochabers		Inverurie	247	Mey	295	Renfrew
144	Forfar	195	Kettle		Moy	296	Rhynie
145	Forres		Kildonan	248	Mintlaw	297	Rothes
146	Fort Augustus	196	Kenmore	249	Methlick	298	Rothesay
147	Fortrose		Kirkliston		Macduff	299	Rothiemay
148	Fort William	197	Kennoway	250	Moneymusk		Rogart
149	Fort George		Kilmartin		Milnathort	300	St. Andrews
150	Fraserburgh	198	Killin	251	Montrose	301	St. Boswell's Green
151	Fushie Bridge	199	Kirknewton	252	St. Cyrus		St. Boswell's
	Fossoway	200	Kingussie		Monkton	302	Saltcoats
152	Finhaven	201	Kintore	253	Mossat	303	Sanquhar
	Finstown	202	Kilsyth		Millport	304	Scourie
153	Farr		Kirn	254	Mortlach		St. Monance
	Greenlaw	203	Kilmarnock		Methil	305	Selkirk
154	Fyvie	204	Kincardine	255	Midcalder	306	South Queensferry
155	Galashiels		Kilwinning	256	Moffat	307	Stewarton
157	Garlieston	205	Kinghorn	257	Moniaive	308	Stirling
	Garmouth	206	Kinross		Mossend	309	Stonehaven
157	Gatehouse	207	Kirkwall	258	Morvern	310	Stornoway
158	Girvan	208	Kippen	259	Moy	311	Stow
		209	Kirkcudbright		Montgreenan	312	Stranraer

313 Strathaven	364 Bridge of Allan	426 George St.,	492 Blairmore
314 Strathdon	365 Ladybank	Edinburgh	493 Rowardennan
Stanley	366 Insch	427 Auchinleck	494 West Wemyss
315 Strichen	367 Barrhead	428 Reston	495 Tighnabruaich
Salen	368 Stobo	429 Earlston	496 Monifieth
316 Stromness	369 Coatbridge	430 Arrochar	497 Strichen
317 Strontian	370 Milngavie	431 Lochawe	498 Brucklay
318 Skene	Stevenston	432 Auldgirth	499 Douglas N.B.
Strathmiglo	371 Maryhill	433 Ardrishaig	500 Kilchrennan
319 St. Margaret's Hope	372 Baillieston	434 Abernethy	Kilchrenan
Tullypowrie	St. Ninians	435 Alford	501 Port Sonachan
Strathtay	373 Whiting Bay	436 Auchencairn	502 Renton
320 Tain	374 Lennoxtown	437 Lauder	503 Crianlarich
321 Tarbert	Upper Keith	438 Lamington	504 Dalmeny
Muir of Ord	375 Partick	439 Portaskaig	505 Beattock
322 Tarland	376 Cumbernauld	440 Tarbert, Lochfyne	506 Lochinver
323 Thornhill	Tarbet,	441 Bowmore	507 Isle of Whithorn
324 Thurso	Loch Lomond	442 Port Ellen	508 Lilliesleaf
325 Tobermory	377 Fordoun	443 Wemyss Bay	509 Auchmill
326 Tomintoul	378 Dalbeattie	444 Bonnyrigg	Bucksburn
Tayport	379 Aviemore	445 Lower Largo	510 Palnure
327 Tomnavoulin	380 Ballinluig	446 Iona	511 Oyne
Torphins	381 Blackford	447 Whitburn	512 Balblair
328 Tongue	382 Fearn	448 Strathpeffer	513 Kinlochbervie
Taynuilt	383 Portmahomack	449 Roslin	514 Cardross
329 Tranent	384 New Cumnock	450 West Linton	515 Castlebay
330 Troon	385 Leslie	451 Culter Cullen	516 Lochboisdale Pier
331 Turriff	386 Kirkcowan	452 Davidson's Mains	517 Philipstown
332 Tyndrum	387 Newtown St. Boswells	453 Corrie, Arran	Philpstoun
Tiree	388 Menstrie	454 Broxburn	518 Inverie
333 Udney	389 Alva	455 Carron	Knoydart
Uddingston	390 Dollar	456 Redgorton	519 Kinlochewe
334 Ullapool	391 Highland Sorting	457 Armadale Station	520 Friockheim
335 Watten	Carriage	458 Fife Sorting	521 Collieston
336 West Kilbride	392 Muthill	Tender	522 Cove,
Windygates	393 Chirnside	Fife Sorting	Aberdeen
337 Whitburn	394 Edrom	Carriage	523 Lumphanan
West Kilbride	395 Grantshouse	459 Kincardine	524 Broughton
338 Whithorn	396 Charlotte Place,	460 Carradale	525 Old Deer
339 Wick	Edinburgh	461 Clachan	526 Thankerton
340 Whitehouse	Lynedoch Place,	462 Tayinloan	527 Galston
Walkerburn	Edinburgh	463 Moidart	528 Glenboig
341 Wigtown	397 Govan	464 Gourock	529 Tynehead
342 Wishaw	398 Hillhead	465 East Wemyss	530 Bishopton
343 Ford	399 Greenburn	466 Freuchie	531 East Calder
344 Lasswade	New Deer	467 Rousay	532 Lhanbryde
345 Loanhead	400 Shotts	468 Falkland	533 Addiewell
346 North Berwick	401 Pollockshaws	469 East Grange	534 Ardeonaig
347 Pennycuick	402 Perth and Aberdeen	Station	535 Ardtalnaig
Penicuik	Sorting Carriage	470 Fortingal	536 Fearnan
348 Portobello	403 Causewayhead	471 Armadale	537 Lawers
349 Prestonpans	404 Strathyre	472 Blaino	538 Gullane
350 Slateford	405 Murthly Station	473 Laudale	539 Cardenden
Tarbolton	Murthly	474 Ratho Station	540 Archiestown
351 Winchburgh	406 Johnstone	475 New Galloway	541 Craignure
The Mound	407 Storme Ferry	Station	542 Connel
352 Ferryport-on-Craig	(actual spelling used)	476 Longriggend	543 Lochbuie
Altnabreac	408 Currie	477 Bothkennar	544 King Edward
353 Strachur	409 Larbert	478 Guard Bridge	545 Onich
Burghead	410 Dolphington	479 Loanhead	546 Staffin
354 Bonnybridge	411 Murrayfield	480 Dailly	547 Airth Road
355 Dalnacardoch	412 Cambus	481 Roxburgh	Station
Bo'ness	413 Woodside N.B.	482 Juniper Green	548 Skelmorlie
356 Trinafour	414 Cornhill	483 Gorebridge	549 Newmains
Inversnaid	415 Dufftown	484 Johnshaven	550 Stenhousemuir
357 Alexandria	416 Polmont	485 Ormiston	551 Kilbirnie
Stonehouse	417 Dreghorn	486 Yetholm	552 Lochearnhead
358 Tillicoultry	418 Ringford	487 Kettle	Station
359 Drem	419 Twynholm	Kingskettle	Balquhidder
360 Lauder	420 Kirkgunzeon	488 Lesmahago	Station
Slateford	421 Dalry	489 Polmont	553 Crookham
361 Motherwell	422 Prestwick	Station	554 New Mills, Fife
362 Ratho	423 Braemar	490 Balerno	555 Sauchie
363 Liberton	424 Guthrie	491 Glenbarr	556 Bellshill
Eyemouth	425 Port Appin		

557	Shiskine	625	Uphall
558	Law	626	Liberton
559	Caldercruix	627	Polton
560	North Queensferry	628	Rosewell
561	Auchterless Station	629	Rosslyn Castle
562	Strone	630	Gilmerton
563	Kames	631	Fauldhouse
564	Lonmay	632	West Calder
565	Eskbank, Dalkeith	633	Macmerry
566	Avonbridge	634	Milton Bridge
567	Skeabost Bridge	635	King's Cross, Arran
568	Denino		
569	Tyndrum	636	Rumbling Bridge
570	Cove, Helensburgh	637	Fionport
		638	Kirkhill
571	Kilcreggan	639	Tomintoul
572	Struan	640	Drumoak
573	Hollandbush	641	Craighouse, Jura
574	Collessie		
575	Aberfoyle	642	Howwood
576	Uphall Station	643	Kilbarchan
577	Gateside	644	Machany
578	Gartmore Station	645	Dunecht
579	Cladich	646	Tarves
580	Lochwinnoch	647	Balloch
581	Acharacle	648	Conon Bridge
582	Slamannan	649	Meikleour
583	Methven	650	Newcastleton
584	Oxton	651	Ancrum
585	Glendaruel	652	Blairadam Station
586	Urray	653	Kippen Station
587	Strathconon	654	Whitehouse
588	Abernethy	655	Achluachrach Glenborrodale
589	Aberdour, Fife		
590	Thornton, Fife	656	Comrie
591	Tarbolton Station	657	Blacksboat
592	Row	658	Mindrim Mill
593	Garelochhead	659	Shiskine
594	Glenfarg	660	Deanston
595	Shandon	661	Westfield
596	Hollybush	662	St. Fillans
597	Stravithie	663	Springfield
598	Riccarton, Kilmarnock	664	Haywood
		665	Eddleston
599	Carsaig	666	Grenadier Steamer
600	Croggan	667	Lochmaben
601	Rum	668	Auchendinny
602	Gailes Camp, Irvine	669	Aros
		670	Port of Monteith Station
603	Galloway Sorting Tender		
		671	Kilconquhar
	Galloway Sorting Carriage	672	Bridge of Weir
		673	Glengarnock
604	St. Margaret's Hope	674	Kilmacolm
605	Ruthwell	675	Cross Gates
606	Muthill Station	676	Ardlui
607	Newport, Fife	677	Dalbeallie (actual spelling used) Knockando
608	Cobbinshaw		
609	Coalburn		
610	Kilninver	678	Rannoch Station
611	Orton Station	679	Roy Bridge
612	Lismore	680	Spean Bridge
613	Chapelton	681	Tulloch
614	Blackshiels	682	Bridge of Orchy
615	Heriot	683	Amisfield
616	Leadburn	684	Kirkmuirhill
617	Lamancha	685	Kinloch Rannoch
618	Blackhall	686	Maud
619	Cramond	687	Darvel
620	Cramond Bridge	688	Strathcarron
621	Fountainhall	689	Achanalt
622	Crosslee	690	Auchnashellach
623	Gordon	691	Lochbroom
624	Winchburgh	692	Lochluichart

693	Forsinard	720	Arisaig
694	Kinbrace	721	Kettleholm
695	Glenfinnan	722	Bonawe Quarries
696	Blackmill Bay	723	Aberlady
697	Plockton Berriedale	724	Dirleton
		725	Achnacarry
698	Bank Latheron	726	Aberchirder
		727	Cambuslang
699	Toberonochy	728	Newton, Glasgow
700	Cornaig	729	Shettleston
701	Hartwood	730	Carstairs
702	Carron	731	Kenmore
703	Hurlford	732	Craigmillar
704	Kilchoan	733	Rosehearty
705	Kincardine	734	Strath
706	Longmorn	735	Findochty
707	Balvicar	736	Portknockie
708	Blackburn, Bathgate	737	Langbank
		738	Auchenheath
709	Marchmont	739	Netherburn
710	New Lanark	740	Quarter
711	Kyle	741	Roseneath
712	Port Erroll	742	Clynder
713	Kinlocheil	743	Cleland
714	Crawford	744	Colonsay
715	Hatton	745	Kilmun
716	Boddam	746	Sandbank
717	Raasay	747	Toward Point
718	Eskbank, Dalkeith	748	Inchbare
		749	Bieldside
719	Lochailort	755	Canna

Ireland

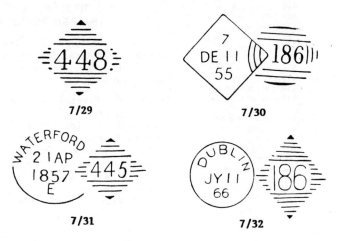

7/29   7/30

7/31   7/32

Numbered cancellations in diamond, from 1844 :

7/27	186/Dublin	3.00
7/28	62/Belfast, 156/Cork, 172/Derry, 303/Limerick, 445/Waterford ...	5.00
7/29	Others	7.50

Spoons 1855–72

No.	Name		English Type	Irish Type
16	Athenry		£125	–
18	Athlone		£50	£50
29	Ballina		£40	£50
32	Ballinasloe		£40	£30
48	Ballymoney		£120	£40
62	Belfast		£15	£15
104	Carrick-on-Shannon		£125	£35
142	Clonmel		£40	£30
156	Cork		£25	£25
172	Derry		£40	£30
186	Dublin		– 7/30	£10
179	Drogheda		£30	£20
211	Ennis		£125	–
214	Enniskillen		£50	£30
232	Galway		£30	£20
269	Kilkenny		£50	£35
272	Killarny		£50	£50
289	Kingstown		£50	£50
291	Ballina (error)		–	£75
303	Limerick		£25	£25
321	Mellow		£120	£70
345	Mullingar		£30	£20
357	Newry		£40	£30
368	Oranmore		£60	£120
397	Roscrea		£40	£25
410	Sligo		£50	£55
412	Strabane		–	£125
435	Tuam		£60	£40
438	Tullamore		£40	£20
445	Waterford	7/31	£40	£20
447	Westport		£18	–
448	Wexford		£25	£35
456	Dalkey		£125	–

Duplex cancellations, from early 1860's :

7/32	186/Dublin	2.50
7/33	62/Belfast, 156/Cork, 172/Derry, 303/Limerick, 445/Waterford ...	5.00
7/34	Others	7.50

Numbers used in Irish numeral and duplex marks:

1 Abbeyleix
2 Adair
  Adare
3 Ahascragh
  Bunratty
4 Ardara
  Cratloe
5 Ardee
6 Ardglass
  Ardrahan
7 Ardrahan
  Abbeyfeale
8 Armagh
9 Ballingarry
10 Arklow
11 Arthurstown
  Armoy
12 Arva
  Ashbourne
13 Ashbourne
  Aghadowey
14 Ashford
15 Athboy
16 Athenry
17 Athleague
  Ardsollus
18 Ardsollus
  Athlone
19 Arva
20 Athy
21 Aughnacloy
22 Aughrim (Galway)
  Aughrim (Wicklow)
23 Antrim
24 Askeaton
25 Bagnalstown
  Bagenalstown
26 Baileyborough
  Baily
27 Balbriggan
28 Ballaghaderin
29 Ballina
30 Ballybay
31 Ballinakill
  Ballinamallard
32 Ballinasloe
33 Ballincollig
  Ballybrack
34 Ballinderry
  Ballybofey
35 Ballingarry
  Ballycassidy
36 Ballinrobe
  Ballybrophy
37 Ballycastle
  Ballybunion
38 Ballyclare
39 Ballyconnell
  Ballylongford
40 Ballybrittas
  Ballygawley
41 Ballygawley
  Ballycastle
42 Ballyglass
  Balla

43 Ballyhaise
  Ballyglunin
44 Ballyjamesduff
  Ballyhaunis
45 Ballymahon
46 Ballymena
47 Ballymoe
48 Ballymoney
49 Ballymore
  Ballymore Eustace
50 Ballymote
51 Ballynacargy
  Balymurry
52 Ballynahinch
53 Ballynamore
  Baltinglass
54 Ballyragget
55 Ballyshannon
56 Ballytore
57 Bangagher
58 Banbridge
59 Bandon
60 Bangor
  Barnesmore
61 Bantry
62 Belfast
63 Bellaghy
  Belleek
64 Belmullet
  Beauparc
65 Belturbet
66 Broadford
  Bessbrook
67 Blackwatertown
  Blackrock
68 Blackrock
  Booterstown
69 Blessington
70 Boyle
71 Booterstown
  Borris
72 Bray
73 Broadway
  Belfast and
    N. Counties
    R.P.O.
74 Brookeborough
  Belmullet
75 Broughshane
  Beragh
76 Bruff
  Bangor Erris
77 Buncrana
  Belmont
78 Bunratty
  Beaufort
79 Burrin
  Blarney
80 Borrisakane
  Bruree, Kilmallock
81 Borrisoleigh
  Brittas
82 Borris-in-Ossory
83 Bushmills
  Bundoran

84 Buttevant
85 Baltinglass
  Burton Port
86 Cabineteely
  Cabinteely
87 Cahirciveen
88 Cahirconlish
  Rathdowney
89 Camp
90 Cahir
91 Caledon
92 Caledon
  Caragh
93 Callan
94 Camolin
95 Cappoquin
96 Carlingford
  Carbury
97 Carlow
98 Carey's Cross
99 Carna
100 Carn
  Carrickmore
101 Carnew
  Carrickmines
102 Carrickfergus
103 Carrickmacross
104 Carrick-on-Shannon
105 Carrick-on-Suir
106 Cashel
107 Castlebar
108 Castlebellingham
109 Castlegregory
110 Castleblakeney
111 Castleblayney
112 Castlecomer
  Castleconnell
113 Castleconnell
114 Castledawson
115 Castlederg
116 Castledermot
  Castleknock
117 Castlefin
118 Castlemartyr
120 Castlepollard
121 Castlerea
122 Castletown
  Castletown Bere
123 Castletown Delvin
  Castletown
    Mullingar
  Castletown
    Geoghegan
124 Castletownroche
125 Castlewellan
126 Cavan
127 Celbridge
128 Charleville
129 Church Hill
  Clifden
130 Clane
131 Clara
  Clanabogan
132 Clare
  Claremorris

133 Clashmore
  Clara
134 Clifden
  Clandeboye
135 Cloghan
136 Clogheen
137 Clogher
  Clonee
138 Cloghnakilty
  Clonakilty
139 Clonard
  Cleggan
140 Clonee
  Clonelly
141 Clones
142 Clonmel
143 Clough (Down)
  Clough, Newry
144 Cloughjordan
  Clonsilla
145 Cloyne
  Cloughjordan
146 Coachford
  Clonbur
147 Coalisland
148 Colehill
  Clogher
149 Coleraine
150 Collon
  Collooney
151 Collooney
  Coachford
152 Cong
  Comber
153 Comber
  Coole
154 Cookstown
155 Cootehill
156 Cork
157 Cove
  Queenstown
158 Carrigart
  Courtmacsherry
159 Craughwell
  Corofin
160 Creeslough
  Craughwell
161 Crookstown
  Crossgar
162 Crossakiel
163 Crossdoney
164 Crossmolina
165 Croome
  Croom
166 Crumlin
  Crossmolina
167 Corofin
  Cullybackey
168 Cushendall
169 Dartrey, Monaghan
170 Dangan
  Draperstown
171 Delgany
172 Derry
173 Dervock

374	Piltown	423	Tallaght
375	Portadown	424	Tallow
376	Portaferry	425	Tanderagee
	Pomeroy	426	Tarbert
377	Portarlington	427	Templemore
378	Portglenone	428	Thomastown
	Patrickswell	429	Thurles
379	Portlaw	430	Tinahely
380	Portumna		Tinode
	Portrush	431	Tipperary
381	Ramelton	432	Toome
	Portstewart		Tinahely
382	Randalstown	433	Tralee
383	Raphoe	434	Trim
384	Rathangan		Trillick
	Raheny	435	Tuam
385	Rathcoole	436	Tubbermore
	Portglenone		Trim
386	Rathcormack	437	Tulla
	Rathcoole	438	Tullamore
387	Rathdowney	439	Tullow
388	Rathdrum	440	Tynan
389	Rathfarnham	441	Tyrrellspass
390	Rathfriland		Urney
391	Rathkeale	442	Valentia
392	Rathowen		Toomebridge
	Rathnew	443	Virginia
393	Red Hills	444	Warrenspoint
	Ratoath		Warrenpoint
394	Rich Hill	445	Waterford
	Rockcorry	446	Waringstown
395	Rochfort Bridge		Woodlawn
	Roundstone	447	Westport
396	Roscommon	448	Wexford
397	Roscrea	449	Wicklow
398	Ross	450	Youghal
	New Ross	451	Clonegal
399	Rosscarbery		Ward
400	Rostrevor		The Ward
401	Ruskey	452	Dunamanagh
	Rush		Tubbermore
402	Saintfield		Tobermore
403	Scarriff	453	Mount Bellew Bridge
	Sandyford		Newton Butler
404	Scrabby		Newtown Butler
	Scarva	454	Ovoca
405	Shanagolden	455	Curragh Camp
	Saggart	456	Templeogue
406	Shinrone		Batterstown
	Skerries	457	Dalkey
407	Sixmilebridge	458	Stillorgan
	Shillelagh		Ballisodare
408	Skibbereen	459	Baldoyle
409	Slane	460	Banteer
	Sixmilebridge	461	Ballinhassig
410	Sligo	462	Ballyneen
411	Stewartstown	463	Castleisland
	Scarriff	464	Carrigtwohill
412	Strabane	465	Clarecastle
413	Stradbally	466	Clashmore
414	Stradone	467	Clondalkin
415	Strangford	468	Drimoleague
	Straffan Station	469	Drumree
416	Stranorlar	470	Enniskean
417	Strokestown	471	Glounthaune
	Shanagolden	473	Innishannon
418	Stoneyford	475	Kilkee
	Strafford on Slaney	476	Killeagh
419	Summerhill	479	Knocklong
	Stewartstown	482	Leap
420	Swinford	483	Millstreet
421	Swords	484	Manorhamilton
	Stranocum	486	Little Island
422	Taghmon	487	Maynooth
	Swords	488	Delgany

490	St. Margarets	530	Cong
491	Templepatrick	531	Sion Mills
492	Templeogue	532	Dromahair
493-8	TPOs	533	Toombeola
499	Welchtown	534	Bangor
500	White Abbey	535	Holywood
501	Doagh	536	Strandtown
502	Ballinamore	537	Donaghadee
503	Doochary	538	Dundrum, Down
505	Upperlands	539	Newcastle, Down
506	Dervock	540	Ardagh
507	Ballinrobe	541	Six Mile Cross
508	Timoleague	542	Maguiresbridge
509	Bailieborough	543	Slane
510	Kingscourt	544	Ardfert
511	Macroom	545	Lisdoonvarna
512	Ballinlough	547	Lisselton Cross
513	Glenanne		Lisselton
514	Limerick Junction	548	Headford, Killarney
515	Hill of Down	549	Ballincollig
516	Moycullen	550	Ballinskelligs
517	Rosscahill	551	Glenbeigh
518	Oughterard	552	Valencia Island
519	Maam Cross	553	Waterville
520	Maam	554	Dunboyne
521	Leenane	555	Annascaul
522	Rusmuck	556	Blennerville
	Rosmuck	557	Woodenbridge
523	Recess	558	Bawnboy
524	Cashel, Galway	559	Ballyconnell
525	Letterfrack	560	Bushmills
526	Ballycroy	561	Ardara
527	Ballyglass	562	Bruckless
528	Tourmakeady	563	Carrick
529	The Neale	564	Mount Charles
	Neale		

8. Squared Circle Postmarks

Experiments to find an improvement to the duplex resulted in the introduction of the Squared Circle at Leeds, Liverpool and London EC in 1879. This was so successful that issues were made to many offices throughout England and Wales. They were not used in Scotland or Ireland. Each office mark (known as a "hammer") is described in accordance with the definitive work, detailed below.

There are six main types (Roman numerals I to VI) with varying numbers of arcs (counted at top left/right) or inner circles. If the hammer has an identity letter or number ("H.I.") it is given an additional sub-type designation (capitals A to G) to show the position of the H.I. Sub-type C denotes any position H.I. other than those illustrated.

In the following simplified lists we show the main types and sub-types used at each office, with any H.I.s in brackets. We do not correlate the use of H.I.s with the sub-types in which they are shown.

It is difficult to place general values on the wide ranges of material available. A strike on a QV cover is usually worth much more than a similar one on a KE VII ppc. In our lists most of the values below £3.50 apply to offices found mainly on KE VII ppc's. Most of the values above £5 apply to offices found mainly on QV covers. * means "few examples known". - means "does not exist" (London Suburban District Offices only).

We strongly recommend to collectors wishing to specialise that they will require "Collecting British Squared Circle Postmarks" by S. Cohen, M. Barette and D. G. Rosenblat, published 1987 and three Supplements published in 1990, 1993 and 1996 including thousands of updates. For details see end of chapter.

We take this opportunity to express our sincere thanks to Stanley Cohen who has assisted us with the thorough review and update that this chapter has received.

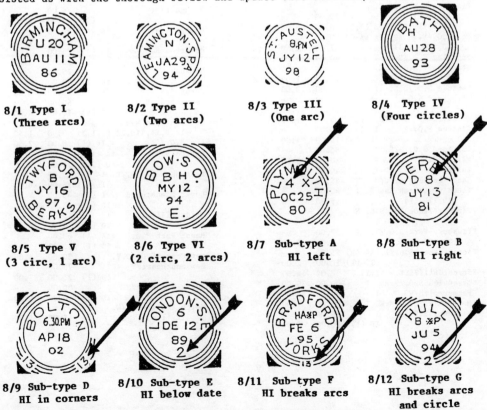

8/1 Type I
(Three arcs)

8/2 Type II
(Two arcs)

8/3 Type III
(One arc)

8/4 Type IV
(Four circles)

8/5 Type V
(3 circ, 1 arc)

8/6 Type VI
(2 circ, 2 arcs)

8/7 Sub-type A
HI left

8/8 Sub-type B
HI right

8/9 Sub-type D
HI in corners

8/10 Sub-type E
HI below date

8/11 Sub-type F
HI breaks arcs

8/12 Sub-type G
HI breaks arcs
and circle

London Head District Offices

London E.C.   1.00
    IA,IIA,VIA (A-L,R)
London E.   1.00
    IA,ID,IE,IIA,IID (A-Z)
    (1-33,41)
London N.   2.50
    IA,ID,IIA,IID,IIIA (A-E,P,X)
    (5,7,9-11,18,19)
London N.W.   1.00
    IA,ID,IF,IIA,IID (1-21,24-26)
London S.E.   1.00
    ID,IE,IID,IIE,IIIE (1-9,11,12,
    18-20,23,24,27-38)

London/S.W.   1.00
    IA,ID,IF,IG,IID,IIF,IIID (1-33)
London W.   1.00
    IE,IG,IIE,IIG,IIIE (18,19,33,
    34,36-38,41,47-53,55,57,60-82)
London W.C.   1.00
    I,IA,ID,IIA,IID,IIIA (A-E,H-P,X)
    (2,5,15,18-30)
Paddington W   1.00
    IA,ID,IE,IID (A-K,O,R,V)
    (8,11,14,21,54,57-72,100)

London Branch Offices

Aldgate B.O./E   15.00
    IA,ID (A,B)(1,2)
Bedford St. S.O./W.C.   3.00
    IA,ID (1,9-13)
Charing Cross W.C.   1.00
    IA,ID,IIA,IID,IIIA (A-F,Z)
    (1-5)
London W.C./C.X.   1.50
    IA,IIA,IIIA (7-11)
Lombard St. B.O./E.C.   4.00 X
    IA (A-E,K,L,O,Q)

Lombard St. S.O./E.C.   20.00 X
    IA (C)
Mark Lane E.C.   4.00
    I,IA,II,III (A-H,J,K)
Stock Exchange/E.C.   *
    I
Threadneedle St. B.O./E.C.   10.00
Throgmorton Avenue/E.C.   *
    I

London Suburban District Offices

The difference in values between QV and KE7 is particularly great for these offices so, for this section only, separate prices are given for covers or cards appropriate to the two reigns.

		QV	KE7
Blackheath S.O./S.E.			
IA (D,E)		20.00	-
I,ID,II,IID,IIID (1,2)		8.00	3.00
Bow S.O./E. IA,VIA (A-C)		20.00	-
ID,VID (1-3)		7.00	1.50
Brockley S.O./S.E. I		40.00	15.00
Camberwell S.O./S.E.			
I,ID,IID,IIID (1,3)		10.00	1.00
Catford S.O./S.E. I		15.00	3.00
Chingford S.O.	IA (A)	60.00	-
	ID (2)	30.00	15.00
Chiswick IE,IIE (1-3)		5.00	1.50
Clapton S.O./E	IA (A)	40.00	-
	ID (1)	15.00	4.00
Deptford S.O./S.E. I		85.00	-
Ealing W.	I	10.00	5.00
Ealing Dean/W.	I	40.00	-
East Finchley S.O./N	I	45.00	-
Finchley/Church End N. I		40.00	-
	ID,IID (1)	15.00	3.00
Finchley/East End S.O. N			
	I	*	-
Finsbury Park S.O./N. I		30.00	-
	ID,IID (1,5,6)	6.00	2.00
Forest Gate S.O./E. IA (B)		75.00	-
	ID (1)	10.00	2.00
Forest Hill/S.E.	I,II	8.00	4.00
Greenwich S.O./S.E. I		100.00	30.00
Hammersmith/W	I	50.00	12.00
Herne Hill S.O./S.E. I		8.00	7.00
Highbury S.O./N.	I	80.00	-
	ID (1)	40.00	3.00

		QV	KE7
Highgate/N.	I	75.00	-
	ID (2)	20.00	10.00
Highgate N.	IA (A)	90.00	-
	I	25.00	12.00
Homerton S.O./E	IA (A)	25.00	-
	ID (1)	15.00	6.00
Hornsey N.	I	75.00	-
	ID (2)	40.00	15.00
Hornsey/N	I,ID (1,3)	10.00	6.00
Kennington S.O./S.E.	I	60.00	-
	ID (1)	10.00	4.00
Kentish Town N.W.			
I,ID,II,IID,IIID (1,3)		3.00	1.50
Lee S.O./S.E.	I,ID (1)	8.00	2.50
Leyton S.O.	IA (A,B)	30.00	-
	ID (2,3)	20.00	4.00
Leytonstone S.O./E. IA (A)		45.00	-
	ID (1)	15.00	8.00
Lower Edmonton S.O. I		45.00	-
	ID (1)	15.00	12.00
Maida Hill/W.	I	15.00	-
	ID (1)	5.00	1.50
Manor Park S.O.	IA (A)	60.00	-
	ID (1)	18.00	3.00
New Cross S.O./S.E. I		20.00	5.00
New Southgate/N	I	75.00	-
	ID (1)	25.00	25.00
North Finchley/N	I	80.00	-
	ID (1)	10.00	6.00
North Kensington/W.			
IE (1,6)		15.00	1.00

		QV	KE7
North Woolwich S.O./E			
IA (A),ID (2)		75.00	50.00
Norwood S.E.	I,II	3.00	2.00
Notting Hill/W.	I	15.00	10.00
Palmers Green S.O./N	I	75.00	8.00
Peckham S.O./S.E.	I	75.00	-
ID,IID (6)		18.00	15.00
Plaistow S.O./E.	IA (A,B)	20.00	-
ID (1,2)		12.00	3.00
Poplar S.O./E.	IA (D)	60.00	-
ID (1)		20.00	6.00
St.John's Wood S.O./N.W.			
IA (1-4)		8.00	-
ID,IID (1-4)		5.00	1.00
Shepherds Bush W.	IE (1)	8.00	5.00
Southgate/N	I	75.00	-
ID (1)		20.00	12.00
South Tottenham S.O.			
I,ID,II (1)		5.00	2.00
South Woodford S.O.			
IA (A)		100.00	-
Stoke Newington S.O./N.			
I,IA (A)(2)		30.00	-
ID (1-3)		8.00	3.00
Stratford S.O./E. IA (A-D)		20.00	-
ID,IID (2-5)		12.00	2.00

		QV	KE7
Tottenham S.O.	I,IA (B)	30.00	-
ID (1,2)		7.00	2.00
Upper Edmonton	IA (A)	85.00	-
Upper Edmonton S.O.			
I,ID (2)		75.00	15.00
Upper Holloway S.O.			
IA (A,C)		25.00	-
ID (1)		8.00	2.00
Victoria Docks S.O./E.			
IA (A)		35.00	-
ID (1)		12.00	2.00
Walthamstow IA (A),ID (1)		25.00	8.00
Walworth S.E.	I,IA (2)	12.00	5.00
West Kensington W.			
ID,IE,IIE (1-5)		4.00	1.00
West Norwood S.E.	I,II	5.00	2.00
Whetstone S.O./N.	I	60.00	-
ID (1)		12.00	6.00
Willesden S.O./N.W.			
I,ID (2)		60.00	40.00
Wimbledon	I	4.00	2.00
Winchmore Hill S.O./N	I	35.00	-
ID (1)		15.00	3.00
Woodford & South Woodford/Essex			
IA (A),ID (2)		45.00	4.00
Wood Green/N	I,ID (1)	25.00	3.00

Provincial Offices

Note : at Birmingham the * is included in the H.I.

Office	Types	Value	Office	Types	Value
Aldbourne	I	35.00	Bedford	I,II	1.50
Alford	I	60.00	Beer	I	2.00
Alfreton	I	3.00	Beer Alston	I	60.00
Alton/Hants	I,II	6.00	Beeston/Notts	I	2.00
Ampthill	I,III	2.00	Belper	I,III	2.00
Andoversford	I	16.00	Berkhamsted	I	30.00
Appledore/Devon	I	25.00	Berwick	I,II,III	3.00
Ardleigh	I	8.00	Bexley	I,II	3.00
Armley	I	65.00	Bicester	I,II	1.00
Arundel	I	2.00	Bideford	I	8.00
Ashbourne	I	4.00	Biggleswade	I,III	2.00
Ashford/Kent	I,II,III	20.00	Bildeston	I	15.00
Ashley Green	I	45.00	Billinghurst	I	75.00
Ashton under Lyne	I	3.00	Bingley	I (A-F)	2.50
Aspley Guise	I	25.00	Birkenhead	IA,ID,IE	
Atherstone	I	15.00	(4-9)		1.50
Atherton	I	15.00	:Liscard/Cheshire	IA (A)	80.00
Axminster	I,II,III	2.50	:New Brighton/		
Aylsham	I	4.00	Cheshire	IA (A,B)	80.00
Aysgarth Station	I	20.00	:Oxton/Birkenhead	I,IA (A,B)	1.50
Bacup	I	5.00	:Rock Ferry/		
Bakewell	I	3.00	Birkenhead	I,IA,ID (A,B)	
Baldock	I,II	3.00	(1,2)		2.00
Barham	I	80.00	:Seacombe/Cheshire	IA (A,B)	70.00
Barnet	I,II	10.00	Birmingham	IA,ID,IID	
Barnetby	I	15.00	(A-H,J-N,P-Z,DD,GG,HH,JJ,		
Barnsley	I,ID (1,2)	1.50	KK,MM,QQ,SS,YY,C*,D*,E*)		
Barnstaple	I,II,III	1.00	(50,56-60,63-79,98)		1.00
Barrasford	I	20.00	Bishop Stortford	I	25.00
Barrow in Furness	I,II	3.00	Bishops Stortford	I	4.00
Barry	I	60.00	Blackheath/Staff	I	2.50
Bath	I,II,III,IV	3.00	Blackley	I	90.00
Bawtry	I	5.00	Blisworth	I	7.00
Baydon	I	50.00	Bloxwich	I	5.00
Beaworthy	I	3.00	Bodmin	I,II,III	0.75
Beckenham	I	20.00			

Place	Classes	Value	Place	Classes	Value
Dawley/Salop	I	5.00	Gloucester	I,ID,IG,II,	
Dawlish	I,III	2.00		IID (1,4,7)	1.00
Deal	I,II	3.00	Gloucester		
:Lower Walmer/			Station	I	4.00
Deal	I	3.00	Godalming	I	5.00
Deepfields	I	100.00	Gomersal	I	20.00
Denton/Lanc	I,II	1.00	Gorton	I	3.00
Derby	IB,II (8)	75.00	Gorton Brook	I	100.00
:Melbourne/			Grampound Road	I,III	2.00
Derby E	I	90.00	Gravesend	I	1.00
Dereham	I,IA,II		Great Somerford	I	5.00
	(1,3)	1.00	Great Yarmouth	I,II	0.50
Devizes	I,II	4.00	Greenstreet/Kent	I	100.00
Devonport	I,IA,IB,II		Grimsby	I,IA,II (B)	1.50
	(2,3)	1.00	Grimsby & Lincoln		
Devoran	I	5.00	Sorting Tender	I	10.00
Didcot	I	2.00	Guernsey	I,II	1.00
Dinas	I	90.00	Guildford	I,II	3.00
Diss	I	1.50	Hadleigh	I	40.00
Doncaster	I,II	7.00	Hafod/Gla	I	*
Dorchester	I,II	6.00	Hailsham	I,II	3.50
Douglas/			Halesworth	I,II	1.50
Isle of Man	I,II	1.00	Halifax	I,IA,II,IID,	
Dover	I,II,III	3.00		IIID (4)	1.00
Downham	I,II,III	1.00	Halstead	I	20.00 X HSL
Droitwich	I,II	1.50	Halstead/Essex	I	35.00
Droylsden	I,II	2.00	Halstead/Kent	I	10.00
Dunmow	I	1.50	Handcross	I,II	3.50
Dunstable	I	1.00	Hanley	I,II	3.00
Dunster	I	1.50	Harleston	I,II	2.00
Eastbourne	I,ID,II,		Harlow	I	1.50
	III (4)	2.00	Harrogate	I,III,IIIB	
Eastwood/Yorks	I	45.00		(A)	2.00
Eccles	I,II	1.50	Harwich	I,II	1.00
Egloskerry	I	1.50	Hastings	I,II	2.50
Eltham	I	1.50	:Gensing Station Rd/		
Ely	I,III	1.00	Hastings	I	25.00
Enfield	I	3.00	Hatfield/Herts	I	2.00
Epping	I,II	2.00	Hatherleigh	I	2.00
Esher	I,II	2.00	Haverfordwest	I	35.00 X Aven
Etchingham	I	20.00	Haverhill	I,II	1.00
Evesham	I,II,III	2.00	Hawkhurst	I,II,III	4.00
Exbourne	I	6.00	Haxby	I	30.00
Exeter	I,II,III	2.00	Hay	I	2.00
Exmouth	I,II	1.00	Hayes/Middx	I	15.00
Eye	I	2.00	Haywards Heath	I	5.00
Fakenham	I	5.00	Heamoor	I	15.00
Fallowfield	I	18.00	Heathfield	I	70.00
Falmouth	I,II	1.00	Hebden Bridge	I,II	10.00
Farnborough Road	V	30.00	Heckington	I	7.50
Farnborough			Helston	I	3.00
Station	I	20.00	Hereford	I	1.50
Farnham	I	1.00	Hertford	I,II	1.00
Faversham	I,II,III	4.00	Hetton le Hole	I	4.50
Felixstowe	I,V	1.50	Hexham	I	45.00
Filey	I,II	1.00	Heytesbury	I	5.00
Finghall	I	40.00	Heywood	I,II	1.50
Fladbury	V	30.00	Higham Ferers	I,II	2.00
Folkestone	I,II,III	1.00	Highampton	I,II	2.00
:Tontine St. B.O.			Highbridge	I	1.00
Folkestone	I	20.00	Hingham	I	*
Foot's Cray	I,II	10.00	Hinstock	I	10.00
Fowey	I	1.00	Hitchin	I,II	1.00
Frome	I	6.00	Hockcliffe	I	20.00
Gainsborough	I,II	4.00	Hoddesdon	I	1.00
Gamlingay	I	5.00	Holbeach	I	1.50
Ganton	V	35.00	Holsworthy	I	10.00
Glaisdale	V	20.00	Holt/Norfolk	I	4.00
Glossop	I	15.00	Honiton	I,II	5.00

Hoo	I	*
Hornchurch	I	15.00
Horndean	I,II	4.00
Houghton-le-Spring	I	3.00
Hounslow	I,II	1.00
Hoylake	I	2.00
Hull	I,IA,ID, IG,II,IIIG (2,3,5)	2.00
Hunmanby	I	2.00
Huntingdon	I,III	2.00
Huttoft	I	40.00
Hyde	I,II	1.50
Ilford	I,II	2.00
Ilfracombe	I,II	1.00
Ilminster	I,II	5.00
Ingatestone	I	2.00
Instow	I	2.00
Ipswich	I,IA,ID,IE, IF,II,IID (1-4)	1.00
:St. John's/ Ipswich	I	100.00
Isleworth	I,II	6.00
Ivybridge	I,II	2.00
Jersey	I,II,III	1.00
Kelvedon	I	2.00
Kettering	I,III	1.00
Kilmington	I	60.00
Kineton	I	6.00
Kingsbridge	I,II,III	2.00
King's Lynn	I,IA,II,III (1-6)	1.00
Kingston-on-Thames	I,II,III	2.00
Kirkby Stephen	I	*
Kirkham	I	60.00
Kirkham Abbey	V	8.00
Kiveton Park	I	20.00
Knockholt	I	10.00
Lakenheath	V	50.00
Lambourn	I,II	1.00
Langport	I	1.00
Launceston	I	1.00
Leamington	I,IA (1-4)	4.00
Leamington Spa	I,IA,ID, II,IID,IIID (1-4)	1.00
Ledbury	I	3.00
Leeds	IA,ID,IID,IIID (A-E,L)	1.00
:Call Lane B.O./ Leeds	I	*
:Chapeltown Rd/ Leeds	I,II	1.50
:Holbeck B.O./ Leeds	I	3.50
:Hyde Park Corner/Leeds	I	1.50
:Market St/Leeds	I	75.00
:Marsh Lane B.O./ Leeds	I,II	1.50
:Marsh Lane S.O./ Leeds	I	12.00
Leicester	I,ID,IID,IIID (1-9)	1.00
Leigh/Lanc	I,II	1.50
Lelant	I	1.50
Levenshulme	I,II	1.50
Lewdown	I	2.00
Lewes	I,II	3.00
Lewes/Station Office	I	2.00
Leyland	I	8.00
Lifton	I	2.00
Lincoln/S.T.	I	3.00
Lincoln/S.C.	I	5.00
Lindfield	I	4.00
Liskeard	I,III	1.00
Littleborough	I	3.00
Liverpool	IA,IB,IIA, IIB,IID,IIIA, IIIB,IIID (A-F,J-L,O,Y,Z,AL,BZ,CL,OL,ZZ) (32,33,35,36,40)	1.00
:Eastern District	IA (ED)	*
:Northern District	IA,IIA (N,ND)	2.00
:Southern District	IA (SD)	2.00
:Liverpool LX (Exchange)	I,IA,II, IIA,IIIA (A-C,E-G)	6.00
:Liverpool/LX (Exchange)	I,IA,IIA, IIIA (B,F)	6.00
:Liverpool.N	I	6.00
:Liverpool/N3	II	2.50
:Liverpool/SD	I,IA (A)	2.50
:Aigburth/ Liverpool	I	3.00
:Blundellsands/ Liverpool	I	3.00
:Bootle/Liverpool	IA (B,D)	10.00
:Bootle-cum-Linacre/ Liverpool	IA (D)	8.00
:Exchange/ Liverpool	IA,II,III (L)	2.50
:Garston/Liverpool	I	15.00
:Lark Lane/ Liverpool	I,IA,II (A,C)	6.00
:Liscard/Liverpool	IA (A)	25.00
:New Brighton/ Liverpool	IA (A,B)	20.00
:Old Swan/ Liverpool	I	15.00
:Rice Lane/ Liverpool	I,II	1.50
:Seacombe/ Liverpool	IA (A,B)	15.00
:Seaforth/ Liverpool	I	2.00
:Walton Rd. Sub D.O./ Liverpool	I,IA,ID (N)(1,2)	1.00
:Waterloo/ Liverpool	I,II	2.00
:Wavertree/ Liverpool	I,IIF (2)	20.00
:West Derby/ Liverpool	I	3.00
(see also Birkenhead)		
Liverpool & London T.P.O.	I	*
Llwynypia	I	8.00
Longfield	I	20.00
Longridge	I	30.00
Long Rock	I	5.00
Long Stratton	I	5.00

Looe	I,II	1.50
Loughborough	I,IA,II (1)	1.00
Louth/Linc.	I	1.00
Lower Sheringham	I	90.00
Lower Sherringham	I	*
Luton	I	1.00
Lyme	I	35.00
Lymington	I,II,III	1.50
Lynmouth	I	4.00
Lynton	I	1.50
Mablethorpe	I	3.00
Macclesfield	I	1.50
:Chestergate B.O./ Macclesfield	I	20.00
Maidenhead	I,II,III	0.50
Maldon	I	2.00
Malmesbury	I	50.00
Malvern	I,II	2.00
Manchester	IA,IIA,IIIA (A,D,U,X-Z,BX,CX,DX,EX, HX,XX,ZX)	1.00
:Manchester/S.W.	I	5.00
:Barlow Moor Rd/ Manchester	I	10.00
:Pendleton D.O./ Salford	I,IA,ID (1,2)	1.50
Manningtree	I	2.00
Marazion	I	75.00
March	I	2.00
Margate	I	20.00
:Northumberland Rd/Margate	I	60.00
Market Harborough	I,II	1.00
Market Rasen	I,III	1.50
Marlborough	I,V	6.00
Marlow	I	1.50
Martock	I	1.50
Matlock Bath	I	6.00
Mawgan	VI	15.00
Melton Constable	I	4.00
Merthyr Vale	I	8.00
Mevagissey	I	10.00
Middleton/Lanc	I	1.50
Midhurst	I,II	3.00
Milborne Port	I	3.00
Milford/Surrey	I	15.00
Minehead	I	1.00
Morchard Bishop	I	3.00
Morpeth	I	2.00
Morthoe	I	50.00
Mossley	I	15.00
Mounts	I	35.00
Narberth	I	3.00
Narborough/ Norfolk	I	35.00
Navigation	I	*
Newbridge/ Cornwall	I	30.00
Newcastle-on- Tyne	I,IE,IIE,IIIE (A-F)(2,3,6)	1.00
Newent	I	2.00
Newhaven	I	75.00
Newhaven/Sussex	I	2.00
Newington/Kent	I,II	45.00
Newmarket	I,III	2.00
Newnham	I	30.00
Newnham/Glos	I,II	1.50
Newport/Mon	I,III	1.00
Newquay/Cornwall	I	30.00
Newton Abbot	I	3.00

Newton le Willows/Yorks	I	12.00
Newtown/Mont	I	4.00
New Tredegar	I	2.50
Neyland	I	14.00
Normanton	I	*
Normanton Station	I	100.00
Northampton	I,II	1.00
North Shields	I	4.00
North Tawton	I	2.00
North Walsham	I	10.00
Norwich	I,ID,IF,IG (A,K)(12,13)	3.00
Nottingham	I,ID,IE,IG (4,5,12)	2.00
Old Brentford	I	45.00
Oldbury	I,II,III	2.00
Old Hill	I	2.00
Ongar	I,II	1.50
Openshaw	I	25.00
Orleton	I	15.00
Orpington	I	25.00
Ossett	I,III	8.00
Ottery St. Mary	I,II	1.50
Oundle	I	2.00
Padstow	I,II	2.00
Par Station	I,II	4.00
Patricroft	I	5.00
Peel/ Isle of Man	V	5.00
Penarth	I,II	5.00
Pendlebury	I	1.50
Penryn	I	25.00
Penzance	I,II	30.00
Perranarworthal	I	*
Perranporth	I	1.50
Perranwell Station	I	6.00
Pershore	I,II	2.00
Peterborough	I,ID,II,V (3)	2.00
Peterborough/ Parcel Post	I	*
Petersfield	I,II	1.00
Plymouth	I,IA,ID,IF (1-10,40,52)	1.00
:Stonehouse/ Devon	I	*
:Stonehouse B.O./ Plymouth	I	2.00
Plympton	I	*
Polegate	I	7.00
Pontefract	I,II	2.00
Pontlottyn	I	20.00
Pontyclown	I	40.00
Pontyclun	I	3.00
Pontypridd	I	10.00
Portscatho	I	4.00
Portsmouth	IA,IIA,III, IIIA,IIID (1-3)	5.00
:Landport/ Portsmouth	I	50.00
:Portsea/ Portsmouth	I,II	10.00
Port Talbot	I	1.50
:Taibach/ Port Talbot	I	*
Poulton Le Fylde	I	2.00
Preston	IA,ID,IG (A)(2)	5.00
Princetown	I	2.50
Radcliffe	I	50.00

Rainham/Essex	I	40.00
Rainham/Kent	I	30.00
Ramsbottom	I	3.00
Ramsey/		
Isle of Man	I	30.00
Ramsgate	I,II,III	1.50
Rawtenstall	I,II	4.00
Rayleigh	I	60.00
Reading	I,II,III	2.00
Redruth	I,II	2.00
Retford	I	1.50
Richmond/Surrey	I,II,III	1.00
Rillington	V	20.00
Ringwood	I,III	1.50
Robertsbridge	I	2.00
Rochdale	I,IA,ID,	
	IID (A)(1)	1.00
Rochester	I,II,III	1.00
Romford	I,II,III	1.00
Ross	I	7.00
Rowley Regis	I	30.00
Royston/Cambs	I,II	4.00
Royston/Herts	I	1.00 X
Ruan Minor	I	2.00
Rugby	I,II,III	4.00
Rugby Station	I,II	4.00
Ryde	I,II	2.00
St. Annes on		
the Sea	I	1.50
St. Austell	I,II,III	1.00
St. Buryan	I	10.00
St. Columb	I,II	2.00
St. Germans/		
Cornwall	I,II	2.00
St. Ives/Cornwall	I,II	3.00
St. Ives/Hunts	I	35.00
St. Just	I	1.50
St. Keverne	I	20.00
S. Mabyn	I	14.00
St. Martin/		
Cornwall	I	15.00
St. Mary Cray	I	20.00
St. Mawes	I	2.00
St. Neots	I	1.50
St. Tudy	I	2.00
Sale	I	1.50
Saltash	I,II	1.50
Sandown	I,III	1.50
Sandwich	I	2.50
Sandy	I	1.50
Saxmundham	VI	25.00
Scarborough	I,IA,IF,	
	IID,IIF	
	(1,2)	0.50
Scorrier	I	25.00
Seaford	I,II	1.00
Sedgley	I	15.00
Selby	I	1.50
Sennen	I	1.00
Sevenoaks	I,II	15.00 X
Shaftesbury	I,III	30.00
Shanklin	I,II	1.00
Sheffield	IA,ID,IE,	
	IID,IIE,IIIE	
	(2,4,10-14)	1.00
Sheffield N	IA,ID (A,B)	
	(1,2)	2.00
Sheffield/S.D.O.	IA,ID (A,B)	
	(1,2)	2.00
Sheffield/W.D.O.	IA,ID (A,B)	
	(1,2)	1.00
Sherborne	I,II	1.00
Shipley/Yorks	I,II	1.00

Shrewsbury	IA,IC,IIA,IIE	
	(1,2)	1.00
Sidcup	I,II	25.00
Sidmouth	I,II	1.00
Sittingbourne	I,II	12.00
:Milton/		
Sittingbourne	I	50.00
Skegness	I	1.00
Slough	I,II	1.00
Snodland	I,II	2.50
Soham	I	5.00
Somerton/		
Somerset	I	1.50
Southampton	IA,IIA,IIIA	
	(1,2)	2.50
:Oxford St. B.O./		
Southampton	I,II	2.50
Southend/Essex	I	5.00
Southend on Sea	I,II	0.50
South Molton	I,II	2.00
South Petherton	I,II	2.50
Southport	I,II	1.00
:Birkdale B.O./		
Southport	I	2.00
South Shields	I	85.00
South Stoke	I	*
Southwick/Sussex	I,II	1.50
Spalding	I	2.00
Spennymoor	I	*
Spilsby	I	2.00
Spondon	I	4.00
Staines	I,III	1.50
Stantonbury	I	15.00
Staplehurst	I	2.00
Stevenage	I	2.00
Stockport	I,ID,II (1)	1.50
Stoke on Trent	I,II,IIID	
	(5)	2.00
Stonham	I	25.00
Stony Stratford	I,II	5.00
Stratton/		
North Devon	I,II	2.00
Strensall	V	16.00
Stretford	I	18.00
Stroud/Glos	I,II	5.00
Sturry	I	2.00
Sudbury/Suffolk	I,II	1.00
Sutton/Linc	I	75.00
Sutton in Ashfield		
	I	2.00
Swaffham	I,II	1.00
Swanley Junction	I,II,III	3.00
Swansea	I	30.00
Tadcaster	I,II,III	2.50
Talybont	I	*
Taunton	I,II,III	1.00
Tavistock	I,II	1.50
Teignmouth	I,IG,II	
	(1,2)	0.50
Tenby	I	2.00
Terrington	VI	70.00
Tetbury	I,II	30.00
Tewkesbury	I	14.00
The Lizard	I	0.50
Thetford	I,II	1.00
Thrapston	I,II	2.00
Tideswell	I	2.00
Tipton Green/		
Tipton	I	*
Tredegar	I,II	2.00
Treen	I	14.00
Tregony	I	20.00
Treharris	I	3.00

Trowbridge	I,II	1.00		West Heslerton	V	*
Truro	I,II	1.00		West Kirby	I	2.00
Tunbridge	I	*		Weston Super Mare	I	5.00
Tunbridge Wells	I	4.00		Wetherby	I	2.00
:Calverley/				Weybridge	I,V	1.50
Tunbridge Wells	I	18.00		Weymouth	I,II	1.00
:Mount Ephraim,				Whitford/Devon	I	50.00
Tunbridge Wells	I	15.00		Wickwar	I	4.00
Twyford/Berks	V	3.00		Wigan	I	1.00
Tyldesley	I	5.00		Williton	I,II	2.00
Upminster	I	45.00		Wilmslow	I	2.00
Uppingham	I	2.00		Winchester	I,II,III	3.00
Wadebridge	I,III	1.50		Windsor	I,II,III	0.50
Wakefield	I	5.00		Wirksworth	I,II,III	1.50
Walmer	I	75.00		Witham	I	25.00
Walmer Road	I	4.50		Witham/Essex	I	1.50
Walsall	I	1.00		Withington	I	20.00
Walsden	I	60.00		Woburn	I	2.00
Walton-on-Naze	I	1.00		Woburn Sands	I	2.00
Ware	I	1.00		Woking	I,III	2.50
Wargrave/Berks	I	2.00		Wokingham	I,II,III	4.00
Warrington	I	4.00		Wolverhampton	I,II,IID,	
Washaway	I	50.00			IIID (11)	1.00
Washford	I	2.00		Wolverton/Bucks	I,II	1.50
Waterfoot	I	2.00		Woodford Green	I	3.50
Wednesbury	I	14.00		Woolpit	I	3.00
Welburn	V	10.00		Woolwich	I,ID,IE,IF	
Wellington College					(2,6)	4.00
Station	I	4.00		Worcester	I,II	3.00
Wellington/Som.	I,II	1.50		Worksop	I	1.50
Wells/Norfolk	I	4.00		Worthing	I,II	40.00
Wells/Somerset	I	8.00		Worthing Station		
Welwyn	I	50.00		B.O./Worthing	I	25.00
Wem	I	12.00		Wrexham	I,II,IID (2)	2.00
West Bromwich	I,II	2.00		Wrington	I	8.00
Westbury/Wilts	I,II	3.00		Wroxall	I,II	2.00
West Hartlepool	I,II,IID (1)	1.50		York	I,II,III	1.00

COLLECTING BRITISH SQUARED CIRCLE POSTMARKS

by Stanley Cohen, F.R.P.S.L.,
Maurice Barette and Daniel Rosenblat

1988 PHILATELIC BOOK OF THE YEAR AWARD

Among the most fascinating of all British postmarks are Squared
Circle postmarks! This book is indispensable as it contains
complete details and explanations with fine illustrations.

You will also need the three 70-page Supplements to the book, with
much additional information, published in 1990, 1993 and 1996

Obtainable from Vera Trinder Ltd, 38 Bedford Street, Strand,
London WC2E 9EU (tel: 0171 836 2365) OR from Bay Stamps, Freepost,
Colwyn Bay, N Wales LL29 9YZ (tel: 01492 516644)

Collect British Squared Circle Postmarks (429 pages) - £18 (+ p&p)
and Supplements Nos 1, 2 and 3 - £6 each (+ p&p).

SPECIAL OFFER - ALL 4 BOOKS - FOR ONLY £32 (+ p&p)

London Fancy Geometric Postmarks

During the 1870s efforts were made to produce a handstamp less cumbersome than the duplex. The most successful and popular replacements undoubtedly were the Squared Circles used in about 800 offices throughout England and Wales. However, three offices in London - Inland Branch, Lombard Street Branch and London E.C. - had similar designs, that (but for one) were based on the octagon. The first of these Fancy Geometrics was issued in 1880. They remained in use until the early 1900s. In each case the left hand letter or number above the date is the H.I, and H.I.s are shown in the listing below in brackets, followed by recorded dates of use for each entry.

A 125-page study of these attractive postmarks, by M. Barette, was published in December 1994, listing all types, rarities and value ranges. The illustrations and reference numbers are from that book, with permission.

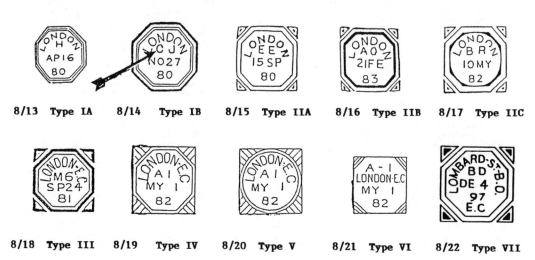

8/13 Type IA   8/14 Type IB   8/15 Type IIA   8/16 Type IIB   8/17 Type IIC

8/18 Type III   8/19 Type IV   8/20 Type V   8/21 Type VI   8/22 Type VII

London Inland Branch	
IA (no HIs)	30.00
(1.5.1880 to 29.7.1880)	
IB (lower case a-f)	15.00
(2.12.1880 to 28.11.1909)	
IIA (capital A,E,F)	12.00
(2.8.1880 to 7.12.1882)	
IIB (capital A-F)	20.00
(17.2.1883 to 1.3.1890)	
IIC (capital A-R)	6.00
(20.2.1882 to 3.12.1895)	

London E.C.	
III (capital H-P)	5.00
(30.11.1880 to 7.3.1898)	
IV (capital A)	15.00
(1.6.1882 to 13.10.1899)	
V (capital A)	15.00
(1.6.1882 to 18.6.1897)	
VI (capital A)	25.00
(31.5.1882 to 3.6.1885)	
Lombard St Branch Office	
VII (capital B,H,I)(7)	10.00
(9.5.1882 to 26.3.1906)	

9.   Later Circular Handstamps

Although they had been in use from the 1850s it was not until the end of the 19th century that the single and double circles ("circular datestamps" or cds's as dubbed by stamp collectors) came into their own. The double circle, with its thick arcs, was designed to cancel stamps: the single circle was for backstamping, but later for post office counter work. A small single circle, the "thimble", had initially been used for backstamping, later for stamp cancelling. Rubber handstamps, widely known as "rubbers" or "village rubbers", were firstly brought in at "postal order money offices", then used on mail but not on the stamp, leaving the larger sorting office to cancel the stamps. Later, stamps were cancelled with these rubbers. The next generation of rubber handstamps (to the present day) were used, at larger sorting offices, for stamping large envelopes or "soft packets", hence the term "packet handstamp".

Readers should note the distinction between a post office sorting office and a post office counter, even though at small offices these were only a few feet apart! The "standard pattern" for the 20th century is as follows (possibly an over-simplification):

- a <u>sorting office</u> is equipped with double circles (with <u>time</u>, or with code A for morning, B for afternoon etc.) for stamping letters, rubber stamps for "soft packets", and "paid" postmarks (if the office is large enough) plus registered handstamps primarily for receipts on incoming items etc.

- a <u>counter</u> is equipped with single circle handstamps (or "SIDs" in modern times) (with <u>no time</u>), with a code identifying the handstamp, used for all paperwork (pensions etc), registered letters and receipts, sometimes used for parcels as well; later if traffic was sufficient a separate parcel handstamp was also supplied.

There are MANY exceptions eg double circles are issued to counters, single circles are used in sorting offices etc etc .... and some in this chapter are not even circular in spite of the chapter heading! Values are for covers/cards (or large piece if from a parcel), but double for handstamp on postal order counterfoil (pre-QEII) and also double, minimum 2.00, for parcel labels.

Single Arcs

	9/1	9/2	9/5

9/1	Undated single arc backstamp, from 1857	....	8.00
9/2	Dated London single arc backstamp	....	3.00
9/3	As above but as Edwardian cancellation	....	5.00
9/4	As above but district initials breaking arc, backstamp	....	4.00
9/5	Dated provincial single arc backstamp	....	4.00

Thimbles (small diameter single circles)

	9/7	

| 9/6 | Undated thimble | .... | 4.00 |
| 9/7 | Dated thimble | .... | 1.50 |

9/8	9/10	9/11	9/15	9/16	9/17

Single Circles

9/8 Small London backstamps, blue (evening), red (morning) 2.50
9/9 Name horizontally across circle, backstamp 2.50
9/10   As above but post-1900 cancellation 3.00
9/11 Single circle backstamps, usually black or blue 2.00
9/12   As above but cancelling stamps, coded or timed before 1900 .... 5.00
9/13   As above, timed, after 1900 .... 0.50
9/14   As above, with inscription altered, such as R of RSO removed 1.50
9/15 Larger Irish type of single circle 1.00
9/16 London mis-sort stamps (code in italic characters) 1.00
9/17 Single circle used for counter duties 0.10

Double Circles

Early types

9/18	9/19	9/20

9/18 Small double circle types 7.50
9/19 Large London double circle, with or without thick arc 3.50
9/20 Continental type double circle ('Hammer'), London or London E.C.
      coded 1-6 .... 40.00

Double arc types

9/21	9/23	9/24

9/21 Scottish type with 1844 office numbers between pairs of arcs, from
      1883 .... 1.50
9/22   As above but larger 0.75
9/23 Double arc with English office numbers, from 1885 :

75	Birmingham	2.00	K34	Haswell (double arcs)	9.00
466	Liverpool	2.50		(single arcs)	20.00
761	Sunderland		K35	Murton Colliery	12.00
	(single arcs)	10.00	K36	South Hetton	6.00

9/24   As above with blank space, Irish 0.50
9/25   As above with cross or stamp number between pairs of arcs,
      English, Scottish or Irish 0.50

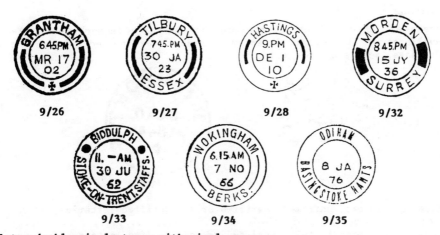

| 9/26 | 9/27 | 9/28 | 9/32 |

| 9/33 | 9/34 | 9/35 |

Later double circle types with single arc

9/26 Medium arc broken by cross pattee or handstamp number 0.30
9/27   as above, post town, county or district at foot 0.30
9/28   as above with 'Station Office' or other inscription removed 1.50
9/29   as above, arc broken by six pointed star 2.00
9/30   as above, arc broken by eight pointed star 3.00
9/31 Thick arc broken by cross pattee, handstamp no. or unbroken arc, 1920s- 0.20
9/32   as above, post town, county or district at foot 0.20
9/33   as above but circular "spacers" instead of thick arcs 0.50
9/34 Thin arcs and post-town, county etc. at foot, from c1950 (different
       letterings) or single unbroken thin arc 0.10
9/35 Unusual type with no side arcs at all 0.30

Coded time

Note : This section is relevant to chapters 7,8,9 and 19; we include it here for convenience.

For the period 1893-5 time was expressed in a coded form, and this was used in various types of handstamp postmark - duplex, squared circle, single & double circle, and so on. For example, about 15% of the offices that used squared circles used coded time; the same applies to duplex postmarks, but not necessarily the same offices. Full details of the usage of these codes can be found in "The Use of the 1894 Coded Time System in English Provincial Offices" by John A E Moy, published in 1991 by the author in conjunction with the British Postmark Society.

9/36   7 p.m.

Simplified details of the codes are as follows, with A-M used to show both hours and minutes :

Code	Hour	Minutes	Code	Hour	Minutes	Code	Hour	Minutes
A	1	5	E	5	25	I	9	45
B	2	10	F	6	30	K	10	50
C	3	15	G	7	35	L	11	55
D	4	20	H	8	40	M	12	-

The normal code consisted of two letters, the first the hour, the second the minutes. A separation device followed, usually an asterisk, alternatively a solid square in Ireland and dots of various sizes in Birmingham. Finally came an A for AM or a P for PM. Thus LI*P = 11.45pm and EF*A = 5.30am. 'Time in clear' officially replaced coded time in March 1895 but at some offices it continued into the 1900s.

Skeletons

Composed of individual characters made up for each temporary use. The terms
'travellers' or 'travelling datestamps' seem to be applied only to the 1840s-
1850s usage, see next two entries.

9/37   9/38

9/37 Office name in arc, unframed, seriffed or non-seriffed lettering, cross
     or index number at foot, 1840s 60.00
9/38 Circular 34mm, year in full, seriffed or non-seriffed letters,
     1840-50's 50.00

9/39 Circular, small 23-24mm, year in 2 or 4 figures, 1890s-1910s 6.00
     (Note: these are easily confused with single circle handstamps of
     same period; in skeletons the lettering is usually irregular and the
     wording asymmetrical)
9/40 Circular, year in two figures, non-seriffed, chiefly 1885 to
     1920, 30-36mm, date in 2 lines (generally no county up to 1906) ...   3.00
     (values higher for villages, lower for seaside resorts, but pre-1900 8.00)
9/41   As above but Camp, railway station or RSO (see chapters 13,15,16) .   4.00
9/42   As above but 28mm design from 1914, date in one line 3.00
9/43   As above but with spelling or other errors 8.00
9/44 Rubber skeletons (particularly difficult to find clear impressions)   20.00
9/45 Irish double rim skeletons 8.00

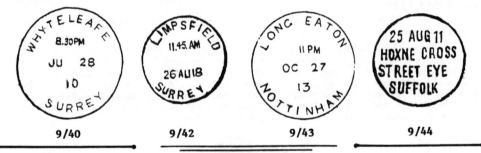

    9/40   9/42   9/43   9/44

Hooded Circles (previously known as 'Scrolls')

9/46 London or London EC, as cancellation, from 1882 (value higher post-1900)   3.00
9/47   As above but modern receiving marks, usually from abroad, red 2.00
9/48 Liverpool, includes 466, pre-1900 ....   8.00
9/49 Liverpool, without 466, 1900s 4.00
9/50   As above but V. Liverpool S, 466 (Victoria St.) 50.00
9/51   As above but E. Low-Hill D., 466 .... 10.00

| 9/46 | 9/52 | 9/53 | 9/54 | 9/55 |

9/52 <u>Irish</u>

Cork	....	15.00	Londonderry	....	40.00
Limerick	....	25.00	Waterford	....	60.00

9/53 <u>Used for late fees:</u> (with 'L' and value ½d, 1d etc; there are inscription variations, ie with/without B.O, E.C. etc)

London (Inland Section) ..	10.00	Leadenhall St. E.C.	.....	10.00
47 Cannon St. B.O. E.C. .	15.00	Liverpool St. E.C.	....	25.00
Eastcheap B.O. E.C.	10.00	Ludgate Circus E.C.	......	25.00
Fenchurch St. B.O. E.C. .	15.00	Mark Lane E.C.	....	10.00
Fleet St. E.C.	10.00	Threadneedle St. B.O. E.C.		10.00
49 Fore St. B.O. E.C. ...	15.00	Throgmorton Avenue B.O. E.C.		15.00
Gracechurch St. E.C.	20.00			

9/54 "Late Box" at Bradford, Leeds, Liverpool, Manchester stations, see chapter 13

   <u>Registered:</u>
9/55 Steel h/s, mainly London, or London District Offices (see also 19/53)   5.00
       (also occasional modern usage eg Haywards Heath, Wolverton etc)
9/56   As above but Official paid, in red (9/55-56 both show month 2 chars)   6.00
9/57 Rubber hooded circle with double rim (month 3 chars)(see also 19/54) .   6.00
9/58   As above but modern version with single rim 7.50

   <u>Parcel Post:</u>
9/59 G.P.O. London/Parcel Post/Depot 15.00
9/60 South West District/Parcel Post/Depot 15.00

9/61 Euston, London Bridge, Paddington, Waterloo stations, see chapter 13

   <u>Precancel</u>
9/62 Stamford Mercury precancel with 742 numeral 4.00

   Note : for further hooded circles see Aviation and Royalty

P/PD (Paid) Handstamps (in red)

| 9/63 | 9/64 | 9/65 |

9/63 Oval P-D or PD on paid letters to Europe, 1840's-1870's, used at
       Southampton and London, sometimes in blue or black 4.00
9/64   As above but P 5.00
9/65   As above but circular PD or PP 4.00

   (Note : unframed or boxed PD marks, all PF marks and most PP marks are French,
so mainly are PPPP marks, indicating passed thro' Paris 'Port Payée Passée Paris')

Rubber handstamps (from 1885)

Climax datestamp : this is distinguished by having the month in three characters and a full stop after month, with the date on revolving wheels.

| 9/66 | 9/67 | 9/68 |

Period 1 - approx to 1930s, known in this period as "rubbers" or "village rubbers", often with post town horizontally above date :

9/66 Cancelling stamps (or stamped alongside), violet/black, 1907-30
(value higher pre-1900 or on postal order) 4.00
9/67 As above but distorted by oil in black ink 7.50

Period 2 - approx from 1930 : in the modern era climax datestamps are plentiful on documents and for "internal purposes" not usually connected with stamping mail. However a good number may also be found used for stamping letters from Post Office departments, usually in black or purple, sometimes in red :

9/68 Modern usage on Post Office letters of handstamps with various
"administrative purposes" wordings, often including phone number
or "duty" eg "Opening duty", "Datapost duty" etc 0.20

Blackwell datestamp

| 9/70 | 9/72 | 9/74 |

Period 1 - approx 1900 to 1980s - this is distinguished by having the month in three letters, no full stop, year as two digits, and the date is composed of loose type, known more usually as "packet handstamp" or "soft packet handstamp"

9/69 Early packet handstamp, approx 1900-40 (various types) 1.00
9/70 Modern handstamps used for packets, some with star at foot 0.10
9/71 As above but London missort mark (code at foot or below London) ... 0.50
9/72 With "bridge", no facility for time 0.20
9/73 Modern usage on Post Office letters of handstamps with various
"administrative purposes" wordings (see **9/68**) 0.20

Period 2 - from 1979 (though period 1 handstamps remained in use until replaced) - this is distinguished by having the month in three letters, no full stop, year as four digits, and the date is on revolving wheels :

9/74 Modern datestamps used for packets, some with star at foot, in
seriffed/unseriffed characters and upper/lower case 0.10
9/75 As above with errors (eg "Fylde Wyre Lancs" with no Blackpool) 0.50
9/76 As above but small lettering used approx 1985-88 .... 0.25
9/77 As above but with narrow date, from approx 1992 .... 0.10
9/78 Modern usage on Post Office letters of handstamps with various
"administrative purposes" wordings (see **9/68**) 0.20

Exceptional types:

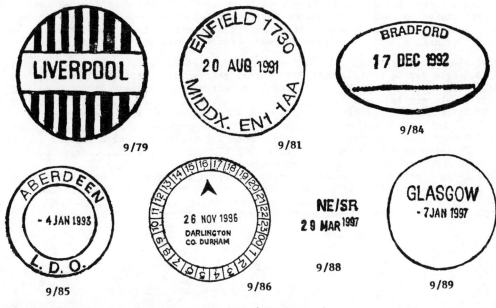

9/79

9/81

9/84

9/85

9/86

9/88

9/89

9/79 Large barred circle eg Liverpool, B.M.(Birmingham) 0.30
          (see similar in chapter 19)
9/80 Double oval eg Cheltenham 1977, others with star at each end 0.40
9/81 Time included in handstamp inscription eg Enfield and Croydon 0.20
9/82 "Label" parcel marks adapted, words "Parcel Post" removed etc 1.50
9/83 Single or double rim oval based on registered design 19/50 .... 0.50
9/84 Oval "rugby ball" at Bradford or double rim oval at Darlington 0.30
9/85 Double circle (rubber) at Aberdeen, 1993- 0.50
9/86 "24 hour" handstamp (rubber, diff sizes) at Southampton, Darlington . 0.50
9/87 Boxed handstamps eg Newmarket, "Tyneside" 0.40
9/88 Unframed NE/SR handstamp at Newcastle upon Tyne, 1996-97 .... 0.40
9/89 Circular handstamp with "Glasgow" in straight line, 1996- 0.40

Note: the "exceptional" items shown above serve to show the range of such handstamps used since about the 1960s: they do not represent an exhaustive list.

Rollers (included here since hand-applied rollers were also used for stamping soft packets, others not shown here were used on parcels; priced for large piece)

9/91

9/93

9/90 London IS between 8 bars, used on newspapers 1930s-1950s 2.50
9/91 Town between parallel double lines, 1950s/60s 0.50
9/92 Swansea trial, 1970-71 .... 2.00
9/93 Swindon trial (device of German manufacture), 1991-94 .... 1.50

Paid Handstamps (in red)

Note : can include value (from 1968 "1st" or "2nd" etc) or "Official Paid"; the latter existed to about 1985, whence Government Departments were required to pay for their own mail. Generally 20th Century Paid handstamps include "Great Britain" as country of origin since no adhesives used. From 1990 occasional use of black.

9/94	Single circle "Official Paid" (metal)(variations)	1.00
9/95	Single circle (metal) with PAID across centre, date at foot, 28mm ...	3.00
9/96	Single circle (metal) with large ½ at centre, PAID above	2.50
9/97	Double circle (metal)	0.50
9/98	Distinctive metal single circle with PAID and value, 32mm (from 1968 1st or 2nd instead of value, or "R" more unusual)	0.20
9/99	Rubber Blackwell Paid handstamps (month 3 characters, year 2 digits) .	0.20
9/100	Skeleton Paid handstamps (chiefly 1907-17)	15.00
9/101	Economy wartime undated rubber handstamps, 1940s	1.50
9/102	Large double circle handstamp with revolving date wheels, from 1980 (known as "lifebelt", year 4 digits, centre revolves to show 1st/2nd etc)	0.20
9/103	As above but used in black on normal mail	1.00
9/104	Modern exceptional types eg Bournemouth with "First Class" included .	0.50

9/94   9/95   9/96   9/97   9/98

9/99   9/100   9/101   9/102

Other types used for backstamping

9/105	Square backstamps in red or black	2.00
9/106	Foreign Office quartered handstamp (sim to **14/24**) with central N ...	10.00

9/105   9/106

Self Inking datestamps (SIDs) (from approx 1985 for various trials, operationally from 1989, counter datestamps generally applicable where computerisation of counter work ('ECCO') has taken place, followed by massive countrywide spread 1993-97, see also page 7)

9/107

9/107 SID datestamp 0.10

Dumb handstamps ("dumb" meaning they say little and have no date)

The first item is included here for convenience. The others are used for cancelling stamps that have been missed by a stamp cancelling machine; there are a series of these, and the most well known examples are shown here:

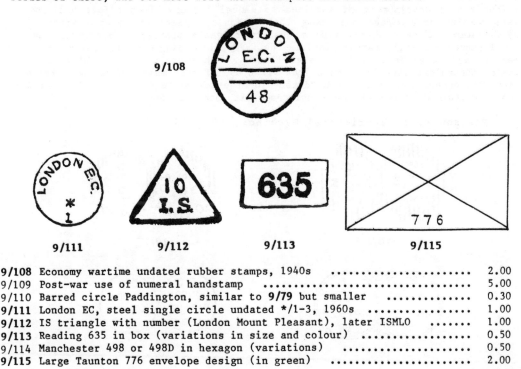

9/108 Economy wartime undated rubber stamps, 1940s 2.00
9/109 Post-war use of numeral handstamp 5.00
9/110 Barred circle Paddington, similar to **9/79** but smaller 0.30
9/111 London EC, steel single circle undated */1-3, 1960s 1.00
9/112 IS triangle with number (London Mount Pleasant), later ISMLO 1.00
9/113 Reading 635 in box (variations in size and colour) 0.50
9/114 Manchester 498 or 498D in hexagon (variations) 0.50
9/115 Large Taunton 776 envelope design (in green) 2.00

Charity appeal mailing handstamps

Some senders of large mailings had for some years preferred to affix stamps to their mailings, usually cancelled by machine (see 10/198 for a typical diamond postmark). In the 1990s there seemed to be an increase in these mailings and Royal Mail decided to permit senders of charity appeals and other large mailings to cancel, with approval, the stamps themselves. See 10/208 for a machine postmark so used. Below is a selection of postmarks believed to be handstamps though it is difficult to ascertain whether handstamp or machine. Numbers of these will continue to grow, no doubt, applied in a variety of designs and colours.

10. Machine Cancellations

Growing volumes of mail, along with the desire to get letters to their destination between one evening and the following morning, have been the driving forces behind development of machines to cancel letters. Much effort has gone into machine development over more than a hundred years, to enable speed of cancellation to be combined with a quality readable postmark. Experiments and developments are still taking place in the 1990s, including machines for stamping packets and large letters (or "large flats" as they are termed). Machines are listed chronologically in order of the first use of each make. In his book Peach (see Bibliography) uses the term "dater" for the town/date portion: we have used the term "town die" instead for consistency with other chapters.

Pearson Hill Experimental Machines, 1857-58

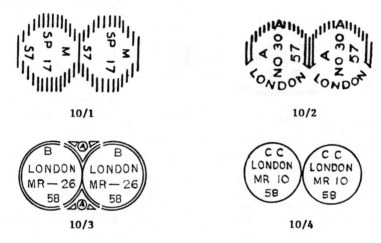

10/1   10/2

10/3   10/4

Note : it is difficult to put precise values on the higher priced items since normally sold only at auction or by private treaty. New information is always welcome.

		⊠	△	○
10/1	Without London, first machine, 1857	5000.00	*	100.00
10/2	With London, coded A or M, second machine 1857-8	450.00	100.00	20.00
10/3	Opera Glass type, prob 2nd machine modified, 1858	3000.00	300.00	75.00
10/4	as above but twin circle type, prob third machine	3000.00	600.00	100.00

Charles Rideout, from 1858

10/5   10/6

10/5	Machine Number 1, coded HS	....	50.00
10/6	Machine Number 2, coded CR	....	60.00

Pearson Hill, from 1858

| 10/7 | 10/8 |

10/7   Parallel Motion machines, London, nos 1-6, 87, 90-92, 97, 100-101   3.00
10/8   Parallel Motion machines, London District offices 3.00

      Note : Pivot machines, listed separately in the Fifth edition, are Parallel Motion machines fixed to special arms; their postmarks are identical.

Azemar, 1869-72 (or Fischer and Maas)

10/9

10/11

10/9   Town die lower at left, dates in 1869 (not used 1870) 150.00
        (bars in 3,4 or 5 sections, varying in sequence)
10/10   As above but town die level with bars, 1871-72 . . . .   75.00
10/11   Rectangular town die, lower at left, along with 89 in diamond
      (see illustration), used January 1871 only on postcards 400.00

Sloper, 1870-75

10/12 Stamped postcard perforated by single hole 25.00
       (doubts exist as to whether this single hole is made by a Sloper machine)
10/13   As above but series of holes in shape of arrow 30.00
10/14   As above but series of holes in shape of orb 200.00

Hoster, 1882-93

Note: care should be exercised in the use of the following summary of this complex topic. Inclusion of stars in the town die is not shown, and with two die heads in each machine, only one of each pair has an asterisk or star at the centre. These in turn should not be confused with side stars, and for simplicity some items with these stars are not shown. The term "mirrored" is used to show bars in the NE/SW direction as opposed to NW/SE, and is shown below as (M). (L) denotes corner bars to the left of town die at top and/or bottom.

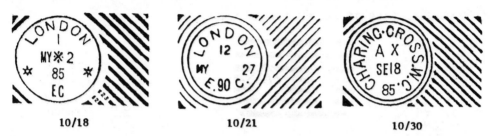

10/18   10/21   10/30

10/15 Single rim London-EC town die 20mm, 18 thick bars but none at left   *
10/16 Single rim London/EC town die 28-30mm, 14 bars but none at left   10.00
10/17   As above but (L) 10.00
10/18   Similar but with numbers in bars to bottom right of town die   12.00
10/19   As above but London/NPB, 14 bars 300.00
10/20 Single rim London/Offl Paid town die, no bars, red 150.00
10/21 Double rim London/E(year)C town die, 18 bars (M)(L) 30.00
10/22   As above but 12/14/15 bars, not (M) 12.00
10/23   Similar but 17 bars and numbers in LH bars 30.00
10/24 Double rim London/EC town die, year above EC, 14 bars (L) 15.00
10/25   As above but with stars and 12 bars 10.00
10/26 Double rim London town die, 12/15/16 bars (L) 10.00
10/27   As above but 16/18 bars (M) 20.00
10/28   As above but square dots for bars 400.00
10/29 Double rim London EC town die, no bars, used as backstamp, blk/red 10.00
10/30 Double rim Charing Cross town die, 17 bars 250.00
10/31 Double rim Bedford St town die, (M) or no bars 600.00

Ethridge, September 1886-April 1887

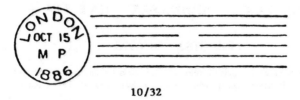

10/32

10/32 Single circle town die, six straight bars with central space ... 400.00

International, 1893-1933 (or Hey & Dolphin, or Flier)

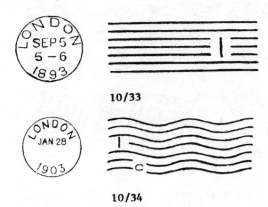

10/33

10/34

10/33	Single circle town die, seven straight bars with 1 (August-September 1893 trials)	250.00
10/34	Single circle town die, seven wavy bars with 1/C (1902-03 trials)	40.00
10/35	As above but Paid town die, without bars, red	50.00
10/36	As above but 1911 trials at London EC	75.00
10/37	As above but 1911-12 trials at Liverpool	100.00

10/38

10/42   10/44 (in red)

10/38	Single circle town die, five wavy bars	1.00
10/39	As above but seven wavy bars	2.00
10/40	Double circle town die, five wavy bars	0.50
10/41	As above but six straight bars	2.00
10/42	As above but seven wavy bars	1.00
10/43	Rectangular Paid die, in red without bars	1.50
10/44	As above but "Official Paid"	2.50

(for continuation see "Universal postmarks from 1933 - summary" on page 143)

Imperial Mail Marking, 1897

10/45

10/46

10/45   Victoria Flag: demonstration trial, June 1897 .... *
10/46   VR Flag: demonstration trial, September/November 1897 .... 500.00

Empire Machine, 1898

10/47

10/47   England Flag: used on four days in March 1898 .... 1000.00

Bickerdike, 1897-1907

10/48

10/53

10/48   V Crown R within bars, non-seriffed, year in full 350.00
10/49   As above but larger VR with serifs 350.00
10/50   As above but VR without serifs and numbers 1-6 beneath crown . 10.00
10/51   As above but year in two digits 10.00
10/52   As above but Liverpool, 1 or 2 beneath crown 40.00
10/53   E Crown R, year in two digits, numbers beneath crown 5.00
10/54   As above but Victoria crown 40.00
10/55   As above but year in full horizontally, no numbers 4.00
10/56   As above but year in full round rim, no numbers 5.00
10/57   As above but Liverpool, 1 or 2 beneath crown 35.00

Boston, 1898-1907

10/58	Trial machine, town die with star within 1898, bars with 1 and ending in zigzags, August-September 1898	350.00
10/59	Town die without star, year in full with dot after, 7 wavy bars	10.00
10/60	Town die with year in two digits, seven wavy bars	10.00
10/61	As above but four bars, numbered 1-6 in centre	5.00
10/62	As above but six bars shaped to town die, numbered 1-6	4.00
10/63	As above but six straight bars, numbered 1-6	4.00
10/64	Town die with year in full, no dot after, six bars, numbered 1-6	2.00
10/65	As above but four bars, numbered in centre	10.00
10/66	As above but six bars shaped to town die, numbered in centre	10.00
10/67	Liverpool town die, 7 wavy bars, inverted 3 in centre	30.00
10/68	As above but upright 4 in centre	25.00

Columbia (single impression machines), 1901-21

10/69	Single arc town die with seven straight bars	10.00
10/70	Single circle town die: London MP, EC, SE, SW, W or WC with seven straight bars	2.00
10/71	As above but with die number in centre of bars	2.50
10/72	As above but London District letters in bars	2.50
10/73	As above but with five wavy bars segmented into three sections, bars above and below and central 3	5.00
10/74	Single circle town die, coded at foot, seven straight bars	1.50
10/75	As above but London District initials in bars	2.00
10/76	As above but with six wavy bars segmented into three sections	3.00
10/77	Paid single circle town die, red, with seven straight bars	5.00
10/78	As above but London District initials in bars	7.50
10/79	As above but with segmented bars	15.00
10/80	As above but with six straight bars and die numbers at left between bars	10.00

10/75

10/76

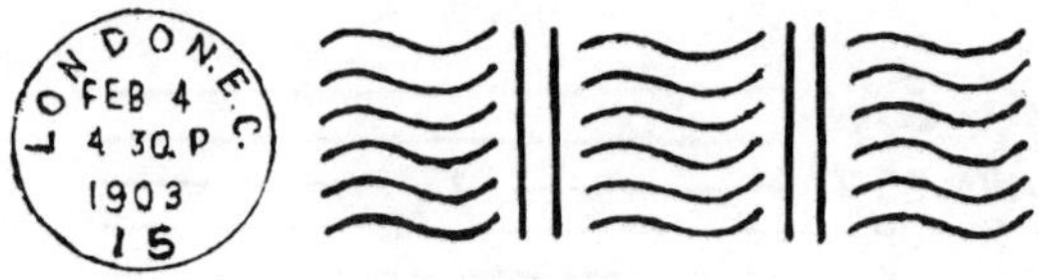

10/81	Three line town die, lines above and below, seven straight bars	2.00
10/82	As above but with six straight bars	5.00
10/83	As above but with six straight bars, and die number at left between central bars: London E (18), EC (2), NW (19 and 20), SE (15 and 19), SW (14), WC (16 and 19), W (17), Paddington W (19 and 21), Aberdeen (1), Birmingham (1), Bristol (1), Cardiff (1), Dublin (1), Edinburgh (1), Glasgow (1), Hull (1), Leeds (1), Liverpool (1 and 2), Manchester (1 and 2), Newcastle-on-Tyne (1), Nottingham (1) .	1.50
10/84	Three line town die without lines, seven straight bars	2.00
10/85	As above but 4 cuts in top 2 bars or 9 cuts in top 3, 1906–07 .	3.00
10/86	As above but with six straight bars	1.00
10/87	As above but with six straight bars segmented into three sections	5.00
10/88	As above but with six straight bars and die number at left between central bars from London and provinces, as listed above (10/83)	2.00
10/89	As above but with five wavy bars	1.00
10/90	As above but with six straight bars in three pairs	10.00
10/91	As above but with eight straight bars in four pairs	20.00
10/92	As above but with large London district letters in 5 wavy bars	3.00
10/93	As above but town die only, no bars, used as receiving mark ..	2.00

10/83

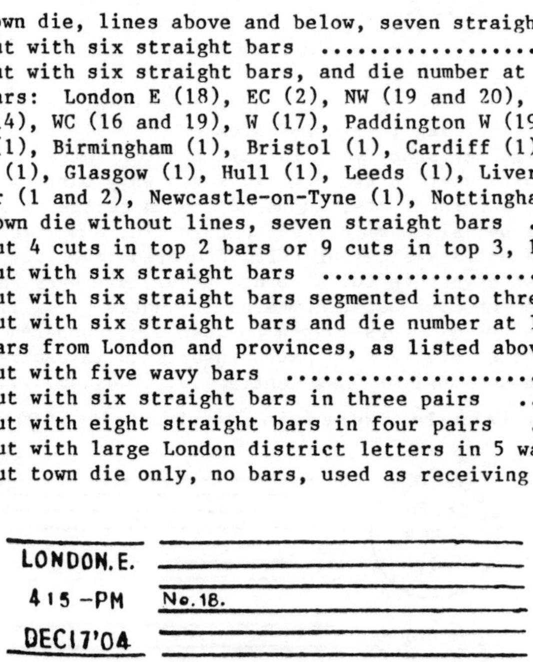

10/87

10/89

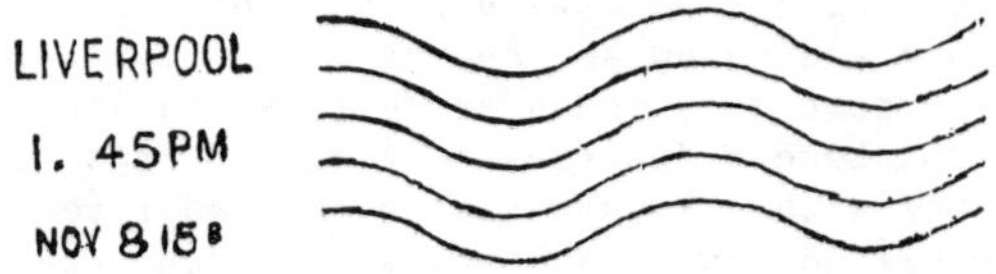

LONDON

10/90   MAR 7 10^A

6.   PM

10/94	Four line Paid town die, 6/7 straight bars or 5 wavy bars, red .	4.00
10/95	As above but Official Paid	4.00
10/96	As above with six bars in three pairs, in red	10.00
10/97	As above, six bars, die number at left between central bars .	8.00
10/98	As above but Paid town die only, no bars, in red	2.50
10/99	As above but Postage Paid town die only, no bars, in red	6.00
10/100	Posted in Advance for Xmas, Manchester, large X and six bars ...	100.00
	(see chapter 20 for details)	
10/101	Triangular die with telegraphic code (eg S.M., M.T.P.I.) with six, seven bars, or bars with central die numbers	5.00
10/102	Dulwich SE21, four-line town die, eight straight bars, 1920 ...	50.00

(for continuation see "Universal postmarks from 1933 - Summary" on page 143)

Krag (continuous impression machines), from 1905

10/103	Continental style town die with seven straight bars (1st trial) .	400.00
10/104	Single circle, London EC, with six straight bars, shaped ends ..	3.00
10/105	As above but Chelsea S.W.	3.00
10/106	As above but London F.S.	8.00
10/107	Three line town die, London W, six straight bars and central 3 .	2.50
10/108	As above but London E.C.	3.00
10/109	As above but six straight bars, London or Provincial	1.00
10/110	Three or four-line town die with five deep wavy bars	1.00
10/111	As above but five wavy bars with large London District in bars	4.00
10/112	As above but wartime dies of bars, crosses or +s, see chapter 14	
10/113	Three line Gt Britain town die with Paid & 6 straight bars, in red	2.00
10/114	As above but with five wavy bars, in red	1.00
10/115	As above but Official Paid with five wavy bars, in red	2.00
10/116	Triangular die with telegraphic code and six straight bars	3.00
10/117	Five shallow wavy bars, from 1950s, with 3 or 4-line town die ...	0.20
10/118	As above but Gt Britain town dies and Paid, red	0.20
	(with value, DP etc, sometimes different in the 2 boxes)	
10/119	As above, but Gt Britain die used in black on normal mail ..	2.00
10/120	As above but with triangular die, code no. or telegraphic code	2.00
10/121	As above but with errors, eg one "box" inverted, dates different	1.50

10/117

```
—————————        JEDBURGH         ————————        JEDBURGH
—————————      ROXBURGHSHIRE      ————————      ROXBURGHSHIRE
—————————        I.  30 PM        ————————        I.  30 PM
—————————        27 JAN 64        ————————        27 JAN 64
                     +
```

Sylbe, 1907-08

10/122 Three line London EC town die similar to Krag but with 9 above
       time, six straight bars 20.00

Columbia (continuous impression machines), 1909-11

Note : many dies were used on trial basis, not all are covered here

```
— LONDON    ———————————————    — LONDON    —
— — SEP 9 -09  —————————————    — — SEP 9 -09 — —
— — — 6——PM  ———————————————    — — 6——PM — —
```

10/123

10/123 Three line London town die with three straight bars 20.00
10/124   As above but with six bars arranged in three pairs 20.00
10/125   As above but Kensington W, with six evenly spaced straight bars 20.00
10/126   As above but Paid town die, three straight bars 20.00

Universal, from 1910

10/129

```
CROYDON
8·45PM
NOV 24
1914
```

10/133

```
MANCHESTER
9 PM
3 SEP
1919
L
```

10/127 London EC single circle, code H or C, seven wavy bars, 1910-11 .. 10.00
10/128   As above, other towns, without inner arc, approx 1912-15 .... 12.00
10/129 Croydon double arc, seven wavy bars, 1914-15, 1920 (5.00 for 1920) 2.50
10/130 Double circle town die, Stockport 1914-15 (Paid die 1917, 50.00) 10.00
10/131   As above but Margate, 1924-25 .... 2.00
10/132   As above Doncaster Yorks, 1926-28 .... 10.00
      (note : Peach shows as 7 wavy bars, but seen with 5 wavy bars)
10/133 Single circle town die with inner arc, and six or seven (or later
      five) continuous wavy bars, later county at foot (variations) . 0.30
10/134 Great Britain circular town die with "Paid" within circle, in red 1.50
10/135   As above but with square Paid die, in red 0.80
10/136   As above but Great Britain die used in black on normal mail . 2.00
10/137 Triangular die used for printed papers [undated but prices are 1.00
10/138 Census diamond die .... [for pre-1933 period ... 0.80

For continuation see "Universal-style postmarks from 1933 - Summary" on page 143

Time Mail Marking Machine Company, 1912-13

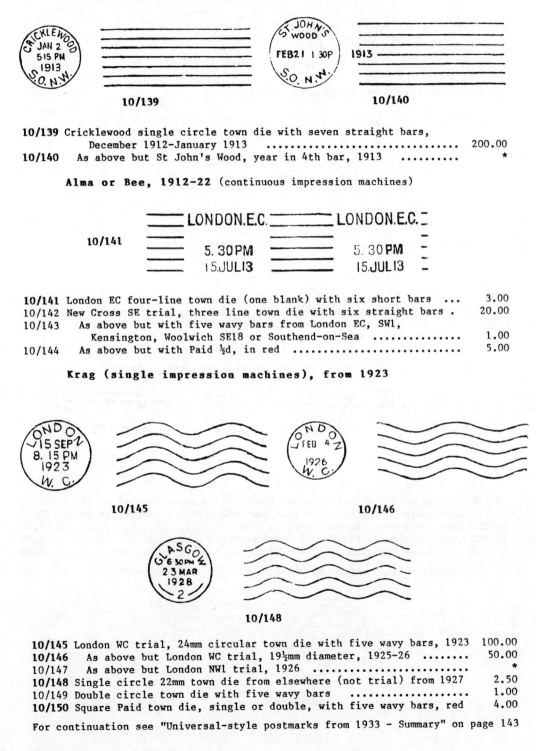

10/139   **10/140**

10/139 Cricklewood single circle town die with seven straight bars,
December 1912-January 1913 .... 200.00
10/140 As above but St John's Wood, year in 4th bar, 1913 .... *

Alma or Bee, 1912-22 (continuous impression machines)

10/141

10/141 London EC four-line town die (one blank) with six short bars ... 3.00
10/142 New Cross SE trial, three line town die with six straight bars . 20.00
10/143 As above but with five wavy bars from London EC, SW1,
Kensington, Woolwich SE18 or Southend-on-Sea 1.00
10/144 As above but with Paid ½d, in red 5.00

Krag (single impression machines), from 1923

10/145   **10/146**

10/148

10/145 London WC trial, 24mm circular town die with five wavy bars, 1923 100.00
10/146 As above but London WC trial, 19½mm diameter, 1925-26 .... 50.00
10/147 As above but London NW1 trial, 1926 .... *
10/148 Single circle 22mm town die from elsewhere (not trial) from 1927 2.50
10/149 Double circle town die with five wavy bars 1.00
10/150 Square Paid town die, single or double, with five wavy bars, red 4.00

For continuation see "Universal-style postmarks from 1933 - Summary" on page 143

10/150 (in red)

Klussendorf (or Standard), 1930-37

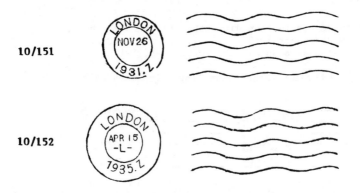

10/151

10/152

10/151 London double circle town die, code Z, five wavy bars, 1930-34 .   10.00
10/152   As above but larger town die, 1935-37 .... 25.00
        (wavy bars changed from those shown later in 1935)
10/153 Double square Paid town die, no bars (with wavy bars - rare), red   25.00

Totometer, 1957-90 (used for stamping magazines/wrappers)

10/155
(in red)

10/156
(in red)

10/154 Postage Paid die in 4 straight lines, lines above and below, red   10.00
10/155 Liverpool/Gt. Britain, circular town die struck sideways, in red   50.00
10/156 Large Paid oval, in red, used to 1980 ....   0.50
10/157   As above but with "Parcel Post" wording 5.00
10/158   As above, exceptional use 1987-90, in black from Bristol 1.00

Machines for stamping "large flats" and/or packets

10/165 (in pink)

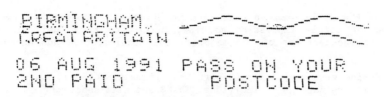

10/167 (in red)

```
10/159 Roddis "Mangle" from 1957, continuous impression similar to Krag
       (normally struck across centre of envelope), red  ............   0.30
10/160 Krag eg London E1,N1, Croydon in black on adhesives, 1980s-90s ..   0.30
10/161 Norwich trial 1959 (3 rows of wavy lines, one with town dies) ..   40.00
10/162 Manchester trial 1963  ........................................   10.00
10/163 Edinburgh trial 1989-90 (black or red), 2 rows of wavy lines  ..    3.00
10/164 Klussendorf, Liverpool (variations in date layout), 1991-92  ...    0.40
10/165   As above but London SE1 Paid, in "luminous pink", 1991-94  ...    0.40
10/166 Birmingham ink jet postmark with/without slogan, 1992-93, black     3.00
10/167   As above but Paid wording (variations), 1991-92, red .........    5.00
10/168 London SW "Please use Postcode" (variations) ink-jet imprint, 1991  5.00
       (this legend is applied at the foot of the envelope, not on stamp)
10/169 Ink jet messages at foot of large envelopes, black or red, 1993-    0.20
10/170 Oxford trial, August 1992 (used few days only)  ................   15.00
10/171 Perth trial, also used short period August 1992  ...............       *
```

Universal-style (unified) postmarks from 1933 — summary

10/172

10/173

10/179

10/183 (in red)

10/191

10/194 (in red)

Note : from 1933 the style of town dies used in Universal machines was adopted for other types of single impression machine, hence the term "unified dies" regardless of the manufacturer of the machine: the manufacturer thus cannot be identified.

10/172	Unified design with wavy lines (3-part wavy lines from 1936) ...	0.05
	(for details/valuations of individual TOWNS see next section)	
10/173	post-1950 use of continuous wavy lines (5 or 7 lines)	0.40
10/174	similar but 6 lines	0.60
10/175	As above but in red, 1990 only (3-part wavy lines)	0.20
10/176	As above but with slogan - see next chapter	0.05
10/177	with double circle town die (eg Bournemouth-Poole to c1950) .	0.50
10/178	with London missort die (usually on reverse of envelope)	0.20
10/179	early ALF dies 1957-62, eg Southampton S, London SE1 T4	0.50
10/180	FCT dies from 1976 with distinguishable codes, eg London EC S1	0.10
10/181	CFC dies from 1989 with distinguishable codes, eg Leicester CFC1	0.05
	(see glossary of terms at end of chapter 27)	
10/182	Square Paid die with continuous lines or 3-part wavy lines, in red	0.50
10/183	same but 1960 or later (values higher with slogans)	1.00
10/184	same but at Guildford, new die 1985-95	0.10
10/185	Circular Gt Brit die with 2d paid/1st paid etc in wavy lines, red	0.05
10/186	same but in black on paid mail from 1990 (eg Watford, Dover)	0.30
10/187	same but NOT Gt Britain die used on paid mail, red	0.05
10/188	same but Slough/Windsor SLO-9 with octagonal die, red, 1995 ..	0.20
10/189	Circ Gt Britain die in black on normal mail with slogan/wavy lines	0.10
10/190	similar but with continuous wavy lines	0.50
10/191	similar on charity mailings eg "R" or "Mailsort" on adhesives	0.50
10/192	same but "Paid" in town die, eg Hastings, 1963-, in red	0.50
10/193	Triangular die with wavy lines, to 1968 (used on printed papers)	0.50
10/194	similar but with "1d paid" etc in wavy lines, in red	1.00
10/195	Census diamond (to 1985 when general use ceased)	0.20
10/196	as above but red or with wavy lines, or narrow type, or other	
	varieties including triangle used instead of diamond	0.50
10/197	same (or triangle in its place) used post-1985	0.40
10/198	Diamond (same but not census!) on charity appeal mailings, 1990s-	0.30
10/199	Dated diamond, first used at Croydon in reserve machines Dec 1996	0.40
10/200	Errors of town die, year inverted, time/date errors etc	0.10
	(note: many of these are very common, but others such as "two	
	years" or "two times", possibly inverted as well, are less so)	
10/201	Errors of wavy lines, centre portion inverted etc	0.10
10/202	- transposed wavy lines (ie to left of town die)	0.25

10/199

10/200

10/202

10/207

```
10/203 Errors of "paid" section eg "2nd paid" in black on normal mail ..    1.00
10/204   pre-decimal "1d"/"2d" used post-1971 with d or d removed, red      0.80
10/205 Date removed (or year only shown) after postal strike July 1964      1.50
10/206 Any postal strike machine postmarks 20 January to 7 March 1971  .    1.00
10/207 Bradford "chess board" design, 1988-93 (used initially for "blacking
         out" incorrect meter postmarks, later for stamp cancelling)   .    0.30
```

Machine used by sender of bulk mailing, from 1993

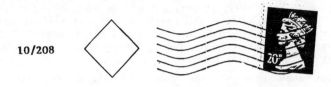

10/208

```
10/208 Diamond with distinctive wavy lines and small gaps, cf 10/198 ..    0.30
       (see note in chapter 9, high density ink jet machine on charity appeals with
       adhesives affixed, Royal Mail agreeing that senders cancel stamps themselves)
10/209 Other machine postmarks applied by senders  ....................    0.50
       (this is an "umbrella entry" covering a large "meter style" red postmark
       inscribed "Thames Valley" used 1996 and others that will no doubt appear!)
```

(numbers 10/210-220 reserved for future use)

Ink jet machines, from 1993

Note : postmarks are in two halves - misalignment of top/bottom does occur

10/221

10/224   10/225

```
10/221 Trials at Gloucester, Darlington etc, 1993-94   ................    2.00
10/222   As above but rectangular Paid die, Swindon, 1994, red   .......    2.50
10/223 London FS ink jet machine, Paid mail (variations), pink, 1995-  .    2.00
10/224 First use in IMP at Watford (5.00 for early dates Aug-Oct 1996) .    0.50
         (Aug-Oct 1996 postmark had no slogan, but imprint on reverse of env)
         (later due for use countrywide)
10/225   same machine but Q of S mark on reverse of meter mail etc, 1996    0.50
```

Note : other machines are listed in the chapters on Meter Marks, Slogan Postmarks (POSB Pitney Bowes machines), Islands (IOM Pitney Bowes machines), Special Event Postmarks ("Swiss Cancelling Machine" and others), and Aviation - Dickinson machine, and more examples of the above types are shown in chapter 14 (Maritime), 15 (Military), 17 (Islands), 21 (Parliamentary) etc.

NOTE : the next section is an A-Z listing of towns showing valuations of Krag and Universal-style dies 1933-96

Towns with Krag and Universal machines from 1933 to 1996

The list that follows is a priced guide to machine postmarks from 1933 (when unified dies started) to 1996. To conserve space it is in compact, heavily abbreviated form. Machines are of the Universal type unless (K) for Krag is shown. (U) denotes use of the Universal type, usually following (K). The following are not specifically indicated in the list :
(a) machine types ie ALFs, FCTs and CFCs, (b) MLO/APC/Royal Mail inscriptions
(c) GB dies used in black or in red on paid mail (including Krag machines used for paid mail, as late as the 1990s, at offices such as Wisbech and Worthing)
(d) old and new counties before/after the county changes of 1974 in England and Wales (in Scotland the old counties remained unchanged in postmarks).
However, use of generic descriptions is shown eg 'North Devon' at Barnstaple.
* denotes towns that no longer have machines.

The following codes show that at the relevant office ONLY the following categories of mail are stamped : (P) paid mail (in red)
 (L) local and/or missorted items; thus mail stamped at this office is not normally seen outside the local area, but MAY be used at Christmas.
 (M) missorted items (postmark usually on the reverse of the envelope)
 (R) restricted collections of outward mail, typically the first morning collection only, or first class mail only; (R)/(L) means (R) later (L)
 (X) mail in the pre-Christmas period

PLEASE – COLLECT MACHINE POSTMARKS COMPLETE WITH WAVY LINES NOT AS SHOWN HERE!

	1933-44	45-60	61-96
Abercarn (L) 94-			0.40
Aberdare (K) 27-33	2.00		
then (U) 35-	0.60	0.30	0.20
then 'Cardiff 10' (L) 89-			0.30
Aberdeen	0.30	0.15	0.05
*Aberdeen DO (M) 88-91			0.40
*Aberdeen Mastrick DO (M) 88-91			0.40
then (X) 94			0.30
*Aberdovey (K) 68-72			0.50
*Aberfeldy (K) 59-60		0.50	
then (U) later (R)-82			0.40
Abergavenny (K) 36-37	3.00		
then (U) later (R)	0.60	0.40	0.20
*Abergele 53-63, (R)-71		0.40	0.30
Abertillery (K) 46-		1.00	
then (U) 51- later (R)		0.40	0.30
Aberystwyth	0.40	0.20	0.10
but (K,X) 77 only			1.50
Abingdon (K) 36-37	2.50		
then (U) later (L)	0.50	0.20	0.20
Accrington -75	0.40	0.20	0.20
then 'Lancashire 15' (M) 89-			0.40
*Airdrie (K) 35-38	2.00		
then (U)-68	0.50	0.30	0.30
then 'Coatbr & Airdrie' (X) 82-85			0.40
Alcester (K) 61-71 then (U,R)/(L)			0.40
*Aldeburgh (K) 61-72			0.50
*Alderley Edge/Manch (K) 55 only	3.00		
then A Edge/Cheshire (K) 56-63	0.50	0.50	
then (U) later (L)-92			0.30
*Aldershot -92	0.40	0.20	0.10
(replaced by Farnborough)			
Aldershot PDO (M) 89-			0.30

	1933-44	45-60	61-96
*Aldridge ?60-?70			0.40
*Alexandria (K) 42-56		0.50	0.40
then (U) 57-?72 then (X)-86		0.30	0.40
(spelling 'Dumbartonshire' 57-59 1.00)			
*Alford 57-77		0.30	0.30
*Alfreton (K) 49-54		1.50	
then (U)-76		0.30	0.30
*Alloa (K) 32-48	1.00	1.00	
then (U)-68		0.30	0.30
Alnwick (K) 36-49	0.70	0.70	
then (U) later (R)/(L)		0.30	0.20
*Alresford (K) 49-57		0.70	
then (U)-768		0.30	0.30
Alton (K) 38-40	1.50		
then (U)-73 then (P,X)	0.40	0.20	0.20
but all mail again 88-92 then (L)			0.20
Altrincham -86	0.40	0.20	0.20
later (M)-90 then (X) 93-			0.40
*Alyth (K) 64-77			0.50
Ambleside (K) 32-60	1.00	0.40	
then (U)			0.20
then 'Lancs & S Lakes 17' (M) 93-			0.40
Amersham 'Chesham & Amersham'			
(K) 33-34	2.00		
then (U) later (L)	0.40	0.20	0.20
Amlwch (K) 62-77			0.40
then (U)			0.20
Ammanford 57- later (R)		0.40	0.20
Andover (K) 32-36	1.00		
then (U) later (L)	0.40	0.20	0.20
Annan (K) 53-58		0.50	
then (U) later (R)-93 then (L)	0.40	0.20	

	1933-44	45-60	61-96
*Anstruther (K) 64-75			0.40
Antrim (K,X) 68-69			5.00
then (U) later (R)/(L)			0.20
*Appleby (K) 60-70			0.40
Arbroath (K) 32-38	1.20		
then (U) later (R)/(L)	0.40	0.20	0.20
*Ardrossan 36-71	0.60	0.30	0.30
Armagh (K) 39-54	4.00	3.00	
then (U) 'Armagh Co Armagh'-56	4.00		
then 'Armagh' later (R)/(L)		0.30	0.20
Arundel (K) 40-55		1.50	0.50
then (U)-77 then again (L) 89-		0.20	0.30
Ascot (K) 29-38	1.00		
then (U) later (L)	0.40	0.30	0.20
*Ashbourne (K) 51-58		1.00	
then (U)-76		0.60	0.30
*Ashby-de-la-Zouch (K) 57-62		1.00	0.80
then (U)-75			0.30
Ashford Kent later (R)	0.40	0.20	0.10
and 'Tonbridge Y' (2nd class) 85-96			0.10
Ashington (K) 38-48	1.00	1.00	
then (U) later (R)/(L)		0.30	0.20
*Ashton-in-Makerfield (K) 59-80		0.80	0.30
*Ashton-u-Lyne later (R)-91	0.40	0.30	0.20
Atherstone (K) 47-59		0.60	
then (U)-70			0.30
then 'Nuneaton' (U,X) 74			0.50
then 'Atherstone' again (U,M) 91-			0.40
Atherton (K) 34-55	0.60	0.40	
then (U) later (R)/(L)		0.30	0.20
*Attleborough (K) 60-77			0.40
*Auchterarder (K) 57-71		0.40	0.40
*Audenshaw (K) 55-69		0.40	0.40
*Aviemore (K) 67-74			0.70
then (U)-86			0.40
*Avonmouth 57-88		0.40	0.30
*Axminster (K) 40-52	0.60	0.60	
then (U)-93		0.30	0.20
Aylesbury -94 then (M)	0.40	0.20	0.10
but 'no Bucks' error 69 & 91			2.50
and (K) in black 75 only GB die			1.50
*Aylsham (K) 62-86			0.40
Ayr -94 then (L)	0.30	0.10	0.10
Bacup (K) 36-37	2.00		
then (U) later (R)/(L)	1.00	0.30	0.30
Baillieston (K) 59-82		0.40	0.40
then (U,R)/(L)			0.30
*Bakewell (K) 50-63		0.40	0.40
then (U)-71			0.30
*Bala (K) 68-83			0.50
*Baldock (K) 58-63		0.40	0.40
then (U)-68			0.40
Balivanich (K) 77-83			0.50
then (U)			0.20
but 'Balavanich' spelling error 83&92			3.00
*Ballater (K) 67-78			0.40
Ballycastle (K) 59-			0.20
Ballymena (K)-48	4.00	3.00	
then (U)		0.40	0.10
Ballymoney (K) 54-57		6.00	
then (U) later (R)/(L)		0.80	0.20
Banbridge (K) 52-59		2.50	
then (U)-93 then (X) 94-			0.20
Banbury later (L)	0.40	0.20	0.20
Banchory (K) no county Dec 63			4.00
then (K) with county 63-78			0.50
then (U,X) 'Aberdeen' 90-92			0.50
then 'Banchory' (U,X) 94-			0.40
Banff (K) 58 only		2.50	
then (U)-76 then (X) 83-		0.40	0.30
Bangor Caern/Gwynedd	0.30	0.20	0.10
also 'Gwynedd N' on Sundays 90-			0.20
Bangor Co Down (K) -36	3.00		
then (U)-93 then (L)	1.00	0.20	0.20

	1933-44	45-60	61-96
*Banstead (K) 45-47		2.00	
then (U)-?61		0.60	0.60
*Bargoed (K) 46-53		2.00	
then (U) 56-75		1.00	0.30
Barking -59	0.40	0.30	
then again 70- later (L)		0.40	0.30
then 'Romford G31' (L) 88-			0.40
Barmouth (K) 37-58	0.40	0.30	
then (U) later (R)		0.30	0.30
*Barnard Castle 45-71		0.30	0.30
Barnet -94 then (L)	0.40	0.20	0.10
*Barnoldswick (K) 61-68			0.40
*Barnsley later (L)-?95	0.40	0.20	0.20
also 'Sheff' (X) 87-90&94			0.30
Barnstaple	0.40	0.20	0.20
then 'North Devon' 70-93 then (R)			0.10
Barrhead 55- later (L)		0.30	0.20
Barrow/Barrow-in-Furness			
-96 then (L)	0.50	0.20	0.10
Barry (K)-33	1.50		
then (U)-76	0.80	0.40	0.30
then 'Cardiff 1' (M) 88-			0.40
*Barry Empire Games Village 58		4.00	
*Barton on Humber (K) 60-66			0.80
Basildon 52-later (R)-94 then (L)		0.20	0.10
Basingstoke (K) 28-35	1.00		
then (U)-94 then (X)	0.60	0.30	0.10
Bath	0.30	0.10	0.05
then NO Avon 96-			0.05
*Bathgate 47-83 then (R)-86		0.40	0.20
then (X) 87-93			0.30
Batley -70 (at Dewsbury)	0.40	0.20	0.20
then 'Wakefield' (X)/(L)			0.20
Battle 53-66		0.30	0.30
then 'Hastings or Tonbridge'(X) 80-			0.30
Beaconsfield (K) 42-44	1.00		
then (U)	0.30	0.20	0.20
then 'High Wycombe' (R) 75-			0.20
then 'Beaconsfield' again (M) 91 only			0.80
then 'Hemel Hempstead' (M) 91-			0.30
Bearsden 54- later (L)		0.30	0.30
*Beauly (K,R) 65-78			0.50
*Beaumaris (K) 64-77, (U)-88			0.50
*Bebington 57-67		0.40	0.40
Beccles (K) 29-59	0.70	0.40	
then (U)-77, and (L) 85-			0.30
Beckenham (R)/(L)	0.40	0.30	0.20
*Bedale (K) 53-75		0.40	0.40
then (K, paid mail only)-83			0.80
Bedford -93 then (L)	0.40	0.20	0.10
*Bedlington Station (K) 58-64		5.00	5.00
then Bedlington (K)-76			0.50
Bedwas Gwent (M) 91-			3.00
then 'Bedwas Newport Gwent'(M) 92-			0.50
*Bedworth 'Nuneaton' (X) 74			0.50
then 'Bedworth' (M) 91-92			1.00
*Beeston (K) 33-38	1.50		
then (U)-76	0.40	0.20	0.20
then again (M) 87-91			0.40
*Beith (K) 64-75 then (K,X) -85			0.70
Belfast	0.40	0.10	0.05
but 'Belf N Ireland'36-40	10.00		
also (K) in reserve -55		5.00	
*Bellshill 51-56, (X) 60-68		0.70	0.50
*Belper (K) 39-62	0.70	0.40	0.40
then (U)-75			0.30
*Belvedere (K) 55-58		1.50	
then (U)-76			0.40
*Bembridge (K) 65-72			0.60
Benfleet 64- later (R)/(L)			0.20
Berkhamsted (K) 36-38	0.60		
then (U) later (M)	0.40	0.20	0.20
Berwick-on-Tweed (K) 28-37	1.50		
then (U) later (L)	0.80	0.20	0.20

	1933-44	45-60	61-96
*Bethesda (K) 64-68			1.00
*Bethlehem Xmas first days 67-76			1.00
*Betws-y-Coed (K) 63-73			0.60
also (U)(at Llanrwst) 66-84			0.40
*Beverley (K)-37	1.50		
then (U) later (R)-88	0.80	0.40	0.30
also (K) again 61-70			0.60
*Bewdley (K) 28-69	1.00	0.40	0.40
then (U,L)-76			0.50
*Bexhill-on-Sea -95	0.40	0.20	0.10
also 'Tonbridge'(X) 87-91 & 93			0.30
Bexleyheath (K) 33-34	1.50		
then (U)	0.50	0.30	0.20
then 'Dartford H' (R) 76-			0.20
Bicester (K) 46-56		0.70	
then (U)-77		0.30	0.20
then again (M) 91-			0.50
*Bideford (K) 36-39	1.50		
then (U)-93	0.40	0.20	0.20
*Biggar (K) 61-			0.30
then (K) 'ML12 Clyde Valley'			
87-93 then (M)-96			0.30
*Biggleswade (K) 39-61	1.00	0.60	0.60
then (U) later (R)-85			0.30
Billericay (K) 53-59		1.00	
then (U)-66		0.40	0.40
then 'Basild'/'Chelmsfd'(U,X) 74-84			0.30
then 'Billericay' (M) 90-			0.50
*Billingham (K) 46-51		2.00	
then (U) 54-69		0.60	0.40
*Billingshurst (K) 61-68			0.60
Bilston -70	0.60	0.40	0.30
then again (M) 92-			0.50
*Bingham (K) 69-77			0.60
*Bingley (K) 37-46	0.80	0.80	
then (U) later (R)-93		0.40	0.20
but (K) used Feb 74 only			2.50
*Birkenhead later (L)-?89	0.40	0.20	0.20
then (X) 96			0.40
Birmingham	0.20	0.10	0.05
('Birmingnam' spelling errors			0.50)
AM (Aston)-37 then 'ADO'-?84 then see +			
CH (Camp Hill)-?76 then see +			

	1933-44	45-60	61-96
Birmingham contd.			
Quinton DO (K) 39-55	1.50	0.40	
then (U)-?65 then +		0.30	0.30
Rednal (K) 58-72 then +		0.40	0.30
Selly Oak (K) 30-36	1.50		
then (U)-69 then +	0.60	0.20	0.20
Shirley (K) 47-55 then +	0.80		
*Yardley 45-?65		0.30	0.30

NOTES (1) Beware of December dates. Dies from above offices used at temp Birmingham offices at Xmas in 1960s-80s eg Acocks Green Dec 1974 +(2) all the following have machines in use (some were new, some were re-uses) 87- (++ initially Solihull/Warley dies) (U,M) (valuation 0.40):

ADO, CH, ED, WDO,	
Castle Bromwich	Kitts Green DO
Chelmsley Wood	++Knowle
Coleshill	Moseley DO
++Cradley Heath	Northfield
Erdington	++Oldbury
Great Barr	Quinton DO
Hall Green	*Rednal -?92
Handsworth	++Rowley Regis
++Henley-in-Arden	Selly Oak
Hockley (not Birm H)	Sheldon
Kings Norton	++Shirley

	1933-44	45-60	61-96
Bishop Auckland (K) 29-37	1.50		
then (U)	0.60	0.30	0.30
then 'SW Co Durham' 70- later (L)			0.40
but 'Darlington' (X) 83 only			0.40
Bishopbriggs 65- later (L)			0.30
Bishops Stortford (K)-37	1.50		
then (U) later (R)-94/(L)	0.60	0.20	0.20
Blackburn -75	0.40	0.20	0.20
also 'Blackb & Accrington' 61-			0.10
then 'B'burn & NE Lancs' 73-			0.30
then 'Lancashire 33' (L) 75-			0.30
Blackpool	0.40	0.20	0.10
then 'Fylde Coast' (variations) 66-			0.30
and (K) 'Fylde Coast' 67-68			2.50

Postmark illustrations:
BILSTON / 1 SEP / 1992 / W.MIDS.
BIRMINGHAM / 7-PM / 16 MAY / 1972 / C.H.
GREAT BARR D.O. / BIRMINGHAM 22 / 9 15 AM / 25 SEP 58
CHELMSLEY WOOD / 11 DEC / 1989 / BIRMINGHAM
CRADLEY-HEATH / 2 JAN / W.MIDS.
BLACKBURN / 22 NOV / 1973 / LANCS.
FYLDE COAST (B'POOL) / 13 DEC / 1966 / LANCS.

Blackpool

	1933-44	45-60	61-96
Birmingham contd			
ED (East)-?86 then see +			
WDO (West)-?86 then see +			
H (Hockley)-?84 (H later used at HO) then +			
- all	0.50	0.20	0.20
*Acocks Green (K) 32-37	1.50		
then (U)-?74	0.40	0.20	0.30
*Blackheath (K) 39-61	1.00	0.50	0.30
then (U)-67			0.30
Erdington (K) 26-34	1.00		
then (U)-?86 then +	0.40	0.20	0.20
Great Barr (K) 55-58		0.80	
then (U)-?65 then +		0.30	0.30
Hall Green (K) 37-58	1.00	0.60	
then (U)-65 then +		0.40	0.30
Handsworth ?39-80 then +	0.40	0.30	0.30
Kings Norton -?65 then +		0.30	0.30
Kitts Green -?65 then +		0.30	0.40
Moseley (K) 29-37	1.00		
then (U) 'DO' -?86 then +		0.20	0.10
Northfield (K) 52-64		0.40	0.40
then (U)-?65 then +			0.30
Oldbury (K) 36-37	2.00		
then (U)-67 then +	0.60	0.30	0.20

	1933-44	45-60	61-96
then (U) 'Fylde B'pool Wyre' 75-95			0.10
then (L), & 'Blackpool' (X) 95-			0.30
Blackwood (K) 53 only		3.50	
then (U) 55- later (R)		0.40	0.30
*Blaenau Ffestiniog (K) 57-59		3.00	
then (U) 60-88		0.30	0.30
*Blairgowrie (K) 56-59		2.00	
then (U) 60-77		0.30	0.30
then 'Perth' (X) 83 only			0.30
*Blandford (K) 37-41	3.50		
then (U)-53	0.40	0.40	
then Blandford Forum later (R)-87		0.30	0.30
Blantyre (K) 55-58		1.50	
(U) 59- later (L)		0.60	0.30
Blaydon-on-Tyne (K) 48-58		1.50	
then (U)-70		0.60	0.30
then Blaydon (X) 73-81, (M) 87-			0.40
*Bletchley 52-73 (then MK)		0.30	0.20
*Blundellsands 53-58		0.70	
Blyth (K) 26-40	1.00		
then (U)-76 then (X)-85		0.30	0.30
then again (M) 88-			0.40
Bodmin (K) 36-39	1.50		
then (U)-92 then (X) 92-	0.60	0.30	0.10
but 'Cornwall 4' Sundays 90-92			0.30

BROADBOTTOM
HYDE CHESHIRE

BROXBURN
WEST LOTHIAN
7 ——PM

21 DEC 63   4 DEC 62

Bolton   Brighton   Brighton

	1933-44	45-60	61-96
Bognor Regis later (L)	0.40	0.20	0.10
Bolton	0.40	0.20	0.10
then 'Bolton & Bury' 74-			0.10
then 'Bury Bolton Wigan' 81-			0.05
but 'Bolton Lancs' Sundays 90-			0.10
*Bo'ness (K) 57 only		3.00	
(U) 59- later (R)-83, (X)-93		0.50	0.30
Bonnyrigg (K) 69- later (R) then (M)			0.40
also (U,X) 'Edinburgh' 81&85			0.40
*Bootle/Liv then Lancs -76	2.00	0.50	0.30
then 'Bootle/Merseyside' 76 only			2.50
then 'GSO Bootle' (M) 86-90			0.50
*Bordon (K) 51-58		1.00	
then (U)-73 then (X)-75			0.20
then again (L,X) 89-91			0.30
*Borehamwood ?46-76	1.50	0.30	0.30
then again (M) 87-?94			0.40
Boston	1.00	0.30	0.10
and (K)(?in reserve) -63		1.50	1.50
*Boston Spa (K) 60-69		0.60	0.60
Bourne (K) 51-63		0.50	0.50
then (U) later (R)			0.20
Bournemouth (K)-?32 or 33	2.00		
then 'Bournemouth-Poole'(K)	3.00	33 only	
then (U)		0.30	0.20	0.05
but 'Bournemouth Dist' Sundays 90-94			0.30
also 'Royal Mail B'th' July 91 only			1.50
then 'Dorset & SW Hants' 94-			0.05
*Bourton-on-Water (K) 68-92			0.40
*Bovington Camp (K) 49-50		10.00	
*Brackley later (L)-89		0.30	0.30
Bracknell (K) 40-54	1.00	0.50	
then (U) later (R)/(L)		0.30	0.20
Bradford	0.30	0.10	0.05
('Yorkshibe' spelling error 65			0.50)
Bradford-on-Avon (K) 53-59		1.00	
then (U)-85 then (L)		0.30	0.30
Braintree 38-93 then (L)	0.50	0.20	0.20
and 'Chelmsford' (X) 85 only			0.30
*Bramhall 'Stockport Z' (R) 86-88			0.40
*Brampton (K) 68-78			0.80
*Brandon (K) 61-78			0.40
*Braunton (K) 67-71			1.00
Brechin 50- later (R)/(L)		0.40	0.30
Brecon (K) 37-43	2.50		
then (U)		0.30	0.10
*Bredbury 'Stockport W' (R) 86-94			0.30
*Brentford (U) 36 seen	2.50		
Brentwood (K) 27-34	2.50		
then (U)-93 then (L)	0.60	0.20	0.10
and 'Chelmsford' (X) 85 only			0.30
*Bridge "First day" 29.4.68 only			2.00
*Bridge of Allan (K) 64-68			0.80
Bridgend 34-?85	0.60	0.30	0.20
then 'Cardiff 15' (M,P) 90-			0.40
Bridgnorth (K) 40-41	2.50		
then (U)-?70		0.40	0.20
then again (M) 88-			0.40
Bridgwater	0.40	0.20	0.10
*Bridlington later (M)-87	0.40	0.20	0.20
*Bridport (K) 36-38	1.50		
then (U)-87	0.40	0.30	0.20
*Brierley Hill (K) 49-58		0.60	
then (U)-?79		0.30	0.30
*Brigg ?50s-66		0.40	0.40
also (K) 62 only			2.00
*Brighouse -67	0.60	0.40	0.30

	1933-44	45-60	61-96
Brightlingsea (K) 63-74			0.60
'Brightlingsea.Colchester' -75			2.00
then (U) later (R)/(L)			0.40
Brighton 'Brighton & Hove'	0.20	0.10	0.05
then 'Sussex Coast' 78-			0.05
but 'South Coast' error 89			6.00
Bristol	0.20	0.10	0.05
*Bristol NDO 45-71		0.50	0.20
*Brixham (K) 37-46	1.00	1.00	
then (U)-70		0.30	0.30
then 'S Devon' (X) ?73-83			0.30
*Broadbottom (K) 62-71			1.00
*Broadstairs	0.40	0.30	0.30
then 'Thanet C' 71-72			0.60
*Broadway (K) 59-66		0.70	0.70
*Brockenhurst (K) 57-60		1.00	
then (U)-69			0.30
Brodick (K) 54-74		0.50	0.30
then (U) later (L)			0.20
'Kilmarnock' on Sats only 83-89			0.60
Bromley 'Brom & Beckenham'	0.40	0.20	0.10
then 'Bromley' 70- later (R)/(L)			0.10
Bromsgrove (K) 34-37	2.00		
then (U) later (M)		0.30	0.20
*Bromyard (K) 62-72			0.80
*Broughty Ferry (K) 42-72		0.40	0.40
*Brownhills (K) 61-63			3.00
then (U)-68			1.00
*Broxburn (K) 58-65		0.40	0.40
then (U)-75 later (X)-93			0.30
*Brynmawr 57-71		0.80	0.40
Buckie (K) 50-59		0.60	
then (U) later (X)		0.30	0.30
Buckingham (K) 40-58	1.50	1.50	0.80
then (U) later (R)		0.30	0.20
Bude (K) 36 only	3.00		
then (U)-92, (X) 94-	0.80	0.30	0.20
*Budleigh Salterton (K) 50-58		0.70	
then (U)-70		0.30	0.30
then 'Exeter Dist' (U,X) 75-92			0.30
Builth Wells (K) 61-74			0.50
then (U) 74-			0.10
(Breconshire short-lived 74-75			0.80)
*Bulford Barracks (U) 45 only	10.00		
then (K) 51-70		1.50	1.50
*Bungay (K) 50-62		0.60	0.50
then (U)-77			0.30
*Buntingford (K) 63-71			0.50
Burgess Hill (K) 49-53		1.00	
then (U) later (M)		0.30	0.20
*Burnham-on-Sea 52-67		0.50	0.40
then 'Bridgwater' (X) 95-96			0.40
Burnley & Nelson (K) 38-42	2.50		
then (U)		0.50	0.20	0.10
then 'Burnley' 67-			0.10
then 'Burnley & Pendle'76-93 then (M)			0.10
Burntisland (K) 59-76			0.40
then (U,L) 95-			0.50
Burslem (U) later (R)	0.80	0.30	0.20
but (K) 63-64			1.00
Burton-on-Trent-86 then (L)	0.40	0.20	0.20
Bury	0.40	0.20	0.20
then 'Bolton & Bury' (R) 74-			0.30
then 'Bury Bolton Wigan' (M) 81-			0.40
Bury St Edmunds-93 then (L)	0.40	0.20	0.20
*Buxton (K) 15-34	0.40		
then (U) later (R)-93	0.30	0.20	0.20

	1933-44	45-60	61-96
*Cadishead (K) 56-65		0.80	0.50
Caernarvon (K) 34-35	4.00		
- Caernarvon/fon (U) 36-	0.80	0.20	0.10
also 'Gwynedd S' Sundays 90-			0.20
Caerphilly (K) 37 only	4.00		
then (U) 45-76		0.30	0.30
then 'Cardiff 16' (L) 89-			0.40
Caldicot (M) 89-			0.50
*Callander (K) 59-61		2.00	2.00
then (U) 62-76			0.40
*Calne (K) 40-49		1.50	
then (U) later (L)-93		0.30	0.30
Camberley (K) 26-33	2.50		
then (U)-76 then (M) 89-	0.60	0.30	0.30
Camborne see Redruth			
Cambridge	0.30	0.10	0.05
Cambuslang (K) 50-53		2.50	
then (U)-86 then (L)		0.30	0.20
*Camelford 87-?92 (R)			0.40
Campbeltown (K) 45-49		2.00	
then (U)-93 then (L)		0.20	0.20
Cannock (K) 39-46	2.00		
then (U)-67		0.30	0.30
then 'Walsall' (X) 79-84			0.30
then 'Cannock' (R)/(L) 87-			0.20
Canterbury	0.30	0.10	0.05
Canvey Island 59- later (L)			0.20
Cardiff	0.30	0.10	0.05
then 'Cardiff Newport' 93-			0.05
Cardiff districts *E,*N,W (M) shown			
as 'Cardiff 4,5,6' 88- (E&N 88 only)			0.40
Cardigan (K) 43-58		0.60	
then (U)-94 then (L)		0.20	0.20
Carlisle	0.30	0.10	0.05
then 'Cumbria Dumfries & Galloway' 93-			0.05
*Carluke (K) 55-58		1.50	
then (U)-68 then (X)-75		0.30	0.30
Carmarthen (K) 28-35	2.00		
then (U)-94 then (L)	0.60	0.20	0.20
Carnforth (K) 51-60		0.60	
then (U) later (R)			0.20
then 'Lancs & S Lakes 15' (M) 93-			0.40
*Carnoustie (K) 54-63		0.60	0.50
then (U)-84			0.30
*Carrickfergus (K) 58-61		3.50	3.50
then (U) later (R)-86			0.30
*Castlederg (K) 68- later (R)-94			0.40
Castle Douglas (K) 49-55		2.50	
then (U) later (R)/(L)		0.30	0.20
*Castleford (K) 28-38	2.00		
then (U)-69	0.60	0.30	0.20
then 'Wakefield' (X) 70-84			0.30
*Caterham (K) 35-39	2.00		
then (U)-70	0.60	0.30	0.20
*Catterick Camp 40-64		2.50	1.50
Chard ?54- later (M)		0.30	0.20
also 'Taunton' (X) 94 only			0.40
*Chatham 'Rochester & Chat'	0.30	0.20	0.10
then 'Medway' 70- later (R)-95			0.10
*Chatteris (K) 60-65			0.40
then (U)-89			0.30
*Cheadle Cheshire (R)-?92	0.80	0.30	0.30
then (X) 96 only			0.30
Cheadle Stoke on Trent (K) 57-63		0.60	0.60
then (U) later (R)/(L)			0.20
Chelmsford	0.30	0.10	0.05
Cheltenham (U)-93 then (L)	0.30	0.10	0.05
also (K) seen 49 & 53 only		2.50	
and 'Gloucestershire' (X) 94-			0.20
Chepstow (K) 36-48	2.50	1.00	
then (U) 51- later (L)-72		0.30	0.30
then again (L) 81-			0.40
*Chertsey (K) ?41-48	2.00	2.00	
then (U)-?61		0.50	0.50

	1933-44	45-60	61-96
Chesham (L) 90- (see also Amersham)			0.40
Chester	0.30	0.10	0.05
also 'Clwyd 1' 72-82			0.10
(used for postings in Deeside area)			
then 'Chester Clwyd Gwynedd' 82-			0.10
then ditto with Gwynedd erased			0.20
also 'Chester/Clwyd 1' 87-			0.10
then 'Chester & Clwyd/-1-' 88-			0.05
*Chesterfield			
later (R)/(L)-93,(X) 96	0.40	0.20	0.20
Chester le Street (K) 33-50	0.60	0.60	
then (U)-?69, 83 and (M) 92-		0.30	0.30
also 'Durham' (X) 81-87			0.40
*Chichester later (M)-96	0.30	0.20	0.20
Chippenham (K) 32-37	2.50		
then (U) later (R)/(L)		0.20	0.20
*Chipping Campden (K) 62-65			1.50
*Chipping Norton (K,L) 60-71			1.00
*Chipping Sodbury P (K) 62-63			1.50
then 'PDO' (U)-72 (then Yate)			0.60
Chislehurst (K) 48-81		0.50	0.20
then (U,R)			0.20
Chorley	0.60	0.30	0.20
then 'Lancashire 40' 75- (R)/(M)			0.30
then 'Chorley Lancs 40' (M) 94-			0.40
Chorlton-c-Hardy (K) 32-34	3.00		
then (U) later (R)/(L)	0.80	0.30	0.20
*Christchurch (K) 30-48	2.50	0.40	
then (U)-71		0.30	0.20
then 'Christchurch Dorset' first day			
posting 77 (stamped at Bournemouth)			0.50
Church Stretton (K) 61-64			0.50
then (U,R)			1.00
			0.30
*Cinderford (K) 52-55			0.60
then (U)-68		0.50	0.40
*Cirencester (K) 37-38	3.00		
then (U)-?72	0.80	0.30	0.20
then 'Gloucestershire' (L) 89-?92			0.50
Clacton-on-Sea later (R)	0.40	0.20	0.20
Clarkston (K) 60-79			0.40
then (U,X) 'Glasgow' 77			0.40
then (U,X) 'Clarkston PSO' 78			0.40
then PSO (U,R) 79-86 then (L)			0.30
*Cleator Moor (K) 70-91			0.40
*Cleckheaton (K) 26-36	1.00		
then (U)-77		0.30	0.20
then 'Wakefield' (X)-80s			0.30
*Cleethorpes (K) 28-48	0.60	0.60	
then (U)-64		0.30	0.30
*Clevedon (K) 39-49	1.00	0.50	
then (U)-78		0.30	0.30
Clitheroe (K) 34-50	1.00		
then (U)-75		0.30	0.30
then (U,M) 'Lancs 16' 89-			0.50
Clydebank (K) 31-37	2.00		
then (U)-86 then (L)	0.60	0.30	0.20
*Coalville to (K) 41-57		1.00	
then on breakdown 70 only			3.00
and (U)-76		0.30	0.20
then 'Leicester' (X) 94-95			0.40
*Coatbridge -68	0.30	0.20	0.20
then 'Coatbridge & Airdrie' -86			0.10
*Cockermouth (K) 53-59		1.50	
then (U) later (R)-91		0.30	0.30
Colchester	0.30	0.10	0.05
*Coldstream (K) 64-75			0.80
*Coleford (K) 53-58		2.00	
then (U)-70		0.40	0.40
Coleraine (K) 37-48	4.00	4.00	
then (U) later (R)		0.30	0.10
*Coleshill (K) 60-63			0.50
then (U)-?78			0.30

	1933-44	45-60	61-96
Colne -76		0.30	0.30
then 'Burnley & Pendle' (X) 81-		/(L)	0.30
Colwyn Bay	0.30	0.10	0.05
(see also Llandudno)			
*Congleton (K) 37-42	2.00		
then (U)-75 (at Macclesfield)		0.30	0.30
then (X) 95 only			0.40
*Consett (K) 46-47		3.00	
then (U)-?83 then (M)-93		0.30	0.30
*Conway (K) 54-60		1.50	
then (U) Conway -72			0.40
then (U) Conwy -?85 then (M)-92			0.30
Cookstown (K) 51-60		2.50	
then (U) later (R)			0.20
Corby Kettering (K) 45-48		3.00	
then (K) NO Kettering 48-52		3.00	
then (U) later (M)		0.30	0.20
*Corsham -69		0.60	0.40
then 'Chippenham' (X) 83-84			0.40
Corwen (K) 60-63			2.50
then (U)-83 then (P,X) later (L)			0.30
Cosham ?52- later (R)/(L)		0.30	0.20
*Cottingham (K) 62-76			0.60
(N Humberside 75-76 only			1.50)
*Coulsdon (K) 24-48	0.80	0.60	
then (U)-?71		0.30	0.30
*Coupar Angus in red with 'Paid' 66-70		4.00	
Coventry	0.30	0.10	0.05
then 'Coventry & Warwickshire' 80-			0.05
*Cowbridge (K) 62-72			0.70
Cowdenbeath (K) 54-57		1.50	
then (U) later (R)/(L)		0.30	0.20

	1933-44	45-60	61-96
*Crook (K) 53 only		3.00	
then (U)-?70		0.40	0.40
*Crosby (U) 59-?70		0.30	0.30
also Crosby 21 and 23 ?58-65		0.30	0.30
*Crosby 22 (K) 64-66			2.50
*Cross Keys (K) 50-51		3.50	
then (U) 57- later (L)-94			0.40
Crowborough (K) 36-55	1.00	0.60	
then (U)-?72		0.20	0.30
then 'T Wells/Tonbridge' (X) 80-91			0.30
and 'Crowborough' again (M) 90-			0.50
Croydon	0.30	0.10	0.05
then 'Croydon/Sutton' 89-			0.05
(but Croydon & Croydon Surrey also)			
and 'SE Div 2' Sundays only 95-			0.10
*Cullompton (K) 57-66		1.00	0.80
then (U)-?70			0.80
Cumbernauld (K) 64-67			0.60
then (U)-86 then (L)			0.30
*Cumnock (K) 50-55		1.00	
then (U) 58-71		0.60	0.40
Cupar (K) 36-37	4.00		
then (U)-76	0.60	0.30	0.30
then 'Kirkcaldy' (X) 81-83			0.30
then 'Cupar' again (R) 87- later (L)			0.30
Cwmbran ?57- later (R)/(L)		0.50	0.20
Dagenham -59	0.40	0.30	
then 'Romford A' later (M) 70-			0.30
*Dalbeattie (K) 61-74			0.60
Dalkeith (K) 50-56		1.00	
then (U) later (R)/(L)		0.20	0.20

	1933-44	45-60	61-96
*Cowes (K) 34-37	3.00		
then (U)-77		0.20	0.20
*Cradley Heath (K) 35-48	1.00		
then (U)-67		0.30	0.30
then see Birmingham entry			
*Cranbrook (K) 53-58		1.50	
then (U)-76		0.30	0.30
then 'T Wells/Tonbridge'(X) 80-91			0.40
Cranleigh (K) 42-58	1.50	1.00	
then (U)-75		0.30	0.30
then 'Guildford' (X) 80-86 then (R)			0.40
then 'Cranleigh' again (R)/(L) 91-			0.30
*Craven Arms (K) 56-60		2.00	
then (U) later (L)-87			0.40
Crawley (K) 33 only	4.00		
then (U) later (M)	0.30	0.20	0.20
*Crediton (K) 49 only		5.00	
then (U)-77		0.30	0.20
then 'Exeter District' (X) ?80-92			0.30
Crewe then 'Cheshire' 83-	0.30	0.20	0.05
but 'Crewe' (M,X) 88-?91			0.30
Crewkerne (K) 51-58		1.50	
then (U) later (P)-86		0.40	0.30
then 'Taunton' (U,X) 94-			0.30
*Criccieth (K) 60-77			0.60
then (U)-87			0.40
*Crickhowell 67-72			1.00
*Crieff (K) 37-38	3.00		
then (U)-83 then (X)-84		0.40	0.20
*Cromer (K) 32-41	0.60		
then (K) 43-50	0.50	0.50	
then (U)-76		0.30	0.30

	1933-44	45-60	61-96
*Dalmuir (K) 59-67		1.50	1.00
then (U,X) 62-65,71			0.60
*Dalry (K) 64-75 then (X)-81			0.80
Darlington (U)	0.30	0.10	0.05
also (K) 48-51		0.50	
then (K) again (X) 55		1.50	
Dartford	0.30	0.10	0.05
*Dartmouth (K) 36-55	0.80	0.80	
then (U)-70		0.30	0.30
then 'S Devon' (X) 74-83			0.30
Darwen -75 (gap 64-65)	0.60	0.30	0.30
then 'Lancashire 17' (M) 89-			0.40
Daventry (K) 62 only			2.50
then (U) later (R)/(L)			0.20
*Dawley (U) 68 only			6.00
*Dawlish (K) 49-56		2.00	
then (U)-70		0.40	0.30
then 'Ex Distr' (X) 75- then (R)-93			0.30
Deal -76	0.60	0.40	0.30
then 'Dover' (X) later (L)			0.30
*Deeside (M) 88-92			0.60
*Denbigh (K) 44-52		2.00	
then (U) 53-71		0.30	0.30
*Denny 59-68		0.80	0.80
Denton (K) 36-38	3.00		
then (U) later (R)/(L)		0.20	0.20
Derby (K) 13-37	0.40		
then (U)	0.30	0.10	0.05
also 'R Mail Midlands' Sundays 93-			0.10
Dereham (K) 39-47	1.50		
then (U)-77		0.20	0.20
then again 83- (L)			0.40

	1933-44	45-60	61-96
Derwentside (M) 93-			0.40
*Desborough (K) 70-71			3.00
Devizes (K) 36-46	0.60	0.60	
then (U) later (L)		0.30	0.20
Dewsbury -70	0.40	0.30	
then 'Wakefield' (X)			0.30
*Didcot -78	0.50	0.30	0.30
*Didsbury (U) 36 only seen	3.00		
Dingwall (K) 50-53		2.00	
then (U) ?56- later (R)/(L)		0.30	0.20
Diss (K) 48-52		2.50	
then (U)-94 then (L)		0.20	0.20
Dolgelley (K) 52-58		3.00	
then (U) 58 only		4.00	
then Dolgellau 58-later (R)/(L)		0.40	0.20
Doncaster	0.30	0.10	0.05
also various DN-LN inscriptions 94-			0.05
and (K) 61 only			2.50
Dorchester then	0.30	0.20	0.20
'Dorch S & W Dorset' 71-94 then (M)			0.10
Dorking (K) 29-35	3.50		
then (U)-72, (M) 96-	0.50	0.30	0.30
*Dornoch (U) summer only 65-72		2.00	
then (K)-95			0.40
*Dover -95 then (X) 96	0.40	0.10	0.05
*Downham Market (K) 57-59		2.00	
then (U)-71		0.70	0.50
Downpatrick (K) 42-54	6.00	4.50	
then (U)-93 then (L)		0.30	0.20
Driffield later (M)		0.40	0.30
Droitwich (K) 44 only	3.50		
then (U)		0.30	0.30
then 'Worc District' (L) 83-			0.40
then 'Droitwich' again (L) 89-			0.40
Droylsden (K) 35-55	1.00	0.80	
then (U) later (R)/(L)		0.20	0.20
Dudley later (L)	0.50	0.20	0.10
*Dulverton (K) 59-76		0.80	0.80
Dumbarton (K) 30-37	2.00		
then (U)-86 then (L)	0.40	0.30	0.20
Dumfries (K) 11-34	1.00		
then (U)-93 then (L)	0.30	0.20	0.10
Dunbar (K) 40-60	2.00	1.50	
then (U) later (L)			0.30
*Dunblane (K) 61-71			0.80
Dundee Angus (K) 34-49	0.30	0.30	
and (U) 29-	0.40	0.20	0.10
then NO Angus 65-83 then (L)			0.10
Dunfermline later (L)	0.40	0.20	0.10
Dungannon (K) 49-55		3.00	
then (U) 57- later (R)		0.20	0.20
*Dunmow (K) 48 only		4.00	
then (U) later (L)-90		0.30	0.30
and 'Chelmsford' (X) 78-89			0.40
Dunoon later (L)	0.40	0.20	0.20
Duns (K) 54-58		0.40	
then (U) 59-84 then (R)		0.30	0.20
Dunstable -82		0.20	0.20
then 'Luton' (L)			0.30
Durham -88 then (M)	0.40	0.20	0.10
also SCD (paid) 64-?77			0.50
*Dursley (K) 50-53		2.00	
then (U)-?72		0.40	0.40
*Dymchurch (U) 62 only			15.00
*Earl Shilton (K) 69-82			0.80
Eastbourne	0.30	0.10	0.05
East Grinstead (K) 28-34	2.00		
then (U) later (R)/(L)	0.40	0.30	0.20
East Kilbride 58-86 then (L)		0.30	0.20
Eastleigh (K) 37-38	3.00		
then (U)-71	0.50	0.30	0.20
then again (L) 90-			0.40

	1933-44	45-60	61-96
*Eastwood (K) 57-63		0.80	0.80
then (U)-77			0.20
Ebbw Vale 49- later (R)		0.30	0.20
but 'Newport Mon NP3' 71-72			0.50
Eccles later (R)/(L)	0.50	0.30	0.20
*Edenbridge (K) 53-59		1.00	
then (U)-76			0.20
then 'T Wells/Tonbridge' (X) 80-91			0.30
Edgware -85 then (M)	0.50	0.20	0.20
Edinburgh	0.20	0.10	0.05
then 'Edinb Lothian Fife Borders' 82-			0.05
then 'Edinburgh' again 95-			0.05
Edinburgh *EC, NW, S, SEDO, SW, W, Dell-DO,			
(EC 59-92, NW 58-, SEDO 68-, Dell-DO 67-)			
- all later (R)/(L)	0.50	0.20	0.20
CDO (Central)'Edinburgh C' (R) 83-			0.30
then 'City & Leith DO' (M) 95-			0.40
*Leith DO later (R)-95	0.40	0.30	0.20
Portobello DO (K) 39-47	0.40		
then (U) later (R)/(L)		0.30	0.20
*Egremont (K) 66-69			0.70
then (U) later (L)-93			0.30
Elgin (K) 29-37	2.00		
then (U) later (R)/(L)	0.50	0.20	0.20
*Elie (K) 61-72			0.40
*Elland (K) 49-75		0.60	0.50
then (K,X) 80,83,84			0.60
*Ellesmere (K) 52-80, (X) -84		0.80	0.50
also (U) 65-75 (at Oswestry)			0.60
*Ellesmere Port (K) 39-40	3.50		
then (U) later (L)-94	0.50	0.30	0.30
(75- 'Wirral' then 78-94 'S Wirral')			
Ellon (K) 68-76			0.70
then (U,X) 'Aberdeen' 89-			0.40
then 'Ellon' (M) 93-			0.40
Ely (K) 33-38	3.00		
then (U)-76		0.30	0.30
then 'Cambridge E' (R)/(L)			0.30
Emsworth (K) 51-		0.60	
then (U) 57- later (R)/(L)		0.30	0.20
*Enfield -?95	0.30	0.10	0.10
also (K) 64 only			1.50
Enniskillen (K) 39-54	3.00	3.00	
then (U) 54- later (R)		0.40	0.20
*Epping ?49- later (R)-93		0.40	0.20
Epsom	0.40	0.20	0.20
then 'Kingston-u-Thames 6,7,8' 87-			0.30
later '9' (L)			0.30
Erith (K) 34 only	5.00		
then (U)	0.50	0.30	0.30
then 'Dartford I' (R) 76-			0.20
*Esher (K) 37-39	4.00		
then (U) -64	0.80	0.50	0.30
Evesham	0.50	0.30	0.20
then 'Worcester District' (L) 83-			0.40
but 'Evesham' again (X) 91 only			0.40
Exeter (K) 38-48	0.60	0.60	
but (U) ?45-		0.10	0.05
then 'Exeter District' 70-			0.05
Exmouth later (L)-?85	0.60	0.20	0.20
but 'Ex District'(X) 82- then (R)/(L)			0.20
*Eyemouth (K) 61-72			0.40
then again (K,L) 90-92			1.50
Failsworth (K) 36-38	3.00		
then (U) later (R)/(L)		0.20	0.20
*Fakenham (K) 39 only	5.00		
then (U)-77	0.40	0.30	0.20
Falkirk -88 then (L)	0.30	0.20	0.10
Falmouth 33-	0.30	0.20	0.10
then 'Cornwall B' (L) 92-			0.40
Fareham (K) 31-38	3.00		
then (U) later (R)/(L)		0.20	0.20

GORING.READING
BERKS.
12 45 PM
9 OCT 76

Glasgow   Glasgow South   Grimsby

	1933-44	45-60	61-96
*Faringdon (K) 55-66		0.80	0.50
then (U)-68			0.50
Farnborough 59-69		0.30	0.30
then again (replaced Aldershot) 92-			0.10
then 'Farnborough & Basingstoke' 95-			0.05
Farnham -76	0.40	0.20	0.20
then 'Aldershot' (X) 89			0.30
then 'Farnham' again (L) 90-			0.40
*Farnworth (K) 60-62			2.50
then (U)-67			0.80
*Faversham (K) 30-38	3.00		
then (U)-90 then (L)-94		0.30	0.30
*Featherstone (K) 57-70		0.40	0.40
Felixstowe later (L)	0.60	0.30	0.30
*Feltham 59-76		0.30	0.30
*Ferndale (K) 61-66			0.80
then 'Rhondda 6' 66-78 then (X)			1.50
then (U,X) 'Ferndale' 80-89			0.40
then 'Cardiff' (X) 90-91			0.40
*Ferryhill (K) 49-57		1.00	
then (U)-63		0.60	0.60
*Filey (K) 38-46	2.00		
then (U)-68		0.30	0.30
Fishguard 60-94 then (L)		0.40	0.20
*Fishponds (K) 34-39	3.00		
then (U) 55-85		0.30	0.30
*Fleetwood -67	0.50	0.30	0.30
then 'Fylde' (X) 81-82			0.40
*Flint (K) 58-59		0.80	
then (U) 60-71			0.30
Folkestone -95 then (L)	0.30	0.10	0.10
*Fordingbridge (K) 58-67		0.50	0.50
*Forfar (K) 34-47	1.00	1.00	
then (U)-83		0.30	0.20
*Formby (R) 59- later (L)-93		0.50	0.40
*Forres (K) 54-59		1.00	
then (U) later (R)/(L)-95		0.30	0.30
Fort William (K) 40-54	1.50	1.00	
then (U) 55- later (R)		0.30	0.20
*Fowey (K) 55-64		0.60	0.40
Fraserburgh (K) 48-58		0.80	
then (U) later (L)		0.30	0.30
*Freshwater (K) 49-61		0.60	0.60
then (U)-77			0.20
Frinton-on-Sea ?51- later (R)		0.40	0.20
*Frodsham (K) 69 only			3.00
Frome (K) 32-40	2.00		
then (U)-86 then (M)		0.30	0.20
Gainsborough (K)-37	1.50		
then (U) later (L)	0.60	0.30	0.20
Galashiels (K) 32-35	2.50		
then (U)-95 then (L)	0.50	0.20	0.10
and 'Scottish Borders' 92-95			0.30
Garstang 64-65			2.50
then (U)-71			0.60
then 'Lancs' (L) ?94-			0.50
*Garston Liv 19 (K) 48-57		1.50	
then (U)-66		0.60	0.60
*Gateshead -33	0.50		
Gerrards Cross 40- later(L)	0.60	0.30	0.20

	1933-44	45-60	61-96
*Giffnock (K) 59-63		0.50	0.50
*Gillingham Dorset (K) 51-58		1.00	
then (U)-68		0.40	0.40
*Gillingham Kent (K) 23-37	1.00		
then (U)-70		0.40	0.30	0.20
then 'BHC' (Bulk Handling Centre) in red			
on paid mail 89-?93			0.50
*Girvan (K) 34-58	0.80	0.60	
then (U) 59-71		0.40	0.40
Glasgow	0.20	0.10	0.05
also 'blank Ayrshire' (X) 91			0.40
*Postmans Office Glasg 80-86			0.40
*Exhib PO 38 only		1.50	
Glasgow SW3 (Savings Bank) 66-			0.60
(all 'paid') then G58 71-93			0.20
(also Pitney Bowes machine still going)			0.20
*Glasgow 2 (Waterloo St) -85		0.30	0.20
*E -57	0.40	0.30	
*E2 (K) 35-39	0.40		
E3 55- then G33 71- later (M)		0.30	0.20
NDO (K) -47	1.00		
then (U) 50-		0.30	0.20
then G21 71- later (M)			0.20
*NWDO (K) -39	1.00		
then (U) 36-		0.40	0.30	0.20
then G20 71-?88			0.20
S then G41 71- later (M)		0.30	0.10
*S4 (K) 35-37	2.50		
*S5 (U,X) 65-66			0.50
*SE then G40 71-?88		0.30	0.20
SW then G51 71- later (M)		0.30	0.20
W then G11 71- later (M)		0.30	0.20
W3 (K) -36	3.00		
and WDO3&4 (U,X) 54-60		0.40	
then (U) then G13 71- later (M)			0.20
*W4 (K) 36-47	2.00	2.00	
*WDO5 (X) 61-65			0.80
then G15 (X) 73-85			0.40
Glastonbury (K) 53 only		4.00	
then (U)		0.40	0.40
then 'Glast & Street' 64-81			0.20
then again (L) 87-			0.40
Glenrothes 64-76			0.40
then 'Kirkcaldy' (X) 78-			0.30
then Glenrothes again (R) 87-			0.30
*Glossop -?87 then (R)-93	0.40	0.30	0.20
Gloucester	0.30	0.10	0.05
then 'Gloucestershire' 70-			0.05
*Godalming (K) 29-36	2.00		
then (U)-77	0.50	0.20	0.20
then 'Guildford' (X) 80-89			0.40
then Godalming again (L) 89-94			0.40
Golspie (K) 65-			0.30
Goole (K) 30-37	1.50		
then (U)-76	0.60	0.30	0.30
then again (M) 88-			0.50
*Gorebridge (K) 69-?87			0.40
*Goring (K) 59-76		0.80	0.60
*Goring by Sea (U,L) 91-93			0.80
*Gorseinon (K) 54-65		0.80	0.60
then 'Swansea 12' (U,L) 87-93			0.40

	1933-44	45-60	61-96
*Gorton (K) 34-37	3.50		
Gosport (K) 34-37	1.50		
then (U) later (R)/(L)	0.70	0.30	0.20
*Gourock (K) 42-64	2.00	1.00	0.50
then (U)-76			0.30
*Grangemouth (K) 45-52		1.50	
then (U) 54- later (R)-95	0.30	0.20	
Grange-over-Sands (K) 50-58		2.00	
then (U) later (R)/(M)		0.30	0.20
Grantham (K) 33 only	5.00		
then (U)-95 then (L)		0.30	0.20
*Grantown-on-Spey (K) 61-72			0.60
then (U)-86			0.30
Gravesend -76	0.60	0.30	0.20
then 'Dartford J' (R)			0.20
Grays (K) 27-34	2.50		
then (U) later (M)	0.30	0.20	0.20
then 'Romford R91' (M) 88-			0.40
Great Missenden (K) 57-60		2.50	
then (U) later (L)			0.30
Great Yarmouth later (L)	0.30	0.20	0.10
*Greenford (K) 34-35	4.00		
then (U)-?70		0.40	0.40
then (M) 90-94			0.50
*Greenock later (L)-?89		0.30	0.20
then 'Paisley' (X) 90-93			0.30
(for later see Inverclyde)			
Grimsby (U)	0.40	0.30	0.20
then 'Gr & Cleethorpes' 64- later (L)			0.20
Guildford	0.30	0.10	0.05
*Guisborough (K) 52-62		1.00	1.00
then (U)-69			0.40
*Guiseley (K) 59-83		0.80	0.40
Haddington (K) 49-59		1.00	
then (U) 60- later (R)/(L)			0.30
*Hadfield Manchester (K) 60-61		2.00	2.00
then 'Hadfield Hyde' -76			0.40
*Hadleigh Ipswich (K) 61-67			1.50
then (U)-73			0.80
Hailsham (K) 40-49	1.50	1.50	
then (U)-76 then (L)		0.30	0.20
Halesowen (K) 47-60		1.50	
then (U) 'Halesowen Birmingham'			0.30
then (U) 'Halesowen Worcs' 67-			
(later W Mids) -92 then (L)			0.20
Halesworth (K) 59-68			0.60
then (U)-93 then (L)			0.30
Halifax (U)	0.30	0.20	0.20
(K) as reserve 54 only		3.00	
then 'Huddersf Halifax B' (U,M) 78-			0.40
Halstead (K) 41-53	2.00	1.50	
then (U) later (R)/(L)		0.30	0.20
*Hamilton -77	0.40	0.30	0.20
then 'Motherwell' (X) 83-86			0.40
*Hampton (K) 48-60		0.60	
then (U)-86			0.30
*Hanley BO Stoke (K) 34-35	4.00		
then (U) 45 seen, see also Stoke		2.00	
*Harleston (K) 59-86		0.50	0.50
Harlow 53-94 then (M)		0.20	0.10
Harold Hill 'Romford C' 70-72			0.50
then 'Romford R31' (M) 90-			0.40
Harpenden (K) 40-41	4.00		
then (U)-70, then (M) 87-	0.60	0.30	0.30
Harrogate -77 then (L,P)	0.40	0.20	0.20
Harrow	0.40	0.10	0.10
then 'Harrow & Wembley' 65-			0.05
then 'Harrow' again 80-			0.05
Harrow PDO (U,M) 90-			0.40
*Hartlepool 'West'	0.60	0.30	0.20
then 'Hartlepool' 67-76			0.30
then 'Cleveland H' (M)-?78			1.00
Harwich later (L)	0.50	0.30	0.20

	1933-44	45-60	61-96
*Haslemere (K) 34-38	2.00		
then (U)-76		0.30	0.30
then 'Guildford' (X) 80-84			0.40
Hassocks (K) 51-57		1.00	
then (U) later (L)		0.30	0.20
Hastings later (R)	0.30	0.20	0.10
Hatfield (K) 43-48	1.50	1.50	
then (U)-71 then (X)-75		0.20	0.20
then again (L) 87-			0.30
Hatfield RM Streamline (R) 95-			0.40
Havant (K) 34-47	1.00		
then (U) later (R)/(L)		0.20	0.20
Haverfordwest (K) 33-37	2.50		
then (U) 37-94 then (L)	0.60	0.20	0.20
but 'Hav/Pembroke' 37	10.00 (error)		
Haverhill (K) 58-59		3.00	
then (U)-92 then (X)			0.20
Hawick -92 then (R)/(L)	0.50	0.20	0.20
and 'Scottish Borders' (R) 92-95			0.30
(but indistinguishable from Galashiels)			
*Hawkhurst 61-72			0.40
*Hawthorn ?44-45		20.00	
Hayes Middx -68	0.60	0.50	0.50
and (K) 61 only			2.00
then Hayes PDO Middx (U,M) 90-			0.40
*Hayle 50-58		0.80	
then (U) later (R)			0.30
then 'Cornwall C' (L) 92-93			1.00
*Hayling Island ?50s-81		0.30	0.30
Haywards Heath later (L)	0.50	0.20	0.20
*Hazel Grove 'Stockport Y' 86-88			0.40
*Heanor 58-76		0.40	0.30
Heathfield (K) 59-60		2.50	
then (U) later (L)			0.30
and 'Tonbridge' (X) 86-91			0.30
*Hebburn (K) 51-58		1.00	
then (U)-77 then (X)-85		0.30	0.30
*Hebden Bridge (K) 39-55	1.00	1.00	
then (U)-75, (L)-76		0.40	0.30
(short lived W Yorks die 75-76			0.60)
Heckmondwike (K) 38-48	2.00	2.00	
then (U)-?70		0.30	0.20
then 'Wakefield' (X)			0.20
Hedge End (L) 90-			0.40
*Helensburgh (K) 26-47	0.80	0.50	
then (U)-77 then (X)-?85		0.30	0.30
Helston (K) 40-50	0.50	0.50	
then (U)		0.30	0.20
then 'Cornwall D' (L) 92-			0.40
Hemel Hempstead	0.40	0.20	0.05
*Hemsworth (K) 60-69			0.40
*Hengoed (K) 52-65		0.40	0.40
then (U)-76			0.30
then 'Cardiff 7' (M) 88 only			0.60
Henley-on-Thames (K) 28-35	2.50		
then (U) later (M)		0.20	0.20
Hereford -93 then (L)	0.30	0.10	0.05
*Herne Bay later (R)/(L)-95	0.30	0.20	0.20
Hertford later (L)	0.30	0.20	0.20
*Hessle (K) 62-75			0.60
(N Humberside only Feb-March 75)			1.00
*Heswall 56- later (R)-?82		0.40	0.40
*Hetton-le-Hole 61 (?X only)			10.00
then 'Durham' (X) 83 only			0.40
Hexham (K) 38 only	5.00		
then (U)-76, then (X)-84		0.40	0.30
then again (M) ?90-			0.40
*Heywood -66	0.70	0.40	0.40
*Highbridge (K) 57-60		2.50	
then (U)-66			0.50
High Wycombe -92 then (L)	0.30	0.10	0.10
*Hinckley -77	0.50	0.30	0.30
then again (M) 89-94			0.40

	1933-44	45-60	61-96
*Hindhead (K) 36-49	1.50	1.50	
then (U) later (R)-76		0.30	0.30
Hitchin later (R)/(L)	0.30	0.10	0.10
Hoddesdon (K) 36-39 & 53	3.00	2.00	
then (U)-68		0.30	0.30
then again (L) 91-			0.40
*Holbeach (K) 50-65		0.60	0.50
then (U)-87			0.30
*Holmfirth (K) 52-57		1.00	
then (U)-67		0.40	0.40
*Holsworthy (K) 58-61		2.50	1.50
then (U) later (R)-93			0.30
*Holt (K) 50-58		1.00	
then (U)-76		0.30	0.30
Holyhead (K) 33-48	1.50	1.50	
then (U) 50-		0.20	0.20

	1933-44	45-60	61-96
Hythe 'Southampton' (K) 63 only			2.00
then 'Hythe Southampton' (U) 63-69			0.60
then again (L) 90-			0.40
Ilford & Barking (K) 32-35	1.50		
then (U) Ilford -59	0.30	0.20	
then Ilford & Barking 51-		0.30	0.10
then Ilford again 70- later (L)			0.10
then 'Romford G11' (L) 89-			0.40
Ilfracombe later (R)/(L)	0.50	0.30	0.20
*Ilkeston (K) 30-38	2.00		
then (U)-?76	0.60	0.30	0.30
Ilkley later (L)	0.60	0.30	0.20
*Ilminster (K) 54-58		1.50	
then (U)-76		0.50	0.40
*Ingatestone (K) 60-65			1.00
then (U)-68, then (X)-74			0.40

IRTHLINGBOROUGH
WELLINGBOROUGH
3 45 PM
15 OCT 65

KINROSS

12 15 PM

15 OCT 74
+

	1933-44	45-60	61-96
*Holywell (K) 50-53		2.00	
then (U) 56-71		0.50	0.40
*Holywood (K) 'Co Down' 58		10.00	
then (K)'Holywood/Belfast'59-60	5.00		
then (U) 60-63			2.00
then 'Holywood/Co Down' -84			0.40
*Honiton 51- later (R)-93		0.30	0.20
*Horden (K) 60-62			1.50
Horley (K) 41-48	2.00	2.00	
then (U)-70		0.40	0.30
then again (M) 92-			0.50
*Horncastle (K) 57 only		3.00	
then (U)-73		0.40	0.30
Hornchurch 'Romford B' 70-72 (R)			0.80
then 'Romford R51' (L) 89-			0.50
also 'Romford G41' (X) 90 only			0.50
*Horsforth (K) 55-63		1.00	1.00
then (U)-66			0.50
Horsham later (L)	0.40	0.30	0.20
*Horwich (K) 61-62			2.00
then (U)-?766			0.50
*Houghton le Spring (U)-67		0.60	0.50
then 'Durham' (X) 82-87			0.40
*Hounslow -86	0.30	0.10	0.10
then (X) 90 only			0.30
*Hove 'Sussex Coast B4' (L) 90-95			0.40
*Hoylake (K) 34-48	1.50	1.50	
then (U) later (L)-76		0.40	0.30
Hucknall (K) 52-55		1.50	
then (U)-?76		0.30	0.30
then (U) again (M) ?90-			0.50
Huddersfield (K) 36-54	0.50	0.30	
and (U) ?45-		0.20	0.10
then 'Hudders Halifax' 76-93 then (L)			0.05
but (K) in reserve 36-54	2.00	2.00	
Hull	0.30	0.10	0.05
but (K) Xmas extra 37-39	3.00		
*Hungerford (K) 43-62		0.60	0.40
then (U)-67			0.30
*Hunstanton (K) 33-39	2.50		
then (U)-71	0.60	0.30	0.30
Huntingdon (U)-92	0.40	0.30	0.20
then again (M) 96-			0.40
also (K) 40-74 in reserve	1.50	1.50	1.50
Huntly (K) 56-60		1.50	
then (U)-77 then (X)			0.30
*Huyton (K) 47 only		3.00	
then (U) later (L)-80		0.30	0.30
Hyde (K) 25-33	2.00		
then (U) later (R)/(L)	0.50	0.30	0.30
Hythe Kent (K) 30-48	2.00	2.00	
then (U) later (R)/(L)		0.30	0.20

	1933-44	45-60	61-96
Inverclyde new office uses variety of Gourock,			
Greenock, Paisley dies (X) 94-			0.40
Invergordon later (R)	0.60	0.20	0.20
Inverness	0.30	0.10	0.05
Inverurie (K) 58-76		0.40	0.40
then (K,X) 85-87			0.40
then (U,X) 'Aberdeen' 90-			0.40
then 'Inverurie' (U,X) 94-			0.40
Ipswich (K) 14-53	0.80	0.60	
and (U)	0.30	0.10	0.05
Irlam (K) 60-67			0.80
then (U) later (R)/(L)			0.30
*Irthlingborough (K) 65-67			1.50
*Irvine (K) 45-55		0.80	
then (U)-79		0.40	0.40
*Iver (K) 59-61		1.50	1.50
then (U)-73			0.50
Jarrow (K) 34-48	1.50	1.50	
then (U)-77 then (X)-85		0.30	0.30
then again (M) ?91-			0.40
*Jedburgh (K) 60-75			0.50
John O'Groats (K) 67- init summer only			0.30
*Johnstone (K) 52-57		1.00	
then (U)-77 then (X)-81		0.30	0.30
Keighley later (L)	0.50	0.20	0.20
also 'Bradford' (X) 84-91			0.30
*Keith (K) 58-76		0.80	0.60
(possibly later X only)			
Kelso (K) 40-56		0.80	
then (U) later (R)/(L)		0.30	0.20
also 'Scottish Borders' 92-95 (R)			0.30
(but indistinguishable from Galashiels)			
*Kempsey (K) 71 only			3.00
then (U,R)-85			0.60
Kendal later (R)	0.50	0.30	0.20
then 'Lancs & S Lakes 18' (M) 94-			0.40
Kenilworth (K) 50-62		0.80	0.70
then (U)-69			0.30
again (M) 91-			0.50
Keswick (K) 32-37	2.00		
then (U)-94 then (L)	0.60	0.30	0.20
Kettering later (M)		0.30	0.20
*Keynsham (K) 56-57		3.00	
then (U)-79		0.40	0.30
*Keyworth (K) 70-77			0.80
Kidderminster later (R)	0.50	0.30	0.10
Kidlington (M) 90-			0.40
*Kidsgrove ?60-88			0.40
*Kilmacolm (K) 66-75			0.60
Kilmarnock -94 then (L)	0.30	0.20	0.10
Kilsyth (K) 54-58		1.00	
then (U) later (L)		0.40	0.30

	1933-44	45-60	61-96
*Kilwinning (K) 59-69		0.80	0.60
then (U)-71			1.50
*Kingsbridge (K) 38-48	1.50	1.50	
then (U)-72		0.40	0.30
then 'S Devon' (X) 73-83			0.30
*Kings Langley 59-78			0.30
then again (M) 85-89, (X)-90			0.40
Kings Lynn	0.30	0.20	0.10
Kingston on/upon Thames	0.30	0.10	0.05
*Kingswood (K) 37-38	3.00		
then (U)-86		0.40	0.30
*Kington (K) 62-71			0.60
*Kingussie (K) 67- later (R)-93			0.40
*Kinross (U) 61-70			0.40
then (K,R) 70-80			0.40
then (U,R) later (M)-90 & (X) 93			0.30
*Kirkby Trading Est -59		0.60	
then Kirkby later (M)-?91		0.40	0.40
*Kirkby-in-Ashfield (K) 55 only		3.00	
then (U)-77		0.30	0.30
then again (M) 87-88			0.60
*Kirkby Lonsdale (K,R) 61-93			0.40
*Kirkby Stephen (K) 61-			0.40
then (U) 83- later (R)-94			0.30
Kirkcaldy later (R)/(L)	0.30	0.20	0.10
*Kirkcudbright (K) 61-74			0.50
*Kirkham (K) 69-70			2.00
(later see Preston West)			
Kirkintilloch (U) 54-86 then (M)		0.20	0.20
also (K,X) 64-65			2.50
Kirkwall (K) 43-54	1.00	1.00	
then (U) 55-		0.30	0.10
*Kirriemuir (K) 58- later (R)-88			0.40
*Knaresborough (K) 49-59		0.80	
then (U)-72			0.40
Knighton (K) 62-72			0.50
then (U) later (L)			0.30
*Knottingley (K) 66-69			1.00
*Knutsford (K) 51-57		1.00	
then (U) later (L)-75		0.30	0.30
Kyle (of Lochalsh) 61-			0.20
*Ladybank (K) 61-76			0.40
Lairg (K) 55-82		0.40	0.40
then (U) later (R)			0.20
*Lambourn (K) 65-66			2.50
Lampeter (K) 59-60		3.00	
then (U) 62-94 then (L)			0.20
*Lanark (K) 36-48	1.00	1.00	
then (U) 50-		0.30	0.20
then 'Clyde Valley ML11' 87-?94			0.20
Lancaster'Lanc & Morecambe' 0.40		0.20	0.10
then 'Lancs & S Lakes 13'(M) 93-			0.40
Lancing -66		0.30	0.40
then again (M) 91-			0.40
Langholm (K) 61-93 then (R)			0.30
*Langport (K) 60-81			0.40
*Larbert 58-68		0.50	0.40
*Largs (K) 34-36	3.00		
then (U)-71	0.60	0.40	0.40
*Larkhall 59-76		0.60	0.40
*Lark Lane Liv (K) 13-37	1.00		
then with district '17' 53 only 2.00			
then (U)-66	0.60	0.50	0.50
then again (M) 91-?92			0.80
*Larne (K) 40s-57		4.00	
then (U) 57-86		0.50	0.30
Launceston (K) 37-48	3.50	2.50	
then (U)-77		0.30	0.30
then 'Plymouth'(X) 80- then (R)-92/(X)			0.30
*Laurencekirk (K) 65-78 then (R)-87			0.60
Leamington Spa : 'Warwick & Leamington Spa'			
later (L)	0.40	0.20	0.10
then 'Leamington Spa' (M) 90-			0.40
Leatherhead (K) 30-35	2.50		
then (U)-86	0.60	0.30	0.20
then 'Kingston-u-T 6,9' (R)/(L) 90-			0.30
*Ledbury (K) 57-68		0.80	0.80
then (U)-72			0.50
then 'Hereford' (M) 91-93			0.30
Leeds	0.20	0.10	0.05
also (K) Xmas reserve 60-67			0.50
*Cross Gates 58-65		0.60	0.40
*Moortown DO 17 -?63		0.60	0.40
(Morley & Yeadon listed separately)			
Leek (K) 28-33	3.00		
then (U) later (R)		0.20	0.20
Leicester	0.30	0.10	0.05
then 'Leicestershire' 93-			0.05
*Leigh Lancs -71	0.60	0.30	0.30
then again (M) 85-90			0.40
Leigh-on-Sea Essex (M) 89-			0.40
Leighton Buzzard (K) 36-38	3.00		
then (U)-92 then (L)		0.20	0.20
*Leiston (K) 60-68			0.50
then (U)-76			0.30
*Leominster (K) 38-52	3.00	2.50	
then (U)-72		0.60	0.40
Lerwick (K) 33-51	1.50	1.00	
then (U) 53-		0.40	0.10
Letchworth (K) 28-48	1.50	1.50	
then (U) later (L)		0.30	0.20
Leven (K) 32-36	3.50		
then (U)	0.60	0.40	0.30
then 'Leven Buckhaven Methil' 64-76			0.40
then 'Kirkcaldy' (X)-85			0.30
then 'Leven' (R)/(L) 88-			0.30
Levenshulme later (R)/(L)	0.60	0.30	0.20
Lewes -75 then (L)	0.50	0.30	0.20
*Leyburn (K) 55-70		0.50	0.30
Leyland (K) 35-38	3.50		
then (U)-?71	0.60	0.50	0.40
then 'Lancs & S Lakes 10' (M) 93-			0.50
*Lichfield (K) 35-38	3.50		
then (U) later (R)-?94	0.60	0.30	0.20
Limavady (K) ?58 only		7.50	
then (U) 60- later (R)			0.30
Lincoln -94 then (L)	0.30	0.20	0.10
*Lingfield (K) 72-75			1.00
then (U)-76 then (L)-79			0.60
*Linlithgow (K) 59-68		0.80	0.40
then (U)-84 then (X)-93			0.40
*Liphook (K) 60-66			0.80
then (U) later (R)-93			0.30
Lisburn (K) 41-48	5.00	5.00	
then (U) 49-93 then (L)		0.30	0.20
Liskeard (K) 50 only		5.00	
then (U)-74		0.40	0.30
then 'Plymouth'(X) 80- then (R)-92/(L)			0.30
*Littleborough (K) 57-60		2.50	
then (U) later (R)-85			0.40
Littlehampton -77	0.40	0.40	0.20
then again (R)/(L) 84-			0.30
Liverpool	0.30	0.10	0.05
*Liverpool ED,ND,SD,			
all later (R)-77		0.30	0.30
*Livingston 74-			0.40
then 'HPO West Lothian' 83-94			0.10
*Llanberis (Empire Games 58)		6.00	
*Llandilo (K) 55-		3.00	
then (K) 'Llandeilo' 58-		3.00	
then (U) 59-75		0.50	0.40
*Llandovery (K) 61-75			0.50
Llandrindod Wells (K) 40-55	1.50	1.00	
then (U) 57- later (R)		0.30	0.20
Llandudno -87 later (M)	0.30	0.20	0.20
(but 'Llandudno-Colwyn Bay' 60-64)			0.20
(also some Xmas periods later -83)			
Llandyssul (K) 60-73			0.30
then (U) 73-			0.40
then 'Llandysul' 80-94 then (L)			0.30
Llanelly -66	0.40	0.30	0.20
then 'Llanelli' later (R)/(L)		0.20	0.20

```
                     1933-44 45-60 61-96                              1933-44 45-60 61-96
*Llanfairfechan (K) 69-77            0.80      Machynlleth (K) 60-63                   0.80
  then (U) later (R)-96              0.30        then (U)                              0.20
Llangefni 57-                  0.50  0.20      Maesteg (K) no Bridgend 49       4.00
Llangollen (K) 40-60      1.50 1.00              then (K) with Bridgend 52      3.00
  then (U) 61-83 then (P,X) then (L) 0.30        then (U) 57-77 (at Bridgend)   0.60  0.30
*Llanidloes (at Newtown) 64-80       0.30        then 'Cardiff 17' (M) 89-            0.40
*Llanrwst (K) 57-62            0.60  0.40      Magherafelt (K) no county 62 only 7.50
  then (U)-?85 (-87 philatelic)      0.30        then (K) with county -68       2.00
*Loanhead (K) 69-85                  0.50        then (U) later (R)                   0.20
Lochgelly 57- later (R)/(L)   0.30  0.30      *Maghull (K) 56-60                2.50
Lochgilphead (K) 59-87        0.80  0.40        then (U)-74                           0.40
  then (U) 'GB' die Jan-Apr 87       5.00      Maidenhead -73 later (L)    0.40 0.20 0.10
  then (U) 'Lochgilp' May 87-93 then (R) 0.30  Maidstone                   0.40 0.20 0.05
*Lochmaddy (K) 68-69 then in reserve-77 3.00     then 'Medway & Maidstone' 83-        0.05
Lockerbie 50- later (R)/(L)   0.30  0.30      Maldon 52- later (L)              0.30  0.20
London (see end of listing)                     but 'Chelmsford' (X) 78-89           0.30
Londonderry later (R)    1.00 0.20  0.10      *Malmesbury (K) 53-57             2.00
*Long Eaton (K) 31-38    2.50                   then (U)-68                     0.60  0.40
  then (U)-77            0.70 0.30  0.20        then 'Swindon' (X) 81-91              0.40
  then again (L) 87-92               0.40      *Malton (K) 36-38           4.00
Longridge (K) 65-71                  0.80        then (U) later (L)-87       1.00 0.30 0.30
  then (U,L) 'Lancs' no number 94-   0.40      Malvern                     0.60 0.30 0.20
Longton (K) 63-67                    0.60        then 'Worc District M' (L) 83-       0.30
  then (U) later (R)                 0.30        but 'Malvern' again (X) 89 only      0.40
```

Lochgilphead

```
*Looe (K) 36-57          0.80  0.80      Manchester                  0.20 0.10 0.05
  then (U)-74 (at Liskeard)    0.40 0.30   and 'Manchester IPS' (M) 83-?95       0.20
*Lossiemouth (K) 61-79               0.50   (Inward Primary Sorting)
*Lostwithiel (K) 61-87               0.50 Manchester districts, later (R)/(L):
  then (U)-92                        0.30   E, N, NE(66-), S, SE, SW  0.30 0.20 0.10
Loughborough later (R)/(L) 0.40 0.30 0.20   and Manch.H (K) 11-51     0.40 0.30
Loughton (K) 53 only         5.00        Manningtree (K) 59-66            0.60  0.60
  then (U) later (L)             0.30 0.30   then (U) later (L)                  0.30
  then 'Romford G41' (M) 90-         0.40 *Mansfield -94               0.40 0.20 0.10
*Louth (K) 35-38        4.00             *March (K) 39-               2.00 2.00
  then (U)-77            0.60 0.40  0.30    then (U) 48-94                  0.30  0.20
  then (U,X) 'Grimsby & Cleeth' 89-92 0.50 *Margate                    0.40 0.20 0.20
*Lowestoft later (M)-94  0.40 0.30  0.20    then 'Thanet A' 71- later (R)/(L)-95 0.20
Ludlow (K) 36-48        1.00 1.00          then again (X) 96                    0.30
  then (U) later (R)/(L)      0.40  0.30  Market Drayton (K) 41-48     2.00 2.00
Lurgan (K) 46-54             3.00          then (U) later (L)             0.40  0.30
  then (U) 56-, then          0.30 0.20  *Market Harborough (K)36-38 3.00
  'Lurgan Craigavon' 73-93 then (L)  0.20   then (U) later (R)/(L)-95 0.80 0.30 0.20
Luton                   0.30 0.10  0.05  *Market Rasen (K) 57-58      3.00
  also (K) in reserve 54-62         1.50    then (U)-73                     0.80  0.30
*Lutterworth Warwicks (K) 60 only 6.00   *Markinch 58-64                  1.00  0.80
  then Lutterworth Rugby (K) 61-    0.80  *Marlborough (K) 37-47      2.00 2.00
  then (U) 'Lutterworth Rugby' 67-  0.60    then (U)-68                     0.60  0.30
  then 'Lutterworth Leics' 73-76    0.40    then 'Swindon' (X) 81-91            0.40
*Lydney (K) 51-54            3.00        Marlow (K) 51-56             1.50
  then (U)-70                   0.40 0.40   then (U)-?66                0.50 0.30
Lyme Regis (K) 50-56         2.00          then again (L) 86-                  0.40
  then (U) later (R)           0.30  0.20 *Marple 'Stockport X' (R) 86-92      0.40
Lymington (K) 33-37     4.00             Maryport (K) 48-59               0.60
  then (U)-75            0.70 0.40  0.30    then (U) later (R)/(L)         0.40  0.30
  then again (L) 90-                 0.40 *Matlock (K) 29-34          2.00
*Lymm (K) 57-64              1.50 1.50      then (U)-78                 0.80 0.30 0.20
*Lyndhurst (K) 52-60        1.00         *Mauchline (K) 59-65             0.60  0.60
Lynton (K) 32-60        1.00 0.50          then (U)-71                         0.40
  then (U) 'Lynton' -65             0.60 *Maybole (K) 60-71               0.80  0.80
  then 'Lynton & Lynmouth' later (R) 0.20 Melksham (K) 39-46          3.00 3.00
Lytham St Annes -?67    0.60 0.40  0.30    then (U) later (R)             0.30  0.30
  then 'Fylde 8' (X) 81- later (L)   0.40 *Melrose (K) 58-65               0.40  0.40
*Mablethorpe -64             0.60  0.50    then (U)-68                         0.40
  then 'Mableth & Sutton on Sea' -77 0.30 *Melton Mowbray (K) 35-44   3.00
Macclesfield -92 then (L) 0.40 0.20 0.20    then (U) later (R)/(M)-95       0.20  0.20
                                         *Menai Bridge '1st day' 29.4.68 only 1.00
                                           (machine at Bethesda)
```

	1933-44	45-60	61-96
Merthyr Tydfil	0.60	0.30	0.20
then 'Cardiff 11' (R) 89-			0.20
Mexborough (K) 33-36	3.00		
then (U)-66	0.80	0.40	0.40
then 'Sheffield' (X) 71- then (M)			0.30
Middlesbrough	0.30	0.20	0.10
then 'Teesside' 69-			0.05
then 'Cleveland' 74-			0.05
Middleton (K) 34-38	2.50		
then (U) later (R)/(L)	0.60	0.30	0.20
*Middlewich (K) 55-64		0.60	0.60
then (U)-75 (at Northwich)			0.40
*Midhurst (K) 43-59		0.80	
then (U) later (R)/(M)-94			0.20
Milford Haven (K) 33-41	3.00		
then (U) later (R)-94 then (L)		0.30	0.20
Millom (K) 58 only		5.00	
then (U) later (R)		0.50	0.20
*Millport (K) 61-92 init summer only			0.60
Milngavie (K, mainly X) 54-79		0.80	0.40
and (U,X) 71-74			0.40
then (U) 79-, then (L) 86-			0.40
Milton Keynes 73- (also see Wolverton)			0.05
Milton Keynes Kiln Farm (M)/(X) 89-			0.40
Minehead (K) 29-39	1.50		
then (U) later (L)	0.40	0.20	0.20
Mirfield (K) 41-57	1.50	1.50	
then (U)-70		0.40	0.30
then 'Wakefield' (X) 71- later (M)			0.20
Mitcham (U) ?33-73	0.80	0.30	0.20
then 'Croydon' (R)-76			0.40
then 'Mitcham' again (M) 89-			0.40
*Moffat (K) 61-77			0.60
Mold 43-71	0.80	0.30	0.30
then again (M) 89-			0.50
Monmouth (K) 49-53		3.00	
then (U) later (R)/(L)		0.40	0.20
Montrose (K) 30-43	2.50		
then (U) later (R)/(L)	0.30	0.20	0.20
Morden 'Sutton' die (M) 87-			0.40
then 'Croydon Sutton/Morden'(M) ?91-			0.50
*Moreton Wirral (K) 57 only		4.00	
then (U)-70		0.50	0.50
*Moreton-in-Marsh (K) 57-59		3.50	
then (U)		0.40	0.40
then 'Worcester District' (L) 83-?89			0.40
*Morley (K) 49 only		4.00	
then (U)-71		0.40	0.40
Morpeth (K) 34-37	3.00		
then (U)	0.60	0.20	0.20
then 'Mid Northumberland' 69-later(L)			0.10
*Morriston (K) 50-55		3.00	
then (U) 57-58		10.00	
Mossley Manchester (U) 50s-61		0.80	0.80
then (K) 61 only			5.00
then Mossley Ashton-u-L 61-82			0.50
and (U,R) 61-76 (at Ashton-u-L)			0.40
then again 91- (R)/(L)			0.50
*Mossley Hill Liv 50s-65		0.50	0.60
Motherwell	0.50	0.30	0.20
then 'Motherwell & Wishaw' 52-		0.20	0.10
but sometimes 'Motherwell' (X)			0.30
then 'Clyde Valley ML1' 87-then (R)/(M)			0.05
Mountain Ash 52- later (R)		0.40	0.30
then 'Cardiff 9' (M) 89-			0.40
*Mumbles 'Swansea 9' (M) 87-93			0.40
Musselburgh (K) 45-48		3.00	
then (U) later (L)		0.30	0.20
Nairn (K) 56-58		2.00	
then (U) 59- later (R)/(L)		0.40	0.30
*Nantwich -82 later (X)-88	0.40	0.30	
Narberth (K) 59-68		2.00	0.60
then (U) later (R)-94 then (L)			0.20
Neath later (R)	0.50	0.30	0.20
then 'West Glam 8' 75- (R)			0.30
then 'Neath' again 80- (R)/(L)			0.30

	1933-44	45-60	61-96
Nelson 'Burnley & Nelson' (L) 93-			0.40
*Newark -94	0.50	0.20	0.10
*Newbridge (K) 57-61		0.80	0.80
then (U) later (R)-94			0.30
Newbury	0.40	0.20	0.10
*Newcastle Co Down (K) 56-60		3.00	
then (U)-95			0.20
Newcastle Staffs (K) 40-43	3.00		
then (U) 65- later (L)			0.30
*Newcastle Emlyn (K) 68-77			0.50
then (U)-86			0.30
Newcastle on/upon Tyne	0.30	0.10	0.05
also NO upon Tyne error 84-95			0.30
then 'Tyneside' 95-			0.05
and (K) in reserve 33-59	2.00	1.50	
Newhaven (K) 49-58		0.80	
then (U)-75 then (R)/(L)		0.40	0.30
*New Malden 33-63	0.60	0.40	0.30
then 'Kingston 5' later (L)-93			0.20
Newmarket later (R)/(L)		0.20	0.10
*New Milton (K) 40-49	2.00	2.00	
then (U)-?71		0.50	0.40
Newport Isle of Wight -77	0.60	0.20	0.20
(error with '6' in die 67-68			4.00)
then 'Isle of Wight' later (L)			0.20
Newport Mon	0.30	0.30	0.10
then 'Gwent' 73-93 then (M)			0.05
Newport Shropshire (K) 54-59		1.00	
then (U) later (L)		0.30	0.30
Newport Pagnell ?60- later (R)/(L)			0.20
Newquay	0.40	0.20	0.10
then 'Cornwall E' (L) 92-			0.40
*New Romney (K) 58-60		2.00	
then (U) later (R)-96			0.30
Newry (K) -45	4.00		
then (U) later (R)		0.40	0.20
*Newton Abbot -83	0.70	0.20	0.20
then again (X) 86-91			0.30
Newton-le-Willows (K) 49 only		4.00	
then (U) later (L)		0.30	0.30
Newton Mearns 65- later (L)			0.30
Newton Stewart (K) 54-66		0.50	0.40
then (U) later (R)-93 then (L)			0.30
Newtown (K) 34-37	3.00		
then (U) later (L)	0.60	0.30	0.20
*Newtownabbey 60-83			0.30
Newtownards (K) 52-53	7.50		
then (U) 54-93 then (L)	0.30	0.20	
*Normanton (K) 62-70			0.50
then 'Wakefield' (U,X) -81			0.30
Northallerton (K) 33-38	3.00		
then (U) later (M,P)/(M)	0.50	0.30	0.20
and 'Darlington'(X) 83-88			0.30
Northampton	0.30	0.10	0.05
then 'Northamptonshire' 85-			0.05
North Berwick (K) 33-58	1.00	0.80	
then (U) later (R)/(L)		0.40	0.20
*Northleach (K) 84-92			0.40
Northolt PDO (M) 90-			0.40
*North Shields -?76	0.50	0.20	0.20
then (X)-85, then (M) 89-95			0.30
*North Walsham (K) 57-60		0.80	
then (U)-76			0.40
Northwich (K) 23-35	1.00		
then (U) later (R)	0.50	0.20	0.20
Northwood (K) 30-38	1.50		
then (U)	0.50	0.30	0.30
then 'Harrow & Wembley N' 70-			0.30
then 'Harrow N' 80- later (L)			0.30
Norwich (K) 31-35	2.50		
and (U)	0.40	0.10	0.05
Nottingham	0.40	0.10	0.05
Nuneaton -?85 then (M)	0.50	0.20	0.20
*Oakengates (K) 56-58		2.50	
then (U) 'Oakengates Salop'		1.00	0.80
then 'Oakengates Telford' 69 only			2.50

	1933-44	45-60	61-96
*Oakham (K) 44-55		0.80	
then (U)-77		0.30	0.30
Oban (K) 26-34	3.50		
then (U)-93 then (R)	0.40	0.30	0.10
*Okehampton (K) 48-49		5.00	
then (U)-93		0.30	0.20
Oldham	0.30	0.10	0.05
then 'Rochdale Oldham Ashton-u-L' 81-			0.05
but 'Oldham' again 92 only			0.20
*Old Swan (K) 16-47		0.80	0.80
then (U)-66		0.50	0.40
Omagh (K) 37-c48	4.00	4.00	
then (U) later (R)		0.30	0.20
*Ongar (K) 58-60		2.00	
then (U)-75			0.30
then 'Chelmsford' (X) 78-90			0.30

	1933-44	45-60	61-96
Penzance	0.30	0.20	0.05
then 'Cornwall F' (R) 92-			0.20
but 'Cornwall 1' Sundays 90-92			0.40
(see also Sennen, stamped at Penzance)			
*Perranporth (K) 60-87			0.40
then (U) later (R)-92			0.40
*Pershore (K) 55-60		2.00	
then (U)-76			0.30
*Perth	0.30	0.10	0.05
then 'Perth Dundee Angus' 83-95			0.05
but 'Perth' on missorts 89-95			0.20
Peterborough (K) 37-47	0.80	0.80	
also (U) (Northants)	0.30	0.20	0.10
then NO Northants 65-			0.05
Peterhead (K) 39-55	1.50	1.50	
then (U)-72 then (M)		0.40	0.30

MITCHAM SURREY 6 45AM 15 MCH 1991 — MOLD 5 45AM 30-XII 1989 CLWYD — CLYDE VALLEY 6 -PM 22 APR 1987 ML1 — NEWTOWN —MONT.— 7. — PM 12 JUL 34 — ROCHDALE OLDHAM ASHTON 22 FEB 1988 LNE 4 BRIM — PENMAENMAWR 10 45AM 19-II 1986 GWYNEDD — CORNWALL 6 15PM 23 JNE 1992 F

| Motherwell | | Oldham | | Penzance |

	1933-44	45-60	61-96
Openshaw later (R)/(L)	0.50	0.40	0.30
*Ormskirk (K) 34-37	4.00		
then (U)-66	1.00	0.40	0.40
then again (M) 89-93			0.40
Orpington later (R)/(L)		0.20	0.20
Ossett (U) ?40s-?70		0.40	0.30
then 'Wakefield L' (X) then (M)			0.30
then 'Ossett' again (X) 94 only			0.40
Oswestry (K) 27-37	2.00		
then (U) later (R)/(L)		0.30	0.20
*Otley (K) 38-47	2.00		
then (U)-?70		0.40	0.30
*Oundle 50s-80		0.40	0.30
Oxford	0.30	0.10	0.05
*Oxted (K) 40-41	4.50		
then (U)-?70		0.50	0.30
*Padstow (K) 58-87		0.60	0.40
then (U) later (R)-92			0.40
Paignton -70	0.40	0.20	0.20
then 'South Devon' (X)			0.20
Paisley -94 then (L)	0.30	0.20	0.10
but (K) in reserve 51 only		3.50	
*Pangbourne (K) 48-59		0.80	
then (U)-67			0.60
*Par (K) 52-62		1.00	1.00
then (U)-68			0.60
*Parkstone -?33	0.80		
later 'Bournemouth-Poole C'-72		0.30	0.30
Peebles (K) 39-53	0.80	0.60	
then (U) later (R)/(L)		0.30	0.30
*Pembroke (K) 59-65		0.50	0.50
Pembroke Dock (K) 54-59		0.50	
then (U) later (R)-94 then (L)		0.30	0.20
Penarth (K) 32-38	2.00		
then (U) 40-67	0.60	0.30	0.30
then 'Cardiff 8' (M) 87-			0.40
Penicuik 61- later (L)			0.20
*Penlan 'Swansea 11' (L) 87-93			0.60
*Penmaenmawr (K) 59-61		3.00	3.00
then (U) later (L)-88			0.30
Penrith (K) 28-35	2.50		
then (U)-93 then (L)	0.30	0.20	0.20
*Pentre (K) 49-50		5.00	
then (U) 53-66		0.50	0.50
then 'Rhondda 4' (K)-69			1.50
*Penygroes (K) 75-77			1.50
then (U)-86			0.50

	1933-44	45-60	61-96
*Peterlee (K) 62-63			2.00
then (U)-82			0.30
Petersfield (K) 32-35	4.00		
then (U)-93 then (L)	0.80	0.20	0.20
*Petworth (K) 31-60	2.50	1.50	
then (U)-93 then (M)-94			0.20
*Pewsey (K) 58-68		1.00	0.80
*Pickering (K) 57-59		2.00	
Pinner ?39-	0.70	0.30	0.20
then 'Harrow & Wembley P' 71-			0.30
then 'Harrow P' (R) 80-			0.30
then Pinner again (L) 93-			0.40
*Pitlochry (K) 39-57	1.00	0.80	
then (U)-83 & (X) 83		0.30	0.30
Plymouth	0.30	0.10	0.05
then 'Plym Cornwall & W Devon' 80-			0.05
but 'Plym & District' Sundays 90-92			0.30
and (K) in reserve 36-56	1.00	1.00	
*Pocklington (K) 49-70		0.80	0.50
Polegate (K) 58-67		1.00	0.60
then (U)-76 then (R)/(L)			0.30
Pontardawe (K) 57-58		5.00	
then (U)-65		1.00	0.60
then 'Swansea 13' (L) 89-			0.30
Pontefract (K) 28-36	2.00		
then (U)-70		0.30	0.30
then 'Wakefield' (X) 70- then (M)			0.30
*Ponteland 65-68			1.50
Pontyclun (K) 60-62			2.00
then (U)-69			0.50
then 'Cardiff 18' (M) 89-			0.40
Pontypool later (R)	0.30	0.20	0.20
Pontypridd	0.30	0.20	0.20
also 'Rhondda 1' 66-71			0.40
then 'Cardiff 2,3' (R) 88-			0.30
Portadown (K) -49	5.00	4.00	
then (U) 50-		0.40	0.20
then 'Porta Craigavon' 83-93 then (R)			0.10
Port Ellen (K) 69-			0.40
*Port Glasgow (K) 50-56		1.00	
then (U)-72		0.50	0.50
Porth (K) 36 then 46	2.50		
then (U) 37-66	0.60	0.30	0.30
then 'Rhondda 2' 66- later (R)			0.30
then 'Cardiff 12' (L) 89-			0.40
Porthcawl 37-77	0.60	0.30	0.20
(stamped at Bridgend 67-77)			
then 'Cardiff 19' (M) 89-			0.40

PLYMOUTH & DISTRICT A
5 AUG 1990

PORTMADOC
CAERNARVONSHIRE
12 45 PM
8 SEP 59

PORTSMOUTH
I
3 DEC 1991
ISLE OF WIGHT

REIGATE
25 APR
1996
SURREY RH2 OPR

ROCK FERRY B'HEAD
II. — AM
15 MAY 40

ROSSENDALE
LANCS
21 DEC 35

SEDBERGH
YORKSHIRE
—PM—
18 DEC 69
+

	1933-44	45-60	61-96
Portishead (K) 59-74		0.40	0.40
then 'Bristol' (X) 94-			0.30
*Portland (K) 61-65			0.60
Portmadoc (K) 53-59		1.00	
then (U) 60-		0.40	0.40
then 'Porthmadog' 72- later (R)			0.20
Portree 60-		0.30	0.20
*Portrush 33-90	1.50	0.50	0.30
Portsmouth			
'Portsmouth & Southsea'	0.30	0.10	0.05
also (K) 33-49	0.60	0.50	
then (U) 'Portsmouth & IOW' 81-			0.05
also 'Portsmouth' 92-?94			0.20
Port Talbot 33-75	0.80	0.40	0.30
then 'West Glam 9' (R) 75-			0.40
then 'Port Talbot' again (R)/(L) 80-			0.30
*Potters Bar 65-71			1.00
*Prescot (K) 39-48	2.50	2.50	
then (U) later (L)-?77		0.50	0.40
*Prestatyn (K) 46-49		4.50	
then (U)-71		0.40	0.30
Preston	0.30	0.10	0.10
then 'Lancashire' 75-			0.05
then 'Lancashire S Lakes' 93-			0.05
Preston DO 70- then (L)			0.50
then 'Lancashire 41' 78-?79			0.40
then 'Lancashire 51' (M) ?81-			0.40
(prev used at North DO)			
and SDO 'Lancashire 55' (M) ?81-			0.40
then 'Lancs S Lakes 11' (M) 94-			0.40
and West DO 'PDO West Lancs' (M) 88-			0.50
*Prestonpans (K,X) 62-63			1.00
then regular use 64-75			0.50
then 'Edinburgh' (U,X) 81-84?			0.30
Prestwich later (R)		0.30	0.20
*Prestwick (K) 39-53	1.50	1.50	
then (U)-?70		0.40	0.30
*Princes Risborough (K) 57-58		4.00	
then (U)-78		0.80	0.30
then NO Aylesbury (L) 90-93			0.40
*Pudsey Leeds (K) 52-		1.50	
then (U) 57-		3.00	
then 'Pudsey Yorkshire' 58-70		0.60	0.40
Pulborough (K) 56-59		2.50	
then (U)-78, then (L)		0.30	0.30
Pwllheli (K) 37 only	5.00		
then (U) 37-	0.80	0.30	0.20
Radcliffe (K) 32-39	3.50		
then (U) later (R)/(L)	0.60	0.20	0.20
*Radcliffe-on-Trent (K) 69-77			0.60
*Radlett (K) 50-59		1.00	
then (U)-68		0.50	0.50
Radstock (K) 53-57		2.50	
then (U)-82		0.50	0.30
then again (L) 86-			0.40
then 'Avon removed' (L) 96-			0.30
Rainham 'Romford R61' (M) 89-			0.50
*Ramsbottom (U) 'Manch' 58-65		0.80	0.80
then (K) 'Bury' 66-68			2.50
*Ramsey Huntingdon (K) 60-			0.40
then (U) 75-89			0.30
*Ramsgate	0.30	0.20	0.10
then 'Thanet B' 71-87 then (X) 96			0.20
Rayleigh (K) 51-59		1.50	
then (U) later (R)-92 then (L)			0.30
Reading	0.30	0.10	0.05

	1933-44	45-60	61-96
*Redcar (K) 29-35	3.00		
then (U)-69	0.60	0.30	0.30
(short lived Teesside county 68-			0.80)
Redditch -96 then (M)	0.50	0.30	0.10
and (K,X) 61			3.00
Redhill:			
'Reigate & Redhill'	0.30	0.10	0.05
then 'MLO Redhill' 76-			0.05
then Redhill 80- then (R)			0.05
also 'Gatwick MLO' 88-			0.05
(Redhill's MLO at Crawley)			
also *'Redhill PDO' 78-?80			0.50
Redruth (K) 33-35	1.00		
then (U) 'Camborne Redruth'		0.20	0.10
then 'Cornwall G' (L) 92-			0.30
Reigate (M) 96-			0.40
*Renfrew (K) 52-63		0.40	0.40
and (U) 58-68		0.40	0.40
Retford (K) 29-33	1.50		
then (U)-76 then (M) 90-	0.50	0.30	0.30
*Rhayader (K) 76-84			0.50
(though philatelic items stamped 87)			
*Rhosllanerchrugog (K) 64-83			0.60
Rhyl	0.30	0.20	0.10
then 'Clwyd'/'Clwyd 2' 72-			0.10
then Rhyl again 83-			0.10
('Clwyd 2' again (X) 87-)			0.30
*Richmond Surrey -45	0.60		
then 'Twickenham' 74-75			0.30
*Richmond Yorks (K) 39-49	1.50	1.50	
then (U)-70		0.40	0.30
*Rickmansworth (K) 37-39	3.00		
then (U)-?80		0.30	0.30
then again (M) 87-?94			0.40
*Ringwood (K) 36-54	2.00	1.00	
then (U)-71		0.40	0.30
*Ripley (K) 53-58		2.50	
then (U)-72 then (X) 74		0.50	0.30
*Ripon (K) 24-44	2.50		
then (U)-72	1.00	0.40	0.30
Rochdale later (R)/(L)	0.50	0.30	0.10
(see also Oldham)			
Rochford (K) 59-60		3.00	
then (U) later (R)-92 then (L)			0.30
*Rock Ferry (K) 25-44	2.00		
then (U)-67		0.60	0.40
Romford -?59	0.30	0.20	
also 'Romf & Dag' 51-		0.20	0.10
and (K) in reserve 66			0.50
then (U) 'Romford' again 70-			0.05
and 'Romford R21' (M) 86-			0.30
*Romsey (K) 43-51	2.00	2.00	
then (U)-69		0.30	0.30
Rossendale (K) 23-35	0.80		
then (U)-71	0.50	0.30	0.20
then (U,M) 'Lancashire 44' 89-			0.50
*Ross-on-Wye (K) 48-49		3.00	
then (U)-72		0.60	0.30
Rotherham later (L)	0.40	0.20	0.20
and (K,X) 64 only			3.00
also 'Sheffield' (U,X) ?75-91			0.30
Rothesay later (L)	0.60	0.40	0.20
Rottingdean (L) 90-			0.40
Royston ?49-77		0.30	0.30
then 'Cambridge' (L)			0.30
*Royton Oldham (K) 49-61			0.80
then (U)-?64			0.60

	1933-44	45-60	61-96
Rugby later (L)	0.40	0.20	0.20
*Rugeley -68		0.40	0.20
Ruislip (K) 36-38	3.50		
then (U)	0.80	0.20	0.20
then 'Harrow & Wembley R' 71-			0.30
then 'Harrow R' 78-			0.20
but 'Ruislip' again (X) 85 & 93-			0.40
Runcorn (K) 35-46	2.00		
then (U) later (L)		0.30	0.20
Rushden (K) 38 only	4.00		
then (U) later (R)	0.80	0.20	0.20
Rutherglen (K) 34-39	3.00		
then (U) 47- later (L)		0.30	0.20
*Ruthin (K) 51-55		2.50	
then (U) 57-71		0.40	0.30
*Ryde -77	0.40	0.30	0.20
Rye (K) 37-52	2.00	2.00	
then (U)-66		0.50	0.30
then 'Hastings or Tonbridge' (X) 80-			0.40
*Ryton (K) 60-70			0.60
Saffron Walden (K) 37-41	3.00		
then (U)-93 then (L)	0.60	0.30	0.20
St Albans later (R)/(L)	0.40	0.20	0.10
and (K) in reserve 33-72	2.00	2.00	2.50
St Andrews -76	0.40	0.30	0.20
then 'Kirkcaldy' (X) 81-			0.30
then 'St Andrews' (R) ?86-			0.20
*St Asaph 67-71			1.00
*St Austell (K) 35-37	3.00		
then (U)	0.60	0.30	0.20
then 'Plymouth R,S,T' 80-92			0.20
and 'Cornwall 3' Sundays 90-92			0.30
*St Columb (K) 69-84			0.50
St Helens later (L)	0.40	0.30	0.20
St Ives Cornwall (K) 32-36	3.00		
then (U)	0.80	0.30	0.30
then 'Cornwall H' (L) 92-			0.40
*St Ives Huntingdon ?58-92		0.30	0.20
St Leonards-on-Sea 'Hastings'(L) 90-			0.40
St Mary's (K) 59-67		0.80	0.60
then (U)			0.20
St Neots (K) 54-60		1.00	
then (U) later (R)		0.20	0.10
*Salcombe (K) 58-69		0.80	0.60
then (U)-72			0.40
Sale (K) 29-36	1.50		
then (U) later (R)/(L)	0.60	0.30	0.20
Salford later (R)/(L)		0.30	0.20
Salisbury -94 then (L)	0.30	0.10	0.10
*Saltash (K) 49-62		0.60	0.60
then (U)-78			0.30
then 'Plymouth' (X) 80-?90 & 95-96			0.30
*Saltburn-by-Sea (K) 42-51	1.50	1.50	
then (U)-?70		0.40	0.40
*Saltcoats 36-80	0.60	0.40	0.40
then (X) 80 only			0.40
*Sandbach (later at Crewe)-?72		0.30	0.30
then again (X) 82 only			0.40
*Sandgate (U)-34	3.00		
*Sandiacre (K) 69-77			0.80
*Sandown (K) 33-35	2.00		
then (U)-77	0.60	0.30	0.20
Sandwich (K) 38-57	2.00	1.50	
then (U)-95 then (L)		0.30	0.20
*Sandy (K) 61-76			0.80
*Sanquhar (K) 74-78			1.50
Sarisbury Green (L) 90-			0.40
*Saundersfoot 67-93 (at Tenby)			0.30
Saxmundham (K) 54-59		1.50	
then (U) later (L)			0.20
Scarborough -90 then (L)	0.30	0.20	0.10
Scunthorpe later (L)	0.40	0.20	0.10

	1933-44	45-60	61-96
Seaford (K) 32-38	3.00		
then (U)-76 then (R)/(L)	0.40	0.20	0.20
*Seaham (K) 40-55	2.00	1.50	
then (U)-?69		0.40	0.30
*Seascale 73-89			0.40
Seaton later(R)-93 then (L)	0.60	0.20	0.20
Sedbergh (K) 60-84			0.50
then (U)			0.30
then 'Lancs S Lakes 20' (M) 94-			0.40
*Selby -71		0.30	0.30
Selkirk (K) 56-60		1.00	
then (U) later (R)/(L)			0.20
*Sennen & Land's End 57-92 (at Penzance)	0.40		
*Settle (K) 60-77			0.50
also (U) used 70 only			1.00
Sevenoaks later (L)	0.50	0.30	0.20
but 'Tonbridge' (L) 84-			0.40
*Shaftesbury (K) 41-50	1.50	1.50	
then (U)-69		0.30	0.30
then 'Salisbury' (X) 76-88			0.30
also 'Bath 5' (R) 87-			0.40
then 'Southampton H' (R) 92-93			0.60
*Shanklin -77	0.40	0.30	0.20
Shaw (K) 52-61		1.00	1.00
then (U) later (R)/(L)			0.30
*Sheerness -71	0.50	0.30	0.20
Sheffield	0.30	0.10	0.05
*Sheffield 5 NEPDO (K,R) 64-92			0.40
*WPDO Sheffield 10 (K,R) 65-66			2.50
then 'West PDO' (K,R) -69			1.00
*Shepperton (K) 49-53 & 58		1.50	
then (U)-61			1.00
Shepton Mallet (K) 51-55		2.00	
then (U)-86 then (L)		0.50	0.30
Sherborne (K) 36-38	3.00		
then (U) later (R)/(L)	0.80	0.20	0.20
*Sheringham (K) 32-41	3.00		
then (U) 61-76			0.40
*Shifnal (K) 60-80			0.50
*Shipley -67	0.60	0.40	0.40
then 'Bradford' (X) 85-91			0.30
*Shipston-on-Stour (K) 61-67			0.80
then (U) later (R)/(L)-95			0.30
*Shoeburyness (K) 61-72			0.80
Shoreham-by-Sea (K) 33-49	2.00	2.00	
then (U)-71 then (L)		0.30	0.30
*Shotts (X) 67-68			3.00
Shrewsbury	0.30	0.10	0.10
and (K) 52-58		0.80	
then (U) 'Salop erased' 80-			0.30
then 'Shropshire & Mid Wales' 82-			0.05
Sidcup (K) 29-34	3.00		
then (U)-76	0.60	0.30	0.20
then 'Dartford K' (R)			0.20
Sidmouth (K) 32-35	3.50		
then (U)-70	0.60	0.40	0.30
then 'Ex District' (X) 75-85			0.30
then 'Sidmouth' (X) 86- later (L)			0.40
*Sittingbourne (K) 29-35	3.50		
then (U)-72	0.60	0.30	0.30
Skegness	0.30	0.20	0.10
*Skelmersdale Ormskirk (K) 61-			3.00
then (K) NO Ormskirk 63-73			0.80
*Sketty 'Swansea 10' (L) 87-91			0.50
Skipton later (R)/(L)	0.40	0.30	0.20
*Sleaford -83		0.40	0.20
then again (M) ?87-93			0.40
Slough	0.30	0.10	0.05
then 'Slough/Windsor SLO-9' 91-			0.05
*Smethwick (K)-37	1.00		
then (U)-67	0.50	0.20	0.20
(then see Warley)			

	1933-44	45-60	61-96
Solihull (K) 40-49	1.50	1.50	
then (U)-?95 then (L)		0.20	0.20
Southall later (R)	0.40	0.20	0.10
Southam (L) 89-			0.40
Southampton	0.30	0.10	0.05
*S Croydon (K) 34-39	2.00		
Southend-on-Sea	0.30	0.10	0.05
also NO on Sea error 93-96			0.20
*South Molton (K) 53-59		1.50	
then (U)-70, then (R) 88-93			0.40
South Ockendon (R) 67-72 then (X)			0.50
then 'Romford R71' (L) 89-			0.40
Southport (U)	0.40	0.30	0.20
also (K) 42-57	1.50	1.50	
then 'Lancashire 32' (U,L) 76-			0.30
South Shields -76	0.40	0.30	0.20
then (X)-85, then (M) 89-			0.30

	1933-44	45-60	61-96
*Stonehouse (K) 55-59		1.50	
then (U)-71			0.40
Stornoway (K) 39-54	2.50	2.00	
then (U)		0.20	0.10
Storrington (K) 61-68			1.00
then (U)-78 then (L)			0.30
*Stourbridge later (L)-95	0.50	0.30	0.30
*Stourport-on-Severn (K) 57 only	3.00		
then (U) later (R)/(M)-95		0.30	0.30
Stowmarket (K) 39-49	2.50	2.50	
then (U)-93 then (L)		0.30	0.10
Strabane (K) 49-58	3.00		
then (U) 60- later (L)		0.20	0.20
Stranraer (K) 39-43	4.00		
then (U) 46-93 then (L)		0.40	0.30
Stratford-u-Av later (R)/(L)	0.40	0.20	0.10
also NO county, stamped at Coventry 92-			0.10
also (K,X) -64 occasionally			0.80

Slough

STAPLEFORD
NOTTINGHAM
10 15 AM
11 DEC 69

STOKESLEY
MIDDLESBROUGH
PAID 1ST
13 FEB 69

Stevenage

TRING
HERTS.
6 30 PM
3 DEC 55

	1933-44	45-60	61-96
*Southwell (K) 63-76			0.50
*Southwold (K) 58-68		0.80	0.60
then (U)-73			0.50
*Sowerby Bridge (K) 40-75	0.60	0.40	0.40
Spalding (K) 35 only	5.00		
then (U) later (R)	0.60	0.30	0.10
*Spennymoor (K) 49-52		2.00	
then (U)-70		0.60	0.50
Spilsby (K) 46-54		2.50	
then (U) later (R)		0.40	0.20
Stafford (U) later (M)	0.50	0.20	0.20
also (K,X) 52 only		3.00	
*Staines (K) 26-37	0.30		
then (U)-?71	0.50	0.30	0.30
*Stalybridge (K) 33-37	2.50		
then (U) later (L)-95	0.60	0.30	0.30
(also die at Ashton-u-L -77)			
*Stamford (K) 26-37	1.50		
then (U)-89	0.80	0.30	0.20
Stanford-le-hope (U,X) 61-64			0.60
then (K) 64-67			0.60
then (U,X) 'Basildon'			0.30
then 'Stanfd-le-hope' again (L) 88-			0.40
*Stanley -82 then (X)-85		0.40	0.30
then again (L) ?90-93			0.40
Stanmore (K) 38-44	1.00		
then (U,M) ?89-			0.40
*Stapleford (K) 69-74			0.80
Stevenage ?50s-		0.20	0.05
and (K) in reserve 50-53		0.60	
and used in power cut 72			4.00
but (U) 'N Herts' error 85			6.00
*Stevenston (U) 59-72		0.60	0.60
Stirling -94 then (L)	0.30	0.10	0.05
Stockport	0.30	0.10	0.05
*Stockton-on-Tees -69	0.40	0.30	0.20
(short-lived Teesside county 68-			(0.80)
then 'Teesside' 69-74 (R)			0.30
then 'Cleveland'-78 then (L)-?80			0.30
Stoke-on-Trent	0.30	0.10	0.05
also Stoke-Hanley (M) 94-			0.40
*Stokesley Middlesbro (K) 59-		0.60	0.60
then NO Yks 68-69			2.00
Stone (K) 48-49		3.00	
then (U)-69, again (M) 95-		0.50	0.40
Stonehaven (K) 57-66		1.00	1.00
then (U) later (L)			0.30

	1933-44	45-60	61-96
*Strathaven (K) 59-77		0.50	0.50
*Street 58-64		0.80	0.60
Stretford (K) 32-35	3.00		
then (U) later (R)/(L)	0.80	0.40	0.20
Stromness (K) 67-			0.40
then (U) 90-			0.20
Stroud -71	0.50	0.30	0.30
then again (L) 86-			0.40
*Sturminster Newton (K) 58-68		0.60	0.60
Sudbury ?40- later (R)		0.30	0.10
*Sunbury on Thames (K) 51-59		0.80	
then (U)-86			0.30
Sunderland -95 then (L)	0.30	0.10	0.05
also (K) seen 44	2.50		
Sutton	0.40	0.20	0.10
then 'Croydon' (M) 86-			0.40
then 'Croydon Sutton/Sutton'(M) 91-			0.50
Sutton Coldfield (K) 33-37	2.50		
then (U) 'Sutton Cd Birm'	0.60	0.20	
then 'Sutton Coldfield Warwickshire'			
58 (later W Mids)-92 then (L)		0.30	0.10
*Sutton-in-Ashfield (K) 41-54		0.80	
then (U)-76, then (M) 87-91		0.30	0.30
*Swadlincote ?60-78		0.30	0.30
*Swaffham (K) 56-58		4.00	
then (U)-71		0.40	0.40
*Swanage 33-71	0.50	0.30	0.30
Swanley (K) 65-81 then (U,R)			0.30
*Swanscombe (K) 67-76			0.60
Swansea	0.30	0.10	0.05
then 'West Glamorgan' 75-			0.05
then 'Swansea' again 80-			0.05
then 'Swansea & SW Wales' 94-			0.05
Swindon	0.30	0.10	0.05
Swinton (K) 35-36	3.00		
then (U) later (R)/(L)	0.80	0.30	0.20
*Tadcaster (K) 57-59		2.00	
then (U)-71		0.30	0.30
Tain (K) 64-84			0.40
then (U) later (R)			0.20
Tamworth (K) 33-39	2.50		
then (U)-?95 then (L)	0.60	0.20	0.20
Tarbert (K) 59-93 then (L)		0.50	0.40
*Tarporley (K) 59-61		2.50	2.50
then (U)-71			0.40
Taunton	0.30	0.10	0.05

	1933-44	45-60	61-96
*Tavistock (K) 42-50	2.00	2.00	
then (U)-76		0.30	0.30
then 'Plymouth' (X)-86			0.30
*Teddington (K) 40-42	4.00		
then (U)-68		0.50	0.40
*Teignmouth ?37-78	0.60	0.40	0.20
then 'S Devon' (X)-83			0.30
Telford 69- later (R)/(L)			0.10
*Tenbury Wells (K) 62-82			0.40
Tenby 33-94 then (L)	1.50	0.40	0.20
Tenterden (K) 56-57		3.00	
then (U) later (R)		0.40	0.20
*Tetbury (K) 57-66		0.80	0.50
Tewkesbury (K) 50-56	2.00		
then (U)-70		0.40	0.20
then 'Gloucester G' (R)/(L) 88-			0.40
(later Tewkesb & Gloucestershire dies seen)			
*Thame (K) 60-62		1.50	1.50
then (U,L)-77			0.40
Thetford later (R)/(L)		0.20	0.20
*Thirsk (K) 36-48	1.50	1.50	
then (U)-71		0.40	0.30
*Thornbury (K) 69-78			0.50
*Thorne (K) 60-76			0.50
(S Yorks only 75-76			2.00)
*Thornhill (K) 59-74		0.50	0.50
*Thornton Heath (L) 88-?92			0.70
*Thrapston (K) 69-74			1.50
Thurso (K) 50-59		1.50	
then (U)-?95 then (L)			0.10
*Tidworth (K) 39-76	2.00	1.20	0.80
Tipton (K) 52-66		0.80	0.80
then (U) later (L)			0.30
Tiverton (K) 34-41	2.50		
then (U)-?75	1.00	0.40	0.20
then 'Exeter District' (X) 79-85			0.30
then 'Tiverton' again (X) 94-			0.30
Tobermory (K) 66-			0.40
Todmorden (K) 36-37	4.00		
then (U) later (R)/(L)	0.60	0.30	0.30
Tonbridge	0.40	0.20	0.05
(mail concentrated on Tonbridge in place of T Wells 83-)			
but 'SE Division 1' on Sundays 94-			0.10
Tonypandy (K) 39-46	4.50		
then (U) 54-66		0.40	0.40
then 'Rhondda 3' 66- later (R)			0.30
then 'Cardiff 13' (L) 89-			0.40
Torquay	0.30	0.20	0.10
'Torquay & Paignton' 40s	0.50		
then 'South Devon' 69-			0.05
*Torrington (K) 58-80		0.40	0.40
then (U,R)-?90			0.30
*Totnes (K) 37-46	1.50	1.50	
then (U)-70		0.30	0.30
then 'S Devon' (X) ?73-83			0.30
Totton (U,L) 90-			0.40
*Towcester (K) 55-60		1.50	
then (U)-?88			0.30
Towyn (K) 60-		0.80	0.80
then (U) 66-			0.80
then 'Tywyn' 68- later (R)/(L)			0.20
*Tranent (K) intermittent 75-79			1.00
then 'Edinburgh' (U,X) 81 only			0.40
Tredegar (K) 50 only	4.00		
then (U) 55- later (R)/(L)		0.40	0.20
Treorchy (K) 50-53	4.00		
then (U) 55-66		0.30	0.30
then 'Rhondda 5' 66- later (R)			0.40
then 'Cardiff 14' (L) 89-			0.40
Tring (K) 49-59		2.00	
then (U) later (L)			0.20

	1933-44	45-60	61-96
*Troon (K) 35-41	3.00		
then (U) 45-72		0.50	0.40
Trowbridge later (R)/(M)	0.40	0.30	0.20
Truro	0.30	0.10	0.10
then 'Cornwall A' 92-			0.05
but 'Cornwall 2' Sundays 90-			0.20
Tunbr Wells -83 then (M)	0.30	0.20	0.10
and 'Tonbridge' (X) 84-91			0.30
and 'Tun Wells' no Kent (X) 92-94			0.30
Turriff (K) 51-76		0.60	0.50
then (K,X) 85-89			0.50
then 'Aberdeen' (U,X) 90-92			0.40
then Turriff (U,L) 94-			0.30
Twickenham (K) 13-35	0.70		
then (U) 'Richm & Twick'	0.40	0.30	0.05
but 'Twickenham' seen 45 only		1.00	
then 'Twickenham' 70-			0.05
and 'Hounslow' (X) 86 only			0.30
*Twyford ?59-65		1.00	0.80
Tyldesley (K) 56-61		0.80	0.80
then (U) later (R)/(L)			0.20
Uckfield (K) 35-48	1.50	1.00	
then (U) later (L)		0.40	0.20
and 'Tonbridge' (X) 86-91			0.30
Uddingston (K) 55-79		0.60	0.60
but (U,X) 54-79		0.60	0.40
then (U) 80- then (L) 86-			0.30
*Ullapool (U) 64 summer only			4.00
then (K) 65 summer only,			4.00
then (U) 66-72 summer only,			1.50
then (K) 73-93			0.40
Ulverston (K) 32-38	3.50		
then (U) later (R)/(L)	1.00	0.30	0.20
Upminster (K) 40-48	3.00	3.00	
then (U)-72 then (M)		0.40	0.30
then 'Romford R81' (M) 89-			0.40
*Uppingham (K) 64-77			0.60
*Upton (L) 65-?79			0.50
*Upton-upon-Severn (K) 71-72			2.00
then (U)-85			0.50
Urmston (K) 34-36	3.50		
then (U) later (R)/(L)	0.30	0.30	0.20
Usk (K) 59-64		1.00	0.80
then (U) later (R)/(L)			0.30
*Uttoxeter (K) 44-49	3.00	2.50	
then (U)-69		0.30	0.30
then again (M) 89-94			0.40
Uxbridge -93 then (L)	0.30	0.10	0.10
*Ventnor (K) 28-38	1.50		
then (U)-77		0.30	0.20
*Virginia Water (X) 67 only			8.00
*Wadebridge 67-92 then (X) 92			0.30
then Cornwall Show 93 only			0.50
*Wadhurst (K) 60-75			0.60
but (U) Sundays only 53-68		1.00	0.80
(stamped at Tunbridge Wells)			
Wakefield later (R)	0.30	0.10	0.05
*Walkden (K) 48-52		1.50	
then (U)-?67		0.30	0.30
*Wallasey later(L)-91,(X)96	0.40	0.30	0.30
*Wallingford (K) 51-61		0.80	0.80
then (U)-77			0.30
Wallington (M) 89-			0.40
*Wallsend (K) 33-48	1.50	1.50	
then (U)-76 then (X)-85		0.30	0.30
then again (M) ?90-95			0.40
Walsall -94 then (L)	0.30	0.10	0.10
*Waltham Cross (K) 30-38	2.50		
then (U)-71		0.30	0.20
then 'Enfield' (X) 79-82			0.50
then 'Waltham X' (R) 85-?94			0.40

ULVERSTON LANCS. 8. — PM 5 MCH36 +

 VIRGINIA WATER 19 DEC 1967 SURREY

 WOOLVILLE 21 JLY 1990 HANTS

WESTBURY ON-TRYM BRISTOL 2. 30 PM 1 JUL 35 +

 WHITCHURCH 29 NOV 1989 SHROPSHIRE

WISHAW LANARKSHIRE 7. — PM 10 MCH 44

 YEADON 5 SEP 1966 LEEDS

	1933-44	45-60	61-96
*Walton Liv (K) 28-45	1.50		
then (U)-?67		0.40	0.30
then again (M) ?91 only			0.50
*Walton-on-Thames (K) 33-38	2.00		
then (U)-?67, (X)-70		0.40	0.30
*Walton-on-the-Naze (K) 58 only	3.50		
then (U)-85, again (R) 93-		0.40	0.20
*Wantage (K) 49-56	1.50		
then (U)-77		0.40	0.20
Ware (K) 44-48	3.00	3.00	
then (U) later (M)		0.20	0.20
*Wareham (K) 49-51	3.00		
then (U)-71		0.30	0.20
Warley 67-92 then (M)			0.10
(incl machine at Smethwick 67-76)			
*Warlingham (K) 54-70		1.00	0.80
Warminster (K) 38-42	4.00		
then (U) later (M)		0.30	0.30
Warrington (K) 11-50	2.50	2.00	
but (U) 30- later (L)	0.30	0.20	0.10
Warwick (M) 91-			0.40
('Warwick & Leamington Spa' see Leamington)			
Washington (K) 60-69		0.50	0.50
then (U,M) 90-			0.50
Waterlooville,Portsmouth ?59-		0.30	0.20
then 'P'mouth erased' 90 only			1.00
then NO Portsmouth (R)/(L) 90-			0.30
Watford	0.30	0.10	0.05
*Wavertree (K) 13-44	1.00		
then (U)-66	0.60	0.30	0.30
*Wednesbury -67	0.60	0.40	0.40
Wellingborough later (L)	0.50	0.30	0.20
*Wellington Salop -69	0.60	0.60	0.40
*Wellington Som (K) 48-49		3.00	
then (U) later (M)-?89		0.40	0.30
then 'Taunton' (X) 94			0.30
then 'Wellington' (X) 96			0.30
Wells (K) 34-48	1.50	1.50	
then (U) later (M) 87-		0.40	0.30
*Wells-next-the-sea (K) 62-76			0.50
Welshpool (K) 51-54		3.50	
then (U) 57- later (R)/(L)		0.40	0.20
Welwyn 'Welwyn' 35-54	0.40	0.40	
then 'W Gdn City' later (L)		0.30	0.20
*Wem (K) 61-70			0.60
then (U,R)-87			0.40
Wembley	0.40	0.30	0.30
then 'Harr & Wembley E,F' 69-			0.20
then 'Harrow E,F' 80- later (L)			0.20
West Bromwich	0.30	0.20	0.20
then 'Birmingham' (R) 93-			0.20
*Westbury (K) 48-58		0.80	
then (U) later (L)-85		0.40	0.20
*Westbury-on-Trym (K) 35	4.00		
then (U), later (R)-87	0.60	0.30	0.30
*West Derby 57- later (L)-?87		0.60	0.40
West Drayton PDO (M) 90-			0.40
*Westerham (K) 60-74			0.60
but (U,X) 70 only			1.50
then 'Sevenoaks' (X) 82-83			0.30
then 'Tonbridge' (X) 84 only			0.30
*Westgate (K) 32-35	3.50		
(W Hartlepool see Hartlepool)			
*Westhoughton (K) 61-68			2.50
*West Kilbride (K) 62-71			2.00

	1933-44	45-60	61-96
*West Kirby (K) 33-38	3.50		
then (U) 59-?70		0.40	0.40
*West Malling (K) 60-63		1.00	1.00
Weston-super-Mare			
later (R)-93 then (X)	0.30	0.20	0.20
West Wickham (K) 48-81		0.50	0.40
then (U,R)			0.30
Wetherby (K) 51-59		2.00	
then (U)-71, again (U,M) 84-			0.50
*Weybridge	0.30	0.20	0.10
then 'Kingston 2,3,4'(L) 87-91			0.20
Weymouth later (L)	0.60	0.30	0.20
and (K) as reserve 55 only	1.50		
*Whitby later (L)-87	0.50	0.30	0.20
*Whitchurch Hants (K) 51-59	1.00		
then (U)-68		0.40	0.40
Whitchurch Shrop ?59- later (L)		0.50	0.30
Whitehaven (K) 29-35	2.50		
then (U)-93 then (R)/(L)	0.60	0.30	0.20
Whitley Bay -76 then (X)-85	0.50	0.40	0.20
then again (M) ?90-			0.40
(continued at new N Tyneside office 95-)			
*Whitstable (K) 28-36	3.50		
then (U) later (R)/(L)-95	0.40	0.30	0.30
*Whittlesey (K) 60-65		0.70	0.70
then (U)-87			0.30
Wick (K) 35-48	3.50	3.00	
then (U)-95 then (L)		0.20	0.20
*Wickford ?58-66		0.60	0.40
then 'Basildon'(X) ?80-88			0.30
Widnes later (L)	0.50	0.30	0.20
Wigan -81 then (L)	0.60	0.30	0.20
*Wigston ?55-76		0.50	0.30
Wigton (K) 54-59		1.50	
then (U) later (R)-95 then (L)			0.20
*Willenhall ?55-65		0.60	0.60
*Willerby (K) 62-75			0.60
Wilmslow Manch'r (K) 39-47	2.50	2.50	
then (U) 'Wilmslow Manchester'		0.40	
then 'Wilmslow Cheshire'			
later (R)/(L)		0.30	0.20
*Wimborne (K) 33-38	2.50		
then (U)-72	0.80	0.40	0.30
then FDCs 77 only			0.50
(stamped at Bournemouth)			
Wincanton (K) 50-70		0.50	0.50
then (U) later (R)/(L)			0.30
Winchester -92 then (L)	0.30	0.20	0.20
Windermere (K) 28-40	1.50		
then (U) later (R)	0.50	0.30	0.30
then 'Lancs & S Lakes 21' (M) 94-			0.40
Windsor -91 then (R)	0.40	0.20	0.10
Winsford (K) 53 only		4.00	
then (U)-75 (at Northwich)		0.30	0.30
then again (U,L) 86-			0.40
*Winslow (K) 62-?87			0.50
then (K,P)-94			0.60
Wisbech	0.50	0.30	0.10
*Wishaw (K) 33-48	1.50	1.50	
then (U)-51 (see Motherwell)		0.80	
then (U,X) 64-68			0.60
*Witham (K) 49 only		4.00	
then (U)-79		0.40	0.20
then 'Chelmsford W' (R)			0.30
& other Chelmsford dies -93			
(note : W later used at Chelmsford)			

	1933-44	45-60	61-96
*Witney (K) 50-51		2.00	
then (U) ?54-77		0.40	0.30
Woking (U)-84 then (L)		0.30	0.20
also (K) 52-61 (?reserve)		0.60	0.60
Wokingham (K) 33-37	3.00		
then (U) later (R)/(L)		0.30	0.20
Wolverhampton	0.30	0.10	0.05
also (K)(reserve) 35-36	2.00		
*Wolverton (K) 42-55	1.50	1.00	
then (U)		0.30	0.20
then 'Milton Keynes 12' 73-85			0.20
*Wombwell (K,R) 54-76		0.80	0.80
Woodbridge (K) 37-40	3.00		
then (U) later (R)/(L)	1.00	0.30	0.20
Woodford Green (K) 32-33	4.00		
then (U) later (L)	1.00	0.30	0.30
*Woolton ?58-66		0.40	0.40
then again (M) 89-?93			0.40
Worcester	0.30	0.20	0.10
then 'Worcester District' 83-			0.05
then 'Hereford & Worcestershire' 93-			0.05
*Worcester Park (K) 45 only		5.00	
Workington -93 then (R)/(L)	0.50	0.30	0.20
Worksop (K) 29-36	3.50		
then (U) later (M)		0.40	0.30	0.20
also 'Sheffield' (X) ?73-82			0.30
Worsley ?60- later (R)/(L)			0.30
Worthing later (R)	0.30	0.20	0.10
*Wotton-u-Edge (K) 57-61		1.00	1.50
then (U)-?69			0.50
Wrexham	0.40	0.20	0.10
also 'Chester' (X) 86 only			0.30
*Wymondham (K) 60 only		5.00	
then (U)-76			0.40
Wythenshawe (K) 48 only		5.00	
then (U) later (R)/(L)		0.30	0.20
*Yate Sodbury 72-78			0.50
(replaced Chipping Sodbury)			
*Yeadon (K) 61-65			0.80
then (U)-70			1.00

	1933-44	45-60	61-96
London contd			
*NW1 then 'NWMLO' 86-95	0.30	0.10	0.05
*districts NW2-11	0.30	0.10	0.10
(incl 'NWMLO' E,F,G,P,S,T,U at these)			
*SE1 -95	0.30	0.10	0.05
districts SE2,18 (K)-?50s	0.40	0.40	
*districts SE2-27 (U)	0.30	0.10	0.10
(SE11,17 merged 66-93			0.20)
also Thamesmead SE28 (R) 92-93			0.50
SW1 then 'SW' 83-	0.30	0.10	0.05
(but SW1 continued on (L) mail-?94)			0.20
then 'London South' 95-			0.05
district SW6 (K) -?50s	0.40	0.40	
*districts SW2-20 (U)	0.30	0.10	0.10
'Gt Britain' error (SW11) 72			10.00
(SW8 stopped but back as (L,X) 91-93, and			
SW20 stopped but back in use 90-?94)			
*W1 -94	0.30	0.10	0.05
W2	0.30	0.10	0.05
then 'Paddington' no district 85-			0.05
then 'West London' 94-			0.05
*districts W3-14	0.30	0.10	0.10
*WC -93 (one m/c continues!)	0.30	0.10	0.05
& *'Lond Temp Office' 35-49	5.00	5.00	
and *'Home District' 35-37	5.00	(Sundays)	

Channel Isles (see also chapter 17)

	1933-44	45-60	61-96
Alderney (Pitney Bowes machine) 92-			3.00
then (U) 93-			0.60
Guernsey	0.40	0.10	0.10
then Guernsey PO 69-			0.05
Jersey	0.40	0.10	0.10
then Jersey CI 69-			0.05
(both used unique straight line canceller			
after independence)			

Winchm Hill   Battersea SW11
N21

	1933-44	45-60	61-96
Yeovil -92 then (L)	0.30	0.20	0.10
York	0.30	0.10	0.05
and (K)(?reserve) 44-56	1.00	1.00	
Ystalyfera 'Swansea 14' (L) 89-			0.40

London (all sub-districts later (R)-about 93,
some ended earlier ?90, see (M) next page)

	1933-44	45-60	61-96
Mount Pleasant 'London'	0.30	0.10	0.05
(used on "country mail" posted in EC, this			
segregation only to 94)			
then 'IS MLO' 80-			0.05
but 'Mount Plesant' error 85			20.00
then 'Mount Pleasant' 96-			0.05
E1 then 'E1-E18' 82-	0.30	0.10	0.05
*districts E2-E18	0.30	0.10	0.10
(E16 Victoria Docks no 's' 67-93			0.20)
(E2/9 merged 77-, then E2/8/9 87-93			0.40)
(E14 'Poplar & Isle of Dogs' 91-93			0.40)
*EC -95 (London mail)	0.30	0.10	0.05
*FS (Foreign Section) -90	0.40	0.20	0.20
N1 then 'London North' 95-	0.30	0.10	0.05
*districts N2-22	0.30	0.10	0.10
(N11 (K) 34),(N13/21 merged 71-93			0.20)

Isle of Man (see also chapter 17)

	1933-44	45-60	61-96
*Ballasalla 90-93			0.60
*Castletown (K) 59-		3.00	1.00
(one-line inscription 75 only			2.00)
then Pit Bowes 76-77 (contin lines)			5.00
then (K) again briefly 77			1.50
then (U) 77-93			0.20
Douglas	0.50	0.30	0.05
Peel (K) 58-		3.00	1.00
then Pit Bowes 76-77 (contin lines)			5.00
then (K) again briefly 77			1.50
then (U) 77- (wavy lines 1.50)			0.30
*Port Erin 66-93 (summer only -77)			0.20
*Port St Mary 67-93 (ditto)			0.20
but Pit Bowes 76-77 (contin lines)			5.00
Ramsey (K) 50-		3.00	
then (U) 57-		0.40	0.20
Southern DO (U,X) 93-			0.50

London missort marks

The code denotes the office concerned. These dies were usually applied to the reverse of missorted letters and Universal dies were normally applied without wavy lines, but sometimes with slogans, less often with wavy lines. The same dies were occasionally used for normal stamping purposes also. Some dates are from British Postmark Society Bulletin. As concentration in London took further steps in the 1990s MOST ENDED BETWEEN 1992-94, but some continue. (H) denotes handstamps only seen.

LONDON
— 75 —
— A —
16 DEC 63

		33-44	45-60	61-96
1	Highgate N6 68-			0.40
2	E Finchley N2 59-		0.50	0.40
3	Whetstone N20 90-			0.40
3B	Hornsey N8 67-			0.40
4	Hampstead NW3 54-		0.50	0.40
	(also used at SW!!)			
4B	Southgate N14 69-			0.40
5	Hendon NW4 64-			0.40
5B	Holloway N7 57-		0.50	0.40
6A	EC Dist Office 50-		0.40	0.20
	(EC/-6A- error 63-64			1.00)
6B	Clapton E5 69-		0.50	0.40
7	Stoke Newington N16 62-			0.40
8	W Brompton SW10 60-			0.40
8B	Hackney E8 60-			0.40
9	Kentish Town NW5 70-			0.40
10	S Kensington SW7 56-		0.50	0.30
11	Chelsea SW3 54-		0.50	0.40
11B	Poplar E14 68-			0.40
12	Bow E3 68-			0.40
13	Stratford E15 69-			0.40
14	E Ham E6 68-			0.40
15	Highbury N5 67-			0.40
16	Woolwich SE18 59-		0.50	0.40
17	Leytonstone E11 69-			0.40
18	Deptford SE8 68-			0.40
19	Finsbury Park N4 58-		0.50	0.40
20	Greenwich SE10 59-		0.50	0.40
21	Charlton SE7 59-		0.50	0.40
21B	Rotherhithe SE16 58-		0.50	0.40
22	Plaistow E13 70-			0.40
23	Brockley SE4 60-		0.50	0.40
23B	Brixton SW2 54-		0.50	0.40
24	Dulwich SE21 58-		0.50	0.40
25	Sydenham SE26 59-		0.50	0.40
26	N Kensington W10 56-		0.50	0.40
26B	S Lambeth SW8 56-		0.50	0.40
27	Clapham SW4 61-			0.40
27B	Stockwell SW9 56-		0.50	0.40
28	Tooting SW17 69-			0.40
28B	Streatham SW16 68-			0.40
29	Forest Gate E7 68-			0.40
30	Lee SE12 66-			0.40
30B	Maida Hill W9 57-		0.50	0.40
31	Wandsworth SW18 69-			0.40
31B	Battersea SW11 49-		0.50	0.30
32	Putney SW15 69-			0.40
33	Mortlake SW14 69-			0.40
34	Earl's Court SW5 55-		0.50	0.40
34B	Acton W3 59-		0.50	0.40
35	Bethnal Green E2 69-			0.40
35B	Ealing W5 57-		0.50	0.40
36	Balham SW12 69-			0.40
36B	Hanwell W7 60-		0/50	0.40
37	Eltham SE9 86-			0.40
37B	Notting Hill W11 57-		0.50	0.40
38	Kensington W8 57-		0.50	0.40
39	Hammersmith W6 57-		0.50	0.40

		33-44	45-60	61-96
39B	Shepherds Bush W12 60-		0.50	0.40
40	Inland Sect MP 58-		0.30	0.20
41	Barnes SW13 69-			0.40
41B	St Johns Wood NW8 68-			0.40
42	Walworth SE17 61-66 (then 45)			1.00
43	Golders Green NW11 68-			0.40
44	Manor Park E12 69-			0.40
44B	The Hyde NW9 68-			0.40
45	Kenn/Walworth SE11/17 66-			0.40
46	Palmers Green N13 (H)			
46B	Fulham SW6 54-		0.50	0.40
47	Finchley Church End N3 90-			0.40
48	N Finchley N12 69-			0.40
48B	Forest Hill SE23 61-			0.40
49	Abbey Wood SE2 64-			0.40
49B	S Norwood SE25 58-		0.50	0.40
50	Victoria Docks E16 69-			0.40
51	New Southgate N11 58-		0.50	0.40
51B	Winchmore Hill N21 78-			0.40
52	Herne Hill SE24 61-			0.40
52B	Wood Green N22 68-			0.40
53	Homerton E9 69-			0.40
53B	Upper Holloway N19 78-			0.40
54	Norwood SE19 60-			0.40
55	W Kensington W14 56-		0.50	0.40
56	S Woodford E18 69-			0.40
57	Chiswick W4 58-		0.50	0.40
58	Mill Hill NW7 68-			0.40
59	W Wimbledon SW20 69-			0.40
60	Kilburn NW6 51-		0.50	0.40
	(Kilburn-60- error 59-80		2.00	2.00)
61	Willesden NW10 38-	1.00	0.50	0.30
62	S Tottenham N15 68-			0.40
63	Wimbledon SW19 63-			0.40
64	W Ealing W13 60-		0.50	0.40
65	Camberwell SE5 63-			0.40
66	Lewisham SE13 59-		0.50	0.40
67	Peckham SE15 58-		0.50	0.40
68	Kennington SE11 62-66 (then 45)			1.00
69	Blackheath SE3 62-			0.40
70	Anerley SE20 (H)			
71	Catford SE6 60-		0.50	0.40
72	W Norwood SE27 59-		0.50	0.40
73	WC Dist Office 35-	1.00	0.40	0.30
	(London WC-73- error 60-62			1.50)
75	Paddington W2 (K)33-63	1.50	1.00	1.00
	and (U) 51-		0.40	0.20
76	New Cross SE14 62-			0.40
77	E Dulwich SE22 59-		0.50	0.40
78	SE District Office 51-		0.50	0.30
79	SW District Office (K) 55-57	2.00		
	and (U) 37-	1.50	0.50	0.30
79B	SW MLO Nine Elms SW8 83-			0.40
80	Tottenham N17 62-			0.40
81	Lower Edmonton N9 60-		0.50	0.40
82	Leyton E10 69-			0.40
83	Upper Edmonton N18 85-			0.40
84	Chingford E4 68-			0.40
85	Walthamstow E17 68-			0.40
86	NW District Office 45-		0.50	0.30
87	North Dist Office 49-		0.50	0.30
88	East Dist Office 36-	0.80	0.50	0.30
89	West Dist Office 13-	0.80	0.40	0.20
90	Muswell Hill N10 58-		0.50	0.40
91	Cricklewood NW2 54-		0.50	0.40

Index to 'generic' identities (see also chapter 27)

The town where a generic or joint town die is used can be identified from this list, then cross reference may be made to the preceding list. London offices are excluded. * is used to denote obsolete inscriptions. Two further generics only used in "First day of issue" handstamps are Herefordshire (Hereford) and South Lakeland (Kendal). Others are confined to meter marks, while obsolete inscriptions such as Coatbridge/Airdrie linger on in meter marks.

Generic/joint description	Town where used
*Blackburn & Accrington	Blackburn
*Blackburn & NE Lancs	Blackburn
*Bolton & Bury	Bolton, Bury
*Bournemouth-Poole	Bournemouth
*Bournemouth District	Bournemouth
*Brighton & Hove	Brighton
*Bromley & Beckenham	Bromley
*Buckhaven Methil Leven	Leven
Burnley & Nelson	*Burnley, Nelson
Burnley & Pendle	Burnley, Colne
Bury Bolton Wigan	Bolton, Bury
*Camborne Redruth	Redruth
Cardiff Newport	Cardiff
Chesham & Amersham	Amersham
Cheshire	Crewe
*Chester Clwyd Gwynedd	Chester
Chester/Clwyd 1	Chester
Chester & Clwyd/1	Chester
Cleveland	Middlesbrough, *Hartlepool, *Stockton-on-Tees
*Clwyd, Clwyd 2	Rhyl
*Clwyd 1	Chester
Clyde Valley	Motherwell, Biggar, *Lanark
*Coatbridge & Airdrie	Coatbridge
Cornwall	Truro, *Bodmin, Falmouth, *Hayle, Helston, Newquay, Penzance, Redruth, *St Austell, St Ives
Coventry & Warwickshire	Coventry
Croydon/Sutton	Croydon, Morden, Sutton
Cumbria Dumfries & Galloway	Carlisle
Dorchester S & W Dorset	Dorchester
Dorset & SW Hants	Bournemouth
*Edinburgh Lothian Fife Borders	Edinburgh
Exeter District (or Exeter & District)	Exeter, *Dawlish, Exmouth etc
*Fylde Coast (variations)	Blackpool
Fylde Blackpool Wyre	Blackpool etc
Gatwick MLO	Redhill's MLO at Crawley
Glastonbury & Street	Glastonbury
Gloucestershire	Gloucester etc
Grimsby & Cleethorpes	Grimsby
Gwent	Newport Gwent
Gwynedd N (North)	Bangor Gwynedd (Sundays)
Gwynedd S (South)	Caernarfon (Sundays)
*Harrow & Wembley	Harrow, Wembley, Northwood, Pinner, Ruislip
*Head Post Office West Lothian	Livingston
Hereford & Worcestershire	Worcester
Huddersfield Halifax	Huddersfield, Halifax
*Ilford & Barking	Ilford

Generic/joint description	Town where used
Isle of Wight	Newport IOW
Lancs, Lancashire and Lancashire & South Lakes	[Preston and other offices in area
*Lancaster & Morecambe	Lancaster
Leicestershire	Leicester
*Llandudno-Colwyn Bay	Colwyn Bay
Lynton & Lynmouth	Lynton
*Mablethorpe & Sutton on Sea	Mablethorpe
*Medway	Chatham
Medway & Maidstone	Maidstone
Royal Mail Midlands	Derby (Sundays)
Mid Northumberland	Morpeth
*Motherwell & Wishaw	Motherwell
*Newport Mon NP3	Ebbw Vale
Northamptonshire	Northampton
North Devon	Barnstaple
*North Herts (error)	Stevenage
*Perth Dundee Angus	Perth
*Plymouth & District	Plymouth (Sundays)
Plymouth Cornwall & W Devon	Plymouth, *St Austell etc
Portsmouth & IOW	Portsmouth
*Portsmouth & Southsea	Portsmouth
*Reigate & Redhill	Redhill
*Rhondda	Pontypridd etc
*Richmond & Twickenham	Twickenham
Rochdale Oldham Ashton-u-Lyne	Oldham
*Rochester & Chatham	Chatham
*Romford & Dagenham	Romford
*Scottish Borders	Galashiels, Hawick, Kelso
*Sennen & Lands End	(used at Penzance)
Shropshire & Mid Wales	Shrewsbury
Slough/Windsor SLO-9	Slough
*South Coast (error)	Brighton
South Devon	Torquay (+ others at Xmas)
SE Division 1	Tonbridge (Sundays)
SE Division 2	Croydon (Sundays)
SW County Durham	Bishop Auckland
Sussex Coast	Brighton, *Hove
Swansea & SW Wales	Swansea
*Teeside	Middlesbrough, Hartlepool, Stockton-on-Tees
*Thanet	Margate, Ramsgate, Broadstairs
*Torquay & Paignton	Torquay
Tyneside-NE-SR	Newcastle upon Tyne
*Warwick & Leamington Spa	Leamington Spa
*West Glamorgan	Swansea etc
Worcester District (see also Hereford & Worcs)	*Worcester, other offices in area

"Collecting Slogan Postmarks" is the flagship
of the series! It includes the story of how
slogans came about in 1917 and how they
developed; gives details of late uses,
inverteds, diamonds, triangles, Paid
dies, Maritime, Savings Bank etc etc

.. and INCLUDES FULL LISTING TO 1969

COLLECTING SLOGAN POSTMARKS

by Cyril R H Parsons, Colin G Peachey & George R Pearson

SLOGAN POSTMARKS OF THE SEVENTIES

An Illustrated Reference Catalogue of slogan postmarks first used or re-introduced in the UK during the 1970s

by Cyril R H Parsons & George R Pearson

PRICE £9.95 plus £1.30 postage & packing (overseas £2)

"Seventies" is 260 pages, crammed with
data on the spread of postcodes,
county change, decimalisation etc.

PRICE £8.50 plus £1.50 postage & packing (overseas £2.30)

SLOGAN POSTMARKS OF THE NINETIES

PART 1: THE FIRST FIVE YEARS 1990-1994

An Illustrated Reference Catalogue of slogan postmarks first used or re-introduced in the UK in 1990-1994

by Cyril R H Parsons, Colin G Peachey & George R Pearson

Published in the U.K. by the Authors, 1995

ISBN 0 904548 06 6

£6.95

SLOGAN POSTMARKS OF THE EIGHTIES

An Illustrated Reference Catalogue of slogan postmarks first used or re-introduced in the UK during the 1980's

WE ♥ LEAD-FREE

R H Parsons, Colin G Peachey
orge R Pearson

"Eighties" **PRICE £5.95 plus £1 postage & packing (overseas £1.50)**

"Nineties part 1 1990-1994" **PRICE £6.95 plus £1 postage & packing (overseas £1.50).** Part 2 is due in 2000 - please enquire.

All available from

C. G. PEACHEY
19 MOORLAND ROAD
HEMEL HEMPSTEAD
HERTS. HP1 1NH

11. Slogan Postmarks

In 1917 the "wavy line" segment of a machine postmark on letters was first used to advertise the Government's War Bond scheme. The idea soon spread to advertising events and Post Office messages eg "Post early for Christmas". The Wembley Exhibition of 1924 was advertised by means of slogans from as early as 1922, then further slogans were used on mail posted at the actual event in 1924 and again in 1925.

In 1956 the first local slogan was used - "Rochdale Centenary" - then from 1963 the first "local publicity" slogan advertised Hastings, with no event or anniversary involved. Also in 1963 came the first "transposed" slogan with the legend to the LEFT of the town die. But the Post Office remained adamant that no commercial advertising could be involved unless an anniversary or event was included eg "Gibbons Centenary Stamp Show" of 1965. The policy changed in the 1980s and advertising is now permitted, indeed actively marketed, hence, for example, the nationwide "Kit Kat" and "Quality Street" slogans in 1995-96.

By 1996 over 7000 slogans have been used. Thus there is ample opportunity for thematic collectors to search the lists for designs representing their own interest. The ever-popular Post Office Savings Bank and meter correction slogans are shown at the end of the chapter.

The reference numbers shown are from the books of Parsons, Peachey and Pearson (for details see Bibliography); these are used with permission. The numbers in brackets show approximate numbers of dies of each slogan (if no number then one die). Listed are all slogans to 1925, then a selection, including most of "the classics".

A pricing guide is shown below. The minimum values are for clean covers, but * indicates a value of the order of £100-£150.

> "Strips" or cut outs .... One quarter valuation shown
>   (slogans separated from town dies should be discarded)
> Slogan with square paid die, in red .... Six times normal
>   (to 1955, modern ones are more scarce; circular paid dies are unusual
>   and impressions with slogans are scarce)
> Slogan with diamond census die (generally to 1985)]
> Slogan with triangular die (generally to 1968) ...] Three times normal
> Slogan with London missort die (number at foot) ...]
> Early or late use .... 1½ times normal

11/1   11/2

	1917				1918 continued		
1	War Bonds Now,						
	single 11/1	(42)	1.50	7	Feed the Guns,		
2	War Bonds Now,				continuous, 34mm	(130)	4.50
	continuous, 33mm	(100)	1.00	7A	Feed the Guns, 38mm	(6)	5.00
3	War Bonds Now, 28mm	(8)	2.50				
					1922		
	1918			8	BIF 1922	(5)	3.50
A4	War Bonds, single	(2)	20.00	9	Cable Canada, boxed	(2)	1.00
4	War Bonds, lines r & l	(30)	0.75	10	Cable Canada, unboxed		*
5	War Bonds, lines rt	(20)	1.50	11	Cable Canada,		
6	Feed the Guns, single	(40)	4.00		continuous, Leicester		20.00

	1922 continued		
12	Post Early boxed, single	(25)	0.50
13	Post Early boxed, continuous, Newcastle		5.00
14	Empire Exhibition, single 11/2	(22)	0.50
15	Empire Exhibition, continuous	(12)	1.00
16	BIF 1923	(10)	3.00
	1923		
17	Ulster Pavilion, single	(2)	25.00
18	Ulster Pavilion, continuous (N Ireland)	(3)	60.00
	1924		
19	BIF 1924	(12)	2.50
A20	Empire Exhib. 55mm		4.00
20	Empire Exhib Wembley (on mail at exhibition)		4.00
21	Pageant of Empire	(30)	2.00
	1925		
22	Empire Exhibition	(30)	0.50
23	Ulster Pavilion	(2)	17.50
24	Empire Exhib Wembley (on mail at exhibition)		5.00
24A	Govt. Pavilion		15.00
25	Join the Fellowship	(5)	3.00
26	London Defended	(25)	1.50
27	Torchlight Tattoo, dates Aug-Sept	(25)	1.50
28	ditto to 10th Oct.	(10)	5.00
29	ditto dates removed	(10)	20.00
30A-E	ditto dots, lines etc.	(29)	10.00
31	British Goods, large	(200)	0.40
32	British Goods, small	(15)	1.50
33	British Goods, continuous, London NW1		50.00
A34	British Made Goods		50.00
34	Christmas -FOR-	(100)	1.00
35	BIF 1926	(12)	1.75

Only a selection of slogans are listed from this point.

	1926		
36	British Goods, framed	(2)	6.00
37	King's Roll	(50)	2.50
38	Say it by Telephone	(125)	1.25
39	Christmas -FOR-	(100)	0.75
	1927		
42	BIF Feb 20-March 2	(12)	1.50

	1928		
44	BIF Feb 18-March 1	(12)	1.50
	1929		
45	Newcastle Exhibition	(30)	1.00
46	Christmas-FOR-	(100)	0.75
	1930		
47	BIF Feb 17-28	(12)	3.00
	1931		
50	BIF Feb 16-27	(12)	3.00
51	BIF Cotton	(30)	3.50
52-62	Series of 10 telephone slogans, 1931-3 then 1934 (25 each)		1.00
	1932		
65	BIF 1932	(18)	2.00
66	BIF Textiles	(20)	2.50
71	BIF 1933, Textiles	(20)	2.00
	1933		
72	Christmas -FOR-)		0.60
73	Christmas FOR)	(150)	0.50
74	BIF 1934, 22 mm	(30)	1.50
75	BIF 1934, 19 mm	(3)	5.00
76	BIF Textiles, 22 mm	(15)	3.00
77	BIF Textiles, 19 mm	(8)	5.00
	1934		
77Ba	Tel. Exhibition		10.00
78	Mt. Pleasant Opening		*
	1935		
84	Christmas -FOR-)		1.20
85	Christmas FOR)	(150)	0.60
86	BIF 1936	(35)	1.50
	1936		
A89	Telephone Habit G.P.O. Exhibition		10.00
91	BIF 1937	(50)	1.00
92	Young People's Exhibition		15.00
	1937		
93	Post Early sunburst	(200)	0.25
94	Post Early, boxed, Leith DO only		40.00
95	As above used at GPO Exhibition		10.00
98	BIF 1938	(50)	1.50
	1938		
M.4	All letters go by air		8.00
100	Glasgow Exhibition		0.25
100a	- Exhibition		1.50
101	- Pavilion		5.00

POST EARLY
— FOR —
CHRISTMAS

11/3

11/4

102	Christmas –FOR-) 11/3	(150)	3.50
103	Christmas FOR)		0.50
104	BIF 1939	(50)	1.00
	1939		
106	Post Early sunburst	(?)	0.50
107	Road Users	(100)	0.50
108	Grow more Food	(75)	0.50
109	Christmas –FOR-)	(100)	10.00
110	Christmas FOR)		0.50
	1940		
111	Post Early sunburst	(?)	0.25
112	Grow more food	(50)	1.50
113	Kitchen Front	(50)	1.50
114	Save waste paper	(50)	1.50
115	Christmas –FOR-	(3)	10.00
116	Christmas FOR	(100)	0.50
	1941		
118	Kitchen Front, Cambridge		5.00
	1942		
122	Post Early sunburst	(?)	1.00
123	Christmas FOR	(50)	1.00
	1945		
128	Post Early sunburst	(8)	1.00
129	Victory Europe	(400)	0.30
130	Victory Japan	(400)	0.30
(129-130 more for smaller offices)			
131	Christmas FOR	(50)	1.00
132	Christmas Holly	(100)	0.50
133	United Nations 11/4	(112)	4.00
	1946		
134	National Savings	(350)	0.40
135	Don't Waste Bread	(350)	0.40
136	Death off road	(350)	0.40
M.A8	c/o ship owner not GPO		*
137	Britain can make it	(350)	0.60
	1947		
140	BIF 1947	(50)	0.50
141	Staggered Holidays	(350)	0.30
142	Blood Donors	(350)	0.30
143	Forces Career	(350)	0.30
144	Britain for Holidays	(50)	0.50
145	Silver Lining	(350)	0.30
147	Royal Wedding	(400)	0.30

	1948		
150	BIF 1948	(50)	0.50
151	Hand on the Land	(350)	0.30
153	Nursing	(350)	0.30
154	As 151 but June	(3)	10.00
155	Edinburgh Festival	(30)	4.00
156	Eisteddfod	(12)	5.00
157	Olympic Games	(2)	1.50
158	Blood Donors	(350)	0.30
159	Save waste paper	(350)	0.30
160	Christmas FOR	(30)	1.00
161	Christmas Holly)	(350)	0.30
162	– Rough Holly)		1.00
	1949		
163	Volunteer Forces	(350)	0.30
164	BIF 1949	(50)	0.50
165	Mind how you go	(350)	0.30
166	Edinburgh Festival	(31)	1.00
167	British Air Lines	(350)	0.40
168	Scottish Industries	(30)	1.25
169	Colonial month	(100)	1.00
170	Food Gifts	(50)	1.00
	1950		
177	Road Users	(350)	0.30
178	Stamp Exhibition	(50)	0.50
179	Edinburgh Festival	(31)	1.50
180	Christmas FOR, Golders Green		30.00
181	Christmas Holly	(350)	0.30
182	– Rough Holly, Stoke		30.00
	1951		
183	Voters List	(350)	0.50
184	BIF 1951	(50)	0.40
185	Blood Donors	(350)	0.30
186	Festival Britain	(40)	1.00
187	– SE1 used at Festival		2.00
188	Civil Defence	(350)	0.30
189	Christmas Holly	(350)	0.30
	1952		
190	BIF 1952	(50)	0.50
191	Voters List	(300)	0.60
192	Postage for Europe	(350)	0.30
193	Christmas rough holly, Sheffield		20.00
194	– holly "outline")	(350)	0.30
195	– holly "solid")		0.30

172

11/5   **11/6**

1953			
196	Voters List	(350)	0.50
197	BIF 1953	(50)	0.40
198	Eisteddfod Rhyl		30.00
199	Coronation	(921)	0.30
	(more for smaller offices)		
202	Check Address	(350)	0.30

1954			
204	Voters, no lines	(350)	0.30
205	Voters, lines at rt		5.00
208	Eisteddf Ystradgynlais	(4)	4.00
210	Buy 2½d stamps in books		
	11/5	(350)	0.30

1955			
220	Eisteddfod Pwllheli	(4)	4.00

1956			
227	BIF Earls Court	(50)	0.40
228	BIF Lond & Birmingham	(50)	0.40
230	Rochdale Centenary		6.00

1957			
235	Licence for Radio-TV	(350)	0.20
237	Stalybridge Centenary		25.00
239	Elgar Centenary Worcester		2.50
242	TT Races Isle of Man		25.00
244	Jamboree	(50)	0.50
245	– used at Jamboree		1.50
	(on FDC of Scout stamps		17.50)
251	Johnstone Centenary		7.50

1958			
254	TA Jubilee	(59)	0.40
255	Bangor Abbey		2.50
258	Empire Games	(45)	0.40
261	– special	(4)	4.00
	(on FDC of Games stamps		50.00)

1959			
277	Bible Society	(10)	1.00
278	Oldham Carnival		4.00

1960			
294	Refugee Year (hand)	(350)	0.30
295	– defaced die, Halifax		30.00
298	– revised design	(350)	0.20
324	Post early candle	(350)	0.20

1961			
341	Aerial Post Windsor	(2)	1.00
347	BBC TV Jubilee	(350)	0.20

1962			
373	Eisteddfod	(6)	0.20
375	Norwich addresses long		1.00
390	Post Early, holly Stafford		3.00

1963			
LP.1	Hastings We're ready		0.40
LP.8t	Bath Assembly Rooms 11/6		0.20
403	London Underground	(50)	0.15
416t	Paisley Abbey	(2)	0.20
NB. t denotes 'transposed' but			
after 1963 t is omitted to save space			

1964			
440	Someone wants a letter		0.75
LP111	Bacup welcomes industry		0.20

1965			
514	Gibbons Cent'y Show	(30)	0.10
523	Bromsgrove Festival		0.20
LP268	Crawley best new town		0.20

1966			
LP298	Basildon faces future		0.20
631	World Cup City Sheffield	(3)	0.20

1967			
LP432	Fly Liverpool Jetport		0.20
839	Southend Illuminations	(2)	0.10

1968			
985	Harlow Charity Ball		1.50
LP653	Back Britain Bridlington		0.20

1969			
LP767	Whitby guide book 1/-		0.20
1287	Ballymena Civic Week		1.00
1302	East of England Show	(14)	0.20

1970			
1459	Vandalism costs money	(2)	2.00
1549	Philympia 70	(4)	0.15
LP963	Prestatyn welcomes you		0.30

1971			
1725	Decimal currency	(143)	0.10
	(used during postal strike		3.00)
LP1101	Londonderry visitors		0.20

1972			
1952	Internatl Book Year	(12)	0.10
LP1285	Industrial dev Consett		0.20

	1973					1983			
LP1366	Lincoln engineering 11/7		0.15		3500	GLC Thames Barrier	(4)	0.40
2190	Leigh Arts Festival		0.20		LP2119	Glasgow's miles better	(5)	0.10
2337	Human Rights	(30)	0.10			(in red from NSB		4.00)
	1974					1984			
2392	Chichester Fest Theatre		0.15		LP2132	Lincoln Philat Counter	(2)	0.10
LP1587	Southampton shopping	(2)	0.20		3593	Middlesex Cricket Lords		0.50
	1975					1985			
2700	Navy Days Portsmouth	(3)	0.20		3620	The Times	(10)	0.10
LP1747	Tenby hol guide 15p	(2)	0.15		LP2148	S Yorks day rovers	(4)	0.10
	1976					1986			
2787	Penfold PGA Sandwich	(3)	0.40		3696	Air Show Sumburgh		0.20
LP1786	Scone Palace	(5)	0.20		3726	N Lighthouse Board 11/8		0.50

11/7 **11/8**

11/9 **11/10**

	1977					1987			
2915	Southampton is MLO	(10)	0.10		LP2197	Shanklin all year hol	(4)	0.30
LP1861	Exeter Speedway		0.15		3810	Ely Cathedral 11/9		4.00
	1978					1988			
LP1903	Wimbledon Tennis Mus'm	(2)	0.10		3844	"Jesus is alive!"	(340)	0.20
3082	Nat Arts Collection	(6)	0.40		3857	Wesley 250th Anniv	(115)	0.10
					3890	Irish Geology Week	(2)	0.50
	1979					1989			
3170	Dutch Week Notts	(4)	0.15		LP2222	Victoria Place		0.30
LP1986	Hagley Hall	(2)	0.10		3944	Lead free (in green)	(370)	0.10
3259	Collect Brit stamps	(100)	0.10		3949	Mailing & Comms Show	(2)	0.30
	1980					1990 (NB: red ink in general			
3293	Sustain Scott scouts	(4)	0.10			use 5 Jan to 16 Sep 1990)			
LP2014	Torquay quality resort		0.20		4078	Stamp World 90	(625)	0.10
					4146	Croydon Business Show	(2)	0.30
	1981								
LP2047	Nat Butterfly Museum		0.30			1991			
3387	Wells 800		0.20		4180	Philips 100 years ahead			
						11/10	(500)	0.10
	1982				4196	Sunday collections	(4)	0.20
3424	Gillette Marathon	(2)	0.30		4200	Crime Line Rugby		0.50
3437	Milt Keynes Station	(12)	0.10					

	1992		
4364	Tusk Force	(15)	0.15
4368	Garden Show M Keynes **11/11**		1.00
4471	Channel 4 (in green) (148)		0.10
	1993		
4524	Safeway open in Newquay		0.30
4544	Three Counties Radio	(6)	0.20
4572	Posted at R Cornwall Show		1.00
	1994		
4660	Valentines Day	(140)	0.10
4666	Colin Richardson 40 **11/12**		1.00
4670	Le Shuttle **11/13**	(150)	0.10
4754	Happy Xmas (snowman)	(400)	0.10
	1995		
4792	Oriana super-liner	(140)	0.10
4811	Charter Day Marazion	(2)	0.40
4835	Nat'l Transplant Week	(2)	0.30
4852	Kit Kat	(154)	0.10
	1996		
4898	Recycle used oil		0.30
4922	Snickers sponsor Euro 96 (2)		0.20
4946	Posted at R Welsh Show		0.50
	(2.00 on commercial cover)		
4980	Newcastle '96 stamp exhib		1.50

MILTON KEYNES GARDEN SHOW — THE BOWL, May Day Weekend, 2nd - 4th May

MILTON KEYNES 7 30 PM 5 MAY 1992

11/11

SOUTH DEVON 1 2 PM 26 FEB 1994 1

COLIN RICHARDSON — THE BIG 40 — 27th FEBRUARY 1994

11/12

WEST LONDON 10 45 AM 24 MCH 1994 CFC 1

le Shuttle — 35 MINUTES — FOLKESTONE TO CALAIS

11/13

Other categories of slogans :
Various special purpose slogans are shown
in chapters 14, 15, 16, 18.

Post Office Savings Bank Slogans

Used in Pitney-Bowes machines at London W14, Acton W3, Richmond & Twickenham,
Harrogate, and Savings Division London N7. All struck in red except S1.

LONDON.W.14 1 JUL 1940 PAID.A?

11/14

LONDON N.7 31 AUG 1947 PAID-D

11/15

S1	OHMS Official Paid, 1926-33 (black or red)	8.00
S2	Save More, Spend Less, 1940 **11/14**	10.00
S3	Serve by Saving, 1940-45	5.00
S4	Win by Saving, 1941-45	8.00
S5	Save to win, 1941-45	8.00
S6	Save for Security, 1942-5	8.00
S7-8B	Keep on Saving (variations), 1947-54	8.00
	(variation shown **11/15**	20.00)
S9	Keep on Saving (new design), 1946-52 (variations)	2.00
S10	Keep on Saving through the Post Office, 1954-59	1.25
S11	As above but with 7 lines at right, 1957-63	0.50
S12	POSB 1861-1961 and key, 1961	4.00
S13	1966 use of S11, London N7	3.50
S14	As above but Univ machine 1966-67	3.00

From the mid 1980s Royal Mail took a closer look at the accuracy of the date in meter postmarks, and applied their own postmark to correct the date if appropriate. Handstamps were sometimes used, or machine-applied meter correction slogans as shown below (year indicates year of introduction, * denotes those believed to be no longer used). The "ref" numbers refer to "Slogan Postmarks of the Eighties" and "Nineties". The slogans are intended for meter correction duties - value from 0.40 - but some are used for stamping normal mail - value from 0.80 - in fact the slogans at Kilmarnock, Lincoln and Southend-on-Sea have only been seen used in this manner.

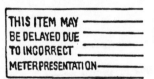

11/16   **11/17**

Ref	Town	Abbrev wording	Year	Colours used
*M.46	Paddington	Paddington meter post processed	1992	black
*M.34	Belfast	Belfast posted on date shown	1988	black/red
*M.41	Belfast	Belfast posting date corrected	1990	black
*M.37	Birmingham	Correct date of posting in black	1988	black
M.30	Birmingham	Incorrectly dated	1990	red/black
M.32	Bolton	Incorrectly dated	1993	black
		("Bury Bolton Wigan" town die)		
M.32	Bournemouth	Incorrectly dated	1988	black/red
		("Bournemouth-Poole" town die, later "Dorset & SW Hants")		
*M.30	Bradford	Incorrectly dated	1991	black
*M.30	Cardiff	Incorrectly dated	1990	black
		(later "Cardiff Newport" town die)		
*M.32	Carlisle	Incorrectly dated	1994	black
		("Cumbria Dumfries & Galloway" town die)		
*M.27	Chester	Correct date of posting in black	1987	black
		("Chester Clwyd Gwynedd" town die)		
M.43	Colchester	Correct date of posting black ink	1991	black
M.39	Crewe	Cheshire meter post	1989	black/red
*M.48	Crewe	Received in 2nd class postings	1995	red
		(both the above used with "Cheshire" town dies)		
*M.38	Doncaster	Doncaster District posted on date	1988	black
M.49	Edinburgh	This item was actually posted on	1996	black
M.30	Glasgow	Incorrectly dated	1987	black
*M.44	Harrow	Harrow meter post posted on date	1992	black
*M.30	Huddersfield	Incorrectly dated	1991	black
		("Huddersfield Halifax" town die)		
*M.35	Hull	Hull meter post	1988	black
*M.30	Kilmarnock	Incorrectly dated	1988	black
*M.31	Leeds	Incorrectly posted in 2nd class	1988	black
M.30	Leeds	Incorrectly dated	1987	black/red
*M.38	Lincoln	Doncaster District posted on date	1990	black
*M.41B	Lisburn	as Belfast M.41 but Lisburn	1990	red
*M.27	Liverpool	Correct date of posting in black	1986	black
M.32	Liverpool	Incorrectly dated	1993	black
*M.41A	Londonderry	as Belfast M.41 but Londonderry	1992	black
*M.26	Manchester	Incorrect meter presentation	1984	black
*M.26	Preston	ditto ("Lancashire" town die)	1986	black
M.30	Preston	Incorrectly dated	1994	black
		("Lancashire" town die, later "Lancashire & South Lakes")		
*M.27	Romford	Correct date of posting in black	1989	black
*M.42	Romford	Correct date shown in red	1990	red
M.47	Romford	Incorrect date Received at Romford	1994	black
M.33	Sheffield	Sheffield meter post posted on date	1988	black/red
M.32	Shrewsbury	Incorrectly dated	1993	black
		("Shropshire & Mid Wales" town die)		
*M.43	Southend on Sea	Correct date of posting black ink	1991	black
*M.32	Stockport	Incorrectly dated	1993	black
*M.45	Uxbridge	Uxbridge meter post posted on date	1992	black
*M.31	Wakefield	Incorrectly posted in 2nd class	1988	black
M.32	Wakefield	Incorrectly dated	1988	black
M.40	Watford	Watford meter post posted on date	1989	black/red
*M.36	York	York meter post posted on date	1988	black/green

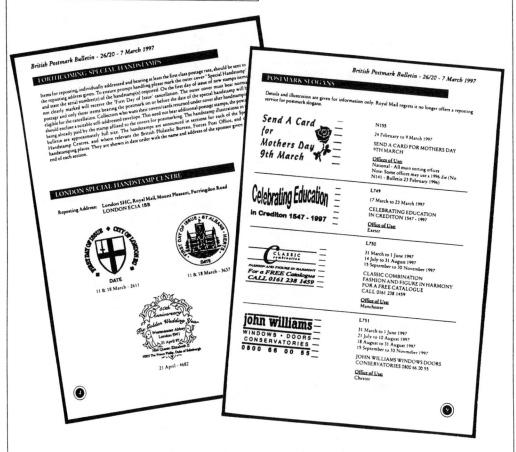

Limited Edition GB fdc New Issue Service

The Heyden Series

An original colour series in limited numbers, started in 1990. Never more than 100 serviced per issue to date. Continuity of design for each numbered issue throughout the year.

All covers competitively priced and satisfaction guaranteed. Some back issues still available.

The Heyden Series

The Alternative Series

We create at least two, often more, alternative fdc designs for each new stamp issue. Limited numbers, never more than 100 per design to date, special postmarks, creative presentations.

Some back issues still available.

Blackpool Tower Centenary

Subscribe Today!

The Alternative Series

Please write for complete details and pricing.

 STAMP SEARCHERS

P.O. Box 11, Arundel, West Sussex BN18 9SS, England

Chapter 12 contains a summary of Special Event postmarks. Full details can be found in "Pearson", regarded as the authority on this topic.

The early period (1851-1962) is now on its Fourth Edition, and Volume I (published 1991) is priced at **£6 plus £1 postage & packing (overseas £1.50)**

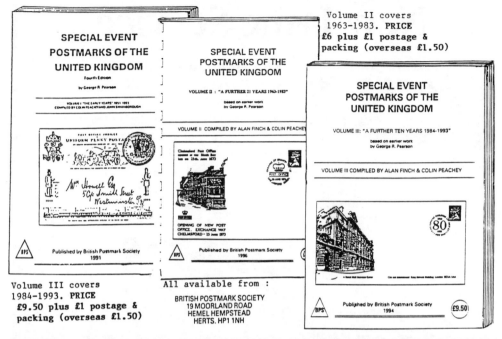

Volume II covers 1963-1983. PRICE £6 plus £1 postage & packing (overseas £1.50)

Volume III covers 1984-1993. PRICE £9.50 plus £1 postage & packing (overseas £1.50)

All available from :

BRITISH POSTMARK SOCIETY
19 MOORLAND ROAD
HEMEL HEMPSTEAD
HERTS. HP1 1NH

12. Special Event Postmarks

Up to about 1960, special event postmarks were only used at post offices set up at relevant events. These were in two categories:

(i) those at which ordinary letters and postcards were stamped, such as the popular White City exhibitions in 1908-14 ("Shepherds Bush" in postmarks). Postcards were posted in large quantities and consequently valuations are low.

(ii) those at which special event marks were used only for counter transactions. The only postal items to receive these postmarks were registered letters and their receipts. Ordinary letters and cards received an ordinary postmark. This applied to many of the agricultural shows of the 1920s and 1930s, which is why many of them are so scarce.

A selection is listed including all the early ones to 1925 and those considered to be "classics". Some early marks are only known in Post Office proof books and these are omitted. So are repeat entries: R denotes an item is repeated in later years. Valuations are shown as * or ** where items appear for sale so seldom that pricing is difficult: * indicates in the region of £100-£200 and ** £250 or more. The reference numbers are, with permission, "Pearson numbers"; see Bibliography for details of Pearson and other suggested books.

Summary 1862 - 1996

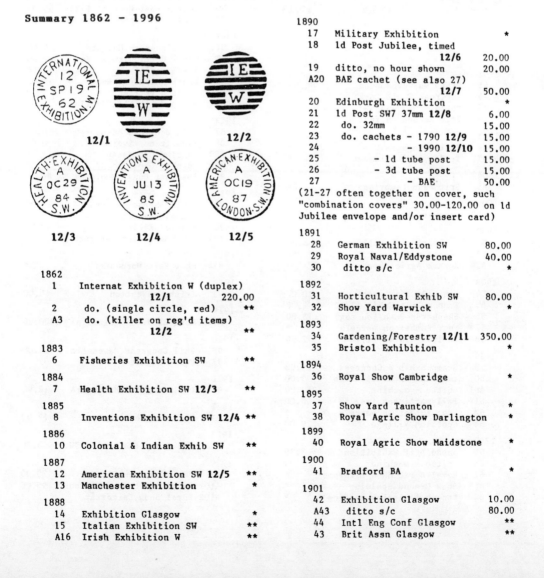

| 12/1 | | 12/2 |
| 12/3 | 12/4 | 12/5 |

1862

1	Internat Exhibition W (duplex)		
	12/1	220.00	
2	do. (single circle, red)	**	
A3	do. (killer on reg'd items)		
	12/2	**	

1883

| 6 | Fisheries Exhibition SW | ** |

1884

| 7 | Health Exhibition SW **12/3** | ** |

1885

| 8 | Inventions Exhibition SW **12/4** | ** |

1886

| 10 | Colonial & Indian Exhib SW | ** |

1887

| 12 | American Exhibition SW **12/5** | ** |
| 13 | Manchester Exhibition | * |

1888

14	Exhibition Glasgow	*
15	Italian Exhibition SW	**
A16	Irish Exhibition W	**

1890

17	Military Exhibition	*
18	1d Post Jubilee, timed		
	12/6	20.00	
19	ditto, no hour shown	20.00	
A20	BAE cachet (see also 27)		
	12/7	50.00	
20	Edinburgh Exhibition	*
21	1d Post SW7 37mm **12/8**	6.00
22	do. 32mm	15.00
23	do. cachets - 1790 **12/9**	15.00
24	- 1990 **12/10**	15.00
25	- 1d tube post	15.00
26	- 3d tube post	15.00
27	- BAE	50.00

(21-27 often together on cover, such "combination covers" 30.00-120.00 on 1d Jubilee envelope and/or insert card)

1891

28	German Exhibition SW	80.00
29	Royal Naval/Eddystone	40.00
30	ditto s/c	*

1892

| 31 | Horticultural Exhib SW | 80.00 |
| 32 | Show Yard Warwick | * |

1893

| 34 | Gardening/Forestry **12/11** | 350.00 |
| 35 | Bristol Exhibition | * |

1894

| 36 | Royal Show Cambridge | * |

1895

| 37 | Show Yard Taunton | * |
| 38 | Royal Agric Show Darlington | * |

1899

| 40 | Royal Agric Show Maidstone | * |

1900

| 41 | Bradford BA | * |

1901

42	Exhibition Glasgow	10.00
A43	ditto s/c	80.00
44	Intl Eng Conf Glasgow	**
43	Brit Assn Glasgow	**

12/6

12/7

12/8

12/9

12/10

12/11

12/12

12/13

1902		
45	Exhib Wolverhampton	80.00
R 46	Internat Exhib Cork	*
47	Botanic Gardens NW	200.00
48	Brit Assocn Belfast	*
1903		
49	Henley Regatta	*
R A51	Trades Exhib Plymouth	*
1904		
A52	Brit Assn Cambridge	*
1905		
C52	Showyard Bath	*
1907		
53	Exhibition BO Dublin	5.00
53A	ditto s/c	**
A54	Newark Agric Show	*
1908		
54	Exhib BO Edinburgh	10.00
55	Franco-Brit Exhib **12/12**	2.00
56	Shepherds Bush (on reg)	75.00
57	do. rubber on parcels	*
58	Ballymaclinton **12/13**	2.50
1909		
59	Stamp Exhib & Congress	15.00
60	Imperial Internat Exhib	3.00
A61	ditto - machine	250.00
61	Ballymaclinton (see 58)	5.00
62	do. rubber on parcels	*
64	Scottish Village	20.00
1910		
65	Japan Brit Exhibition	3.00
66	ditto - machine	9.00
67	Royal Agric Show Liverpool	*
A68	Show Ground Spalding	*
68	Lanark (Aviation meeting)	*

1911		
69	Exhibition BO Glasgow	10.00
70	Crystal Palace Fest 1-4	15.00
71	ditto reg no.7	90.00
72	Royal Hortic Ex (see 82)	*
73	Stamp Exhib & Congress	30.00
74	Coronation Exhib **12/14**	17.50
75	Royal Show Norwich	*
76	St Andrews (?golf event)	**
79	Aerial Post London 1-6	17.50
80	Aerial Post Windsor 1-2	45.00
(79-80 only on special cards/envelopes)		
1912		
81	Phil Congress Margate	20.00
82	Royal Horticultural Ex	40.00
84	Royal Society W	*
85	Exhib Shepherds Bush (Latin British)	15.00
86	Stamp Exhibition Jubilee	5.00
1913		
87	Phil Congress Edinburgh	30.00
88	Exhibition Liverpool	90.00
A89	Paisley Grandstand	*
A90	Burnley Show Ground	*
90	Internat Congr Medicine SW	80.00
1914		
92	Exhib Shepherds Bush (Anglo-American)	15.00
93	Bristol Exhib	40.00
A94	UMC (Methodist) Redruth	*
1915		
B94	Show Yard Worcester	*
1917		
95	Irish Convention	60.00
1919		
A96	Lond 213/ R34 (airship)	1300.00
1920		
96	Phil Congress Newcastle	12.00
97	Cowes Regatta	*
1921		
98	Phil Congress Harrogate	12.00
1922		
99	Phil Congress Bath	12.00
1923		
100	Int Stamp Exhibition SW1	3.00
1924		
101	Phil Congress Glasgow	20.00
A102	Royal Agric Show Windsor	90.00
B102	Royal Show Leicester	*

| **12/14** | **12/15** | **12/16** | **12/17** |

The Empire Exhibition of 1924 was GB's first commemorative stamp issue. We here introduce valuations of commemorative <u>First Day Covers</u> since the valuation of FDCs with complete sets of stamps (1d and 1½d in the case of the Empire Exhibition) is considerably higher than covers with the same postmark on other dates or bearing one stamp only. We thus include in our selection the "postmark" valuation and the "FDC" valuation on each relevant occasion. The latter is for FDCs with special postmark on illustrated envelopes (except where "plain" noted).

(for all of 102-123A, covers - or large pieces for the parcel postmarks - would normally bear the Wembley commem stamps, except for "paid" postmarks in red)

102	Empire Exhib Wembley m/c	4.00
	(on Wembley 1d stamp, any date)	
	(FDC with both stamps	250.00)
103	do. but red ("paid")	90.00
104	do. but large h/s **12/15**	7.00
105	do. but red ("paid")	80.00
106	do. double rim packet h/s	40.00
107	do. purple oval regist'd	*
108	Palace of Engineering	25.00
109	Engineering parcel	*
109A	do. but 'British' wording	*
110	Palace of Industry h/s	25.00
111	do. parcel	*
A112	Stadium used on reg'd cover	**

1925

112	Empire Exhib Wembley m/c	10.00
	(on Wembley 1d stamp, any date)	
	(FDC, both stamps, plain cover	1000.00)
113	do. but red ("paid")	90.00
114	PO Exhibit h/s (with two	
	parts of souvenir telegram)	350.00
115	PO Exhibit machine	12.00
116	Empire Exhib large h/s	10.00
117	do. but red ("paid")	80.00
118	Brit Empire Ex large h/s	30.00
A119	do. double rim packet h/s	60.00
119	do. purple oval regist'd	80.00
120	small rubber stamp	50.00
121	Brit Empire Exhib parcel	*
122	Palace of Industry h/s	30.00
123	do. parcel (confirmed)	80.00
123A	do. parcel with 'British' wording as 109A	*
C124	Show Ground Watford	*
D124	Show Yard Maidstone	*
E124	Portsmouth Show Yard	*
124	Phil Congress Cambridge	15.00
125	Railway Congress **12/16**	**
126	Chester Royal Show	80.00
A127	Show Yard Newcastle	*
B127	S Y (Show Yard) Glasgow	*
C127	Yorks Show Bradford	*

Selection only shown from this point.

1926

128	Phil Congress Liverpool	12.00
A129	Show Yard Kelso	*
129	Reading Royal Show	80.00

1927

132	Phil Congress Nottingham	12.00
133A	Newport Mon Royal Show A	*

1928

R 135	Br Industries Fair Birm	40.00
136	Phil Congress London NW1	7.50
B138	Showyard Aberdeen	*
139	London Stamp Exhibition	5.00
140	ditto s/c	12.00

1929

142	Newcastle Exhibition	40.00
144	Postal Union Congress	10.00
	(FDC ½d-2½d, plain cover	800.00)
145	ditto reg oval in purple	25.00
146	ditto packet h/s	60.00
153	Arrowepk Camp	**
B154	Calshot Aerodrome (Schneider Trophy Race)	*

1930

154	London Naval Conference	40.00
157	Margate Sanitary Congress	50.00
161	Oxford Esperanto	30.00
162	SAT London WC1	60.00
R 164	Indian Conference	40.00

1931

A167	Christian Endeavour	*
172	Lincs Show	60.00
174A	Warwick Royal Show A	40.00
178	Congr Hall Bristol (TUC)	50.00
182	Burma Conference	40.00

1932

R 184	Telephone Exhib slogan	12.00
R 185	Chelsea Flower Show	30.00
187	Sutton Coldfield Show	50.00

1933

| A194 | Bath W of England Show | 60.00 |

197	Monetary & Economic Conf	30.00
198	ditto s/c on reg'd cover	45.00
199	ditto parcel	*
200	ditto hooded packet	*
202A	Derby Show A	*

1934

204	Air Post Exhib **12/17**	5.00
R 209	Peterborough Show Yard	*
215	Mildenhall A'dme(Air Race)	25.00
	(more for flown covers)	
216	Mt Pleasant Opening slogan	**

1935

R 222	Edinburgh Ch of Scotland	40.00
B229	Mildenhall Royal Review	70.00
A230	Scientific Management SW1	*

1936

R 232	BIF s/c	10.00
R 233	BIF registered oval	12.00
235	Phil Congress Paignton	3.00
240	Royal Show Bristol	50.00
241	Mt Edgcumbe scout camp	**
	(look for two different handstamps!!)	
A243	Jamboree Camp Darlington	**
244	Stamp Exhibition London	3.00
245	Young People Exhib slogan	15.00

1945

298	CCIF (telephone conf)	*

1946

299	Phil Congress Brighton	2.00

1947

R 301	BIF s/c 1-3	10.00
R 302	BIF reg oval (purple)	20.00
A305	Wimbledon skeleton	40.00

1948

A315	Royal Show York	40.00
315	Olympic Rings (machine)	2.00
	(FDC whole set 45.00, airletter 25.00)	
315A	Wembley skeleton	10.00
	(FDC usually with 315, but 315A	
	on stamps missed by machine	70.00)

1949

R A316	BIF d/c	10.00
319	Chelsea Flower MY over date	10.00
A324	Keswick Convention	*

1950

325	Int Stamp Exhib (machine)	0.75
326	ditto h/s no time	5.00
327	ditto h/s with time	5.00
A338	Marine Insurance	*

12/18

12/19

12/20

12/21

1937

R 252	Henley Regatta (reg label)	80.00
253A	Royal Show Wolverhampton A	40.00
R E255	Birmingham Dog Show	50.00

1938

259	Empire Exhib Glasgow slogan	1.50
260	ditto wavy lines last day	3.00
261	ditto s/c 1-4	6.00
262	ditto d/c 5-6	6.00
263	ditto parcel violet	40.00
264	ditto packets violet	10.00
265	ditto PO Pavilion slogan	6.00
A271	Town Moor Newcastle	*
274	ILO London W1	*

1939

282	Phil Congress Liverpool	3.00
A283	Diss Norfolk Showground	80.00
	(new discovery!)	
284A	R Windsor Show rectangle	22.00
286	Dundee Brit Assoc	60.00

1940

287	Phil Congr Bournem'th **12/18**	2.50
288	Stamp Cent'y Bournemouth	2.50
A289	Pavilion/Bournemouth	45.00
289	Stamp Centy (in red) London	2.50
	(FDC of complete set	55.00)

338	GATT s/c 1 and 2	30.00
339	GATT reg oval	30.00
	(338-39 often on same cover)	

1951

343	Festival of Britain machine	1.00
344	ditto handstamp **12/19**	3.00
345	ditto parcel	30.00
355	Int Air Transport	25.00
356	Farnborough SBAC	40.00
357	SBAC Farnborough Hants	40.00
358	SBAC Farnborough Hts	30.00

1952

365	Phil Congress Southampton	2.00
369	Royal Show Newton Abbot	6.00
370	Int Dental Congress	25.00

1953

373	Coronation Yr Stamp Exhib	0.75
A379	Esperanto Bournemouth	40.00
388	TUC Douglas	120.00
390	Canadian PS Exhib	1.50

1954

392	Table Tennis Wembley	15.00
397	Int Railway Congress	10.00
401	Liverpool Show	8.00

```
1955
R 406  Ideal Home                    5.00
R 407  Ideal Home reg                6.00
  415  Royal Highland Show Edinb    10.00
  416   ditto parcel                25.00
  417  Abergeldie Castle            30.00
R 418  Banking Summer School 12/20  2.00


1956
  A424  Empr of Brit Maiden Voyage  15.00
  427   Health Congress Blackpool    0.75
  A429  SS Reina del Mar M Voyage   30.00
  429   Phil Congress Brighton       1.00
  A430  Showgrounds Helston             *
  433   Fish Docks Grimsby           1.50
  435   Pier Pavilion Llandudno     12.00


1957
R 436  Gifts & Fancy Goods           1.50
  439  Stampex                       0.75
  A440 Empr of England Maiden V     15.00
  A441 Mayflower II                  2.00
  447  Festival of Women Wembley     3.00
  452  Scout Jamboree slogan         2.00
  (FDC of whole set                20.00)
  453-454A 4 Sutt Coldf skeletons   25.00
  (difficult to find good impressions)
  455  Sutton Coldf 'J' parcel      50.00
  456  46th Parliamentary 12/21      3.00
  (FDC 80.00, airletter 25.00)
```

```
1958
  462  RHAS Ayr                      5.00
  463  Wimbledon Tennis timed        1.50
  464  Empire Games Village m/c      2.00
  (FDC of complete set             80.00)
  465  Empire Games d/c              4.00
  466   ditto s/c                    5.00
  (FDC of complete set 465/66     200.00)
  467  Empire Games packet h/s      40.00
  468   hooded registered h/s       30.00
  469   parcel handstamp            40.00

1959
  A470 Alloway d/c                   2.00
  477  Olympex Brighton              1.00

1960
  479  Seaborne Mail SE10            0.80
  481  Rotary Douglas               40.00
  483  Int Stamp Exhib slogan        0.50
  484  ditto large h/s (if clear!)  1.50
  (7.00 if clear on reg letter + GLO set)
  485  Phil Congress slogan          0.50
  A490 Arlanza Maiden Voyage        60.00

1961
  A492 Empr of Canada Maiden Vyge   8.00
  499  Int Scout Training Reunion    0.50
  500  Midland Stampex Birmingham    0.50

1962
R 511  Royal Highl Show Ingliston   0.50
  514-5 Rhyl-Wallasey Hovercraft    2.00
  (more on flown covers)
  517/A Pier Pavilion Llandudno    12.00
```

From about 1963 the nature of special event postmarks changed considerably. Most since that date have been used to produce philatelic souvenirs rather than to fulfil a postal need at a given location/exhibition/event. Although attractive postmarks, items are not usually stamped at the event and often not on the date concerned. In 1990 seven "Special handstamp centres" were established and since then most covers for stamping have been sent to these locations. In many cases there is now no posting box at the actual events. Many postmarks are associated with stamp issue days as the popularity of First Day Covers has increased.

From 1972 Swiss cancelling machines were used, with a grey but even postmark, then from 1992 "PAD machines" installed to give a black high-definition postmark.

Modern Special Event postmarks are on their own worth little - a standard 0.25 on a small envelope with single stamp; most however can be obtained on a special postcard, souvenir cover or first day cover. Amongst the selection of modern postmarks shown below, valuations of those marked "C" are for postmarks with relevant postcard or souvenir cover etc. For First Day Covers (marked "F") this is with complete set of the appropriate stamp issue and on relevant envelope. There are several specialist publications which will help the collector and give fuller guidance: see Bibliography for details.

```
1963
F 525  Dover Packet Service         25.00
  528  Brownsea Island               0.30

1964
F 542  Shakespeare's 400th Anniv    25.00
  546  Middlesex Philat Socs W3      0.30
  (first self-inking handstamp)
F 559-562 S & N Queensferry         20.00
  (but more for the plastic dies)

1965
  574  Gibbons Centenary             0.30
```

```
  585  Wilts Convention Chippenham   2.00
  (first 3-coloured postmark)
  590  Lincs Show Lincoln skel'n    30.00
  592  Talyllyn Centenary            0.50

1966
  637  Seaspeed Hovercraft Cowes     0.30
C 640-664 World Cup matches (each)  2.50
  (pair of two diff Final h/s       6.00)
C 665  1d Post repeat of 18          1.50
F 682  Hastings Battlefield          7.00
  694  Stamp Exhib BFPS 1000         0.30
```

12/22	12/23	12/24	12/25

1967
```
    717  Sir Francis Chichester Plym 0.30
R   721  Dulwich Millennium          0.40
R   730  BFPS 1000 (Aldershot)       0.40
    A765 Queen Mary (last voyage)    1.50
    A770 Queen Mary (last cruise)    1.50
    A774 Queen Mary slogan           0.50
```
1968
```
    820  Rathfriland Civic Week      0.50
C   838  TUC Manchester (4d only)    1.50
    859  Berlin Air lift BFPO 45     0.50
    862  Portsmouth Alec Rose        0.30
    866  RAF Wildenrath Open Day     0.50
    871  Open Golf Final Day         0.25
    891  Philatex Woburn             0.25
    909  Ulster Tattoo BFPS 1072     0.40
F   949  HMS Hermes BFPS 1074 12/22 100.00
```
1969
```
    956  Closure Waverley Route      0.30
F   958  Cutty Sark SE10            25.00
C   969  Investiture Caernarvon      2.00
(used only on 5/- Caernarvon stamps but
12.00 for 1 March as h/s not announced)
    973  (League Cup) Swindon        0.25
    1042 Cactus & Succulent Whit Bay 0.25
    A1115 Darlington Show 12/23       1.50
C   1206 Christm Marshf'd Chippenham 2.50
```
1970
```
    1292 (Harbour opening) P Talbot  0.25
    1308 Somerset Jamboree           0.25
    1336 Mayflower Boston            0.25
F   1481 Philympia Opening Day       3.00
```
1971
```
C   1559 R'1 Green Jackets BFPS1221  1.00
C   1642 Air Day RAF Henlow BFPS1166 1.00
```
1972
```
F   1863 Tutankhamun Exhibition     25.00
    1882 Vaughan Will'ms Down Ampney 0.40
C   2018 John Knox Edinburgh         2.00
```
1973
```
F   2139 Westonbirt Arboretum 12/24  9.00
    2189 David Livingstone Blantyre  0.25
R   2270 Royal Show Stoneleigh s/c   1.50
C   2275 Douglas IOM 12/25           1.50
    (souvenir cover, IOM regional stamps)
```

1974
```
C   2477 Duddon Valley Post Bus     40.00
    (on postcard with cachet etc)
    2538 Electric Scots Glasgow      0.25
    2625 Scout Camp Blair Atholl     0.25
    2728 Churchill Centen Woodstock  0.30
```
1975
```
F   2777 Chester Heritage City      15.00
    2888 Stephenson Birthplace Wylam 0.30
C   2952 Easy View Sorting Redhill   2.50
```
1976
```
C   2973 Concorde 1st scheduled flt  1.50
    3046 Opening Bridge Conwy        0.30
```
1977
```
C   3187 MLO Open Day Doncaster     20.00
    3228 Queens Silver Jub Glasgow   0.30
    3418 Liverpool into Europe       0.50
```
1978
```
F   3466 Hampton Court Tennis        5.00
C   3522 Barnes Cross Postcard       2.00
    3667 RNLI Stand Boat Show So'ton 0.30
```
1979
```
C   3741 Scotland v Wales rugby      2.50
    A3911 Kent County Show Maidstone   ?
    (only recently discovered)
```
1980
```
C   4130 To London 1980 by ship      2.00
    4382 Austral v Engl cricket Birm 0.30
C   4460 Welsh rugby centen Cardiff  1.50
```
1981
```
C   4564 Victoria Cross Exhib (red)  7.00
F   4838 Royal Wedding Canterbury    5.00
```
1982
```
F   5058 Darwin Man of Vision SW7    2.50
    5079 Opening Barbican Centre     0.30
C   5270 S Atlantic Fund Phil Bureau 2.50
C   5290 Blackpool Tram Post Office  2.00
    (postcard with "posted on .." cachet)
```
1983
```
C   5592 Nat Stamp Day               0.50
C   5846 SWDO Nine Elms Opening      1.50
```

1984

C 5878	Manchester (Kelloggs)	1.00
C 5886	Oxfordshire PO cards (set)	4.00
C 6018	Smallest TPO Garden Fest	1.50
6208	Last day of the ½p	0.30

1985

6390	Life-boat Dedic'n Ramsgate	0.30
6481	Elvis Presley 50th El	0.30

1986

C 6606	Golf Show Barbican	1.50
C 6702	York PO postcard	0.50
C 6789	Hemel Hempstead PO opening	6.00

1987

6964	World Snooker Sheffield	0.30
C 6998	Exhib Card 1 + Capex cachet	7.00
C 7063	Victorian Britain Bakewell	6.00

1988

C 7120	TPO Anniv Nat Post Museum (on postcard 88/1,2 or 3)	2.00
F 7335	Edward Lear Knowsley	6.00

1989

C 7444	Stamp Printing Walsall (on £1 stamp book, PO envelope)	5.00
F 7540	Pontcysyllte Aqueduct	5.00
C 7645	Roadside Pillar Box (red)	1.50

1990

F 7649	150th Ann 1d Post London EC (full set definitive stamps)	6.00
F 7747	Opening Day Stamp World N22	6.00
7868	Benson & Hedges Cricket NW8	0.30

1991

C 8031	Edwardian Exhib EC(set of 4)	3.00
F 8079	Greetings Clowne Derbyshire	6.00
C 8262	Rugby World Cup Twickenham (single stamp, PO souvenir cover)	1.00

1992

8421	Garden Festival parcel h/s	3.00
C 8433	'People in post' cards(set)	3.00
F 8601	Autumn Stampex	3.00

1993

F 8661	Wildfowl Caerlaverock	5.00
F 8712	£10 Britannia Porth	20.00
C 8827	Postbus 25 years Scotland	1.50
C 8856	Goodwin Sands CT16 1GS	2.00

1994

F 9056	Orlando Marmalade Cat W1	5.00
C 9099	RNLI Boathouse Tobermory	2.00
F 9248	Greg Norman champ Turnberry	5.00
C 9369	Final Despatch Aylesbury	3.00

1995

F 9450	Readers Digest coil Swindon	3.00
C 9478	Edinburgh (magnifying glass)	1.00
F 9503	Glasgow School of Art (first day of aerogramme)	2.50

1996

C 9870	K Edward VIII Sandringham	2.50
F 9913	Cartoon Art Trust London	7.00
C 10067	RHS Chelsea Flower Show	2.50
10291	Duxford Air Show Duxford	0.50

Exhibition sites

Not inscribed for particular events or exhibitions, these marks were usually used only for the duration of such events. Most Crystal Palace marks are extremely scarce. Full details in Pearson, as for special event postmarks.

| 12/27 | 12/30 | 12/31 | 12/36 |

12/26	Crystal Palace 1856-1936 (various inscriptions)	20.00
12/27	Alexandra Palace 1876 (but see operational handstamp used at Alexandra Palace in 1990, mentioned later in this chapter) ...	*
12/28	Earls Court 1893-1980 (various inscriptions)	6.00
12/29	Agricultural Hall London N 1894-1922	50.00
12/30	Shepherds Bush (White City) 1926-1937	20.00
12/31	Olympia 1892-1970 (various inscriptions, skeleton as shown 40.00)	6.00
12/32	Athletic Ground Richmond Surrey 1900-53	8.00
12/33	Balmoral Showground Belfast 1937-75	6.00
12/34	Kelvin Hall Glasgow 1949-69 (various inscriptions)	5.00
12/35	National Exhibition Centre Birmingham 1976-	3.00
12/36	RASE Showground Stoneleigh Kenilworth Warwickshire 1980-	3.00

"First Day of Issue" postmarks

12/37   12/40   12/42

Introduced in 1963, these are used on stamp issue days but ONLY ON THE NEW STAMPS. The other major feature is that these are Post Office-provided postmarks, unlike most sponsored special event handstamps. However, on stamp issue days all are available for the collector, including "philatelic handstamps" featured in the next section but one. Special posting boxes were provided at initially 30 offices but this was expanded to about 210 offices, later reduced to about 200 offices. In addition, pictorial "first day" marks are provided by the Philatelic Bureau (at Edinburgh since 1966) and at (usually) one town or city relevant to the stamp issue. Like modern special event marks, valuations depend largely on the envelope used, the stamps affixed and how the address is written (hand written addresses should be discounted). Valuations shown below are basic prices for clean plain covers with ONE stamp only.

Technical developments enabled the Philatelic Bureau postmarks and those of the "special offices" to be applied by a combination of "Swiss cancelling machines" (used from 1972), "high speed machine" (from 1985) and "PAD cancellers" (from 1992), though in most cases handstamps have been used as well.

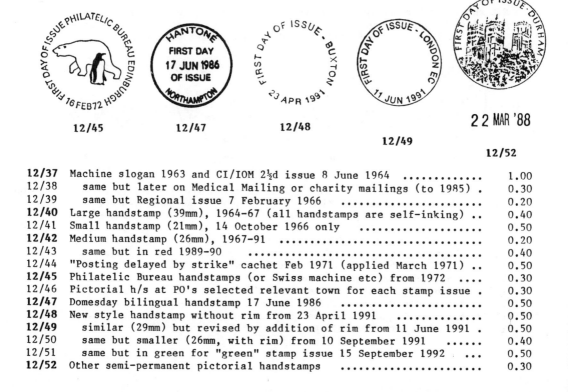

12/45   12/47   12/48   12/49   12/52

12/37	Machine slogan 1963 and CI/IOM 2½d issue 8 June 1964	1.00
12/38	same but later on Medical Mailing or charity mailings (to 1985) .	0.30
12/39	same but Regional issue 7 February 1966	0.20
12/40	Large handstamp (39mm), 1964-67 (all handstamps are self-inking) ..	0.40
12/41	Small handstamp (21mm), 14 October 1966 only	0.50
12/42	Medium handstamp (26mm), 1967-91	0.20
12/43	same but in red 1989-90	0.40
12/44	"Posting delayed by strike" cachet Feb 1971 (applied March 1971) ..	0.50
12/45	Philatelic Bureau handstamps (or Swiss machine etc) from 1972	0.30
12/46	Pictorial h/s at PO's selected relevant town for each stamp issue .	0.30
12/47	Domesday bilingual handstamp 17 June 1986	0.50
12/48	New style handstamp without rim from 23 April 1991	0.50
12/49	similar (29mm) but revised by addition of rim from 11 June 1991 .	0.50
12/50	same but smaller (26mm, with rim) from 10 September 1991	0.40
12/51	same but in green for "green" stamp issue 15 September 1992 ...	0.50
12/52	Other semi-permanent pictorial handstamps	0.30

Special Occasions

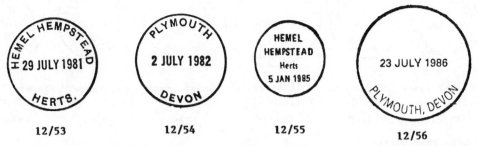

12/53   12/54   12/55   12/56

On the four occasions listed below the Post Office offered facilities for purchase of special envelopes and for posting them at the 200-or-so offices countrywide, similar to "first days" but the dates were NOT stamp issue days. Thus, for example, for the wedding of Prince Charles and Lady Diana Spencer the stamps were issued on 22 July 1981 and the "Wedding Day" postmarks were provided on 29 July. Inscriptions do NOT show the events, and datestamps were "fixed date" (prices are for covers with single stamp):

12/53	Royal Wedding 1981 (14p stamp on souvenir cover or PHQ card)	0.40
12/54	South Atlantic Fund 1982 (15½p Maritime stamp on souvenir cover) ...	0.60
12/55	Africa Appeal 1985 (31p Xmas stamp on souvenir cover)	0.60
12/56	Royal Wedding 1986 (12p stamp on souvenir cover or PHQ card)	0.40

Philatelic handstamps

These are semi-permanent handstamps which are available for all dates, not just stamp issue dates. Locations are a combination of tourist resorts (hence the alternative term "tourist handstamps") and philatelic counters. All are valued at 0.30 on small envelope with one stamp, but 1.00 for 14 Aug 1972, the (unannounced) first day of Trafalgar Square (shown here) and Chief Office London, or 5.00 each on souvenir cover. Four examples are illustrated.

12/57   12/58   12/59   12/60

Relevant Operational handstamps on FDCs

Although Royal Mail has attempted to satisfy FDC collectors' requirements by providing first day posting facilities (usually at one town relevant to each stamp issue), collectors have an interest in ALL relevant postmarks. FDCs are consequently posted, usually by registered post, and with a full set of stamps, at post offices with names relevant to a specific stamp issue. Obviously such covers have to be addressed, but the other FDC requirements described earlier apply here in order to attract the relevant values. We show here a few examples. A further allied topic is FDCs with relevant SLOGAN postmarks.

"Green" issue	Xmas issue	QEII Accession	Sport issue	Dogs issue	Flowers issue
Val. 6.00	Val. 8.00	Val. 100.00	Val. 7.00	Val. 15.00	Val. 30.00
12/61	**12/62**	**12/63**	**12/64**	**12/65**	**12/66**

Mobile Post Offices

These were introduced in 1936, initially one vehicle but later three, with a full programme of events attended from May-October each year (except 1940-46). We list the events intended for 1936-9 (two MPOs only at this stage) but some may have been cancelled. Datestamps are generally inscribed "MPO" or "MPO 1" for number 1, "MPO 2" and "MPO 3" and lettered A to F in each case. Usually used on registered mail only, valuations are for registered covers; receipts are often offered alone and these are valued at approx one third of the registered cover. Pressure on costs of attending events forced the programme to be cut back in the 1980s. MPO postmarks were last used in 1988, though the vehicles have occasionally been used since.

During the war arrangements were made for temporary post offices to be set up in the event of bomb damage, though not using the same MPO vehicles. A series of 3-digit MPO numbered datestamps were issued, but few were used.

Following publication of the pre-war list (below) in our Sixth Edition we received several enquiries concerning the details of post-war MPOs. We have details of most from about 1960 onwards (courtesy "Stamp Collecting" etc) but although the list would be too large to include in a future edition of this book, we would be interested in hearing from any collector with details of the 1946-60 period.

12/67 Golf event Little Aston	**12/68**	**12/69**	**12/71** Horse Show Derby

12/67 MPO handstamp on pre-war registered cover 30.00
(but non-registered cover from initial publicity event on 30 Sep 1936 100.00, registered covers from the other 1936 events 60.00)
12/68 Edinburgh skeleton 31 Aug 1937 (one-day publicity event) 60.00
12/69 Wartime use, London Aug 1941 rubber one-day handstamp 160.00
12/70 MPO 121 and similar numbering, wartime use on registered cover ... 100.00
12/71 Post-war events (1.00 for certificate or receipt) 5.00

Notes : AS = Agricultural Show — also note dates may include day before the event, when MPO arrived

MPO1 - 1936

6-8 Oct	Fruit Show Marden Kent	8-9 Feb	Races Nottingham	26-29 May	Bath AS Trowbridge
18-20 Nov	Races Derby	15-16 Feb	Races Derby	1-4 Jun	Races Epsom
26-28 Nov	Races Manchester	22-23 Mar	Races Nottingham	10-12 Jun	Horse Show Richmond
21-22 Dec	Races Derby	31 Mar-1 Apr	Races Leicester	15-18 Jun	Races Ascot
1937		7-9 Apr	Golf Little Aston	23-24 Jun	AS Hatfield
18-19 Jan	Races Derby	20-22 Apr	Races Epsom	25-26 Jun	Cricket Eton
		28-29 Apr	AS Ayr	30 Jun- 3 Jul	Henley Regatta
		10 May	Races Derby	5-6 Jul	Races Nottingham
		14-15 May	AS Newark	12-16 Jul	Yorkshire AS York
		18-19 May	AS Banbury	19-20 Jul	Races Leicester

22 Jul   AS Ampthill
24-27 Jul Cricket Manchester
29 Jul-2 Aug Lancs AS Manchester
5 Aug   AS Bakewell
9-10 Aug   Races Nottingham
18-19 Aug Music&Floral Shrewsbury
27-28 Aug Highland Games Dunoon
31 Aug   On exhib at Edinburgh
           (2 hours only)
3-4 Sep   Races Manchester
8-10 Sep   AS Yeovil
14-15 Sep AS Altrincham
20-21 Sep Races Leicester
24 Sep-1 Oct Golf Wadebridge
5-7 Oct   Fruit Show Marden
8-9 Nov   Races Leicester
17-19 Nov Races Derby
25-27 Nov Races Manchester
13-14 Dec Races Nottingham

1938
10-11 Jan Races Leicester
17-18 Jan Races Derby
31 Jan-1 Feb Races Leicester
9-10 Feb   Races Derby
14-15 Feb Races Nottingham
21-22 Feb Races Derby
21-23 Mar Races Lincoln
30-31 Mar Races Leicester
2 Apr Hunt Race Meeting Bolton
11-12 Apr Races Nottingham
19-21 Apr Races Epsom
27-28 Apr Cattle Show Ayr
3-4 May   Races Kelso
9 May   Races Derby
13-14 May AS Newark
18-19 May AS Wallingford
25-28 May Bath AS Plymouth
31 May-3 Jun Races Epsom
9-11 Jun   Horse Show Richmond
14-17 Jun Races Ascot
22-23 Jun AS Hatfield
29 Jun-2 Jul Henley Regatta

5 Jul   Dog Show Richmond
12-16 Jul Yorks AS Doncaster
19-20 Jul AS Tunbridge Wells
28-31 Jul Lancs AS Liverpool
4 Aug   AS Bakewell
8-9 Aug   Races Nottingham
13 Aug   AS Ulverston
17-18 Aug Floral Fete Shrewsb
25 Aug   AS Sandy
30 Aug-1 Sep Races Derby
7-8 Sep   AS Yeovil
15 Sep   AS Thame
19-20 Sep Races Leicester
24 Sep   Races Newark
28 Sep   AS Frome
3-4 Oct   Races Nottingham
22-24 Oct ditto
7-8 Nov   Races Leicester
16-18 Nov Races Derby
24-26 Nov Races Manchester
5-6 Dec   Races Leicester
12-13 Dec Races Nottingham
1939
9-10 Jan   Races Leicester
16-17 Jan Races Derby
30-31 Jan Races Leicester
8-9 Feb   Races Derby
13-14 Feb Races Nottingham
20-21 Feb Races Derby
18 Mar   Races Newark
29-30 Mar Races Leicester
3-4 Apr   Races Nottingham
8 Apr   Races Stockton-on-Tees
15 Apr   Steeplechases, Wrexham
8-10 Jun   R Horse Sh Richmond
19-24 Jun Highland Show Edinb
29 Jun-1 Jul Milty Displ Aldershot
5-8 Jul   Henley Regatta
15-25 Jul World Scout Moot Crieff
2-5 Aug   Lancs AS Lancaster
10 Aug   AS Bakewell
16-17 Aug Music&Floral Shrewsbury
30 Aug   AS Shaftesbury

MPO2 - 1938
16-18 Apr Races Manchester
21-30 Apr Golf Moortown Leeds
7 May   Races Stratford-upon-Av
13-20 May Golf Burnham on Sea
25-26 May AS Shrewsbury
2-3 Jun   Suffolk AS Bury St Ed
7-9 Jun   AS Helston
15-16 Jun AS Midhurst
21-24 Jun R Highland AS Dumfries
28-30 Jun AS Peterborough
4-5 Jul   Races Nottingham
8-12 Jul   Cricket Test Manchester
18-19 Jul Races Leicester
21 Jul   Beds AS Ampthill
6 Aug   AS Perth
20 Aug Highland Gathering Crieff
26-27 Aug Cowal Games Dunoon
2-3 Sep   AS Chester
6-10 Sep   Races Doncaster
20-21 Sep AS Altrincham
28-29 Sep Hunt Race Meeting Scone
4-7 Oct   Horse Sale Lanark
22 Oct   Races Stockton-on-Tees
1939
29-31 Mar D Mail Golf Bournemouth
8 Apr   Races Newark
15 Apr Hunt Races Meeting Bolton
18-20 Apr Races Epsom
9-10 Jun   AS Leicester
13-16 Jun Races Ascot
21-22 Jun AS Hatfield
24 Jun   Regatta Marlow
26 Jun-8 Jul Tennis Wimbledon
11-15 Jul Yorks AS Halifax
17-18 Jul Races Leicester
20 Jul   Beds AS Ampthill
26-27 Jul R Welsh AS Caernarvon
7 Aug   AS Uxbridge
21-26 Aug Boys Golf Carnoustie
4 Nov   Races Stockton-on-Tees

Operational handstamps used at events

Operational datestamps are sometimes used at temporary post offices; these can be skeleton, s/c, d/c or rubber stamps. They have replaced MPO handstamps from 1989. A selection is shown here, including one of the "Wood Green" handstamps used at the Mobile Post Office outside "Stamp World 90" at Alexandra Palace. Valuations from 5.00 on registered covers.

12/72
White Rock Pav
Royal Sanitary
Congress
Val: 10.00

12/73
Open Golf
Championship

Val: 40.00

12/74
World Scout
camp

Val: 25.00

12/75
"Stamp World 90"
MPO outside
Alexandra Palace

Val: 10.00 on FDC

12/76
Chelsea
Flower Show

Val: 6.00 on
souvenir cover

Seasonal Post Offices ie summer only

At one time about 23 offices were open for the summer season each year, largely Butlins Holiday Camps (which later either closed or changed their names). By 1996 about a dozen seasonal offices were still in operation.

12/77   12/78

12/79

12/77   Single/double circle on cert of posting (pre-1960 3.00) 1.50
                (multiply by 4 for value of registered cover)
12/78   As above but Douglas Hol Camp/IOM Hol Centre (on registered cover) 40.00
12/79   Parcel handstamp (pre-1960 16.00) 4.00

Thematic collecting

Many stamp/postmark collectors use both SPECIAL EVENT POSTMARKS and SLOGAN POSTMARKS to complement their collecting themes. These themes may be those represented by some of the chapters of this book - Royalty, Islands, Railways etc. Here are some others to show the collecting possibilities.

a) Letter boxes   Val : 0.25   Val : 0.25 (used 1983 not 1982 as
                                                      listed in Fifth Edition)

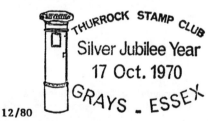

12/80

12/81

b) United Nations   Val : 4.00   Val : 0.25

12/82

12/83

c) Birds/animals   Val : 0.15   Val : 25.00 on reg cover   Val : 3.50 on FDC

12/84   **12/85**   **12/86**

d) Music   Val : 0.30   Val: 2.50 on FDC (Elgar's birthplace)

12/87   **12/88**

e) Rugby Football   Val : 0.50   Val : 1.50 on souvenir cover

12/89   **12/90**

f) Scouting   Val : 0.25   Val : 0.25

12/91   **12/92**

g) Police/crime   Val : 0.25   Val : 0.25

HELP POLICE

- POSTCODE

VALUABLES

12/93   **12/94**

h) Christmas   Val: 2.50 on FDC   Val: 2.00 on compliments card

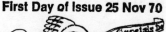

12/95   **12/96**

13. Railway Postmarks

Stations

"Postmarks of British Railway Stations" by Pipe and Blackman (see Bibliography) was published in 1994 by the Railway Philatelic Group and permission was granted for inclusion here of some of the data. The Editors are grateful to the RPG, also particularly to Grahame Blackman, Nigel Davidson, Keith Downing, Roger Dymond and Bill Pipe who have kindly helped with the careful revision that has been applied to all sections of the chapter in this Edition.

Many station postmarks are difficult to find. Many are known used on one date only: some are not known at all and these we have deleted. As we go to press some recent discoveries have come to our notice and these will be included in the Eighth Edition. Additional reports are always welcome.

A	Dated double arc	F	Double circle
B	Numeral	G	Single circle
C	Duplex	H	Skeleton
D	Squared circle	I	Rubber handstamp
E	Double circle, Scottish double arc	S	Self-inking handstamp

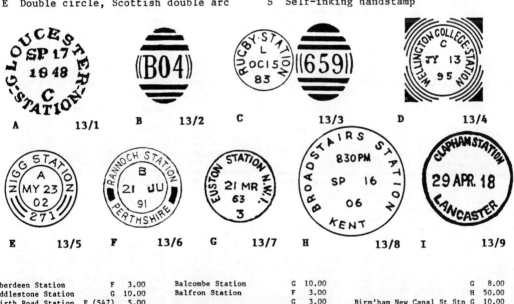

Aberdeen Station	F	3.00
Addlestone Station	G	10.00
Airth Road Station	E (547)	5.00
Airth Station	F	8.00
	I	10.00
Angmering Station	C (G73)	30.00
	G	2.00
	H	12.00
Annbank Station	F	6.00
	G	4.00
	I	12.00
Armadale Station	E (457)	5.00
Ashbourne Station	F	6.00
Ashford St'n Kent	C (31)	4.00
	G	2.00
registered		10.00
instructional		15.00
Ashford St'n Middlesex	F	2.00
	G	5.00
	H	12.00
Ash Vale Station	F	5.00
	G	2.50
parcel		4.00
Atherstone Station	parcel	10.00
Auchterless Station	E (561)	4.00
	F	4.00
	G	5.00
Aysgarth Station	D	20.00
	G	15.00

Balcombe Station	G	10.00
Balfron Station	F	3.00
	G	3.00
Balquhidder Station	E (cross)	5.00
Barnham Junction	G	5.00
Bath Station	F	6.00
	G	1.50
Beaconsfield Station	G	10.00
Bedlington Station	F	4.00
	G	4.00
Krag machine		5.00
meter mark		30.00
parcel		5.00
Bekesbourne Station	I	25.00
Belvedere Station	F	2.00
	G	3.00
Berney Arms Station	F	10.00
	I	25.00
Berwick Station N'thumbld	A	12.00
	B (66)	25.00
	C (66)	20.00
	G	4.00
Berwick Station Sussex	F	2.50
	G	10.00
Bexhill Station	C (K27)	35.00
	F	10.00
	G	6.00
Bickley Station	B (B12)	25.00
	C (B12)	35.00

	G	8.00
	H	50.00
Birm'ham New Canal St Stn	G	10.00
Birmingham Snow Hill Stn	G	10.00
Blair-Adam Station	E (652)	12.00
	H	20.00
Blantyre Station Scots local		60.00
Bletchley Station	A	50.00
	A (single arc)	50.00
	B (025)	20.00
	C (025)	8.00
	F	8.00
	G	5.00
parcel		10.00
Bogside Station	F	8.00
	G	6.00
	I	20.00
Bootle Station	C (K58)	15.00
(Cumberland)	F	2.00
	G	3.00
Bosham Station	F	2.00
	G	3.00
	H	20.00
parcel		5.00
Bournemouth Central Stn	G	1.00
Bournemouth West Station	G	15.00
Bradford Station		
"late box" hooded circle		75.00

Braidwood Station	G	6.00
	H	15.00
Brampton Junction	F	25.00
	G	3.00
	I	20.00
Brayton Station	C (K38)	35.00
Bridlington Station	F	0.50
	G	4.00
Krag machine		2.00
do. with War bonds slogan		2.50
Brighton Station registered		10.00
"R.L" (returned letter)	G	12.00
Bristol Station	A	50.00
	G	12.00
mis-sent		75.00
Broad Clyst Station	F	5.00
	H	20.00
	I	10.00
Broadstairs Station	C (737)	8.00
	F	0.50
	G	1.50
	H	8.00
registered		10.00
parcel		8.00
postage due		10.00
Buckhurst Hill Station	G	10.00
Byfleet Station	G	10.00
Caerwys Station	F	5.00
Cambridge Station	parcel	10.00
Carlton Station	G	3.00
Carron Station	G	8.00
parcel		10.00
Carstairs Junction	B (70)	30.00
	E (70)	4.00
	F	3.00
	G	3.00
	H	15.00
Castle Cary Station	G	3.00
Castle Eden Station		
	A (undated)	25.00
	A (single arc)	20.00
	B (737)	20.00
	B (D70)	15.00
	C (D70)	20.00
	G	8.00
Caterham Junction	B (C79)	20.00
Charing Cross Station	G	8.00
Chester Station	C (180)	12.00
	D	1.00
	G	2.50
straight line		75.00
registered		10.00
parcel		8.00
postage due		10.00
Chichester Station	C (190)	12.00
(Sussex)	D	1.00
	F	2.00
	G	3.50
parcel		10.00
postage due		10.00
Chislehurst Station	C (D05)	10.00
	G	4.00
parcel		15.00
Chollerton Station	I	20.00
Clapham Junction	G	20.00
Clapham Station Lancaster	I	8.00
Craigellachie Station	C (86)	50.00
	E (86)	30.00
	G	10.00
Crewe Station	A	40.00
	B (047)	25.00
	C (047)	10.00
	D	3.00
	F	1.00
	G	1.00
parcel		8.00
postage due		10.00
mis-sent		50.00
Crowthorne Station	G	2.00
parcel		8.00
Croy Station	F	5.00
	I	20.00
Cumbernauld Station	F	5.00
	G	4.00
Custom House Station	G	12.00
Derby Station	G	8.00
mis-sent		35.00

Dess Station	G	3.00
Douglas Station	G	50.00
Dover Station	C (258)	8.00
	G	1.50
registered		15.00
parcel		10.00
postage due		10.00
Drymen Station	F	3.00
	G	2.00
Eaglescliffe Junction	G	8.00
Eastbourne Station	G	12.00
East Grange Station	E (469)	8.00
Central Station Edinburgh	G	2.00
Effingham Junction	G	8.00
parcel		4.00
Euston Station	F	3.00
	G	3.00
I modern packet stamp		7.50
parcel hooded circle		50.00
registered		12.00
parcel (Euston Central)		10.00
Euston Station Irish Mail (see TPO)		
Euston Square Station		
A (single & double arcs)		40.00
	B (964)	50.00
straight line		75.00
	G	4.00
Exeter Station	A	75.00
	G	35.00
Farnboro Station		
	A (single arc)	35.00
	B (023)	20.00
	C (023)	6.00
s/ways duplex (023) large		75.00
s/ways duplex (023) small		45.00
	G	3.00
too late		30.00
Farnborough Station	A	35.00
	D	20.00
	G	3.00
Fawley Station Hereford	G	3.00
	H	15.00
Fimber Station	G	5.00
	I	20.00
Flaxton Station	A (undated)	50.00
undated s/c		50.00
	G	4.00
	I	20.00
Folkestone Harbour Stn	G	8.00
Fort George Station	B (14)	30.00
	G	12.00
	H	25.00
parcel		12.00
Freshwater Station	C (H06)	5.00
	F	1.50
	G	2.00
	H	8.00
Gartmore Station	E (578)	6.00
Gartness Station	G	10.00
Gloster Station	C (312)	6.00
	G	3.00
Gloucester Station	A	15.00
	B (312 & E94)	25.00
	C (312 & E94)	6.00
	D	4.00
	G	3.00
	H "traveller"	100.00
Godstone Station	C (874)	30.00
	G	15.00
Greenford Station	F	10.00
Hampstead Heath Station	G	4.00
Hamworthy Junction	G	4.00
Harperley Station	G	3.00
Harrogate Station	G	8.00
Harrow Station	G	12.00
Haslemere Station (Hants)	G	10.00
Hastings Station	C (342)	8.00
	F	1.00
	G	1.00
parcel		8.00
postage due		8.00
instructional		12.00
Heathfield Station	C (H54)	30.00
	G	10.00
Hendon Central Station	F	4.00
registered		4.00
Henlow Station	F	4.00

Hereford Station registered		4.00
High Peak Junction	I	15.00
Holytown Station	G	12.00
Horley Station	C (H37)	20.00
Horsham Station	C (381)	10.00
	G	4.00
parcel		10.00
postage due		15.00
Hull Station	G	10.00
Ilkeston Junction	G	8.00
Inverness Station	G	10.00
Ipswich Station	G	8.00
Killearn Station	G	3.50
Kings Cross Station	G	12.00
	H	35.00
Kippen Station	E (653)	4.00
	F	4.00
Kirkby Station Liverpool	G	3.00
Kiveton Park Station	F	5.00
	G	5.00
Knapton Station	G	8.00
	I	15.00
Knebworth Station	F	8.00
	G	2.00
	H	20.00
Knowle Station	G	15.00
Laindon Station	F	10.00
	G	3.00
	H	15.00
Lancing Station	G	15.00
Langwith Junction	F	3.00
Leeds Station	F	8.00
"late box" hooded circle		75.00
Central Station Leith	G	3.00
Lewes Station	C (451)	12.00
	D	2.00
	F	3.00
	G	4.00
parcel		10.00
postage due		10.00
Lintz Green Station	C (F77)	35.00
	G	30.00
Liverpool Lime Street Stn	F	10.00
	G	10.00
	I	12.00
"late box" hooded circle		100.00
Liverpool St Station	G	2.00
parcel		10.00
Livingston Station	F	6.00
	G	4.00
	I	15.00
Llandudno Junction	F	1.00
	G	2.00
	H	15.00
parcel		5.00
Lochearnhead Station	E (552)	5.00
Lockington Station	G	3.00
London Bridge Station	G	4.00
	H	40.00
parcel hooded circle		100.00
Lowthorpe Station	G	2.50
Ludgate Hill Station	G	12.00
Maghull Station	G	2.00
Maidstone Station	C (493)	15.00
Manchester Station	G	12.00
"late box" hooded circle		100.00
Manchester Exchange Stn	G	10.00
Manchester Hunts Bank Stn	G	10.00
Manchester London Rd Stn	F	12.00
	G	12.00
	I	30.00
Martin Mill Station	F	3.00
	G	3.00
	I	6.00
rubber skeleton		75.00
Marylebone Station	G	12.00
Meopham Station	F	6.00
	G	3.00
	H	20.00
Micheldever Station	A	35.00
	B (22)	15.00
	C (22)	4.00
	F	12.00
	G	3.00
	H	15.00
parcel		10.00
instructional		10.00

Middleton Junction	F	8.00
	G	3.00
Milford Junction	A	30.00
	A (single arc)	35.00
	B (015)	25.00
	G	30.00
Mintlaw Station	E (cross)	3.00
	F	2.00
	G	3.00
	H	20.00
	parcel	10.00
Misterton Station	F	2.50
Moorgate St Station	G	15.00
Murthly Station	E (405)	20.00
Murton Station	G	4.00
Muthill Station	E (606)	15.00
Newcastle on Tyne Station	B (A16)	40.00
	G	40.00
New Galloway Stat'n E (475)		6.00
	H	40.00
New Killearn Station	G	10.00
New Southgate Station	F	10.00
Nigg Station	B (271)	40.00
	E (271)	5.00
	F	5.00
	G	8.00
Normanton Station	C (48)	8.00
(new discovery)	D	100.00
	G	3.00
	registered	8.00
	parcel	20.00
Northampton Castle Statn	G	10.00
Nottingham Station	G	10.00
Nunburnholme Station	G	4.00
Nunthorpe Station	F	4.00
	G	4.00
	I	20.00
	S	2.00
Old Steine Station	G	8.00
Orpington Station	F	1.00
	G	12.00
	H	12.00
	I	15.00
Orton Station	E (611)	4.00
	G	3.00
	H	20.00
Paddington Station	A	50.00
	B (049)	40.00
	G	3.00
parcel hooded circle		100.00
	registered	10.00
	parcel	10.00
Par Station	B (B04)	15.00
	D	4.00
	F	1.00
	G	1.50
	H	12.00
	parcel	10.00
Park Station	G	2.50
	parcel	10.00
Parkeston Quay Station	G	2.50
Penybont Station	G	2.50
Perranwell Station	D	6.00
	F	4.00
	G	2.00
Peterborough North Stn	G	10.00
Pevensey Station	G	2.50
Pilmoor Station	G	10.00
Pluckley Station	F	3.00
	G	3.00
Plumpton Station	G	12.00
Plymouth Station	G	10.00
Polmont Station	E (489)	3.00
	G	4.00
Port of Monteith Station		
	B (288)	60.00
	E (288 and 670)	4.00
	G	20.00
Portswood Junction	G	8.00
Preston Station	G	10.00
	parcel	15.00
Prudhoe Station A (undated)		40.00
	F	4.00
	G	12.00
Queensbury Station	G	4.00
Queen St Glasgow Scots local		60.00
Rannoch Station	E (678)	2.50
	F	1.50
Rathen Station	G	5.00
Ratho Station	E (474)	6.00
	F	4.00
	G	3.50
	H	20.00
Redhill Station	C (A21)	12.00
	F	4.00
	G	4.00
	registered	15.00
	parcel	10.00
	postage due	10.00
Robin Hoods Bay Station	F	3.00
	G	1.50
	H	40.00
Rugby Station	B (659)	50.00
	C (659)	8.00
	D	4.00
	F	1.00
	G	1.00
	H	30.00
	registered	10.00
	parcel	10.00
	postage due	10.00
St Budeaux Station	F	5.00
	G	3.00
(St Enoch thought to be "Square" not Station)		
St Leonards on Sea Station		
	C (342)	8.00
	F	1.50
	G	1.50
	parcel	10.00
St Pancras Goods Station	G	15.00
Scotstounhill Station	I	15.00
Semley Station	G	4.00
Sheffield Station	G	10.00
Sheffield Park Station	I	8.00
Sherburn Station undated s/c		50.00
Shortlands Station	G	15.00
Shrewsbury Station	G	12.00
Sleights Station	F	3.00
	G	4.00
Southampton Station	G	12.00
	mis-sent	250.00
South Kensington Station	F	3.00
	G	3.00
	I	2.00
	S	1.00
	registered	12.00
parcel (or Kensington)		5.00
Stafford Station	C (730)	12.00
	F	1.50
	G	1.00
	registered	10.00
	parcel	8.00
Stoke Newington Station	G	8.00
Stoke upon Trent Station	A	35.00
then Stoke Station	A	40.00
Sunningdale Station	G	8.00
Swanley Junction	D	3.00
	F	2.00
	G	2.50
	H	12.00
	parcel	10.00
Swindon Station A (undated)		50.00
	B (881)	60.00
	C (881)	6.00
	F	30.00
	G	2.50
	H	15.00
	registered	10.00
	parcel	10.00
	postage due	10.00
Tarbolton Station	E (591)	5.00
Taunton Station	G	10.00
Thorntonhall Station	G	5.00
Thornton Heath Station	F	3.00
	instructional	12.00
Tilbury Station	G	8.00
Timperley Station	G	1.50
	S	2.00
	parcel	4.00
Tonbridge Station	B (818)	40.00
	C (818)	8.00
(see also Tunbridge)	F	3.00
	H	12.00
	parcel	10.00
Tooting Junction	G	10.00
Trimdon Station	F	8.00
Tunbridge Station	C (818)	8.00
	G	25.00
	registered	15.00
Udny Station	E (cross)	3.00
	F	6.00
	G	8.00
Uphall Station	E (576)	6.00
Victoria Station	G	3.00
Virginia Water Station	F	8.00
Wadhurst Station	C (J82)	30.00
Warlingham Station	G	10.00
	H	50.00
Warrington Station str line		100.00
Washington Station	C (B43)	12.00
	F	3.00
	G	6.00
	H	20.00
	S	1.50
	instructional	12.00
Waterloo Station	G	3.00
	H	25.00
	I	25.00
parcel hooded circle		100.00
	registered	12.00
	parcel	10.00
	instructional	20.00
Waverley Station	G	12.00
Wellington College	B (J09)	50.00
Station	D	4.00
	F	3.00
	G	2.50
	H	20.00
West Ealing Station	G	12.00
West Grinstead Station	I	20.00
West Station Hounslow	G	5.00
Weybridge Station	B (B87)	25.00
	C (B87)	15.00
	G	4.00
Whitmore Station A (undated)		45.00
Wingate Station	C (H49)	15.00
	G	12.00
Woking Station	B (C66)	20.00
	C (C66)	12.00
Wolverton Station A undated		100.00
Woodland Station	G	8.00
Worcester Station	G	12.00
Worthing Station	C (923)	15.00
	D	25.00
	G	6.00
	registered	15.00
	parcel	10.00
York Station	G	10.00
	Framed oval "R.W"	40.00

Irish

Athenry Station str line		100.00
Ballycarry Station	F	5.00
	G	6.00
	I	20.00
Chichester Station str line		75.00
Dunkettle St'n RSO	B (195)	30.00
	G	25.00
Greenisland Station	G	8.00
Limerick Junction	C (514)	50.00
	G	8.00
	H	30.00
Portadown Station	G	5.00
Portarlington Station	G	20.00
Queenstown Railway	G	40.00
Straffan Station	B (415)	75.00
	G	6.00
	H	25.00
Whitehead Station	H	40.00
	I	40.00

Travelling Post Offices (TPO's)

A TPO is a specially adapted railway coach (or a "set" of them) in which mail is sorted during the course of a journey. The first one was introduced in 1838 on the Grand Junction Railway. Although the TPO network still runs, much rationalisation has taken place in recent years, with appropriate changes to postmarks. Although the 1993 changes were included in our Sixth Edition, further changes have taken place since then. Postal markings include (a) mis-sort marks; (b) marks used by the Inland Office sent to a TPO for sorting; (c) sorting marks used by the TPO on mail in transit. Datestamps also cancel postage stamps on mail posted directly into letter boxes on TPOs or collected from Late Fee boxes at stations, though late fees are no longer applicable to TPO letters.

Routes operating in England, Wales and Scotland

If a service runs both ways, it is listed under the first alphabetical reference (eg Bangor-Crewe is listed under Bangor but marks also exist worded Crewe-Bangor) and they are marked +. Some of the others, not marked +, ran Up/Down, East/West etc. TPOs for which no marks are known have been excluded: these include Chester-Crewe Parcel TPO, Chester-Holyhead RPO, Dartmoor RST, Gt Western Sunday ST, London-Doncaster ST, London-Dover SC (Ostend Day Mail)(1887), Perth-Dingwall RSC and Shrewsbury & Normanton TPO (1893-94). The rubber handstamps (type R) of 1986 were used for a two-week period of repair to the Birmingham Proof Bridge during which time TPOs were re-routed. "AM index" refers to special arrangements for stamp issue days during 1953-80 when new stamps were on sale from midnight and AM handstamps were used instead of applying to new stamps the previous day's date. Doubts have been expressed about the meaning of "LCR" shown here under "Caledonian"; it now appears to be the "Lancaster & Carlisle" section of the TPO.

The list that follows is a summary of Frank Wilson's 1991 book (see Bibliography) published by the Railway Philatelic Group, who have kindly given permission to use this data.

Notes on values :
(a) All registered covers, complete with registration labels, are worth a premium; modern registered covers are worth a minimum of 4.00
(b) Bag Tenders (BT) replace TPOs for the pre-Christmas period each year; mail is not normally postmarked but philatelic "by favour" items are sometimes produced
(c) All values given are for the most common marks, generally the most recent; naturally earlier marks are normally priced higher, and Queen Victoria marks at not less than 8.00

A	Missent types	H	Double circles, medium or thick arcs
B	Small circles with initials	J	Double circles, thin arcs
C	Unframed circular	K	Skeletons
D	Star stamps	L	Parcel types (**13/20** or **19/10-12**)
E	Single circles, many types	M	'Late fee not paid' seen on this route
F	Numeral and duplex, English type	N	Squared circles
G	Duplex, Scottish type	R	Rubber handstamps

MS̱ - N-W
R·P·O-NIGHT

A	13/10	B	13/11	C	13/12	D	13/13

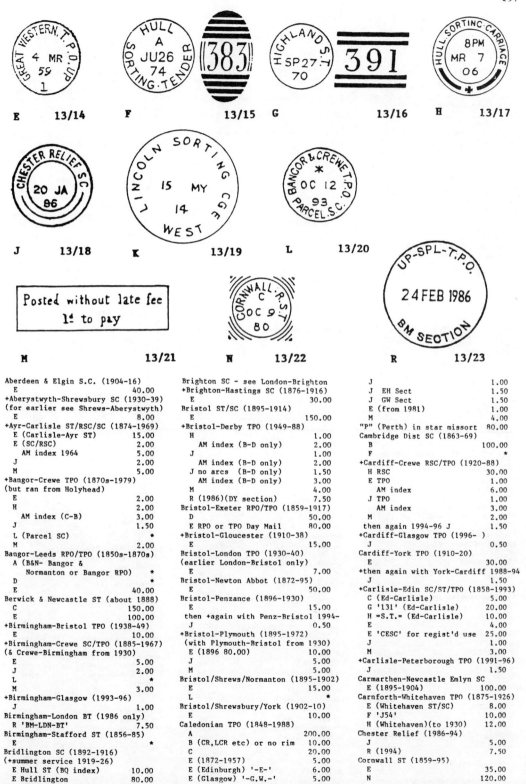

E 13/14 **F** 13/15 **G** 13/16 **H** 13/17

J 13/18 **K** 13/19 **L** 13/20

M 13/21 **N** 13/22 **R** 13/23

Aberdeen & Elgin S.C. (1904-16)	
E	40.00
+Aberystwyth-Shrewsbury SC (1930-39)	
(for earlier see Shrews-Aberystwyth)	
E	8.00
+Ayr-Carlisle ST/RSC/SC (1874-1969)	
E (Carlisle-Ayr ST)	15.00
E (SC/RSC)	2.00
AM index 1964	5.00
J	2.00
M	5.00
+Bangor-Crewe TPO (1870s-1979)	
(but ran from Holyhead)	
E	2.00
H	2.00
AM index (C-B)	3.00
J	1.50
L (Parcel SC)	*
M	2.00
Bangor-Leeds RPO/TPO (1850s-1870s)	
A (B&N- Bangor &	
Normanton or Bangor RPO)	*
D	*
E	40.00
Berwick & Newcastle ST (about 1888)	
C	150.00
E	100.00
+Birmingham-Bristol TPO (1938-49)	
E	10.00
+Birmingham-Crewe SC/TPO (1885-1967)	
(& Crewe-Birmingham from 1930)	
E	5.00
J	2.00
L	*
M	3.00
+Birmingham-Glasgow (1993-96)	
J	1.00
Birmingham-London BT (1986 only)	
R 'BM-LDN-BT'	7.50
Birmingham-Stafford ST (1856-85)	
E	*
Bridlington SC (1892-1916)	
(+summer service 1919-26)	
E Hull ST (BQ index)	10.00
E Bridlington	80.00

Brighton SC - see London-Brighton	
+Brighton-Hastings SC (1876-1916)	
E	30.00
Bristol ST/SC (1895-1914)	
E	150.00
+Bristol-Derby TPO (1949-88)	
H	1.00
AM index (B-D only)	2.00
J	1.00
AM index (B-D only)	2.00
J no arcs (B-D only)	1.50
AM index (B-D only)	3.00
M	4.00
R (1986)(DY section)	7.50
Bristol-Exeter RPO/TPO (1859-1917)	
D	50.00
E RPO or TPO Day Mail	80.00
+Bristol-Gloucester (1910-38)	
E	15.00
Bristol-London TPO (1930-40)	
(earlier London-Bristol only)	
E	7.00
Bristol-Newton Abbot (1872-95)	
E	50.00
Bristol-Penzance (1896-1930)	
E	15.00
then +again with Penz-Bristol 1994-	
J	0.50
+Bristol-Plymouth (1895-1972)	
(with Plymouth-Bristol from 1930)	
E (1896 80.00)	10.00
J	5.00
M	5.00
Bristol/Shrews/Normanton (1895-1902)	
E	15.00
L	*
Bristol/Shrewsbury/York (1902-10)	
E	10.00
Caledonian TPO (1848-1988)	
A	200.00
B (CR,LCR etc) or no rim	10.00
C	20.00
E (1872-1957)	5.00
E (Edinburgh) '-E-'	6.00
E (Glasgow) '-G.W.-'	5.00

J	1.00
J EH Sect	1.50
J GW Sect	1.50
E (from 1981)	1.00
M	4.00
"P" (Perth) in star missort	80.00
Cambridge Dist SC (1863-69)	
B	100.00
F	*
+Cardiff-Crewe RSC/TPO (1920-88)	
H RSC	30.00
E TPO	1.00
AM index	6.00
J TPO	1.00
AM index	3.00
M	2.00
then again 1994-96 J	1.50
+Cardiff-Glasgow TPO (1996-)	
J	0.50
Cardiff-York TPO (1910-20)	
E	30.00
+then again with York-Cardiff 1988-94	
J	1.50
+Carlisle-Edin SC/ST/TPO (1858-1993)	
C (Ed-Carlisle)	5.00
G '131' (Ed-Carlisle)	20.00
H =S.T.= (Ed-Carlisle)	10.00
E	4.00
E 'CESC' for regist'd use	25.00
J	1.00
M	3.00
+Carlisle-Peterborough TPO (1991-96)	
J	1.50
Carmarthen-Newcastle Emlyn SC	
E (1895-1904)	100.00
Carnforth-Whitehaven TPO (1875-1926)	
E (Whitehaven ST/SC)	8.00
F 'J54'	10.00
H (Whitehaven)(to 1930)	12.00
Chester Relief (1986-94)	
J	5.00
R (1994)	7.50
Cornwall ST (1859-95)	
E	35.00
N	120.00

Crewe-Glasgow RSC/SC (1926-93)
E (RSC)	15.00
E (SC)	5.00
J	1.00
AM index 1964	3.00
M	4.00

Crewe-Liverpool SC (1885-1939)
E	15.00

+Crewe-Manchester SC (1908-39)
H	10.00

+Crewe-Peterborough (1966-91)
J	0.50
AM index	2.00
J (Lincoln Section)	0.50
AM index	2.00
E	2.00
K (1974)	*
M	4.00

Derby-London TPO (1988-95)
J	1.00

+Derby-Penzance TPO (1988-94)
J	1.00

Dingwall-Perth RSC (1917-30)
E	35.00

Doncaster-London TPO (1932-40)
E	20.00

+Dover-London RSC (1922-23)
(earlier London-Dover only)
H	*

+Dover-Manchester TPO (1988-96)
J	0.50

Down Special TPO (1923-93)
E	2.00
H	2.00
J	0.50
side A (Aberdeen Section)	5.00
AM index 1964	5.00
M	3.00
R (1939)	50.00
R (BM sect 1986)	7.50

East Anglian TPO (1929-)
E	10.00
H	5.00
J	0.50
AM index	2.00
M	3.00

E Anglian K Lynn Section (1929-49)
E	15.00
H	15.00

E Anglian Peterboro Sect (1949-90)
J	0.50
AM index	2.00

Edinburgh-Berwick ST (c1866-85)
G numeral '131/ST'	250.00
C	40.00
E (Edinburgh ST)	20.00

Edinburgh-Carstairs ST (1877-1914)
C	5.00
G (unframed) '131'	*

Edinburgh-Glasgow ST (c1869-70)
C	50.00
G (unframed) '131'	50.00

Edinburgh-Newc'le ST/SC (c1869-1922)
C	10.00
E	10.00

Edinburgh-York SC/TPO (1926-85)
E	2.00
J	1.00
M	3.00

Exeter-Torrington SC (1906-17)
E	10.00
K (1906)	100.00

Fife ST/SC (1884-1917)
H ST =458=	15.00
H SC	*

Galloway ST/SC/TPO (1871-1940)
E	15.00
H ST =603=	35.00
H TPO	10.00
M	10.00

Glasg-Carlisle RPO/ST/SC (1858-1914)
B (C & G)	20.00
D on missorts	35.00
E (incl Glasgow ST)	5.00
G '159'	8.00
E registered (Glasgow ST)	35.00
Reg crown oval (Glasg ST)	80.00

+Glasgow-Preston RSC (1914-26)
E	60.00

Gloucester-Tamworth RPO (1850-55)
A	*

Grand Junction Railway (1838)
A	150.00

Grand Northern Railroad (?1844-59)
B (ENR, MNR)	20.00

Grand Northern RPO (1838-65)
A (no Day)	130.00
A (Day)	200.00

Great Northern Night Mail (1910-22)
E	10.00

Great Northern SC Day (1877-1922)
E	5.00

Great Northern ST (1875-1902)
E	25.00
Box (GNSC, GNST)	100.00

Gt N'th'n TPO Midday Mail (1885-1915)
E	15.00

Great Western Dist SC (1859-69)
Two line	75.00

Great Western RPO (1847-1904?)
A	*
B (E/GW)	25.00

Great Western TPO (1896-)
E	1.00
H	5.00
J	0.50
AM index	2.00
M	2.00

Greenock ST (1866-79)
E	15.00

Grimsby-Lincoln SC (1850s-1915)
E	10.00
H	6.00
N	12.00

Grimsby-Peterborough SC (1900-17)
E/H (ST)	10.00
E (SC)	10.00
H (SC)	5.00
K (1910)	40.00
Tax 'K.97'	75.00

Halifax ST (1871-c79)
E	50.00

Helmsdale-Dingwall RSC (1923-30)
E	60.00

Highland ST/SC/TPO (1870-1978)
G '391'	60.00
E	10.00
H	3.00
J	1.50
L	*
M	5.00

Huddersfield, see Liv'l, Whitehaven
Hull Sorting Carriage (1867-1917)
E (ST 19mm)	45.00
E (ST or SC)	8.00
F '383'	5.00
H	2.00

+Hull-Leeds SC (1914-17)
E (Leeds-Hull)	80.00
H (Hull-Leeds)	15.00

Ipswich ST/SC (1858-1929)
Box (IST)	150.00
Two line (DSC)	*
E (ST/SC)	5.00

+Ipswich-London TPO (1929-31)
E	15.00
K (1929)	*

Lincoln ST/SC (1867-1919)
E 'Tender' or ST/SC	5.00
F '458'	*
H (SC)	20.00
K (1914)	150.00
L ('Tender')	*
N (ST)(1891)	5.00
N (1905)	4.00

+Lincoln-Tamworth SC (1919-40)
E	15.00
registered oval	100.00

Liverpool-Huddersf'd TPO (1899-1965)
H (Rly SC)	50.00
E	5.00
J	5.00
M	5.00
Liverpool Late Fee	10.00

(20.00 for 1930s use)
Liverpool-London TPO (c1863-1918)
E & N - on piece	10.00

Llandyssil ST (1875-95)
F 'D25'	120.00
E	50.00
L	120.00

London-Birmingham RPO (1838)
A	*

London-Brighton SC Day (1880s-1916)
E (incl Brighton SC)	5.00

London-Brighton SC Night (?1864-1916)
E	8.00

London-Bristol SC/ST (1868-1930)
(then see Bristol-London)
E or box (ST)	*
E (SC)	15.00

London-Crewe ST/SC (1876-1918)
E (ST)	22.00
Box (SC)	100.00
E (SC)	17.00

London-Derby SC (1908-18)
Box (1896)	50.00
E	20.00

London-Dover SC, Continental
Night Mail (1884-1923)
E (TPO/SC)	15.00
Reg oval FNM	22.00
H (+RSC)	*

and inscribed Continental Night Mail –
F (CS/2 Cannon St)	40.00
F (CX/1 Charing Cross)	80.00
H	30.00

London-Dover SC, French Day Mail
(1860-1918)
B (LD/SC)	80.00
F numeral 'C68'	8.00
E (FDM)	20.00
E (SC)	12.00
Reg oval	30.00
Tax (hexagon T/C68,72)	3.00

London-Exeter RPO/TPO (1855-95)
A	*
B	15.00
D	30.00
Diamond L&E/TPO/E	40.00
E (TPO)	15.00
F numeral 'G01'	50.00
L	50.00

London-Folkestone SC (1911-15)
E	15.00
Reg hooded circle	30.00

London-Holyhead Day TPO (1860-1939)
A	140.00
Large X (used with above)	*
E Euston Statn Irish Mail	200.00
F numeral 'B34'	*
E (TPO)	15.00

London-Holyhead Night TPO (1860-1940)
A & large X	180.00
Box	80.00
E	6.00

London-Holyhead TPO Canadian
(1895-1908) & USA Mails (1895-1914)
E Canadian	*
E US + F numeral 'K49'	120.00
H London-Holyh'd index US	120.00
Tax (T/L&H)	200.00

+London-Leeds ST/SC/TPO (1901-32)
Box L&L/ST	60.00
E (ST/SC)	22.00
H (SC/TPO)	15.00

+London-Newhaven RSC/SC (1923-39)
E	15.00

+London-Norwich TPO (1931-90)
E (London-Norwich to 1939)	8.00
E (Norwich-London)	1.00
J (ditto)	1.00

London-Queenboro ST (1891-1911)
E	22.00
Reg hooded circle	50.00
Tax (hexagon L.01)	30.00

+London-Shrewsbury TPO (1988-93)
J	1.00

London-York-Edinburgh (1922-85)
E	3.00
H	3.00
K (1930)	120.00
J	0.50
M	3.00

Manchester ST (1864-1908)
  E 5.00
Manchester-Glasgow SC (1951-77)
  J 4.00
  M 4.00
Midland District SC (1859-69)
  Two line *
Midland TPO (1855-)
  A 150.00
  B (EMR) 20.00
  D 50.00
  E 1.00
  K (South)(1949) *
  H 2.00
  J 0.50
    AM index (South) 2.00
  M 3.00
Newcastle-on-Tyne ST/SC (1876-1914)
  E 8.00
Newcastle-London RSC (1922-26)
  H 10.00
Normanton-Stalybridge (1870s-1893)
  E 50.00
North of Scotland SC (1886-1904)
  E 60.00
NETPO (Day) (1895-1926)
  E 5.00
  K (South)(1911) 40.00
NETPO Night (1926-95)
  E 2.00
    AM index (Up) 3.00
  H (Up) 4.00
  H (index K,Z - Leeds Sect) 10.00
  J 0.50
    AM index (Down 1964 only) 4.00
  M 3.00
NETPO (1995-)
  J 1.00
NW District SC (1857-69)
  A (boxed) 70.00
NWTPO Day Mail (1847-c1922)
  A *
  B (NW/RPO/M) 22.00
  C 35.00
  D 35.00
  Diamond NW/TPO/M 40.00
  E 15.00
NWTPO Midday (1883-1915)
  Hooded circle *
  E 15.00
NWTPO 10PM Mail (1886-1926)
  E 15.00
NWTPO Night Down (1847-1993)
  A *
  Box (NWST)(Sunday) 100.00
  B (NW/RPO/E) 22.00
  C 22.00
  diamond NW/TPO/E 40.00
  D (NW Ry) 22.00
  E 3.00
  H 1.00
  J 1.00
    AM index 4.00
  M 4.00
  R (BM Sect)(1986) 7.50
NWTPO Night Up (1847-c1918)
  E 15.00
  diamond NW/TPO/E 25.00
North West TPO (1993-)
  J 0.50
Norwich SC/ST (1869-1929)
  E 4.00
  K (Up)(1909) *
  Tax (L.05, O15) 50.00
Perth-Aberdeen SC (1871-93)
  G '402' 250.00
Perth-Helmsdale RSC (1919)
  E on piece 60.00
Peterborough DSC/ST (1858-1916)
  Two line (DSC) *
  E (ST) 20.00
Peterborough-Ely SC (1908-12?)
  E 30.00

Plym-Bristol(Foreign Mails)(1869-1920s)
  F numeral 'B16' 75.00
  E 20.00
  Tax 'B16' 20.00
Plym & Ex'r Nt Mail Tender (1880-94)
  F 'C24' 30.00
  E 30.00
Portsmouth SC (1865-1923)
  D/E together 150.00
  E 8.00
Preston, see Whitehaven
Rugby-Leeds RPO (1852-62)
  A *
Rugby-Newcastle RPO (1845-52)
  A 120.00
St Pancras & Derby (1877-1908)
  E 15.00
Scarboro-Whitby SC (c1864)
  E (S.W./York in str lines) 25.00
Shrewsbury-Aberystwyth (1883-1930)
then see Aberyst-Shrewsbury
  E 10.00
  H 15.00
Shrewsbury-Crewe SC (1891-92)
  E *
Shrewsbury-Hereford SC (1885-1902)
  E 15.00
+Shrewsbury-Stafford SC (1985 only)
  R in red 10.00
+Shrews-Tamworth SC/TPO (1857-1917)
(also Tamworth-Shrewsb'y from 1914)
  Two line *
  Box (RPO) 120.00
  Box (TPO) 150.00
  E 15.00
  E (RSC from 1914) 22.00
+Shrewsbury-York TPO (1920-88)
  H (SC) 30.00
  E 0.50
  J 0.50
    AM index 3.00
  M 3.00
South East DSC/RPO/TPO (1860-1977)
  Box (DSC) *
  B (E/SE) *
  B (SE/RPO) 30.00
  E 4.00
    AM index (Down) 3.00
  F (SE Ry PO) *
  H 10.00
  J 1.00
    AM index (Up) 2.00
  M 3.00
  then again (1996-) J 0.50
South Wales SC/ST/TPO (1869-)
  E 1.00
  H 1.50
  J 0.50
    AM index (Down) 2.00
  R (1988, BT with BT removed) 5.00
  M 3.00
S Wales SC/TPO (Nth Mail)(1884-1923)
  E 15.00
South Western DSC (1860-69)
  Box or 2-line *
South West TPO (Day) (1866-1940)
  E 6.00
South Western Night TPO (1862-1988)
  Box (RPO) 50.00
  B (L&SW/RPO) 22.00
  E 2.00
    AM index (Up) 4.00
  H 20.00
  J 0.50
    AM index (Down) 3.00
  K (Up)(1910) 60.00
  M 3.00
Stalybridge, see Whitehaven
Tamworth-Hereford SC (1902-14)
  E 8.00
Truro-Falmouth ST (1864-1916)
  E 35.00
Up Special TPO (1886-1993)
  E 'Mail TPO' 15.00
  H 5.00
  E (TPO) 4.00
    AM index (1953) 5.00

  J 0.50
    AM index (1961-) 2.00
  R (1936,1948) 50.00
  R (Birm Sect) 1986 7.50
  J -A- (Aberdeen duty) 4.00
  M 3.00
Up Spec Edinburgh Section (1922-93)
  E 8.00
  H 5.00
  J 1.00
  M 3.00
Up Spec Glasgow Section (1917-93)
  E 5.00
  H 0.50
  J 1.00
  K *
  M 3.00
West Cornwall Tender (1884-92)
    *
Whitehaven ST - see Carnforth-Whiteh'n
+Whitehaven-Huddersf'd TPO (1966-91)
  J 1.00
    AM index (Hudd-Wh'haven) 2.00
  M 4.00
+Whitehaven-Preston TPO (1926-65)
  H 4.00
  J 2.00
  M 4.00
+Whitehaven-Stalybridge TPO (1965)
  J 10.00
  M 10.00
York-Newcastle TPO (1853-95)
  E 15.00
York-Scarborough SC (1899-1928)
  E 12.00
Yorkshire TPO (1988-95)
  J 1.00

Irish TPOs (Southern Ireland to 1922)

Ballybrophy ST (1900)
  E 150.00
Belfast & North'n Counties (1881-1940)
  Diamond in bars '190' *
  E 8.00
  H 15.00
  K (1923) *
Dublin-Belfast RPO/TPO (1868-1923)
  E 5.00
Dublin & Derry TPO (1912-24)
  E 15.00
  H 60.00
Dublin-Queenstown TPO (1892-1907)
  C 'Dublin-Cork American Mail'
    60.00
  C 25.00
Dublin-Wexford RPO/TPO (1894-1965)
  E 15.00
  K (1904) *
Gt South & West'n TPO (1884-1994)
  Diamond in bars 'TPO 498' *
  E (Cork TPO, GS&W or
    Dublin & Cork TPO) 15.00
  K (double rim skeleton) 35.00
  R *
Kildare ST (1900)
  E *
Limerick ST/SC (1903-18 & 1938-39)
  E 35.00
  K (1938-39) 25.00
Midland TPO (1893-1994)
  E (Midland, MGW or
    Dublin & Galway TPO) 15.00
  K (double rim) 40.00
Mullingar-Sligo ST/SC (1903-76)
  E 15.00
  R 40.00
Portadown-Derry SC/ST/TPO (1887-1940)
(& Derry-Portadown from 1930)
  E 8.00
  K (1910) *
Ulster TPO (1895-1902)
  E (& Portadown-Derry Night) 15.00
    *
Waterford ST/SC (1903-17)
  E 30.00

Two further railway postmarks

(a) single circle shown as **13/24**; first used pre-war (the one shown here is a 1991 replacement), it was used at TPO publicity events approx 1987-94 (value 5.00) then from 1994 it was made available for collectors as a "philatelic handstamp" (value 0.30) (b) "Cruise of the Northern Belle" cachet (previously listed in chapter 24) - this train "cruise" first ran

13/24   **13/25**

from King's Cross 16-30 June 1933 covering 4000 miles, with separate day and night portions accommodating 60 passengers and a crew of 20. Similar trips were made in 1934-39 and the cachet **13/25** was used in purple in 1936-38 - value 75.00.

Railway Sub Offices

The story of RSOs is long and complex. The term RSO was originally introduced in 1856 as an accounting device, whereby a number of smaller offices could be down-graded from Head Office status. The original offices were served by TPOs, but the designation was later extended to indicate offices which received the bulk of their mail from a TPO instead of from their own Head Office. Thus towns well away from railways became RSOs. Datestamps generally did not include "RSO", however, until after 1900. The designation was abolished in 1905 but datestamps continued in use after that date, some with the "R" removed. * indicates an item in the list about which we are uncertain, or of which confirmation would be appreciated.

13/26   **13/27**   **13/28**   **13/29**

A Single Circle   **AR** Single Circle   **B** Double Circle   **BR** Double Circle
with R removed   with R removed

13/30   **13/31**   **13/32**

C Duplex   **D** Skeleton   **F** Rubber

E Irish skeleton, double rim   **G** Undated parcel types   **H** Paid skeleton

England, Scotland, Wales

Abbey Cwmhir/Penybont Stn RSO A	8.00	Allendale RSO/Northd A	1.50	
Abergele RSO/ Denbighshire G	10.00	D	15.00	
Abertillery RSO/Mon A	1.50	All Stretton/Church Stretton RSO Salop A	4.00	
B	2.00	Alperton/Wembley RSO Middlesex A	1.50	
BR	2.00	Alphamstone/Bures RSO/ Suffolk F	8.00	
D	20.00	Alveston RSO/Glos A	2.50	
Adelaide Rd/Gillingham RSO Kent A	10.00	Ancrum RSO/ Roxburghshire A	2.50	
Alcester RSO/Warwickshire G	10.00	Apethorpe/Wansford RSO Northants A	5.00	
Alexandra Rd Morecambe RSO/Lanc A	12.00	F	15.00	
		Appin RSO Argyllshire A	2.00	

Appledore RSO/N Devon B	1.50
D	10.00
Ardens Grafton/Alcester RSO/Warwickshire F	15.00
Ashburton RSO/Devon B	1.50
BR	2.00
Ashbury/Shrivenham RSO Berks A	3.00
Ashington/Pulborough RSO Sussex A	12.00
Ashurst/Lyndhurst RSO Hants A	1.50
Ashwater Beaworthy RSO/ Devon A	3.50
Ashwell/Baldock RSO Herts A	2.50

Aspenden/Buntingford	
RSO/Herts F	8.00
Aviemore RSO Inverness-	
shire A	1.00
Aylsham RSO/Norfolk A	2.50
Bainbridge Askrigg	
RSO/Yorks A	3.00
Bala RSO/Merioneth A	5.00
Baldock RSO D	15.00
Banavie RSO	
Inverness-shire/+ A	2.50
Barton Stacey RSO/	
Hants A	2.50
Batley Rd/Heckmondwike	
RSO Yorks A	10.00
Bawtry/RSO Yorks D	10.00
*Bawtry RSO/Yorks D	12.00
Beaconsfield RSO/Bucks D	10.00
Beal RSO/	
Northumberland A	2.50
Beamish RSO/Durham A	2.50
Beaufort RSO/Brecon A	2.50
Beaumont/Weeley RSO/	
Essex F	15.00
Beaworthy RSO/N Devon A	2.00
*Berkeley RSO/	
Gloucestershire A	15.00
Berrow/Burnham RSO	
Somerset A	15.00
Betchworth RSO/Sy D	8.00
Bettws RSO A	15.00
Beulah RSO/	
Cardiganshire A	3.00
Beulah/Garth RSO	
Brecon A	2.00
Bexhill on Sea RSO/	
Sussex B	1.00
Bexley RSO/Kent B	1.00
D	8.00
Bickley RSO/Kent D	12.00
Billingford/Scole RSO/	
Norfolk F	7.00
Billy Row/Crook RSO	
Durham A	5.00
Birchgrove/Llansamlet RSO	
Glam A	4.00
Birtley RSO/Co Durham A	4.00
B	2.00
BR	3.50
Blackhill RSO/Co Durham	
A	2.00
AR	3.00
Blackwater/Scorrier	
RSO Cornwall A	3.00
Blaina RSO/Mon A	1.50
Blisworth RSO/	
Northants D	8.00
Bolam/Heighington RSO/	
Co Durham F	15.00
Boldon Colliery RSO/	
Co Durham A	8.00
Bolingey/Perranporth RSO/	
Cornwall F	15.00
Borth RSO/Cardiganshire	
D	10.00
Bourton/Shrivenham	
RSO Berks F	12.00
Bourtoh(error)/Shrivenham	
RSO/Berks F	25.00
Branch End/Stocksfield RSO/	
Northumberland F	15.00
Brandeston/Wickham Market	
RSO/Suffolk F	15.00
Brantingham/Brough RSO/	
Yorks F	15.00
Brixham/RSO G	10.00
Broad Haven RSO/	
Pembrokeshire A	3.50

Broadway RSO/	
Worcestershire A	4.00
Brockenhurst RSO/Hants A	1.00
G	10.00
Brocklesby/RSO (Lincs) G	10.00
Bromfield RSO/Salop A	3.00
Brompton RSO/Yorks A	2.50
Brompton Regis/	
Dulverton RSO Som A	12.00
Broomfleet/Newport	
RSO Yorks A	2.00
Brough RSO/Yorks A	1.50
B	1.50
Broxbourne/RSO G	10.00
Bryncethin Aberkenfig RSO/	
Glam A	5.00
Bryncethin/Aberkenfig RSO	
Glam A	4.00
Brynna/Pontyclun RSO	
Glam A	20.00
Brynsaddler Pontyclun	
RSO/Glamorgan A	3.00
(same but Glam) A	2.00
Bucknell RSO/Salop A	4.00
Bude RSO/North Cornwall A	5.00
Budleigh Salterton/RSO G	8.00
Builth-Wells RSO/	
Breconshire A	1.50
AR	2.00
D	20.00
Buntingford RSO/Herts A	5.00
G	10.00
Burgess Hill RSO Sussex/	
-1- B	1.50
BR	2.00
G	15.00
Burgh RSO/Linc A	1.50
B	1.50
Burgh/Aylsham RSO/	
Norfolk F	7.00
Burnham RSO/Somerset B	1.00
BR	1.50
D	15.00
Burnham/RSO Som D	15.00
Burnham on Crouch RSO/	
Essex A	1.50
AR	2.00
Burry Port RSO/	
Carmarthenshire A	2.00
AR	10.00
Butley/Tunstall RSO/	
Suffolk F	8.00
Byron Rd/New Brompton	
RSO Kent A	10.00
Caergeiliog Valley RSO/	
Anglesey A	4.00
Camp/Bridestowe RSO	
Devon A	3.50
Campden RSO/Gloucestershire	
D	20.00
G (Glos)	8.00
Campton/Shefford RSO/Beds	
F	15.00
Canterbury St/	
Gillingham RSO Kent A	10.00
Capel Celyn/Bala RSO/	
Merionethshire F	15.00
Cardington/Church	
Stretton RSO Salop A	12.00
Carharrack/Scorrier RSO/	
Cornwall F	15.00
Carnetown/Abercynon	
RSO Glam A	15.00
Carrbridge RSO	
Inverness-shire A	2.00
Carrington/Gorebridge RSO/	
Midlothian F	20.00

Castle Cary RSO/Somerset	
A	1.50
B	1.50
BR	2.00
Castle Eden RSO/Co Durham	
A	1.50
AR	2.00
B	1.50
Castleton/Grosmont	
RSO Yorks A	10.00
Caton RSO/Lanc BR	12.00
D (Lancashire)	10.00
Chadwell Heath RSO/	
Essex B	2.50
Chalfont St Giles/	
Gerrards Cross RSO A	1.50
Chapel Amble/Wadebridge	
RSO/Cornwall F	15.00
Chappel/Earl's Colne RSO	
Essex A	4.00
Charmouth RSO/Dorset G	8.00
Chathill RSO/Northd D	15.00
Chathill/RSO G	7.00
Chatteris RSO/Cambs B	1.50
BR	2.00
Chelsfield Lane/Orpington	
RSO/Kent F	15.00
Chenies/Rickmansworth	
RSO/Herts F	7.00
Chesham RSO/Bucks A	12.00
D	10.00
Chollerton Station/Wall	
RSO/Northumberland F	15.00
Chopwell/Ebchester RSO	
Co Durham A	3.50
Church/Freshwater Stn	
RSO IOW A	12.00
Church Crookham/	
Fleet RSO Hants A	2.50
Church St/Gillingham	
RSO Kent A	12.00
Clearbrook Yelverton	
RSO/Devon A	3.00
Cleckheaton/RSO G	8.00
Cleckheaton RSO/Yorks H	20.00
Clydach RSO/Glamorgan A	2.50
AR	2.00
Cockfield RSO/	
Co Durham A	2.50
Colinsburgh RSO/	
Fifeshire B	2.50
Colne Engaine/Earls Colne	
RSO/Essex F	8.00
Colwell/Barrasford RSO/	
Northumberland F	8.00
Combe Martin RSO/Devon B	2.00
Commondale Grosmont RSO/	
Yorks A	3.50
Coniston RSO/Lanc A	2.00
AR	2.00
Consett RSO/Durham D	15.00
Cootham/Pulborough	
RSO/Sussex F	5.00
Copley/Butterknowle RSO	
Durham A	10.00
Corbridge RSO/	
Northumberland A	3.00
Cosham RSO/Hants B	1.50
BR	2.00
G	7.00
Cotes Heath Eccleshall	
RSO/Staff A	3.50
Coughton RSO/	
Warwickshire A	3.00
Court Hill/Swanage RSO	
Dorset A	8.00
Cowdenbeath RSO/	
Fifeshire B	2.00

Stoke Rivers RSO/	
N Devon A	3.00
Stokesley RSO/Yorkshire A	1.50
Stow on the Wold RSO/	
Glos A	2.50
Strachan/Banchory RSO/	
Kincardineshire F	12.00
Sudbourne/Orford RSO/	
Suffolk F	8.00
Sunnyside/Tow Law RSO A	3.50
Sutton on Sea RSO/Linc B	1.50
BR	2.00
Swanage RSO/Dorset A	1.50
Swanland/Brough RSO	
Yorks A	3.50
Swinton/Masham RSO/	
Yorkshire F	12.00
Swinton/Masham RSO G	8.00
Tanygroes RSO/	
Cardiganshire A	2.50
Tebay RSO/Westmorland A	10.00
Templecombe RSO/Somt A	1.00
B	2.00
BR	1.00
The Parade/Wealdstone RSO	
Middx A	8.00
The Roe/St Asaph RSO	
Flintshire A	5.00
Thornbury RSO/Glos A	1.50
B	1.50
Thornley RSO/Durham D	15.00
Thorpe Abbotts/Scole RSO	
Norfolk A	10.00
Thundersley/Rayleigh RSO	
Essex A	10.00
Tilbury RSO/Essex A	8.00
D	10.00
Tintagel RSO/Cornwall A	1.50
AR	2.00
D (two layouts)	12.00
Tiptree Kelvedon	
RSO/Essex A	2.50
Tisbury RSO/Wilts A	2.00
B	1.50
D	15.00
Toddington/Winchcombe RSO/	
Glos F	15.00
Torpoint RSO/Cornwall A	3.00
AR	2.00
Towyn RSO/Merioneth A	1.50
AR	1.50
Towyn/Abergele RSO/	
Denbighshire F	12.00
Trawsfynydd RSO/	
Merionethshire B	1.50

Ireland

Abbeyfeale RSO B	5.00
Aghadowey RSO/	
Co.L'derry A	5.00
Ardagh RSO/Co.Lim'k A	3.00
Ardrahan RSO/Co.Galway A	4.00
Ardsollus/RSO A	10.00
Armoy RSO/Co.Antrim A	4.00
Askeaton RSO/Co.Lim'k A	5.00
Augher RSO/Co.Tyrone A	4.00
Aughnacliffe/Granard RSO/	
Co.Longford F	15.00
Aughrim RSO/Co.Wicklow A	4.00
Balbriggan RSO/	
Co.Dublin A	4.00
Ballagh/Goolds Cross RSO/	
Co.Tipperary F	15.00

Treboeth/Landore RSO	
Glamorgan A	10.00
Trefnant/RSO G	8.00
Tregaron RSO A	8.00
Treharris RSO/Glamorgan A	2.00
Trimdon/Trimdon Grange	
RSO Durham A	2.00
Trimsaran Kidwelly RSO/	
Carmarthen A	4.00
Twatt/Stromness RSO/	
Orkney F	12.00
Twyford RSO/Berks D	15.00
Tycroes RSO/Anglesey A	2.50
Tynllechwedd/Llanidloes	
RSO/Mont F	12.00
Ulceby RSO/Linc A	2.00
Upton Cross/Callington	
RSO A	3.50
Van/Llanidloes RSO/	
Montgomeryshire F	15.00
Victoria St./Gillingham	
RSO Kent A	6.00
Wainfleet RSO/	
Lincolnshire B	1.50
Walberswick/Southwold	
RSO Suff A	3.00
Walkden/Farnworth RSO	
Lanc B	5.00
Wallbottle/Newburn RSO	
Northd A	3.00
Wall-under-Heywood/	
Church Stretton RSO/	
Salop F	10.00
Wansford RSO/	
Northamptonshire A	10.00
Wansford RSO/Northants G	8.00
Washington/Pulboro RSO F	8.00
Waterloo Rd/	
Llandrindod Wells RSO	
Radnor A	10.00
Wavendon/Woburn Sands RSO	
Beds A	2.50
Wealdstone RSO/	
Middlesex A	3.00
B	1.50
Weeley RSO/Essex A	2.50
AR	5.00
Weldon Bridge/	
Longframlington RSO/	
Northumberland F	8.00
Welton/Brough RSO Yorks A	2.50
Wembley RSO/Middlesex A	1.50
AR	2.00
B	1.50
BR	2.00

Ballinamallard/RSO A	5.00
Ballinamore/RSO A	20.00
Ballineen RSO/Co.Cork A	4.00
Ballingarry RSO/	
Co.Lim'k A	5.00
Ballinlough RSO	
Co.Roscommon B	5.00
Ballintogher/Collooney	
RSO A	12.00
Ballybay/RSO E	20.00
Ballybay RSO/	
Co.Monaghan A	5.00
Ballybunion RSO/	
Co.Kerry A	4.00
Ballycassidy/Ballinamallard	
RSO/Co.Fermanagh F	15.00
Ballycastle RSO/Co.Mayo	
A	12.00

West Cornforth RSO/	
Co Durham A	3.00
Westgate on Sea RSO/	
Kent A	3.50
*D	15.00
West Mill/Buntingford RSO/	
Herts F	8.00
West Pelton/Beamish RSO/	
Co Durham F	15.00
Westward Ho RSO/	
North Devon A	2.00
Whitchurch RSO/Hants G	10.00
White Colne/Earls Colne	
RSO/Essex F	12.00
Whitland RSO C (F24)	20.00
Whitley Bay RSO/	
Northumberland A	1.00
AR	2.00
B	1.00
BR	2.00
Wickham Market RSO/	
Suffolk G	10.00
Wickwar RSO (Glos) D	15.00
Widecombe in the Moor/	
Ashburton RSO A	3.50
Willingham RSO/Cambs A	10.00
Winsford RSO/Cheshire A	1.50
B	2.00
G	10.00
Wiston/Clarbeston Road RSO	
Pem A	3.50
Wiston/Steyning RSO/	
Sussex F	8.00
Wiveliscombe RSO/	
Somerset B	1.50
BR	2.00
Woburn Sands RSO/Beds D	15.00
Wolverton RSO/Bucks A	2.50
AR	2.00
Woodleigh Loddiswell RSO/	
Devon A	4.00
Wooler RSO/Northd A	3.50
Wootton/Ulceby RSO Linc A	8.00
Wotton-under-Edge RSO/	
Glos B	1.50
Wragby RSO Lincolnshire B	1.50
Wykeham RSO/Yorkshire A	3.50
Yarm RSO/Yorks D	12.00
Yarmouth RSO/	
Isle of Wight A	1.00
Yeoford/Copplestone RSO A	4.00
Yiewsley RSO/Middlesex A	2.50
D	10.00
G	8.00
Ystrad Meurig RSO A	5.00

Ballycroy RSO/Co.Mayo A	6.00
Ballycumber RSO/	
Kings Co. A	7.00
Ballydavid/Dingle RSO A	15.00
Ballyduff, Lixnaw RSO/	
Co.Kerry A	6.00
Ballyglass RSO/Co.Mayo A	5.00
Ballylanders/	
Knocklong RSO A	5.00
Baltimore RSO/Co.Cork A	4.00
Bangor RSO/Co.Down A	3.00
Bansha RSO/Co.Tip. A	4.00
Bellaghy/Castledawson RSO	
A	6.00
Belleek RSO/	
Co.Fermanagh A	3.00
Belmullet RSO/Co.Mayo A	20.00
Beltra/Ballisodare RSO A	5.00

Entry	Value
Blarney RSO/Co.Cork A	3.50
Bloomfield RSO/Co.Down A	2.00
E (no county)	15.00
Bonmahon/	
Kilmacthomas RSO A	5.00
Borris RSO/Co.Carlow A	4.00
Borris-in-Ossory/	
RSO Queens Co. A	4.00
Brosna Abbeyfeale RSO/	
Co.Limk A	6.00
Bruckless RSO	
Co.Donegal B	6.00
Cabinteely RSO/	
Co.Dublin A	5.00
B	6.00
Cahirciveen RSO/Co.Kerry	
A	20.00
Caledon RSO/Co.Tyrone A	4.00
Caledon RSO/Tyrone E	15.00
Callan RSO/Co.Kilkenny A	3.00
Callow RSO/Co.Mayo A	6.00
Camolin RSO/Co.Wexford A	6.00
Camp RSO/Co.Kerry A	6.00
Carah RSO A	15.00
Carrigtwohill RSO/	
Co.Cork A	6.00
Cashel RSO/Co.Galway A	3.50
Castlecomer RSO/	
Co.Kilkenny A	5.00
Castlecomer RSO E	20.00
Castleconnell RSO/	
Co.Lim'k A	4.00
Castlecor/Kanturk RSO A	8.00
Castledermot RSO/	
Co.Kildare A	5.00
Castlegregory RSO/	
Co.Kerry A	8.00
Castleisland RSO/	
Co.Kerry A	5.00
Castlemahon/	
Newcastle West RSO/	
Co.Limerick F	10.00
Castlemaine RSO/	
Co.Kerry A	20.00
Castlemaine RSO/=1= B	5.00
Castlemartyr RSO/	
Co.Cork A	3.00
Celbridge RSO/	
Co.Kildare A	4.00
Chapelizod RSO/	
Co.Dublin A	8.00
Clane RSO/Co.Kildare A	10.00
Clara RSO Kings Co. B	5.00
Clarin Bridge RSO/	
Co.Galway A	6.00
Cleggan RSO/Co.Galway A	4.00
Clifden RSO/Co.Galway A	10.00
Cloghan/RSO A	15.00
Clonakilty RSO/Co.Cork A	4.50
Clonbur RSO/Co.Galway A	5.00
Clondalkin RSO/	
Co.Dublin A	4.00
Clooney Glenties RSO/	
Co.Donegal A	6.00
Cloughjordan RSO/	
Co.Tip A	5.00
Coagh/Moneymore RSO A	8.00
Collinstown/	
Castlepollard RSO A	5.00
Cong RSO/Co.Mayo A	4.00
Coole RSO/Co.Westmeath A	5.00
Corofin RSO/Co.Clare A	5.00
Courtmacsherry RSO/	
Co.Cork A	4.00
Cratloe RSO/Co.Clare A	7.00
Creagh RSO/Co.Cork A	5.00
Cross Cong RSO/Co.Mayo A	12.00
Crossgar RSO Co.Down B	5.00
Curry RSO/Co.Sligo A	10.00
Dalkey RSO/Co.Dublin A	12.00
Dartrey RSO/	
Co.Monaghan A	5.00
Derinagree/Banteer RSO/	
Co.Cork F	10.00
Dervock RSO/Co.Antrim A	4.00
Doonagore Lahinch RSO/	
Co.Clare A	6.00
Dromard/Ballisodare	
RSO/Co.Sligo F	12.00
Dundrum RSO/Co.Down A	4.00
Dundrum RSO Co.Tip A	4.00
Dunkettle Stn/-RSO- A	10.00
Dunleer RSO B	12.00
Dunleer/RSO A	8.00
E	20.00
Dunmanway RSO/Co.Cork A	5.00
Edenderry RSO/Kings Co. A	4.00
Enniskeen RSO/Co.Cork A	6.00
Errill Ballybrophy RSO/	
Queens Co A	5.00
Favor Royal/Aughnacloy	
RSO/Co.Tyrone F	15.00
Ferbane RSO/Kings Co A	4.00
Fiddown Piltown RSO/	
Co.Kilkenny A	5.00
Foynes RSO Co.Limerick B	4.00
Garranlahan/Ballinlough	
RSO/Co.Roscommon F	8.00
Glandore, Leap RSO/	
Co.Cork A	4.00
Glanmire RSO/Co.Cork A	4.00
Glasslough RSO	
Co.Monaghan B	5.00
Glenbeigh RSO/Co.Kerry A	5.00
Glenfarne RSO/	
Co.Leitrim A	6.00
Glin RSO/Co.Limerick A	4.50
Gneeveguilla/	
Rathmore RSO A	12.00
Goold's Cross RSO/	
Co.Tip A	5.00
Greenore RSO/Co.Louth A	4.00
Helen's Bay RSO/	
Co.Down A	3.00
Herbertstown Knocklong	
RSO/Co.Limerick A	8.00
Hillsboro/RSO C (250)	30.00
Hollymount RSO/Co.Mayo A	6.00
Holywood RSO/Co.Down A	2.00
E (no county)	12.00
Hospital/Knocklong RSO A	8.00
Howe's Strand/Kilbrittain	
RSO/Co.Cork F	10.00
Innismore/Lisbellaw RSO/	
Co.Fermanagh F	12.00
Inver RSO Co.Donegal B	5.00
Kanturk RSO/Co.Cork A	6.00
Kells RSO/Killarney	
C (258)	20.00
Kells RSO/Co.Kerry A	12.00
Kenmare RSO/Co.Kerry A	3.00
AR	7.00
Kilbrittain RSO/Co.Cork A	7.00
Kilcock RSO Co.Kildare B	5.00
Kilfenora RSO/Co.Clare A	6.00
Kilkee RSO/Co.Clare A	4.00
Kill/Kilmacthomas	
RSO/Co.Waterford F	15.00
Killala RSO/Co.Mayo A	4.00
Killaloe RSO/Co.Clare A	4.00
Killeagh RSO/Cork A	5.00
Killinkere/Virginia RSO/	
Co.Cavan F	15.00
Killoscully/Newport RSO/	
Co.Tipperary F	15.00
Killylea RSO/Co.Armagh A	5.00
Kilmeedy/Ballingarry	
RSO A	5.00
Kilmore/Drumsna RSO A	8.00
Kilnaboy RSO/Co.Clare A	6.00
Kilpedder RSO/	
Co.Wicklow A	5.00
Kilskeery RSO/	
Co.Tyrone A	5.00
Kiltyclogher RSO/	
Co.Leitrim A	5.00
Kilworth RSO/Co.Cork A	5.00
Kingwilliamstown Rathmore	
RSO/Co.Kerry A	12.00
Knockcroghery RSO/	
Co.Roscommon A	8.00
(spelling error one c A 12.00)	
Knocklong RSO/	
Co.Limerick A	6.00
E (no county)	20.00
Knocknagashel/	
Abbeyfeale RSO A	8.00
Kylemore RSO/	
Co.Galway A	5.00
AR	6.00
Lahinch RSO/Co.Clare A	4.00
Laurencetown/	
Gilford RSO A	5.00
Leap/RSO A	8.00
C (482)	15.00
Leenane RSO/Co.Galway A	4.00
Leixlip RSO/Co.Kildare A	5.00
Letterfrack RSO/	
Co.Galway A	5.00
Limerick Junct RSO/	
Co.Tip A	8.00
Lisbellaw RSO/	
Co.Fermanagh A	5.00
Lisdeen RSO/Co.Clare A	6.00
Lisdoonvarna RSO/	
Co.Clare A	5.00
Lismore RSO/	
Co.Waterford A	4.00
Lisnagry RSO/Co.Limk A	6.00
Lisnalong/Rockcorry RSO/	
Co.Monaghan F	15.00
Lisnamuck/Maghera RSO/	
Co.Derry F	15.00
Lisnaskea RSO/	
Co.Fermanagh A	4.00
Lissleton RSO/Co.Kerry A	12.00
Listowel RSO/Co.Kerry A	12.00
Longwood/Moy Valley RSO A	6.00
Lough Rynn RSO/	
Co.Leitrim A	6.00
Louth Inniskeen/RSO A	8.00
Lucan RSO/Co.Dublin A	3.00
Maam Cross Roads/RSO A	15.00
Macmine RSO/Co.Wexford A	6.00
Madden/Keady RSO/	
Co.Armagh F (red)	12.00
Manorcunningham RSO/	
Co.Donegal A	4.00
Manorhamilton RSO/	
Co.Leitrim A	4.00
Maynooth RSO	
Co.Kildare B	4.00
Middletown, Tynan RSO/	
Co.Armagh A	6.00
Millstreet RSO/Co.Cork A	4.00
Mitchelstown RSO/	
Co.Cork A	8.00
Moira RSO/Co.Down A	5.00
Monasteraden RSO/	
Co.Sligo A	6.00

Monasterevan RSO/ Co.Kildare A	5.00
Mount Bellew RSO/ Co.Galway A	5.00
Mountcharles RSO Co.Donegal B	6.00
Mountmellick RSO/ Queens Co. A	3.00
Mountrath RSO Queens Co. B	5.00
Moycullen RSO/Co.Galway A	5.00
Mullagh/Milltown Malbay RSO A	7.00
Murroe Newport RSO/ Co.Tip A	6.00
Narin/Glenties RSO A	7.00
Neale/RSO A	5.00
C (529)	20.00
Newbliss RSO Co.Monaghan B	8.00
Newcastle West RSO/ Co.Lim A	6.00
Newmarket on Fergus RSO/Co.Clare A	6.00
Newport RSO/Co.Tip A	7.00
Newtown Butler RSO/ Co.Fermanagh A	4.00
Oldcastle RSO/Co.Meath A	3.00
Pallasgreen RSO/ Co.Limerick A	5.00
(also without county)	
Passage West RSO/ Co.Cork A	3.00

Patrickswell RSO/ Co.Lim'k A	5.00
Philipstown RSO/ Kings Co. A	5.00
Piltown RSO/ Co.Kilkenny A	4.00
Portlaw RSO/ Co.Waterford A	8.00
Portmagee/ Valencia Island RSO A	12.00
Portrush RSO/Co.Galway A	12.00
Portumna RSO/Co.Galway A	4.00
Poyntzpass RSO/ Co.Armagh A	5.00
Quin RSO/Co.Clare A	5.00
Rathaspic/Rathowen RSO/ Co.Westmeath F	8.00
Rathdangan/Baltinglass RSO/ Co.Wicklow F	15.00
Rathdowney Ballybrophy RSO/ Queens A	5.00
Rathfarnham RSO/ Co.Dublin A	4.00
Rathkeale RSO/Co.Lim'k A	12.00
Rathmore RSO/Co.Kerry A	6.00
Rathnew RSO/Co.Wicklow A	5.00
Robertstown RSO/ Co.Kildare A	10.00
Rosmuck RSO/Co.Galway A	10.00
Rosscahill RSO/ Co.Galway A	6.00
Rosscarbery RSO/ Co.Cork A	12.00
Sixmile Bridge/RSO A	10.00
Sixmilebridge RSO B	4.00

Sneem Kenmare RSO/ Co.Kerry A	5.00
Spanish Point/ Miltown Malbay RSO F	12.00
Stamullen/Balbriggan RSO A	8.00
Stewartstown RSO/ Co.Tyrone A	3.00
Stradbally RSO/ Queen's Co. A	5.00
Street RSO Co.Westmeath B	6.00
Swords RSO Co.Dublin B	6.00
Tallow/RSO A	10.00
Tallow RSO/Co.Waterford A	7.00
Tarbert RSO/Co.Kerry A	4.00
Tarbert RSO/ Co.Limerick A	10.00
Templeorum/Piltown RSO/ Co.Kilkenny F	15.00
Tourmakeady RSO/ Co.Mayo A	7.00
Tullow RSO Co.Carlow B	4.00
Tummery RSO/Co.Tyrone A	12.00
Tynan RSO Co.Armagh B	4.50
Union Hall Leap RSO/ Co.Cork A	5.00
Upperlands RSO/ Co.Derry A	5.00
Upton RSO/Co.Cork A	6.00
Valencia Island RSO/ Co.Kerry A	7.50
Whiteabbey RSO/ Co.Antrim A	5.00
Woodlawn/RSO E	15.00

14. Maritime Markings

The sections in this chapter, showing some of the varied forms of maritime postal markings of the British Isles, are generally in the sequence of the earliest marking of each section. As well as postmarks there are privately produced cachets which are included only because they form an important element of maritime postal history and where the presence of such cachets (usually on postcards) alters the card's value considerably.

Ship Letters and India Letters

Applied to mail landed from private trading ships and carried by them from the port of departure, 1760s-1840s.

Note re type A below : inscription alternatively LRE. or LE. or LETR.

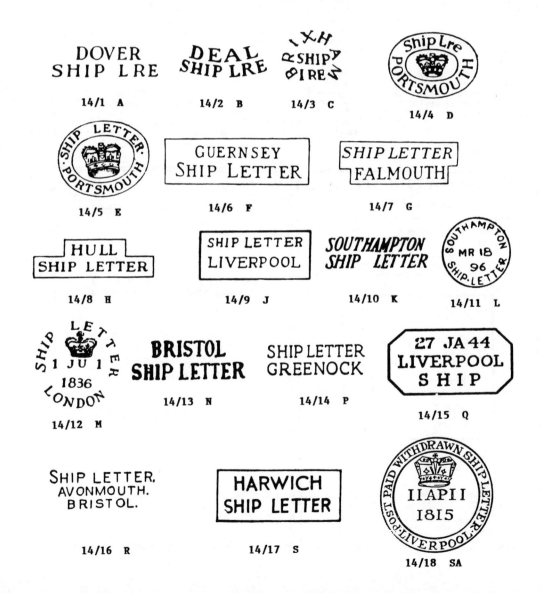

INDIA LETTER PORTSMOUTH	INDIA LETTER WEYMOUTH	
14/19 T	14/20 V	14/21 W

London Ship Letters:

A with or without hyphen	£50	SA	£400
E	£50	T	£25
H	£50	W	£30
L	£25	Paid Ship Letters	£25
L Paid	£15	Post Paid Ship Letters	£50
M	£25	Exempt Ship Letters	£75
M double circle	£75	Ship Letter/from/India	£750
M single circle	£60		

Provincial Ship Letters:

Aberdeen E dated	£300	N	£40	T	£25
H	£150	T	£80	T (port at top)	£40
Aldborough B	£300	Brixham C	£300	V	£100
Anstruther J	£300	E	£100	Deal A	£50
Ardrossan S (dated)	£300	G	£25	B	£75
Arundel H	£300	H	£15	C	£250
T	£300	N	£100	E	£75
Avonmouth R	£50	T	£60	G	£75
Ayr H	£300	Burntisland P	£300	H	£15
Bangor (Wales) S	£250	Cambleton A	£300	T	£30
Barnstable D	£200	Campbelton Steam		Derry E	£300
Barnstaple A	£200	Boat (2 lines)	£300	Devonport G	£25
H	£40	Campbleton S	£300	N	£100
Beaumaris A	£250	Cardiff H	£250	T	£60
H	£200	L	£50	V	£100
T	£300	Carlisle H	£250	Packet Letter	
Belfast F	£60	Carnarvon E	£250	two lines	£25
N	£250	Castletown		Dingle A	£450
Bideford H	£300	(Ireland) N	£100	Donegal F	£100
Birmingham/Ship		Castletown		Douglas (IOM) A	£3000
(double circle)	£50	(Portland) R	£75	Dover A	£50
Blyth North.d. P	£250	Colchester E (dated)	£500	B	£100
Bowmore Ship:Lre:		H	£300	E	£75
(2 lines)	£300	Cork F	£75	G	£30
Bridlington D	£250	N	£60	H	£50
Bridport B	£200	T	£100	P	£75
Bright Helm Stone		Cove A	£120	SA	£250
A (4 lines)	£300	N	£50	T	£50
Brighton B	£200	V	£75	T (port at top)	£50
E	£300	Cowes A (Lres)	£100	V	£75
G	£100	G	£60	Dublin J	£120
H	£60	H	£200	N	£60
K	£80	K	£15	Crown dated	£100
T	£60	T	£80	Dumfries J	£300
Bristol A	£80	Cromarty E (dated)	£300	Dunbar J	£300
A with port at top		SA	£300	Dundee	
and mileage	£200	Dartmouth A	£40	E (with cypher)	£300
E	£80	D	£100	H	£300
E with port at top	£200	G	£40	Eastbourne D	£200
G	£100	H	£40	H	£100
H	£60	P	£200	T	£100
K	£100	SA	£300		

Edinburgh A	£300	Guernsey E	£300	Liverpool A	£40
D (with ship)	£300	F	£500	A (Ship only)	£40
E	£220	H	£4000	D	£40
H	£100	J	£2000	E	£40
Octagon Ship Letter	£75	Harwich E	£200	E dated	£60
Exeter A	£200	G	£80	G	£25
E	£200	H	£200	H	£25
H	£200	S	£100	J	£25
T	£200	T	£300	L (Ship)	£25
Exmouth H	£100	Hastings A	£200	M	£60
T	£200	E	£200	N	£25
Falmouth A	£200	G	£60	Q	£25
C	£80	H	£60	Q (Paid)	£200
D	£80	N	£200	S	£25
E	£100	T	£60	SA	£200
G	£80	Haverford West A		T	£40
H	£40	(3 lines)	£250	T (India Ship Lr	
L	£200	Helston G	£100	at top)	£40
P	£300	Hithe C	£250	Exempt Ship	£80
SA	£300	Holyhead A	£250	Looe G	£150
T	£40	H	£100	Lowestoff C	£500
V	£100	T	£150	Lyme A	£200
Circular, dated,		Hubberstone A	£250	D	£200
double arcs	£300	Hull E	£150	G	£200
Packet Lre, circ	£100	G	£50	H	£200
Packet Letter,		H	£50	T	£200
2 lines	£300	L	£25	Lymington A	£80
L (Packet)	£200	N	£50	D	£200
Faversham H	£250	Q	£50	T	£100
Fleetwood P	£50	SA	£250	Lynn E	£300
Folkestone D	£150	T	£250	Maldon A	£400
H	£80	Hythe H	£250	Marazion A	
K	£80	Ilfracombe G		(289 mileage)	£250
T	£100	(port at bottom)	£300	H	£200
Fowey H	£500	T	£300	Margate A	£75
T	£200	W (port at top)	£300	G	£75
Fraserburgh J	£300	I. Man G	£3000	H	£75
Glasgow E	£75	Ipswich H	£300	SA	£250
F	£50	Irvine A	£300	T	£50
F dated	£50	Isle of Wight D	£500	Mevagissey H	£200
Gloucester H	£250	T	£100	Middlesbrough L	£60
Goole H	£250	Jersey F	£3000	Milford (Wales) E	£250
Gosport A	£350	H	£4000	H	£250
E	£350	K	£500	T	£250
Grangemouth E		S	£500	Montrose J	£300
(with cypher)	£300	Kingsbridge G	£15	Newburgh F dated	£300
S	£300	H	£25	Newcastle (Northd) D	£250
Granton S	£100	T	£25	Newcastle-Tyne P	£250
Gravesend A	£150	Kinsale N	£100	Newcastle.u.T. P	£250
D	£250	Kirkcaldy J	£300	New Romney S	£75
E	£250	Kirkwall J	£300	T	£75
G	£50	Lancaster C	£350	New Rumney D	£250
H	£50	D	£250	Newry N	£150
N	£100	E	£250	Oval fancy	£500
S (italic)	£30	H	£150	Newton Abbot H	£200
T	£50	Leith E	£75	North Shields E	£350
T (italic)	£50	E (with cypher)	£300	H	£250
V	£75	E dated	£150	S	£250
Greenock C		H	£150	Oban A	£300
(single circle)	£300	Oval, Ship Letter	£150	Padstow E	£200
D	£50	ditto, dated	£150	Pembroke G	£250
E	£50	Shipletter thimble	£150	Penzance A	£200
H	£30	L	£50	D	£100
J (dated)	£50	T	£300	H	£60
N	£30	Lerwick H	£150	P	£100
P	£30	J	£300	T (double frame)	£60
P (dated)	£50	Lewes G	£200	V	£80
SA (2 types)	£300	H	£80	Peterhead P	£300
India	£50	T	£60	Plym.Dock H	£25
Grimsby E	£300	Limerick F	£100	Packet letter	
N	£250	Limington A	£300	2 lines	£200

Plymouth A	£25	G	£150	Swanage E	£200
D	£40	H	£75	G	£200
E	£25	H (port at bottom)	£150	H	£200
G	£15	T	£75	J	£200
H (port in bottom line)	£15	Rochester E	£150	N	£200
T	£15	G	£150	S	£100
V	£25	H	£150	T	£200
Plymouth Dock C	£300	Rochford H	£300	T (port at top)	£200
D	£100	Romney T	£100	W (port at top)	£200
T	£200	Ross N	£200	Swansea H	£250
Polpero S	£300	Rostrevor N	£300	L	£50
Pool A	£100	Rothesay J	£300	N	£250
E	£200	Ryde E	£200	Swanzey A	£400
Poole G	£200	H	£100	Teignmouth G	£200
H	£80	K	£100	H	£200
K	£200	P	£200	T	£300
SA	£200	V	£100	Tenby J	£250
T	£100	V (port at top)	£100	Thurso J	£300
Portaskaig, Ship (single circle)	£300	W	£200	Tobermory A (double circle)	£300
Port Glasgow A	£75	Rye E	£300	Torquay N	£100
E dated	£300	G	£200	Totness A	£300
E with cypher	£75	H	£200	C	£300
H	£50	St.Ives H	£300	Troon E (with cypher)	£300
N	£50	T (Corn.)	£300	J	£200
SA	£300	St.Mawes G	£100	Tyne Dock/South Shields R (3 lines)	£200
India	£50	Saltcoats J	£300	Warren N	£500
Portsmouth A	£60	S (three lines)	£300	Warrens Pt N	£500
B	£80	Sheerness D	£250	Waterford N	£50
D	£60	H	£250	Wexford N	£450
E	£60	T	£250	Weymouth A	£200
E small single oval	£200	Shoreham H	£300	D	£200
H	£40	Sidmouth G	£300	E dated	£200
K	£40	Sittingbourne H (port at bottom)	£250	G	£100
P (Packet Letter two lines)	£200	Skibbereen A	£100	H (spaced)	£60
SA	£200	N ('Ship letter' script)	£250	T	£80
T	£40	Southampton A	£80	V	£200
T (port at top)	£60	D	£100	Whitby H	£250
Preston H	£250	E	£80	Whitehaven B	£250
Pteerhd Ship letter (Peterhead)(1 line)	£300	G	£40	H	£250
Pt Glasgo A	£150	H	£60	Worthing H	£200
Pwllheli S (italic)	£250	K	£60	Yarmouth (Norfolk) A	£300
Qn.Borough A	£250	L	£15	D	£300
Queenboro G	£75	N	£40	H	£200
T	£250	P	£60	Yarmouth IOW G (three line with "Sihp" for "Ship")	£300
Queenborough B	£250	S	£60	Yarmouth IW E	£300
H	£150	T	£60	Yarmouth.N (Norfolk) G	£300
Queenstown N	£75	South Shields P	£50	T	£200
Ramsgate A	£150	Southwold E	£350	Youghal N	£300
E	£250	Stranraer A	£300		
		H	£300		
		Sunderland H	£250		

Packet Letters

Carried by vessels hired by the Post Office to carry letters, from 1802

PACKET-LETTER

14/23

14/24

14/27

14/29

(14/22 number not used)

London
14/23 Packet Letter, boxed or unboxed, 1802-63 .... 30.00

London Foreign Branch
14/24 Quartered handstamp, red or black, 1864-1902, with L (London),
       D (Devonport), H (Holyhead), I (Ireland - Cork), N (underpaid)
       - also known with C or blank centre (meanings unclear) 15.00

Dartmouth
14/25 Dartmouth Packet Letter, circular unframed, 1857 .... 300.00

Devonport
14/26 Packet Letter/Devonport, 1839-50 .... 70.00
14/27 Devonport/Packet Letter, circular unframed, 1858-66 .... 100.00
14/28 Cape Packet/Devonport, circular unframed, 1858-67 .... 70.00
14/29 Paid/Devonport/Cape Packet, 1863-67 .... 15.00
14/30 Cape Packet/Devonport, 1869-70 .... 80.00

Dublin
14/31 America/Paid/Dublin, with side arcs, black,green or blue, 1856-59 250.00

14/32

LISBO
5 MY 5Z
1813
F

14/34

14/40

Falmouth

14/32	Falmouth Packt Lre, unframed circular, green or black, 1807-14 .	80.00
14/33	Falmouth/Packet Letter, 2-line unframed, green or black, 1809-15	120.00
14/34	Unframed, with F (Falmouth) in green, 1810-47:	

America	£150	Jamaica	£300
Brazil	£150	Leeward Islands	£400
Cadiz	£120	Lisbon	£60
Gibraltar	£300	Malta	£600
		India (with double arc)	£1000

14/35	Falmouth Packet, single circle, 1869-84	50.00

Glasgow

14/36	Glasgow Packet/Paid/date, four line unframed, 1860-81	40.00
14/37	As above but unpaid, 1865	50.00
14/38	Glasgow Packet/Col. Paid, four line unframed, black/blue, 1860-63	40.00
14/39	As above but unpaid, 1863	50.00
14/40	Packet Letter/Glasgow, oval, 1879-94	40.00
14/41	Paid/Glasgow/Packet, single circle, 1883-90	40.00
14/42	As above but unpaid, 1883	50.00

Liverpool

14/45	14/47	14/55	14/65	14/67

14/43	America/L, double circle undated, 1840-41	....	200.00
14/44	America/L, oval undated, 1840-44	....	100.00
14/45	As above but dated, black or green, 1850-55	....	60.00
14/46	America (enclosed)/Liverpool/date, 1844	....	?
14/47	As above but not enclosed, black, 1845-58	....	12.00
14/48	As above but in green, 1858	....	40.00
14/49	America/Paid/Liverpool, with side arcs, red or black, 1848-70	..	25.00
14/50	Paid in/America/Liverpool, tombstone, red 1850-58	....	60.00
14/51	American Mail, in horseshoe, 1857-58	....	?
14/52	Pkt. Letter/Liverpool/date, tombstone, black or green, 1852-58	.	20.00
14/53	As above but with Paid, black or red, 1852-58	....	20.00
14/54	Liverpool/U.S. Packet, circular, black, 1858-1903	....	15.00
14/55	As above but with Paid, red, 1858-1903	....	8.00
14/56	Liverpool/BR Packet, circular, black, 1858-74	....	25.00
14/57	As above but with Paid, red or black, 1858-1902	....	6.00
14/58	Liverpool/Col. Packet, circular, black, 1859	....	50.00
14/59	As above but with Paid, red, 1859-1903	....	10.00
14/60	Liverpool/DE Packet (Londonderry), circular, black, 1859	....	200.00
14/61	Paid/Liverpool/LB Packet, circular, 1814	....	?
14/62	Liverpool P.S. Packet, circular, 1872	....	?
14/63	Liverpool.P.L.O. (Packet Letter Office), circular, 1858-1902	...	50.00
14/64	South Amern/Liverpool/Packet, with side arcs, black or green, 1854-55	....	100.00
14/65	Australian/Liverpool/Packet, with double side arcs, black or green, 1855-56	....	80.00
14/66	As above but with Paid, red, 1855-57	....	80.00
14/67	Liverpool/F.R.H. (Floating Receiving House), with double side arcs, black, red or blue, 1859-64	....	250.00
14/68	(no entry, for Quartered handstamp see **14/24**)		

14/74

14/79

14/80

Londonderry

14/69	Paid/Derry/Col. Packet, circular, black or red, 1862-75	80.00
14/70	Londonderry/Paid/Col. Packet, circular, red, 1877-89	50.00
14/71	Londonderry Colonial Pkt., circular, black or red, 1897-1906 ...	40.00

Plymouth

14/72	Packet Letter/Plymouth, boxed, 1811-15	300.00
14/73	Plymouth/Packet Letter, circular with side arcs, black, red, blue, yellow or green, 1853-56	60.00
14/74	Cape Packet/Plymouth, 1870-78	30.00
14/75	Paid/Plymouth/Cape-Packet, 1870	75.00

Plymouth Dock (later Devonport)

14/76	Packet Letter/Plym. Dock, boxed, 1813	200.00

Portsmouth

14/77	Packet Letter/Portsmouth, unframed, 1847-49	100.00

Southampton

14/78	Packet Letter/Southampton, unframed, blue, red, green or black, 1844-55	75.00
14/79	Southampton/Packet Letter, circ unframed, black or blue, 1857-67	30.00
14/80	As above but framed, 1881-1917	8.00

Moveable Box Marks on Mail to France

14/81

14/83

14/84

14/81 Boxed MB from 1844:
Brighton   London
Dover   Southampton
Folkestone   from   50.00

14/82 Milestone type with year in four digits, from 1856:
Dover   London
Folkestone   Newhaven
Guernsey   Southampton
Jersey   Weymouth   from   30.00

14/83 As above but with year in two digits, from 1884 .... 25.00

14/84 Circular MB types, 1893-1939:
London   12.00   Southampton   10.00

British Coastal Steamers

Skye Packet Services

UIST to DUNVEGAN

14/85

14/85 Uist to/Dunvegan, 1836-41 .... 200.00

Fleetwood to Belfast Steamer Service

      14/86   14/87

14/86 Prince of Wales,   ) circular cachets struck on mail
14/87 Fleetwood & Belfast) from the 'Prince of Wales' 1843-44 .... 250.00

Holyhead and Kingstown Service
(City of Dublin Steam Packet Co.) 1860-1925

    14/88   14/89   14/91   14/93

      14/95   14/97

14/88 H & K Pact duplex with diamond numeral 186, from 1860 .... 75.00
14/89 H & K Pact, with side arcs, from 1860 (value as cancellation) .. 75.00
14/90   As above but surmounted by 'Night Mail', known used 1870 & 1883 200.00
14/91 H & K Packet, double circle (various), 1884-93 .... 50.00
14/92   H & K Packet, single circle (various), 25mm, 1894-1900 .... 50.00
14/93   As above but 27mm, C1-4 (Connaught), L1-4 (Leinster), M1-4
          (Munster), U1-4 (Ulster), from 1901 .... 20.00
14/94   As above but H & K Packet PO - C5, L5, M5, U5 - rubber, purple 150.00
14/95 H & K Packet, double circle thick arcs with cross at foot, 1919-25 25.00
14/96 H and K Packet/Day Boat, double circle, 1922-23 .... 150.00
14/97 H and D L Pkt, double rim skeleton, 1922 .... 300.00

14/98 Mis-sent to Hd & Kn Packet, 1862 .... 150.00
14/99 Posted without late fee, boxed, 1897-1907 .... 25.00
14/100 Late fee paid, boxed, 1922 .... 25.00

Clyde Steamers

Greenock & Ardrishaig Floating Post Offices (David MacBrayne Ltd), 1879-1917:

14/101   14/104   14/105

14/106   14/107   14/108

14/101 Greenock & Ardrishaig Packet, duplex 163, 1879 only 250.00
14/102 Columba Steamer/Greenock, duplex 163, 1879-1900 .... 50.00
14/103 As above but without small side arcs in datestamp 50.00
14/104 Iona Steamer/Greenock, duplex 163, 1879-84 .... 50.00
14/105 Iona Steamer/163, small double circle, 1884-1900 .... 40.00
14/106 Grenadier Steamer/666, double circle, 1895-1901 .... 200.00

14/107 Gk. & Ardrishaig Packet, double circle 30mm, 1901-08 (see note below)
        - Columba 15.00, Iona 35.00, Grenadier 100.00, Chevalier .. 250.00

14/108 Greenock & Ardrishaig Pkt, double circle 30mm, 1903-09 (see note below)
        - Columba 50.00, Iona 35.00, Grenadier 150.00

14/109 Gk. & Ardrishaig Packet, double circle 27mm, 1909-15 (see note below)
        - Columba 20.00, Iona 40.00, Grenadier 120.00, Chevalier .. 250.00

14/110 As above but without ship's name, 1916 only 120.00

Note : Valuations are for index B, afternoon return trip from Ardrishaig to Greenock, used as cancellations. Index A, morning trip, merits a premium. Backstamps should be discounted slightly.

      Private Cachets

      D. Hutcheson & Co.
14/111 Posted on Board/"Columba"/date/D. Hutcheson & Co., oval, 1878 . 250.00
14/112 As above but Iona 250.00

      Glasgow and Inveraray Steamboat Co.
14/113 Posted on Board/Lord of the Isles/Steamer, unframed, magenta,
       1878-79 .... 150.00
14/114 Steamer Lord of the Isles, double oval with date, violet, 1903 150.00
14/115 R.M.S."Lord of the Isles", oval belt & buckle, violet, 1904-12 25.00
14/116 Posted on Board S.S."Fairy Queen"/Loch Eck/Argyllshire, 1903-10 50.00

      Lochgoil and Lochlong Steamboat Co.
14/117 Posted on Board/"Edinburgh Castle"/Steamer, violet, 1881 ..... 200.00

      Glasgow and South Western Railway
14/118 Glasgow and South Western Rly/P.S./Juno/Steam Vessels, 1905- .. 85.00
14/119 As above but P.S. Jupiter, 1905 .... 85.00

      Caledonian Steam Packet Co. Ltd.
14/120 Caledonian Steam Packet Co./Limited/Duchess/of Argyll, 1908- .. 50.00
14/121 As above but P.S./Duchess of/Rothesay, ?date 60.00
14/122 As above but P.S./Duchess of/Hamilton, 1906- 50.00

14/111

14/116

14/113

14/114

14/115

14/117

14/118

14/122

Loch Lomond

14/123 Posted on board "The Queen", violet, 1892 .... 300.00

14/123

14/125

14/128

14/131

North Wales Coastal Services

14/124 Per Passgr S.'Trefiw-Belle', small violet cachet, 1904- 175.00
14/125 Posted on "La Marguerite", blue, 1905-10 .... 35.00
14/126   As above but double circle in violet (sim to 14/128) 1911-14 . 85.00
14/127   As above but sans-serif letters and crosses, 1914 only 100.00
14/128 Posted on St. Elvies, violet, 1912-14 .... 175.00
14/129   As above but Posted on Snowdon, 1911-13 .... 175.00
14/130   As above but Posted on St. Tudno, 1911 only 175.00
14/131 Posted on Board St. Tudno, violet, 1926 only 150.00
14/132 St. Tudno, straight line, black or violet, 1926-29 .... 100.00
14/133 Passed by Censor HMS Marguerite, violet, 1917 only 100.00

Tay Pleasure Steamers

14/134   **14/135**

14/134 Tay Pleasure Steamer/Marchioness of Bute, 1913 .... 100.00
14/135 P.S.Slieve Bearnach/Tay/Pleasure/Steamer, 1913-14 .... 100.00

Later period

Of the items shown above in the "British Coastal Steamers" section nos 14/86-87 and 14/111-135 are cachets and not Post Office postmarks. We have retained in this chapter the cachets of the "classic period" up to 1930 (except "Ivanhoe 1904" of which we do not have details). Subsequent to this there are a wealth of further cachets from steamers all round the UK coasts. We show here six examples, but the listing of these is outside the scope of this book.

MONA'S ISLE

14/137 (Isle of Man 1963)

14/138 (1981)

14/136 (see **14/120-22**)

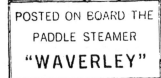

AT SEA
m.v. ROYAL EAGLE

RMS HEBRIDES

14/141
(Southend 1950)

14/139 (Isle of Skye 1985)   **14/140** (IOW 1979)

Ocean Going Steamers

The same remarks concerning cachets apply here as in the previous section. This is a large topic and we only show here the RMSP Co cachets, thanks to the book by Michael Rego, otherwise this large topic is outside the scope of this book.

Royal Mail Steam Packet Company

Cachets without Ships' names:

14/142 Oval belt & buckle cachet, violet or purple-black, 1905-12 ....   6.00
14/143   As above but Posted on/the High Seas in 2 lines, violet, 1905-09 8.00
14/144 Posted on the/High Seas, 2 lines, violet, purple or black, 1906-09 5.00
14/145   As above but date in second line, blue, 1912 .... 15.00
14/146   As above but single line, no date shown, violet, 1913 ...... 25.00
14/147 Posted on the/High Seas, oval, violet or black, 1910-13 ......   5.00

POSTED ON THE HIGH SEAS.

14/142

14/144

A **14/150**

R.M.S.P. above,
Ship name below

B **14/151**

'Posted on the High Seas' above
Ship name below

C **14/152**

Company name above
'Posted on the High Seas' below

Cachets with Ships' names:

14/148   Straight Line, name of Ship only (1900-04):

Eden	£250	Yare	£100
Esk	£100	Yare & Tagus	£100
Solent	£100		

14/149   Dated three or five line cachets (1922-26):

Chaleur	£40	Darro	£15
Chaudiere	£40	Teviot	£40

D **14/153**

Ship name above,
'Posted on the High Seas' below

Oval cachets (1908-69) (see **14/150** to **14/153**):

Alcantara C	£12	Beresina D	£6	Highland Brigade	
D	£6	Caraquet C (large		D	£5
Almanzora D	£6	single oval)	£40	Highland Chieftain	
Amazon A	£10	Chaleur D	£40	D	£12
B	£5	Chaudiere C	£40	Highland Monarch	
C	£8	D (single oval)	£40	D	£5
Andes D	£4	Chignecto C	£40	Highland Patriot	
Aragon A	£8	Clyde A	£20	D	£6
Araguaya A	£5	Danube C	£20	Highland Princess	
B	£20	Darro B	£12	D	£5
C	£8	C	£8	Lochgoil C	£15
D	£6	D	£12	Lombardy D	£15
Arcadian D	£12	Demerara C	£10	Ohio D	£6
Arlanza B	£5	D	£6	Orbita D	£15
D	£6	Deseado B	£12	Orca D	£7
Asturias A	£10	C	£10	Orduna B	£12
D	£5	D	£6	D	£15
Atlantis D	£4	Desna B	£10	Oruba A	£20
Atrato A	£20	C	£6	Sabor A	£20
Avon A	£10	Essequibo B	£6	Tagus A	£20
B	£12	C	£10	Trent A	£20
D	£5	Gascony D	£7		

Paquebot

Applied from 1890s to the present day to mail posted on board ship. A and B applied either as cachets or to cancel stamps, but C to H cancelling stamps. This is one of the few circumstances under which stamps of an overseas country may be legitimately cancelled in the country where the ship berths.

A selection of overseas Paquebot marks is shown at the end of the chapter.

PAQUEBOT

14/154

A. Straight Line
(size and spacing of
letters vary)
(or "Paquebots")

PAQUEBOT.

14/155

B. Boxed
(size of letters and
box vary)

14/156

C. Distinctive
'Posted at sea'
steel handstamps

PAQUEBOT
POSTED AT SEA

14/157

D. Machines
(eg. Universal machine with Paquebot
slogan or town die or both -
Paquebot town die shown as D*)

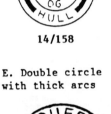

14/158

E. Double circle
with thick arcs

14/159

F. Single circle

14/160

G. Double circle
with thin arcs

14/161

H. Rubber stamps
(various designs)

Aberdeen B with port	£6	Chatham A	£4	Grangemouth A	£50
H	£6	B	£4	B	£6
Ardrossan A	£25	Chelmsford B	£8	Grays B	£4
Ayr A	£6	Cowes A	£4	D* Universal	£6
Basildon A	£10	Dartford A	£5	Great Yarmouth A	£4
Belfast B	£6	B	£6	Greenock A	£10
C	£6	Dartmouth A	£40	D Universal	£3
D Hey Dolphin	£10	Douglas G	£100	Grimsby A	£4
D Universal	£3	Dover A	£50	Guernsey A	£40
Berwick A	£6	C red	£4	Harwich B	£3
Blackpool A	£6	H red	£3	Holyhead C	£3
Blyth B	£10	Dundee B	£6	Hull A	£4
Boston A	£6	Edinburgh A	£6	D Universal	£25
triangular	£8	D/D* Universal	£5	E	£10
Bournemouth B	£5	D/D* slogan	£8	Ilford A	£25
Bridgwater A navire	£10	E	£4	H	£6
Bristol A	£6	Falmouth A	£10	Invergordon A	£10
D* Krag	£40	F	£6	B	£6
D Hey Dolphin	£6	Felixstowe B	£4	Inverness B	£6
D Universal	£4	Fishguard C	£6	Ipswich B	£4
Brixham A	£10	Folkestone A	£4	Jersey A	£50
D Universal	£4	A mis-spelt	£30	Kings Lynn A	£6
G	£8	B	£3	Kirkcaldy A	?
(then see Torquay)		Glasgow A	£10	Kirkwall A	£10
Buckie A	£25	B	£4	B	£10
Burnham on Crouch A	£6	D Universal	£3	Lancaster boxed	£4
Cardiff C	£4	Gloucester A	£10	Leith A	£60
D* Krag	£6	Goole B	£5		

Lerwick A	£75	Newport A	£10	Shoreham by Sea A	£6
F without		C "Newport Mon"	£10	Southampton A	£10
'Shetland'	£25	C "Newport Gwent"	£6	C	£4
F with 'Shetland'	£6	North Shields A	£6	D* Columbia	£6
Liverpool A	£6	Oban A	£5	D/D* Universal,	
C	£4	Pembroke Dock H	£5	wavy lines	£3
D Columbia	£6	Plymouth A	£6	D/D* Universal,	
D Hey Dolphin	£3	D Columbia	£3	with slogans	£4
D Universal	£4	D* Hey Dolphin s/c	£25	E	£6
E	£3	D Hey Dolphin d/c	£4	South Shields A	£10
F	£6	D* Krag 'Paquebot'	£3	Stornoway A	£25
London A	£4	D Krag 'Posted		B	£25
D* Krag	£3	at sea'	£50	F	£8
D Hey Dolphin	£3	D Universal		Stromness B	£10
D Universal		(several)	£3	Sunderland A	£6
(London/London FS)		E	£3	B	£6
(several)	£3	Portree H	£10	Swansea E	£6
F	£3	Portsmouth A	£4	G "Swansea"	£6
G	£4	B	£3	G "West Glam"	£8
H	£3	G no arcs (1953)	£20	Tayport with map ref	£10
Londonderry A	£8	H	£25	Thurso B	£6
B	£6	Port Talbot F	£20	Torquay ("South Devon")	
H	£8	G	£20	D	£6
Lowestoft A	£6	Preston B	£6	G	£6
Maldon A	£25	Queenstown A	£25	Weymouth D* Univ	£8
Manchester A	£6	(incl used with Dublin/Cork		F	£10
Methil A	£50	& Dublin/Queenstown TPOs)		skeleton	£40
Middlesbrough A	£6	E (double arcs)	£6	H	£6
Milford Haven G	£6	Ramsgate A	£4	Wick B	£10
H	£6	B	£4	Wisbech, special B	£10
Newcastle upon Tyne A	£6	Romford B	£6	Workington A	£10
B	£6	Ryde A	£6		
Newhaven A	£4	St.Mary's B	£10		
D Universal	£4	Saltcoats A	£6		
G	£4	Scarborough A	£10		
H	£5	Selby B	£10		

Sea Post Offices

14/162	14/163	14/164	14/165	14/166

Transatlantic Post Office:

In 1904 GB and USA agreed to the establishment of joint post offices on board seven White Star liners and four ships of the American Line. This joint service operated 1905-14. British postmarks were used in the post offices aboard the ships, but tax and mis-sent marks were of US style on all eleven ships.

14/162 British Sea Post Office Liverpool/nos 1-7, double circle, 1905-07   40.00

14/163 British Sea Post Office/Southampton, nos 1-10, single circle, 1907-08 .... 25.00

14/164 Transatlantic Post Office Plymouth/nos 1-4, double circle, 1905-07 .... 150.00

14/165 Transatlantic Post Office/nos 1-11, single circle, 1908-14 .... 15.00

U.K. & South Africa Sea Post Office:

The service operated 1913-14 and was the successor to South Africa administered Ocean Post Offices. One British handstamp was used as shown below, plus tax mark.

14/166 United Kingdom & S. Africa Sea P.O./nos 1-9, double circle (index letters N North or S South above date) 50.00

14/167 Tax mark T in hexagon above "UK-SA/Sea Post" 20.00

Royal Navy

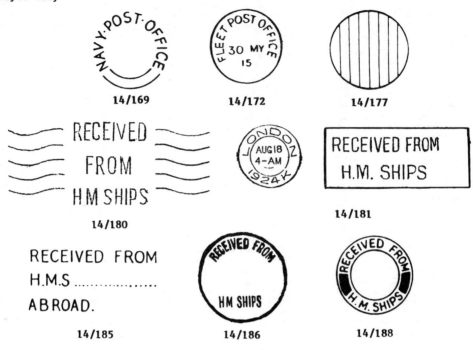

14/169   14/172   14/177

14/180   14/181

14/185   14/186   14/188

14/168	Navy Post Office, straight line, unframed, 1840s	250.00
14/169	Navy Post Office, circular double arc, blue, 1850s	150.00
14/170	Duplex: Plymouth/H.M.S. with numeral 620, 1852-	150.00
14/171	Duplex: Devonport/H.M.S. with numeral 250, 1860s	150.00
	World War I period:	
14/172	Fleet Post Office, single circle, 1914-	8.00
14/173	Fleet PO, single circle, 1915-	8.00
14/174	Krag machine, with FPOa dies for anonymity	3.00
14/175	Krag machine with town dies of bars, crosses or plus signs	5.00
14/176	Locally made crosses, circles etc, probably rubber or cork ...	5.00
14/177	Dumb cancel of seven or eight vertical bars across circle	1.00
14/178	Received from H.M. Ship./No Charge to be Raised, framed/unframed	3.00
14/179	As above but machine die (framed or unframed), 1915-20	2.50
	(see "Collecting Slogan Postmarks" for details)	
14/180	Received from HM Ships, Krag machine (undated)	25.00
	From 1920s onwards, including World War II period:	
14/181	Received from H.M. Ships, machine die	3.00
	(framed/unframed, see "Collecting Slogan Postmarks" for details)	
14/182	As above but without town die, 1939-40	3.00
14/183	As above but with census diamond instead of town die, 1939-40	5.00
14/184	London IS/H.M. Ships, rubber handstamp, 1931	6.00
14/185	Received from/H.M.S. .../Abroad, unframed	10.00
14/186	Received from/H.M. Ships, undated rubber handstamp, 1939	5.00
14/187	Received from/H.M. Ships, single circle, dated, 1939	4.00
14/188	Received from/H.M. Ships, double circle thick arcs, 1939	4.00
14/189	London/H.M. Ships, double circle thick arcs, 1939	5.00
14/190	Edinburgh/H.M. Ships, double circle thick arcs, 1939	5.00

Maritime Mail postmarks 1943-95:

MARITIME MAIL

14/191   **14/197**   **14/200**

14/191 Machine die with undated "Post Office" town die, red or black .   0.50
        (variations, see "Collecting Slogan Postmarks" for details)
14/192   As above but dated London town die (& unusually Plymouth), 1968-   0.30
14/193 Post Office/Maritime Mail, double circle thick arcs, 1943- 3.00
14/194 Post Office/Maritime Mail, rubber handstamps (various) 5.00
14/195 London I.S./Maritime Mail, rubber handstamp, 43mm diameter, 1967-   4.00
14/196   As above but Plymouth or Portsmouth, 1969- 6.00
14/197 London I.S./Maritime Mail, rubber handstamps (various) 33mm, 1977-   1.50
14/198 Maritime Mail/Bristol, steel single circle, 1960s 6.00
14/199 Parcel Post/Post Office/Maritime Mail, parcel handstamp 10.00
14/200 Town/Maritime Mail, steel double circle 33mm diam, 1968- 2.50
14/201 Received from Ships, Postage Paid, triangular, red, 1980s 5.00
        (seen used in conjunction with **14/197**)

   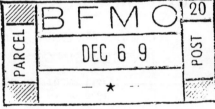

14/201   **14/202**   **14/203** (+ wavy lines)   **14/204**

14/202 British Fleet Mail/number, double circle with thick/thin arcs .   4.00
14/203 Base Fleet Mail Office/20, Universal machine die (Singapore) 1960s   5.00
14/204 B F M O parcel handstamp 10.00

British Fleet Mail Offices 1944-1982 :

1	Ceylon	13	India	27	Netherlands E Indies,
2	India, Japan	14	USA		Ceylon
3	Malaya	15	Gibraltar	28	India
4	Egypt	16	Australia	29	South Africa
5	Australia	17	India	30	Germany
6	USA	18	Egypt, Germany	31	India
8	Italy	19	Kenya	32	Germany
9	Australia, UK, Hong Kong	20	Burma, Ceylon, Singapore	33	Malaya, Singapore
10	Malta	22	Netherlands E Indies	35	Pakistan
11	Germany, Sierra Leone	24	Belgium, Italy, Denmark	36	Egypt
12	Australia, Palestine, Israel, Greece	25	Papua New Guinea	37	Ceylon
		26	Singapore	38	Germany
				39	Egypt
				40	Germany
				41	Japan

Note: a large variety of ships' cachets are available on naval covers, either on
official use or posted on ships' Open Days (eg HMS Eagle shown on page 176 of
the Fifth Edition, used 1936). These are beyond the scope of this handbook.

Naval Censor marks – Second World War

Censorship and censor marks are large topics, and a representative selection of censor marks is shown below, with values. The source of these is "World War Two Censor Marks" edited by John Daynes, see Bibliography. Further censor marks from the same source are included in chapters 15 and 16. To aid cross reference to that book we include the reference numbers used by John Daynes.

14/205 N100 0.10
1939-45 (also Suez 1956)

PASSED CENSOR H.M.S. HOOD

14/206 N201 20.00
1939 only

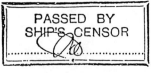

14/207 N216 40.00
1939 only

14/208 N421 2.50

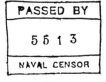

14/209 N412 5.00

PASSED BY CENSOR

14/210 N604 1.00
1939 only

ON ACTIVE SERVICE PASSED BY CENSOR

14/211 N802 10.00
1939 only

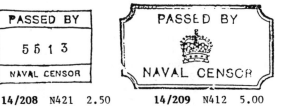

14/212 N904 9.00

Naval Establishments

D	Single circle
E	Double circle

F	Skeleton handstamp
J	Parcel handstamp

14/213

Note the entries are abbreviated, similar to Camps in chap 15.

Admiralty SW F	20.00	Naval Barracks Keyham Devonport		Plymouth Devon, Naval	
Naval Camp Blandford E	5.00	D	5.00	Barracks J	8.00
F	12.00	F	15.00	Portland Dock, Portland	
J	10.00	Dover Naval Mail Office		Dorset D	3.00
*HMS Cabbala, Stafford D	?	rubber	20.00	*Portsmouth, Fort Grange D	10.00
registered	?	Drake Hall Stafford D	8.00	Portsmouth, Naval Barracks	
Naval Barracks Chatham D	3.00	RNC Eaton, Chester rubber	6.00	D	3.00
J	8.00	HMS Excellent Whale Island		Raleigh, Torpoint Cornwall	
Dockyard Chatham D	3.00	F	20.00	D	3.00
Churchill, Helensburgh D	3.00	*Fort Matilda Camp, Greenock		E	3.00
Clyde Submarine Base,		D	?	J	8.00
Helensburgh D	3.00	FMO Greenock D	4.00	Scapa Pier, Kirkwall Orkney	
J	6.00	Haslar Hospital, Gosport D	8.00	E	10.00
Collingwood (or HMS), Fareham,		*Inverness AMO D	6.00	Sultan, Gosport Hants D	6.00
Hants D	4.00	Naval Barracks, Lee on the Solent		Whale Island, Portsmouth	
J	8.00	D	4.00	Hants D	6.00
Dockyard Devonport D	5.00	J	8.00	J	8.00
Devonport, Naval Barracks J	10.00	(HMS) Nelson Portsmouth F	20.00	*Woolwich Royal Dockyard SE D	?

Special Events (a selection of earlier events)(see chap 12 for further details)

```
14/214  Royal Naval Exhibition, London SW, 1891  .....................  40.00
14/215  Cowes Regatta, 1920, skeleton  .................................  *
14/216  London Naval Conference, 1930, single circle  ................  40.00
14/217  Marine Insurance Conference Eastbourne, 1950,  ................  *
14/218  SS Empress of Britain Maiden Voyage, 1956, double circle  .....  15.00
14/219  SS Reina del Mar Maiden Voyage, 1956, double circle  ..........  30.00
14/220  Fish Docks Centenary Exhib Grimsby, 1956  .....................  1.00
14/221  SS Empress of England Maiden Voyage, 1957, double circle  .....  15.00
14/222  Mayflower II Maiden Voyage, 1957, double circle  ..............  2.00
14/223  Anglo-Danish Festival (shows Viking ship) Hull, 1957  .........  1.00
14/224  Seaborne Mail Exhibition SE10, 1960  ..........................  0.50
14/225  Arlanza Maiden Voyage, 1960, double circle  ...................  50.00
14/226  Empress of Canada Maiden Voyage, 1961, double circle  .........  6.00
```

Disaster/Wreck and Salvaged Mail

THIS SECTION IS APPLICABLE TO CHAPTERS 14, 15 and 16.

This is a large subject, but in general cachets may or may not be applied to covers that are rescued - THIS APPLIES TO PLANES AS WELL AS SHIPS. Not always is this the case; items may be forwarded with no cachet, or forwarded under cover with an explanatory letter.

DAMAGED BY SEA WATER	Saved from wreck of s.s. "Eider"	RECOVERED FROM WRECK OF SS 'LABRADOR'
14/229	**14/239**	**14/240**

General cachets :
```
14/227   Damaged as a result of enemy action
14/228   Damaged by fire and water
```

Ship wreck cachets without ships' names:
```
14/229   Damaged by Sea Water          14/232   Recovered from the sea
14/230   Damaged by water              14/233   Salved from submerged mail
14/231   Damaged by Immersion in       14/234   Salved from the sea
         Sea Water                     14/235   Salved Letter
```

Wreck cachets from disasters within British territorial waters:
```
14/236   1833 Brothers                 14/241   1900 Ibex
14/237   1838 Lady Charlotte           14/242   1907 Jebba
14/238   1875 Schiller                 14/243   1915 Hesperian
14/239   1892 Eider                    14/244   1918 Leinster
14/240   1899 Labrador
```

GPO cachets on mail from disasters outside British territorial waters:
```
14/245   1799 Lutine
14/246   1846 Great Liverpool          14/250   1862 Cleopatra
14/247   1858 Ava                      14/251   1871 Rangoon
14/248   1860 Malabar                  14/252   1900 Mexican
14/249   1862 Colombo                  14/253   1930 Comorin
```

All wreck mail bearing cachets with ships' names is scarce. Most of the above are sold so infrequently that no realistic prices can be given.

Particular thanks go to Messrs Cowell, Daynes, Densham, Frost and Hosking for their help with updated listings in this chapter.

Appendix - Overseas Paquebot marks

Shown below are some foreign Paquebot marks to be found on mail franked with British stamps. Due to popular demand we have retained this section in this chapter.

Aden:	Boxed Paquebot, from 1894	3.00
	Circular with shaded bottom half, from 1908	4.00
	Paquebot/Aden, shaded background, from 1933	4.00
	Paquebot/Aden G.P.O., single circle, from 1953	3.00
	Paquebot machine marks	3.00
Alexandria:	Boxed Paquebot, from 1902	4.50
	Circular Paquebot/Alexandrie, with Arabic, from 1924	3.00
	Straight line types	8.00
Balboa:	Duplex types, from 1917	2.00
	Straight line types, from 1920	8.00
	Machine types, from 1931	2.00
Bergen:	Straight line types, from 1925	3.00
	Boxed types, from 1905	3.50
	Machine types, from 1938	3.00
Bombay:	Boxed Paquebot, from 1904	3.00
	Straight line types, from 1900	8.00
	Circular Bombay Foreign types, from 1913	2.00
Capetown:	Circular types, from 1914	2.00
	Machine types, from 1914	2.00
Cherbourg:	Straight line types, from 1920	2.00
	Continuous impression machine, Paquebot between bars, from 1926	2.00
	Machine with tourist slogan, from 1955	3.50
	Machine with boxed Paquebot between wavy bars, from 1965	2.00
Cobh (formerly Queenstown):	Irish skeleton types, 1922	25.00
	British-type double circle, from 1924	2.00
	Machine types from 1963	2.00
Colombo:	Straight line types, from 1894	3.00
	Circular types, from 1912	3.00
	Machine types, slogans or bars, from 1927	3.00
Dublin:	Circular Baile Atha Cliath types, from 1935	3.00
Dun Laoghaire:	Posted at Sea type, from 1923	2.00
Durban:	Double circle types, from 1937	2.00
	Machine types, from 1941	3.00
Funchal:	Straight line types, from 1904	3.50
	Paquebot in oval frame, from 1910	8.00
	Boxed Paquebot, from 1913	2.00
	Circular dated type, from 1968	5.00
Gibraltar:	Straight line types, from 1894	3.00
	Gibraltar/Paquebot single circle, from 1910	4.00
	Pictorial mark with ship, from 1967	3.00
Hamilton, Bermuda:	Straight line types, from 1907	3.00
	Paquebot/Bermuda, single circles, from 1947	2.00
	Machine with Paquebot boxed, from 1951	20.00
Lisbon:	Paquete, straight line types, from 1895	3.00
	Paquebot, straight line types, from 1897	2.00
	Double circle types with Paquete at base, from 1906	2.50
	Double circle types with Lisboa at base, from 1949	2.00
Malta:	All types	4.00

Marseille:	Single or double circle types	2.50
New York:	Straight line types with (N.Y. 2D Div) from 1894	2.50
	As above but (N.Y.P.O. For. Sec.) from 1913	20.00
	Single circle types, from 1905	3.50
	Duplex types, from 1915	2.00
	Machine types, from 1924	2.00
Oslo:	Boxed Paquebot, from 1931	2.00
	Machine type, from 1937	8.00
	Paquebot straight line type, from 1972	5.00
Port Said:	Straight line type, from 1905	3.50
	Pleine Mer, unframed, from 1896	8.00
	Boxed Paquebot, from 1899	2.00
	Circular type, from 1912	2.00
Port Sudan:	Boxed Paquebot, from 1927	2.50
Port Taufiq:	Boxed Paquebot, from 1901	2.00
	Circular type with wording inside arcs, from 1939	2.00
	Circular type with wording across, from 1957	2.00
Quebec:	Straight line types, from 1914	8.00
	Two line, Exempt from War tax, from 1915	30.00
	Boxed, Exempt from War Tax, from 1919	8.00
	Mailed on the High Seas, unframed, from 1920	3.50
	Mailed on High Seas, unframed, from 1923	3.50
	Depose en mer/mailed on high sea, unframed, from 1937	2.00
	Machine with Paquebot/Posted/At Sea, from 1926	2.00
Suez:	Boxed or unboxed Paquebot, from 1902	2.50

Full details of all Paquebot marks are given by Roger Hosking including many not included in the above lists.

15. Military and Camp Postmarks

15/1　　　　**15/2**　　　　**15/5**

War of the Austrian Succession: 1740-48

15/1 Circled AB ('Armée Britannique') 800.00

French Revolutionary War: 1799

15/2 Army Bag, circular, in black 1000.00
15/3 Post Paid/Army Bag, double oval, in red 2000.00

Napoleonic and Peninsular Wars: 1803-15

15/4 Lisbon town marks on campaign letters 75.00
15/5 Transport office oval on Prisoner of War mail 300.00

Crimean War: 1854-56

15/6　　　　　**15/7**

15/6 Barred type with crown and stars, 1854-55 .... 250.00
15/7 Barred type with star and cyphers, 1855-56 .... 150.00
15/8 Post Office/British Army, unframed circular types, black, blue, red
　　　 or green from 1854 .... 50.00

On pieces the first two of the above postmarks are worth about a
half of the prices quoted, on loose stamps about a third.

British Expeditions to Egypt (1882) and Sudan (1885)

15/9

15/9 British Army Post Office/Egypt, single circle 250.00
15/10 Barred type with B.A./E. .... *

On pieces these postmarks are worth about a third of the prices
quoted, on loose stamps about a quarter.

South African War 1899-1902

15/11   **15/12**   **15/19**

15/11	Field Post Office B.O./British Army S. Africa, double circle	17.50
15/12	As above but without B.O.	20.00
15/13	Field P.O./British Army S. Africa, single circle	7.00
15/14	Army Post Office/South Africa, large double rim circle with town or code	40.00
15/15	Army Post Office/town, double circle	7.00
15/16	Army Post Office/T.P.O. double circle	25.00
15/17	Army PO 43/S. Africa single circle (nos 43-55)	10.00
15/18	Registered/Army Post Office/(place name), hooded circle	50.00
15/19	Octagonal Natal Field Force marks	50.00
15/20	Parcel marks with NFF/FPO etc.	50.00
15/21	Instructional marks, 'Not to be found' etc.	25.00

Section II : First World War 1914-19

Most mail passed free and so bears datestamp and censor mark but no stamp. Values vary considerably according to location of unit and date. Some marks were used in more than one theatre of war; Palestine and Russia being highly sought, Western Front, plentiful and cheap. Examination of the censor mark often helps decide from which theatre an item comes. Full details are in Kennedy/Crabb and Proud.

15/22   **15/23**   **15/24**   **15/25**

France 1914-15   France 1914-15   France 1915-16   France 1916
Russia 1919 with   Middle East 1915-16 Middle East 1915-19
Suffix R   East Africa 1916-17 East Africa, Mesopotamia
                     Balkans 1916   E. Mediterranean

15/26   **15/27**   **15/28**   **15/29**

France 1916-17   France 1917-20   Salonica, Egypt   Italy 1918-19
Italy 1917   Italy 1917-18   and Palestine 1917-19,
                                          Turkey 1918-20,
                                          Balkans, S. Russia 1919

(Censor illustrations reduced by different amounts)

15/30	Advance Base Post Office, double circle	7.50
15/31	Army Base Post Office, single circle, 1913 manoeuvres only ..	15.00
15/32	As above but indexes 18-19 at foot (pre-war manoeuvres only)	17.50
15/33	Army Base Post Office, double circle	1.50
15/34	Army Courier Office/S5, single circle, 1920-21	30.00
15/35	Army Letter Office/London, double circle	6.00
15/36	D.A.L.O. London, double circle	6.00

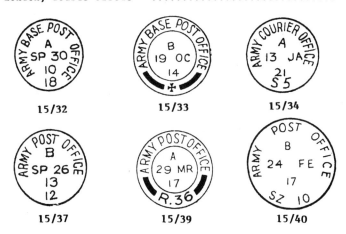

15/32   15/33   15/34

15/37   15/39   15/40

15/37 Army Post Office, single circles with number of infantry brigade at
foot (used pre-1914 in England, 1914-15 in France and Belgium) :

1	2.00	5	2.00	9	2.00	13	2.00	17	2.00
2	2.00	6	4.00	10	2.00	14	2.00	18	2.00
3	2.00	7	2.00	11	2.00	15	2.00		
4	4.00	8	2.00	12	2.00	16	2.00		

These APO single circles used pre-1914 are worth from 7.50

15/38 Army Post Office/HD1 (Malta) 7.50

15/39 Army Post Office, double circle with index at foot, and –
15/40 skeletons, various sizes, chiefly with index at foot :

Index	Used by	d/c	sk	Index	Used by	d/c	sk	Index	Used by	d/c	sk
no index			6.00	41	I Corps	1.50		66	22 Bde.	2.00	
1	Base APO 1 Havre	0.50	1.00	42	II Corps	1.50		67	IV Corps HQ	3.00	
2	Base APO 2 Rouen	0.50		43	III Corps	1.00		68	8 Div. HQ	2.00	
3	Base APO 3			44	19 Inf. Bde.	1.50		69	8 Div. Train	2.00	
	Boulogne	0.60		45	2 Cav. Div.	2.00		70	23 Bde.	2.00	
4	Base APO 4 Calais	0.60		46	W. Front	1.50		71	24 Bde.	3.00	
19	1 Inf. Div.	2.00		47	Rouen	0.60		72	25 Bde.	3.00	
20	2 Inf. Div.	3.00		48	Orleans	1.50		73	W. Front	4.00	
21	3 Inf. Div.	3.00		49	Nantes	1.00		74	W. Front	4.00	
22	4 Inf. Div.	1.00		50	Le Mans	2.00		75	Paris	3.00	
23	5 Inf. Div.	1.00		51	I Corps Railhead	0.60		76	W. Front	4.00	
24	6 Inf. Div.	1.00		52	II Corps			77	W. Front	3.00	
25	1 Inf. Div.	1.00			Railhead	1.00		78	Dunkirk	3.00	
26	2 Inf. Div.	1.00		53	III Corps			79	W. Front	1.50	
27	3 Inf. Div.	1.50			Railhead	1.50		80	W. Front	1.50	
28	4 Inf. Div.	1.00		54	W. Front	2.00		81	W. Front	3.00	
29	5 Inf. Div.	1.00		55	Lahore Div.			82	Etretat	3.00	
30	6 Inf. Div.	1.00			Train	3.00		83	80 Bde.	5.00	
31	1 Cav. Bde.	2.00		56	W. Front	2.00		84	81 Bde.	5.00	
32	2 Cav. Bde.	1.00		57	W. Front	2.00		85	82 Bde.	5.00	
33	3 Cav. Bde.	3.00		58	W. Front	1.50		86	27 Div. HQ	5.00	
34	4 Cav. Bde.	1.00		59	W. Front	2.00		87	27 Div. Train	5.00	
35	5 Cav. Bde.	1.00		60	7 Cav. Bde.	1.50		88	W. Front	10.00	
36	1 Cav. Div.	1.00		61	W. Front	2.00		89	W. Front	5.00	
37	Boulogne	0.50		62	7 Div. HQ	2.00		94	W. Front	10.00	
38	St.Nazaire	1.00		63	7 Div. Train	2.00		100	Etaples	5.00	
39	Army Troops	1.50		64	20 Bde.	2.00		A	Rouen		1.00
40	?	1.50		65	21 Bde.	2.00		B	France		5.00

Index	Used by	d/c	sk	Index	Used by	d/c	sk	Index	Used by	d/c	sk
C	France		4.00	R62	62 Div Railhead	1.00		S46	France	0.60	4.00
D	France		4.00	R63	63 Div Railhead	1.00		S47	France	0.60	4.00
E	France		5.00	R66	66 Div	1.00		S48	France	1.00	
F2	Abbassia		4.00	R74	74 Div	2.00		S49	France	1.60	
G	France		5.00	RA1	1 Ammunition			S50	Cherbourg	0.60	3.00
GR	Germany	10.00			Railhead	0.60		S51	France	0.60	
L1	Italy, Base	2.00		RA2	2 Ammunition			S52	France	0.60	
L2	Italy	3.00			Railhead	1.00		S53	France	0.60	
L3	Italy	4.00		RB	Guards Div			S54	France	0.60	
L4	Italy	6.00			Railhead	0.60		S55	Marseilles	2.00	
L5	Italy	6.00		RC1	1 Cav. Div			S56	France	0.60	5.00
L6	Italy	6.00			Railhead	1.00		S57	France	1.00	
L7	Italy	5.00		RC2	2 Cav. Div			S58	France	1.00	
L8	Italy	4.00			Railhead	1.00		S59	France	0.60	2.50
L9	Italy	5.00		RC3	3 Cav. Div			S60	France	0.60	
L11	Italy	5.00			Railhead	1.00		S61	France	1.00	
L12	Italy	7.50		RC4	Cav. Div Railhead	4.00		S62	France	0.60	
L13	France	7.50		RG	GHQ Railhead	4.00		S63	France	0.60	
L14	Italy	30.00		RHD	51 Div Railhead	2.50		S64	France	1.00	
L15	Austria	30.00		RK	American Div			S65	France	0.60	
L16	Yugoslavia	30.00			Railheads	10.00		S66	France	0.60	
PB1	Russia	15.00		RK2-8	ditto	10.00		S67	France	3.00	
PB2	Russia	15.00		RL	47 Div Railhead	10.00		S68	France	1.00	
PP1	Italy	3.00		RN	50 Div Railhead	1.00		S69	France	10.00	
R1	1 Div Railhead	0.60		RP1-4	Canadian Div			S70	Italy	3.00	
R2	2 Div Railhead	0.60			Railheads	5.00		S71	France	1.00	
R2A	27 Div Railhead	5.00		RSM	48 Div Railhead	5.00		S72	France	2.00	9.00
R3	3 Div Railhead	0.50		RW	Egypt		10.00	S73	Vendroux	0.60	
R4	4 Div Railhead	0.50		RW1-5	Australian Div			S74	France	1.00	
R5	5 Div Railhead	0.50			Railheads	5.00		S75	France	0.60	
Note	: R1-5 were initially			RWR	49 Div Railhead	5.00		S76	France	0.60	5.00
	Corps railheads			RX	Canadian Div			S77	France	0.60	5.00
R5A	28 Div Railhead	5.00	5.00		Railhead	5.00	10.00	S78	France	0.60	
R6	6 Div Railhead	0.50		RX2-4	ditto	5.00		S79	Le Touquet	0.60	
R7	7 Div Railhead	1.00		RX16	XVI Corps Rail	20.00	20.00	S80	France	0.60	
R8	8 Div Railhead	0.60		RY	59-63 Div	1.00		S81	France	0.60	2.50
R9	9 Div Railhead	0.60		RZ	N Zealand Div			S82	Rue	3.00	
R10	10 Div Railhead	15.00			Railhead	5.00	3.00	S83	Trouville	0.60	1.50
R11	11 Div Railhead	1.00		S1	Abbeville	0.50		S84	Lilliers	2.00	
R12	12 Div Railhead	0.60		S2	France	0.60		S85	France	3.00	
R14	14 Div Railhead	0.60		S3	France	1.00		S86	France	2.00	6.00
R15	15 Div Railhead	0.60		S4	France/Belgium	1.00		S87	France	2.00	
R16	16 Div Railhead	0.50		S5	Paris	0.60		S88	Boulogne	3.00	
R17	17 Div Railhead	0.50		S6	France	0.60		S89	France	5.00	
R18	18 Div Railhead	0.60		S7	Marseilles	0.60		S90	France	2.00	
R19	19 Div Railhead	0.50		S8	Dieppe	0.60		S91	France	4.00	12.00
R20	20 Div Railhead	0.50		S9	Etratat	1.00		S92	France	2.00	
R21	21 Div Railhead	1.00		S10	Dunkirk	0.60		S93	Courban	5.00	
R22	22 Div Railhead	2.00	10.00	S11	Etaples	0.50		S94	Hesdin	1.00	5.00
R23	23 Div Railhead	1.00		S12	Harfleur	0.60		S95	St. Pol	3.00	6.00
R24	24 Div Railhead	0.60		S13	Le Treport	0.60		S97	France	7.50	15.00
R25	25 Div Railhead	1.00		S14	France	0.60		S98	France	4.00	
R26	26 Div Railhead	2.00	10.00	S15	Rouen	0.50	2.00	S99	France	2.00	
R27	27 Div Railhead	3.00	10.00	S16	Serqueux	0.60		S100	Taranto	3.00	
R28	28 Div Railhead	2.00	10.00	S17	Etaples	0.50	10.00	S101	Arquata	4.50	13.50
R29	29 Div Railhead	1.00		S18	Camiers	0.60		S102	France	3.00	
R30	30 Div Railhead	1.00		S19	France	0.60		S103	Aulnois	5.00	
R31	31 Div Railhead	2.00		S20	France	0.60		S104	Nancy	10.00	
R32	32 Div Railhead	2.00		S21	France	0.60		S105	France	4.00	
R33	33 Div Railhead	1.00		S22	France	1.00			& Rotterdam (1919)	15.00	
R34	34 Div Railhead	1.00		S23	France	0.60		S106	Brussels	5.00	
R35	35 Div Railhead	0.60		S24	Calais	0.60		S107	Belgium	4.00	
R36	36 Div Railhead	0.60		S25	France	0.60		S108	France	4.00	
R37	37 Div Railhead	1.00		S26	France	0.60		S109	Motteville	7.50	
R38	38 Div Railhead	1.00		S27	Caudebec	1.50		S110	Antwerp	12.00	
R39	39 Div Railhead	0.60		S28	St. Saens	1.00	3.00	S111	Dieppe	5.00	5.00
R40	40 Div Railhead	1.00		S29	France	1.50		S114	Spa	5.00	
R41	41 Div Railhead	1.00		S30	France	0.60		S115	Charleroi	4.00	
R42	42 Div Railhead	1.00		S31	France	0.60		S116	France	4.00	
R46	46 Div Railhead	0.60		S32	France	0.60		S117	Belgium	2.00	
R47	47 Div Railhead	1.00		S33	France	0.60		S118	Lille	5.00	
R48	48 Div Railhead	0.60		S34	France	1.00		S119	France	4.00	
R49	49 Div Railhead	1.00		S35	France	1.00	6.00	S120	Germany	5.00	
R50	50 Div Railhead	1.00		S36	Zeneghem	2.00		Note:	Usages in France may		
R51	51 Div Railhead	0.60		S37	France	0.60			include Belgium		
R52	52 Div Railhead	5.00		S38	Wimereaux	0.60		SW1	France	3.00	
R55	55 Div Railhead	0.60		S39	Dannes	0.60		SW2	Harfleur	5.00	
R56	56 Div Railhead	1.00		S40	France/Germany	1.00		SW3	France	5.00	
R57	57 Div Railhead	2.00		S41	France	0.60		SW4	France	6.00	
R58	58 Div Railhead	1.00		S42	France	0.60		SWZ	France	5.00	
R59	59 Div Railhead	1.00		S43	France	0.60		SWZ2	Etaples	6.00	
R60	60 Div Railhead	3.00		S44	Buchy	1.00		SX1	Greece	1.00	4.00
R61	61 Div Railhead	1.00		S45	France	1.00		SX2	Salonika	2.00	6.00

Index	Used by	d/c	sk	Index	Used by	d/c	sk	Index	Used by	d/c	sk
SX3	Greece	4.00	4.00	SZ6	Greece/Egypt?		6.00	SZ38	Palestine		25.00
SX4	Salonika	3.00	3.00	SZ7	Malta/Palestine		5.00	SZ39	Palestine		25.00
SX5	Greece	2.00	6.00	SZ8	Greece/Egypt/			SZ40	Jaffa		20.00
SX6	Vertekop		7.50		Lebanon		7.50	SZ41	Egypt		10.00
SX7	Stavros	7.50	15.00	SZ9	Egypt/Lebanon		5.00	SZ42	Egypt		12.50
SX8	Greece	3.00	3.00	SZ10	Cairo		1.00	SZ43	Rafa		15.00
SX9	Greece	7.50	10.00	SZ10T	Cairo		5.00	SZ44	Jerusalem		10.00
SX10	Greece		7.50	SZ11	Egypt		4.00	SZ45	Jaffa		20.00
SX11	Greece	4.00	10.00	SZ12	Egypt		3.00	SZ46	Palestine		25.00
SX12	Greece	7.50	10.00	SZ13	Egypt/Lebanon		5.00	SZ47	Palestine		25.00
SX13	Eurendzik	5.00	5.00	SZ14	Egypt		5.00	SZ48	Palestine		25.00
SX14	Greece	15.00	15.00	SZ15	Egypt		5.00	SZ49	Mulebbis		20.00
SX15	Greece		10.00	SZ16	Egypt/Palestine		10.00	SZ50	Turkey		30.00
SX16	Greece		20.00	SZ17	Egypt/Palestine		5.00	SZ51	Egypt/Palestine/Syria		20.00
SX17	Sarigol		15.00	SZ18	Egypt/Palestine		7.50	SZ52	Palestine		30.00
SX18	Burgas		?	SZ19	Egypt		7.50	SZ53	Palestine		25.00
SX19	Rupel		20.00	SZ20	Egypt/Palestine		7.50	SZ54	Egypt		15.00
SX20	Hirsova		20.00	SZ21	Egypt		6.00	SZ56	Syria		7.50
SX21	Bulgaria		30.00	SZ22	Port Said		2.00	SZ58	Egypt		7.50
SX22	Batum		50.00	SZ23	Egypt/Palestine		15.00	SZ61	Safed		30.00
SX23	Greece		10.00	SZ24	Suez		4.00	SZ62	Damascus		15.00
SX24	Greece		10.00	SZ24T	Egypt		4.00	T42	France	1.00	
SY1	Chanak		10.00	SZ25	Egypt		7.50	T62	France	1.00	
SY2	Turkey		15.00	SZ26	Egypt		10.00	X	Greece		2.00
SY3	Turkey		15.00	SZ26T	Egypt		15.00	Y1	Turkey	12.50	10.00
SY4	Turkey		10.00	SZ27	Egypt/Palestine		7.50	Y2	Turkey	15.00	15.00
SY5	Turkey		30.00	SZ28	Egypt		7.50	Y3	Bostanji?		15.00
SZ1	Turkey/Egypt	3.00	3.00	SZ32	Palestine		25.00	Abbassia			15.00
SZ2	Greece/Egypt/			SZ33	Palestine		10.00	Base X	Greece		2.00
	Palestine	3.00	4.00	SZ34	Palestine		15.00	Cairo			15.00
SZ3	Turkey/Egypt	5.00	3.00	SZ35	Palestine		17.50	Kantara			12.00
SZ4	Turkey/Egypt		2.00	SZ36	Egypt		10.00	Mustapha			20.00
SZ5	Turkey/Egypt/Syria		4.00	SZ37	Palestine		12.50	Port Said			20.00

15/41 Army Post Office, Krag machines:

Army Post Office 1	1.00
Army Post Office 2	0.80
Army Post Office 3	0.50
Army P.O.1	0.50
Army P.O.2	0.50
Army P.O.3	0.50
Army P.O.4	0.60
A.P.O. S12 Harfleur	1.00
Army P.O.S15	1.00
A.P.O. S17	1.00
A.P.O. S40	3.00
A.P.O. S60	6.00

15/41

15/42 Army Post Office (HD), for Home Defence, single ring with index at base:

1	3.00	14	5.00	27	6.00	45	5.00	D14	30.00
2	5.00	15	6.00	28	7.50	46	7.50	D16	7.50
3	5.00	16	5.00	29	5.00	47	7.50	M6	7.50
4	5.00	17	6.00	30	6.00	54	6.00	M7	7.50
5	5.00	18	6.00	31	5.00	59	6.00	M8	7.50
6	5.00	19	6.00	32	6.00	70	6.00	M9	7.50
7	5.00	20	6.00	33	6.00	A1	6.00	M10	7.50
8	5.00	21	6.00	34	6.00	A3	6.00	M11	7.50
9	5.00	22	6.00	35	5.00	D1	6.00	R1	10.00
10	5.00	23	6.00	36	6.00	D3	5.00	R5	7.50
11	5.00	24	6.00	40	25.00	D5	4.00	R19	10.00
12	7.50	25	6.00	41	25.00	D11	6.00		
13	6.00	26	6.00	42	25.00	D12	7.50		

15/43 Army Post Office HD/A, skeleton 20.00
15/44 Army R.L.O./London, single circle 10.00
15/45 R.E. Postal Section/R.L.O. single circle 10.00

15/46 Base Army Post Office, double circles with index at base:

1	Le Havre	0.50	W	Brindisi	30.00
2	Rouen	0.50	X	Salonica	2.00
3	Boulogne	0.50	Y	Greece	3.00
4	Calais	1.60	Z	Egypt	1.00

15/47 Base Army P.O. skeletons:

K	Kantara	2.50	X	Salonica	3.00
T	Port Said	2.50	Z	Egypt	2.50

Field Post Office, double circles **15/48** or skeletons with index at base:

Most Field Post Offices were allotted to formations. A simple number indicated a Brigade, a prefix D or T indicated a Division, H a Corps, and A an Army. Additional codes were B for Guards, C for Cavalry, G for GHQ, K for American, P for Canadian, Q for Tanks, W for Western Frontier Force, Adriatic Mission or Australian, X for Canadian, Y for Yeomanry or Mounted, Z for New Zealand. Territorial formations were at first designated by an

15/48

abbreviation of their name (eg SM = South Midland) before being numbered. However these descriptions do not hold good throughout, eg on the Western Front from June 1916 to February 1919 datestamps were periodically changed round for security reasons. Example : datestamp FPO DW4 was used initially by 4th Australian Division, then in turn by the 3rd Canadian, 49th, Guards, 63rd and 57th Divisions before reverting to 4th Australian Division.

Index	Used by	d/c	sk	Index	Used by	d/c	sk	Index	Used by	d/c	sk
no number	GHQ B.E.F.		1.00	57		0.60		114		0.60	
1		0.60	1.00	58		0.60		115		0.60	
2		0.60		59		0.60		116		0.60	
3		0.60		60		0.60		117		0.60	
4		1.00		61		0.60		118		0.60	
5		0.60		62		0.60		119		1.00	
6		0.60		63		0.60		120		1.00	
7		0.60		64		0.60		121		0.60	
8		0.60		65		2.00		122		0.60	
9		0.60		66		2.00		123		0.60	
10		0.60		67		2.00		124		0.60	
11		0.60		68		0.60		125		0.60	
12		0.60		69		0.60		126		0.60	
13		0.60		70		0.60		127		0.60	
14		0.60		71		0.60		137		0.60	
15		0.60		72		0.60		138		0.60	
16		0.60		73		0.60		139		0.60	
17		0.60		74		0.60		140		0.60	
18		6.00		75		0.60		141		0.60	
19		0.50		76		0.60		142		0.60	
20		0.60		77		2.00		143		0.60	
21		0.60		78		2.00		144		0.60	
22		0.60		79		3.00		145		0.60	
23		0.60		80		1.00		146		0.60	
24		0.60		81		0.60		147		0.60	
25		0.60		82		0.60		148		0.60	
26		0.60		83		0.60		149		0.60	
27		0.60		84		0.60		150		0.60	
28		0.60		85		0.60		151		0.60	
29		6.00		86		0.60		152		0.60	
30		5.00		87		0.60		153		0.60	
31		5.00	10.00	88		0.60		154		0.60	
32		5.00		89		0.60		155		1.00	
33		0.60		90		0.60		156		1.00	
34		0.60		91		0.60		157		1.00	
35		0.60		92		0.60		158		10.00	
36		0.60		93		0.60		159		7.50	
37		0.60		94		0.60		160		10.00	
38		10.00		95		0.60		161		7.50	
39		10.00		96		0.60		161T			1.00
40		10.00		97		0.60		162		6.00	
41		0.60		98		0.60		163		6.00	
42		0.60		99		0.60		164		0.60	
43		0.60		100		0.60		165		0.60	
44		0.60		101		0.60		166		0.60	
45		0.60		102		0.60		167		0.60	
46		0.60		103		0.60		168		1.00	
47		0.60		104		0.60		169		0.60	
48		0.60		105		0.60		170		1.00	
49		0.60		106		0.60		171		1.00	
50		0.60		107		0.60		172		1.00	
51		0.60		108		0.60		173		0.60	
52		0.60		109		0.60		173		0.60	
53		0.60		110		0.60		174		1.00	
54		0.60		111		0.60		175		0.60	
55		0.60		112		0.60		176		1.00	
56		0.60		113		0.60		177		2.00	

Index	Used by	d/c	sk
178		1.00	
179		1.00	1.50
X179			2.50
180		1.00	10.00
180X			1.50
181		1.00	1.50
X181			1.50
182		1.00	
183		1.00	
184			1.00
185		1.00	
186		1.00	
187		1.00	
188		1.00	
189		1.00	
190		0.60	
197		1.00	
198		1.00	
199		1.00	
200	N. Russia	30.00	
201	Russia	25.00	
202	N. Ireland	25.00	
228	Salonika	10.00	10.00
229		1.00	
230		1.00	1.50
231		1.50	
232		7.50	7.50
233		7.50	20.00
234		7.50	7.50
A1	1 Army HQ	0.60	
A2	2 Army HQ	0.60	2.50
A2A	Adv. Army HQ		1.00
A3	3 Army HQ	0.60	
A4	4 Army HQ	0.60	
A4X	Adv. Army HQ	1.20	
A5	5 Army HQ	0.60	
AD1	1 A.D.O.	0.60	1.00
AD2	2 A.D.O.	0.60	
AD3	3 A.D.O.	0.60	
AD4	4 A.D.O.	1.00	
AD5	5 A.D.O.	1.00	
AGX	Adv. G.H.Q.	25.00	
AH16			6.00
AN8,12-15		20.00	
AR	5 Army HQ	0.60	
AT1	Army Troops	0.60	
1B		0.60	
2B		0.60	
3B		0.60	
4B		0.60	
C1		0.60	
C2		0.60	
C3		0.60	
C4		0.60	
C5		0.60	
C6		0.60	
C7		0.60	
C8		0.60	
C9		0.70	
C10		20.00	20.00
C11		15.00	
C12		20.00	
C13		20.00	20.00
C14		20.00	25.00
C15		?	?
CD3	Kantara	15.00	
CIB	Composite Infantry Brigade		25.00
CZ		20.00	20.00
D1		0.60	
D2		0.60	
D3		0.60	
D4		0.60	
D5		0.60	
D6		0.60	
D7		1.00	
D8		0.60	
D9		0.60	
D10		5.00	
D11		0.60	
D12		0.60	
D13		15.00	
D14		0.60	
D15		0.60	
D16		0.60	

Index	Used by	d/c	sk
D17		0.60	
D18		0.60	
D19		0.60	
D20		0.60	
D21		0.60	
D22		2.00	
D23		0.60	
D24		0.60	
D25		1.00	
D26		2.00	
D27		0.60	
D28		2.00	
D29		0.60	
D30		0.60	
D31		0.60	
D32		1.00	
D33		0.60	
D34		0.60	
D35		0.60	
D36		0.60	
D37		0.60	
D38		0.60	
D39		0.60	
D40		1.00	
D41		0.60	
D42		0.60	
D46		0.60	
D47		0.60	
D48		0.60	
D49		0.50	
D50		0.60	
D51		0.60	
D52		2.00	
D53		10.00	
D54		10.00	
D55		0.60	
D56		1.00	
D57		1.00	
D58		1.00	
D59		1.00	
D60		20.00	1.00
D61		1.00	
D62		1.00	
D63		1.00	
D66		1.00	
66D	APO S66		5.00
D74		2.00	4.00
D75		10.00	
DAN4		3.00	
DAN5		3.00	
DB		0.60	
DC1		0.60	
DC2		0.60	
DC3		0.60	
DC4		3.00	
DC5		20.00	
DHD		1.00	
DK		1.00	
DL2		2.50	
DLL		20.00	
DM		2.50	
DM1		5.00	
DM2		5.00	
DM3		20.00	
DM4		15.00	
DN		2.00	
DNL		15.00	
DP1-4		1.00	
DQ		1.00	
DSM		1.50	
DW	Egypt		25.00
DW1-5		2.00	
DWR		3.00	
DX1-4		1.00	
DY		15.00	
2DY			10.00
3DY			15.00
4DY			20.00
DZ	N.Z. Div. HQ	1.50	
EY		20.00	
F1	Eastern Force HQ		10.00
F2	Abbassia		4.00
FD1	Field Depot Italy	3.00	
FD2	Field Depot Italy	7.00	
FD3	Field Depot Italy	7.50	

Index	Used by	d/c	sk
FD4	Field Depot Italy	7.50	
FD5	Field Depot Italy	6.00	
FD8	Field Depot Italy	5.00	
FD9	Field Depot Italy	5.00	
G	GHQ B.E.F.	0.80	
GM	GHQ B.E.F		5.00
GM1	GHQ E.E.F.		10.00
GM2	GHQ E.E.F.		5.00
GQ	Italy GHQ	4.00	
GQ2	Italy GHQ	4.00	
GX	British Salonika Army	3.00	
GZ	GHQ M.E.F.	7.50	
H1		0.60	
H2		0.60	
H3		0.60	
H4		0.60	
H5		0.60	
H6		0.60	
H7		0.60	
H8		0.60	
H9		0.60	
H10		0.60	
H11		0.60	
H12		2.00	
H13		0.60	
H14		0.60	
H15		0.60	20.00
H16			6.00
H17		0.60	
H18		0.60	2.00
H19		0.60	
H20			15.00
H20T			20.00
H21			20.00
H22		0.60	
HC1		0.60	
HC2		0.60	
HC3		0.60	
1HD		3.00	
2HD		4.00	
3HD		1.00	
HK	II American Corps	1.60	
HM	HQ Desert Column	15.00	20.00
HP	Canadian Corps	2.00	
HR		2.00	
HW		3.00	
HW2		2.50	
HX		2.50	
HY		15.00	10.00
1K-3K	Security purposes	2.50	
4L		1.20	
5L		1.20	
6L		1.20	
1LL		1.00	
2LL		2.00	
3LL		1.00	
LY	Lowland Mtd. Bde.	20.00	
M1		20.00	20.00
1M		1.00	
2M		1.00	
3M		1.00	
MD1	Anzac Mtd. Div.	15.00	
MD2	Imperial Mtd. Div.	15.00	
MDT1	Anzac Mtd. Div. Train	15.00	
MH2	VIII Corps HQ	15.00	
MH3	IX Corps	15.00	
MX1	Mtd. Bde.	30.00	
1N		3.00	
2N		3.00	
3N		3.00	
NL1		1.00	
NL2		1.00	
NL3		1.00	
NMY		5.00	
1P-12P	Canadian Bde. HQ	2.00	
PB1	Egypt		20.00
PB11	Russia	50.00	
PB12	Russia	40.00	
PB13	Russia	40.00	
PB14	Russia	40.00	
PB15	Russia	40.00	
PB22	Russia	40.00	
PB33	Russia	40.00	
PB44	Russia	40.00	

Index	Used by	d/c	sk
PB55	Russia	40.00	
PB66	Russia	40.00	
PB77	Russia	45.00	
PB88	Russia	45.00	
PB99	Russia	50.00	
Q1		1.50	
Q2		1.50	
Q3		1.50	
Q4		2.50	
Q5		2.50	
R10	10 Div. Railhead		15.00
S26	France	2.00	
S58	France	4.00	
S62	France	1.50	
S63	W. Front	4.00	
S64	France	4.00	
S66	France		4.00
S74	France	3.00	
S77	France	0.60	
SA1		2.00	
SEY	S.E. Mtd. Bde.	15.00	
1SM		1.00	
2SM		1.00	
3SM		1.00	
SWY2		15.00	
SX2	Greece		6.00
SX3	Salonica		10.00
SZ1	Turkey	3.00	
SZ1T	Egypt	3.00	
SZ5	Syria	20.00	
SZ8	Lebanon	15.00	
SZ9	Lebanon	20.00	
SZ11	Egypt	4.00	
SZ15	Egypt	5.00	
SZ16	Haifa	25.00	
SZ18	Egypt	15.00	
SZ19	Lebanon	15.00	
SZ19T	Egypt	7.50	
SZ20	Ludd	7.50	
SZ21	Egypt	6.00	
SZ23	Egypt	15.00	
SZ34	Jaffa	10.00	
SZ36	Egypt	10.00	
SZ48	Palestine	20.00	
SZ49	Mulebbis	20.00	
SZ53	Palestine	20.00	
SZ55	Egypt	15.00	
SZ57	Haifa	20.00	
SZ58	Jericho	15.00	
SZ59	Tul Karem	25.00	
SZ60	Tiberias	25.00	
SZ61	Palestine	25.00	
SZ62	Damascus	15.00	

Index	Used by	d/c	sk
T1		0.60	
T2		0.60	
T3		0.60	
T4		0.60	
T5		0.60	
T6		0.60	
T7		1.00	
T8		0.60	
T9		0.60	
T10		5.00	
T11		1.00	
T12		0.60	
T14		0.60	
T15		0.60	
T16		0.60	
T17		0.60	
T18		0.60	
T19		0.60	
T20		0.60	
T21		0.60	
T22		2.00	
T23		0.60	
T24		0.60	
T25		0.60	
T26		2.00	
T27		0.60	
T28		2.00	
T29		0.60	
T30		0.60	
T31		0.60	
T32		0.60	
T33		0.60	
T34		0.60	
T35		0.60	
T36		0.60	
T37		0.60	
T38		0.60	
T39		0.60	
T40		0.60	
T41		0.60	
T46		0.60	
T47		0.60	
T48		0.60	
T49		0.60	
T50		0.50	
T51		0.60	
T52		5.00	
T53		20.00	
T55		0.60	
T56		0.60	
T57		2.00	
T58		2.00	
T59		1.00	

Index	Used by	d/c	sk
T60		15.00	
T61		1.00	
T62		1.00	
T63		0.60	
T66		2.00	
T74		1.00	
TAN4	4 Aust. Div. Train	2.00	
TAN5	5 Aust. Div. Train	2.00	
TB	Guards Div. Train	1.00	
TC	Cav. Div. Train		2.00
TC4	Cav. Div. Train	2.00	
TG	GHQ Train	1.00	
THD	51 Div. Train	6.00	
TK	Spare D/S	1.00	
TL2	47 Div. Train	2.00	
TLL	52 Div. Train	12.00	
TM	46 Div. Train	2.00	
TN	50 Div. Train	3.20	
TNL	RN Div. Train	25.00	
TP1-5		?	
TSM	48 Div. Train	2.50	
TW	W.F.F. Train	20.00	
TW1-5		2.00	
TWR	49 Div. Train	3.20	
TX-TX4		2.00	
TY	Spare D/S	1.00	
TZ		1.00	
W1	W.F.F. Egypt		15.00
W1	B.M.M. Italy	20.00	
W2	W.F.F. Egypt		17.50
W2	B.M.M. Greece		15.00
W2	B.M.M. Greece	15.00	
W3	B.M.M.	20.00	
W4	Greece	20.00	
W9-W11		1.00	
1W-8W		1.00	
12W-15W		1.00	
WBY		7.50	
1WR		1.60	
2WR		1.60	
3WR		1.00	
WSY	Mtd. Bde.	3.00	
1X-12X	Canadian Bdes.	1.00	
1Y	Mtd. Bdes.	10.00	
2Y		25.00	
3Y			6.00
4Y		15.00	
5Y		10.00	
6Y		20.00	
7Y		6.00	6.00
8Y		15.00	
22Y	Mtd. Bdes.	25.00	15.00
1Z-4Z		1.00	

15/49   Instructional marks, 'Present location uncertain' etc., many types 3.00
15/50   Packet handstamp 2.00
15/51   Parcel handstamp (on piece) 2.00
15/52   P.O.W. mail from UK camps with P.C. markings 7.50
15/53   As above but from Isle of Man 25.00
15/54   P.O.W. mail from UK camps with camp cachets 10.00
15/55   As above but from Isle of Man 30.00
        Travelling Post Office markings, see below 20.00

TPO handstamps : the full inscriptions are not shown here, and some include more than one variety, but all include the letters "TPO". Most are skeleton handstamps :

15/56 Egypt & Palestine : BAR, RAB, CAT, TAC,
DAL, LAD, JAP, PAJ, KAL, LAK,
KAR, RAK, LAP, PAL, SAT, TAS,
Upper Egypt, Z and W
15/57 France & Germany : BEF Main Line
15/58 Russia : NREF
15/59 Turkey : TPO1

15/56

15/57

Dublin marks used after Easter rising, 1916

These are civilian marks but are occasionally found on soldiers' mail :

15/60 Parcel post handstamps 15.00
15/61 Single rim/double rim skeletons 25.00

Section III : Between the Two World Wars

15/60   15/63   15/64

In 1921 new styles of postmarks were introduced, rubber stamps 15/63 very briefly and single circle datestamps 15/64. In Germany single circle Army Post Office datestamps as 15/37 were used, with offices designated S40, or S40A to S40H (with letter above the date or at foot of circle, see below). From 1927 a new series of double circle datestamps came into use, numbered from 1 upwards, 26 being the highest number used before 1939. These new double circle datestamps were the forerunners of the Second World War series, and the earlier datestamps were not used after 1929 apart from some odd exceptions.

Ireland 1920-23

15/62 First World War datestamps (as 15/48) used 1920-23 :
          FPO 202, D41, 3K, T29, W16 .... 20.00
          New rubber datestamps 15/63 (1921) or single circle 15/64 (1921-23) :
          FPO 5,6,7,8,9,10 (not all known used in both types) 30.00

Germany 1922-29

For earlier postmarks see section II. In 1922 the offices were reorganised as sub offices of APO S40, identified by a letter suffix. In 1926 the Army of the Rhine transferred from the Cologne area to Wiesbaden area and the APOs were also moved.

15/65 APO S40, as 15/37 and 15/39 .... 3.00
15/66 APO S40A to S40C, as 15/37 but with code A,B,C above date 10.00
15/67 APO S40D to S40H, as 15/37 S40 after Office, codes D-H at foot 10.00
15/68 FPO X, as 15/48 .... 30.00

Turkey 1922-23

For earlier postmarks see section II.

15/69 FPO 1,2, as 15/48 .... 20.00
15/70 FPO 11,12,13,14,15, as 15/64 .... 15.00

15/71 China 1927-40

AP01	Shanghai	as 15/39	2.00	4	various	as 15/48	15.00
FP01	Tientsin	as 15/48	3.00	5	Hong Kong	as 15/48	?
2	Hong Kong	as 15/48	?	8	HMT Dorsetshire		
3	Shanghai	as 15/48	15.00		(single circle)		20.00

15/72 Egpyt 1932-39

These datestamps were used at Egyptian post offices but on British Forces mail bearing the Army Post stamps (see Gibbons catalogues). They also appear on covers bearing NAAFI seals affixed to the backs of envelopes, which are cancelled with a dotted diamond obliterator.

Abu-Qir	5.00	Cairo	1.00	Moascar	1.50
Abu-Sueir	3.00	El Daba	*	15/73 Port Said	7.50
Alexandria	1.00	Mera Matrhu	5.00		

15/73

15/74 Saar 1935

FPO 10, as **15/48** 20.00

15/75 Palestine 1936

FPOs 12,15,16,17,18,20,22,23,24,25,26, as **15/48** 15.00

UK Manoeuvres

15/76 1925 : FPO 1-16, skeleton as **15/40** but 'Field' .. 25.00
15/77 1933-7 : Base Army PO 1 .... 15.00
15/78   FPO 1-12, as **15/48** 15.00

15/77

We gratefully acknowledge the assistance of Alistair Kennedy of the Forces Postal History Society in checking, revising and adding to the contents of sections II and III of this chapter.

Section IV : Second World War 1939-46

Most military postmarks of this period were Field Post Office handstamps type **15/79**, though Krag machines **15/80** were also in use - value 1.00. In the simplified listing on the pages that follow these types are not differentiated. Universal machine FPO 676 **15/81** was used at Inverness where much military mail was handled - value 2.00. Only from 1944 other styles of machine postmarks were used, with Army Post Office wording, see **15/82** and **15/83** though these specimens are from shortly after the end of the war - value 1.00.

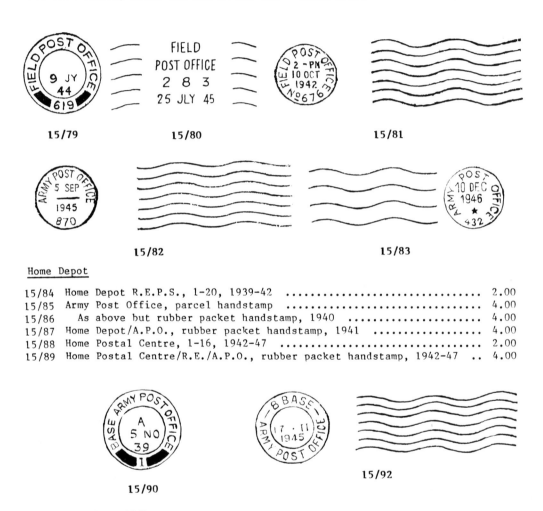

15/79	15/80	15/81

15/82	15/83

Home Depot

15/84	Home Depot R.E.P.S., 1-20, 1939-42	....	2.00
15/85	Army Post Office, parcel handstamp	....	4.00
15/86	As above but rubber packet handstamp, 1940	....	4.00
15/87	Home Depot/A.P.O., rubber packet handstamp, 1941	....	4.00
15/88	Home Postal Centre, 1-16, 1942-47	....	2.00
15/89	Home Postal Centre/R.E./A.P.O., rubber packet handstamp, 1942-47	..	4.00

15/90	15/92

Base Army Post Offices

Either handstamp **15/90** or Krag machine 15/91 similar to **15/80** or Universal type machine as **15/92** but with several different types of town die:

1	France	1.00 (Machine 1.50)	8 Belgium	0.50 (Machine 0.80)
4	Egypt	0.40	15 Italy	0.50 (Machine 0.80)
5	Algiers	1.00 (Machine 1.00)	17 Singapore	10.00
6	Italy	3.00	18 Dieppe	?
7	Rangoon	1.00		

15/93 S.E.A (South East Asia) Base A.P.O. double circle or Krag machine 2.00

British Expeditionary Force in France, 1939-40

5	1.00	22	1.00	39	0.80	56	0.60	73	3.00	102	2.50
6	1.20	23	0.80	40	0.70	57	0.50	74	0.70	103	2.50
7	2.00	24	1.50	41	0.40	58	0.50	75	1.20	104	2.50
8	0.50	25	0.80	42	0.70	59	0.40	76	1.20	110	1.50
9	1.50	26	0.40	43	1.50	60	2.50	77	2.50	111	3.00
10	0.60	27	0.40	44	0.80	61	0.70	78	1.50	112	5.00
11	0.60	28	2.00	45	0.50	62	2.50	79	1.50	113	3.00
12	0.60	29	0.80	46	0.50	63	2.00	80	0.40	114	3.00
13	0.70	30	0.50	47	3.00	64	2.00	81	0.80	130	4.00
14	0.80	31	1.50	48	1.00	65	3.00	82	5.00	132	4.00
15	0.60	32	0.80	49	1.00	66	0.40	85	0.70	135	5.00
16	1.00	33	0.60	50	2.50	67	3.00	86	1.20	136	4.00
17	0.60	34	5.00	51	2.00	68	0.40	87	1.20	137	5.00
18	0.70	35	0.60	52	2.50	69	0.70	88	2.00	140	5.00
19	0.60	36	4.00	53	2.50	70	2.50	89	2.00	181	5.00
20	1.00	37	0.70	54	2.00	71	5.00	100	3.00	182	5.00
21	0.40	38	0.70	55	0.40	72	2.50	101	4.00		

Channel Islands Liberation, 1945

138 Guernsey 25.00   302 Jersey 25.00

Cyprus

124	25.00	168	5.00	291	12.50	293	20.00	552	?	726	20.00
164	5.00	290	?	292	?						

Egypt

15/94 Military Post Offices, redesignated numeral types M.P.O. or B.P.O., from 1939:

E601	2.00	E603	3.00	E605	5.00	E607	7.00	E609	15.00	E611	7.00
E602	2.00	E604	3.00	E606	5.00	E608	5.00	E611	7.00	E615	6.00

15/94

15/95

15/95 Egyptian Pre-Paid marks :

1	0.40	19	0.50	36	0.50	53	0.80	70	?	87	?
2	0.40	20	0.50	37	1.00	54	1.50	71	0.40	88	0.50
3	0.40	21	0.50	38	0.80	55	0.50	72	0.40	89	0.50
4	0.40	22	2.50	39	1.50	56	0.40	73	?	90	0.40
5	1.00	23	2.50	40	0.50	57	0.40	74	?	91	1.00
6	0.40	24	0.40	41	1.00	58	0.50	75	0.60	92	?
7	0.50	25	0.60	42	1.00	59	?	76	0.80	93	0.40
8	0.50	26	0.40	43	0.50	60	?	77	1.00	94	1.50
10	0.50	27	0.50	44	0.60	61	0.40	78	?	95	2.00
11	0.40	28	1.00	45	0.40	62	?	79	1.00	96	0.40
12	0.80	29	0.50	46	1.00	63	1.00	80	0.50	97	0.40
13	1.00	30	0.50	47	1.00	64	0.60	81	2.00	98	0.40
14	0.40	31	1.00	48	0.40	65	1.00	82	0.60	99	?
15	5.00	32	5.00	49	?	66	0.60	83	?	100	?
16	0.40	33	0.60	50	1.50	67	2.00	84	0.50	101	?
17	0.40	34	0.50	51	0.40	68	0.60	85	1.00	102	0.60
18	0.40	35	0.50	52	0.60	69	0.50	86	0.50	103	0.60

104	?	113	0.80	123	0.50	134	3.00	142	0.80	149	1.50
105	3.00	114	0.60	124	0.50	135	4.00	143	1.00	151	1.20
106	2.50	115	1.50	129	0.60	137	2.50	144	2.00	152	1.50
109	2.00	117	2.00	130	4.00	139	2.50	145	5.00	153	1.00
111	1.50	118	0.60	131	0.50	140	2.00	146	2.00	154	1.00
112	1.00	121	0.60	132	0.50	141	1.50	148	0.80	155	5.00

Field Post Offices 1939-46 (used in diff locations, some continued later)

13	1.00	139	?	196	0.60	264	?	327	?
15	2.00	140	1.00	197	0.50	265	5.00	368	5.00
17	3.00	147	4.00	198	0.70	267	?	369	?
35	2.00	148	1.00	199	0.50	284	?	370	3.00
36	2.00	156	3.00	201	1.00	285	?	371	?
37	2.00	161	7.50	217	2.00	287	?	372	2.50
38	2.00	165	6.00	218	1.00	288	?	375	0.80
39	4.00	167	1.00	220	1.00	289	?	394	?
67	0.60	168	1.00	224	?	290	3.00	395	4.00
68	1.00	169	0.50	225	?	291	4.00	396	?
69	1.00	170	0.40	226	?	292	3.00	397	5.00
74	1.50	171	0.40	232	2.00	293	3.00	445	3.00
76	1.00	172	1.00	233	?	299	1.50	448	?
96	0.70	173	0.60	234	3.00	309	0.70	451	5.00
113	1.50	174	0.60	235	1.00	315	1.50	481	?
123	1.50	177	1.00	236	2.00	317	1.50	482	?
124	2.00	178	2.00	242	1.50	318	?	503	4.00
129	?	186	0.50	243	1.50	319	?	513	1.50
134	?	187	0.60	244	1.50	323	?	515	1.50
135	0.40	188	1.00	245	1.50	324	3.00	517	2.00
136	0.40	189	2.00	246	1.00	325	?	519	1.50
137	0.80	190	0.40	255	1.50	326	?	525	?
138	1.00	191	0.50						

530	1.00
531	1.50
533	2.50
546	5.00
550	1.50
551	0.50
554	2.00
555	?
557	5.00
568	2.00
569	1.50
572	0.50
575	4.00
576	0.70
605	?
655	0.80
659	5.00
708	?
716	5.00
717	2.00
777	2.00

Liberation of Europe (France, Belgium, Germany, Austria), 1944-46

3	1.00	285	1.50	432	0.40	541	4.00	706	1.50	801	0.50
8	1.00	286	1.00	439	2.00	546	1.00	716	0.80	809	0.70
9	1.00	287	3.00	467	?	584	1.50	734	1.20	810	0.40
20	0.60	288	3.00	468	2.50	605	?	736	1.00	820	2.00
89	1.00	294	1.00	481	3.00	606	1.50	737	0.80	829	2.00
158	1.00	295	1.00	482	1.00	607	1.00	738	0.60	830	4.00
223	0.50	296	2.00	493	1.00	617	5.00	739	1.00	832	0.70
225	1.00	339	1.00	503	2.00	618	3.00	740	0.60	841	0.60
228	1.00	350	0.60	506	0.60	620	1.00	741	1.00	842	0.60
229	1.00	351	1.00	507	0.60	660	1.50	742	1.00	867	0.50
279	1.00	352	2.50	508	0.70	660	1.50	743	2.00	868	0.80
280	1.50	381	1.00	525	3.00	690	1.50	744	1.00	870	0.50
284	3.00	385	1.00	533	?	692	0.40	792	0.60	899	0.60

Gibraltar

475	2.00

Greece and Crete

69	7.50	194	50.00	266	5.00	288	4.00	567	3.00	776	5.00
137	3.50	195	?	267	5.00	400	3.00	654	4.00	777	4.00
139	10.00	250	5.00	285	3.00	402	10.00	709	12.50	778	?
175	35.00	264	4.00	286	4.00	454	7.50	727	?	782	?
176	?	265	4.00	287	4.00	514	2.00	732	?	783	1.00
193	12.00										

Iceland and the Faroes

2	10.00	128	?	304	12.50	306	10.00	308	17.50	611	30.00
3	17.50	219	?	305	20.00	307	50.00	526	12.50	695	25.00
89	50.00										

India and Burma

6	1.00	198	0.50	261	1.00	389	1.00	670	4.00	770	0.60
8	?	224	?	262	1.00	390	0.60	696	0.50	771	4.00
30	1.00	225	2.00	263	1.00	449	0.50	697	0.80	772	2.00
37	0.80	226	?	352	?	517	6.00	698	0.50	773	0.80
39	1.50	259	1.00	366	0.80	545	3.00	699	0.60	781	?
145	0.50	260	1.00	388	5.00	557	2.00	769	2.50	873	2.00

Iraq

171	0.50	224	5.00	244	2.50	290	?	375	?	397	2.00
222	?	225	?	269	5.00	291	?	394	2.50	398	3.00
223	?	226	?	289	5.00	292	?	395	5.00	533	1.50

Italy and Sicily

1	2.00	232	1.00	300	0.50	501	1.00	604	0.80	715	1.00
16	2.00	236	1.50	315	2.00	503	?	605	1.00	720	0.80
32	?	238	2.00	317	1.00	510	1.00	609	5.00	721	1.00
36	0.50	239	2.00	323	?	520	1.00	612	?	722	0.80
110	0.50	250	1.00	324	1.50	525	?	613	2.50	723	0.80
116	0.50	254	1.00	325	3.00	530	0.60	614	6.00	724	1.00
120	1.50	255	2.00	327	0.60	531	0.80	615	3.00	725	0.60
126	1.00	256	2.00	370	0.50	533	0.80	627	0.80	726	5.00
134	0.50	257	2.00	385	0.60	546	1.00	629	0.60	728	0.60
135	0.60	258	3.00	387	0.60	550	4.00	632	?	730	0.80
136	?	265	3.00	395	1.50	558	2.00	642	0.60	746	0.50
137	0.80	266	4.00	396	2.00	568	1.00	657	?	748	0.80
139	5.00	267	4.00	397	1.00	570	?	661	2.00	750	1.50
167	1.00	284	1.50	398	2.00	577	?	662	1.20	751	0.50
168	2.00	285	1.50	399	2.00	578	0.80	663	2.00	754	0.50
196	0.50	286	1.50	402	0.80	581	0.40	708	2.00	755	0.50
214	1.00	287	1.50	448	1.50	583	2.00	709	4.00	756	1.50
217	1.00	288	1.00	451	2.00	583	1.00	710	3.00	793	1.00
223	1.50	290	2.00	462	1.00	594	2.00	711	1.00	796	1.00
224	1.00	291	2.00	481	1.20	600	2.50	712	0.80	797	1.50
225	?	292	2.00	482	1.00	603	3.00				

Lebanon

141	4.00	223	?	550	2.50

Libya

33	0.50	178	?	315	2.50	327	?	395	?	515	2.00
40	2.50	197	1.00	316	3.00	368	?	396	2.50	516	3.00
51	1.50	199	7.50	317	1.50	369	?	397	3.00	518	1.00
111	3.00	218	5.00	318	3.00	370	5.00	398	?	571	5.00
134	3.00	233	2.00	323	3.00	371	?	448	3.00	572	3.00
135	5.00	234	2.00	324	4.00	372	?	451	4.00	653	3.00
156	4.00	244	3.00	325	6.00	394	?	499	3.00	656	1.00
168	1.50	289	5.00	326	6.00						

Madagascar

226	7.50	596	12.50

Malaya

1939-42:

15/96

SP501	Singapore	1.00	SP504	Kelantan	10.00
SP502	Penang	3.00	SP505	?	10.00
SP503	Kedah	7.50	SP506	Perak	10.00

1945-7:

259	5.00	261	6.00	262	6.00

FIELD POST OFFICE / 30 SP 1939 / S.P.501

15/96

Malta

188	2.00	443	1.00	570	1.50

North African Campaign, 1943-45

13	2.50	218	1.00	285	2.00	398	3.00	571	3.00	661	4.00
15	3.00	238	2.00	286	2.00	448	?	572	2.00	662	4.00
17	2.00	250	3.00	288	2.00	451	1.50	580	1.00	701	1.00
51	1.50	253	2.00	289	2.50	462	1.00	581	2.00	702	2.00
111	2.00	254	2.00	317	2.00	464	?	582	1.00	703	1.00
116	1.00	255	2.00	323	6.00	481	1.50	583	0.80	704	2.00
117	1.50	256	2.00	324	2.50	482	1.50	589	1.50	705	?
118	1.00	257	1.50	325	2.00	497	1.50	591	2.00	706	2.00
136	3.00	258	?	326	5.00	500	1.50	594	2.50	707	1.00
137	3.00	264	2.50	327	5.00	520	3.00	601	2.50	708	4.00
159	1.00	265	4.00	370	4.00	525	1.50	603	3.00	712	2.00
168	1.50	266	3.00	385	1.00	532	2.00	605	1.50	713	?
178	2.50	267	3.50	395	3.00	546	2.00	632	?	720	1.00
189	1.00	284	2.50	397	?	568	1.50	658	2.50		

Norway

1940:

115	50.00	125	100.00	127	85.00

1945:

150	7.50	343	10.00	785	10.00	786	7.50	787	25.00	788	17.50

Palestine, 1940-48

28	5.00	143	2.00	171	6.00	254	7.50	316	20.00	525	15.00
38	8.00	146	?	172	7.50	256	7.50	373	10.00	533	?
69	6.00	148	2.00	201	5.00	257	10.00	394	?	534	7.50
120	1.50	149	2.00	222	8.00	258	10.00	395	?	535	5.00
121	1.50	154	2.00	223	8.00	284	?	397	?	550	3.50
122	1.50	155	3.50	224	?	285	?	398	?	553	3.00
123	3.00	156	5.00	225	7.50	286	6.00	448	?	588	3.00
124	7.50	164	2.00	226	7.50	287	10.00	454	12.50	708	25.00
139	2.00	166	10.00	233	4.00	288	10.00	511	20.00	731	3.50
141	?	167	7.50	234	?	299	7.50				

Persia

222	?	223	5.00	224	5.00	225	4.00	226	4.00	375	?

Sudan

174	2.00	186	2.50	214	3.00	549	1.50	718	1.00	782	4.00

Syria

61	1.00	172	0.60	225	6.00	289	5.00	292	3.00	533	3.00
66	1.50	222	?	226	4.00	290	5.00	316	?	552	4.00
80	1.50	223	5.00	257	?	291	4.00	370	7.50	567	2.00
140	10.00	224	6.00	269	7.50						

West Africa

41	Sierra Leone	1.00	536	Gold Coast	7.50	563	Nigeria	5.00	699	W. Africa GHQ	?
45	Gold Coast	1.50	537	Sierra Leone	2.50	564	Gold Coast	10.00	769	Nigeria	5.00
46	Nigeria	1.50	538	W.A. Force	?	565	W. Africa APS	?	770	Nigeria	7.50
106	Gold Coast	1.00	559	Nigeria	1.50	670	W. Africa GHQ	?	771	Nigeria	7.50
107	Gold Coast	?	560	Nigeria	7.50	696	W. Africa GHQ	?	772	Nigeria	?
108	Gold Coast	?	561	W. Africa APS	5.00	697	W. Africa GHQ	?	773	Nigeria	?
109	Gambia	3.00	562	W. Africa APS	?	698	W. Africa GHQ	?			

Army Censor marks – Second World War

See note concerning Censor marks in chapter 14 (Naval censor marks section).

Further marks used throughout the Empire have not been included, but a representative selection is shown here. Prisoner of War and civilian censor marks are included here also.

15/97 A100 0.50
Chiefly France 1939-40

15/98
A200
0.50

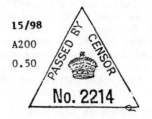

Chiefly UK 1940-41

15/99 A300 0.50
Egypt 1939-42

15/100 A500 0.30
Worldwide from 1942

15/101 A600 0.30
Worldwide 1944-45

15/102 A700 5.00
Middle East etc 1945

15/103 B100 0.40   **15/104** B403 1.50
North Africa, CMF & NW Europe

15/105 FC303 1.00
Middle East

UK Prisoners of War

15/106 GBPW100 1.00

15/107 GBPW210
(machine) 5.00

British Civil Censor marks

15/108 GBC3 0.50   **15/109** GBC5 0.50

Section V : Post War Operations

An alphabetical listing of FPO locations is shown below. While handstamps of the thick arc type **15/79** continued in use (a more up to date specimen is shown at **15/112**), the thin arcs type **15/113** later took over, with alternative wording as **15/114**. Single circle handstamps **15/115** (alternatively Field Post Office or Forces Post Office) were also plentiful. These are all shown as "steel" in the list. Krag machines **15/116** or Universal machines **15/117** (mostly with continuous wavy lines or with slogans) were also used; there were inscription variations in both cases. Many Field Post Offices also used rubber 'Blackwell' types (see chapter 9), as **15/118** or **15/119** (or other variations). Parcel handstamps (see **15/120** - variations) were also used but are not valued in the list: these are generally about three times the value of the rubber handstamps. The list gives basic values but not dates, thus the address on the envelope (usually a BFPO number) or contents have to be used to confirm the source of an envelope.

United Kingdom FPOs are not included as the list is extensive, also exercises in the UK or overseas, but Northern Ireland is included in the list. FPOs were used at various UK publicity events, also the annual tour of the RE Recruiting Display which over some years used machine 8 and steel handstamps 172 254 258 390 519 643 999 1015 1021 1050 1054 and rubber and parcel handstamps as well.

Gulf War : stationary FPOs are listed under the relevant country; under the heading "Gulf War" are listed those FPOs attached to fighting units, some of which travelled from Saudi Arabia into Iraq and/or Kuwait.

We are indebted to John Daynes of the Forces Postal History Society who has helped with the updated list that follows and with the illustrations.

15/110   Home Postal Depot R.E., 1,4,6,8,16, thick arcs, 1949-53   .... 2.00
15/111   As above but thin arcs, 51-53,63,68, from 1952   .... 1.00

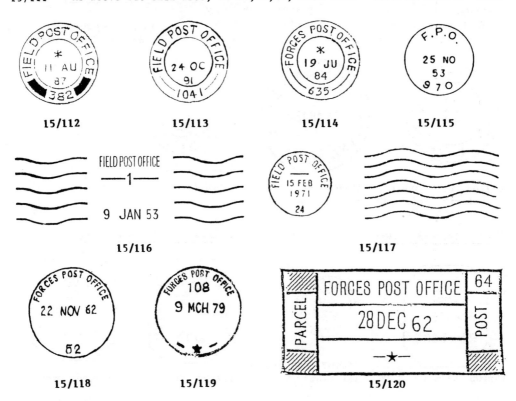

| 15/112 | 15/113 | 15/114 | 15/115 |

| 15/116 | | 15/117 | |

| 15/118 | 15/119 | 15/120 |

Aden

Machines:
1	0.50	2	0.50	21	0.50

Steel:
124	0.75	190	0.75	255	0.50	567	0.75	941	0.75	1002	0.75	1056	0.75
148	0.75	218	0.75	257	0.75	937	0.50	955	0.50	1041	1.00	1057	0.75
186	0.75	250	0.75	293	0.50	938	0.75	999	1.00	1055	0.75		

Rubber:
81	1.00	92	1.00	95	1.00	100	1.00	110	1.00	116	1.00	120	1.00
90	1.00	93	1.00	96	1.00	102	1.00	112	1.00	118	1.00	186	1.00
91	1.00	94	1.00	98	1.00								

Angola

Steel:
707 5.00 (also in blue ink)   795 12.00

Anguilla/Antigua

Steel:
701 3.00   1046 1.00

Rubber:
143 3.00

Ascension

Steel:
777 2.00   998 2.00

Rubber:
163 4.00

Australia

Steel:
51	2.00	80	2.00	155	2.00	385	2.50	1010	2.50	1033	1.50	1043	5.00
67	2.50	146	1.40	233	4.00	708	5.00	1014	2.00	1035	7.00	1046	1.50
69	2.50	149	5.00	234	5.00	1003	2.00	1016	3.00	1037	5.00		

Rubber:
71	3.00	75	4.00	138	3.50	157	3.50	159	3.50	186	4.00

Austria

Steel:
286	1.00	482	1.50	710	1.00	751	2.00	766	2.00	797	2.00	893	2.50
431	2.00	594	1.50	746	1.00	754	1.50	795	2.00				

Bahrain

Machine:
1 1.00

Steel:
123	2.00	218	1.00	235	2.00	372	3.00	551	1.50	955	1.00	1056	1.50
170	1.50	234	1.50	254	1.50	518	1.50	941	1.50	1013	2.00	1057	2.00
186	1.00												

Rubber:
77	2.50	94	2.00	99	2.50	106	2.50	109	2.50	115	2.50	186	2.50
81	2.50	98	2.50	102	2.50	107	2.50	113	3.00	116	2.50		

Bechuanaland

Steel:
1002 4.00

Belgium (for 1990s machine see listing under Germany heading)

Machine:
18 1.00

Steel:
177	0.50	358	1.50	513	0.50	716	1.00	955	0.50	984	1.00	1030	1.50
350	1.00	376	1.50	516	0.50	916	0.50						

Rubber:
4	1.50	18	1.50	31	1.50	59	1.50	91	1.00	97	1.50	174	1.50
13	2.00	21	1.50	54	1.50								

Bermuda

Steel:
51 10.00   148 12.00   707 12.00

Bosnia & Croatia (see also Italy)

Steel:
```
142  2.00    445  1.50    556  2.00    776  1.00    909  1.50    1027  1.50    1052  1.00
222  2.00    482  3.00    572  2.00    791  1.00    1012  1.00    1029  1.50    1057  1.00
375  3.00    555  1.50    576  1.50
```

Rubber:
```
 32  2.00     44  3.00     95  2.00    108  2.00    119  2.00     132  2.00
```

British Guiana and Guyana

Steel:
```
136  8.00    188  0.50    376  5.00    616  2.00    955  1.00    1022  3.00    1043  5.00
154  3.00    243  1.00    576  5.00    941  3.00    966  4.00
```

British Honduras and Belize

Steel:
```
188  0.50    293  0.75    939  2.00
```

Rubber:
```
177  3.00    193  3.00    200  3.00
```

British Solomon Islands

Steel:
```
136  15.00
```

British Virgin Islands

Steel:
```
148  5.00    385  10.00
```

Brunei

Steel:
```
 51  0.50    234  3.00    656  3.00    964  2.00    1034  5.00    1035  5.00    1044  2.00
156  1.00    635  2.00
```

Rubber:
```
 51  2.00    109  2.00    163  2.50    165  2.50
```

Caicos

Steel:
```
1042  10.00
```

Cameroons

Steel:
```
188  3.00    233  25.00    570  15.00    573  5.00    594  10.00    600  15.00    1032  7.50
```

Canada

Steel:
```
129  3.00    166  3.00    316  3.00    532  3.00    740  3.00    1012  3.00    1042  3.00
136  3.00    234  3.00    372  3.00    558  3.00    766  3.00    1016  3.00    1045  3.00
141  3.00    243  3.00    375  3.00    574  3.00    777  3.00    1018  3.00    1046  3.00
148  3.00    254  3.00    376  3.00    576  3.00    969  3.00    1021  3.00    1062  3.00
155  3.00    260  3.00    443  3.00    616  3.00    984  3.00    1035  3.00    1063  3.00
157  3.00    307  3.00    518  1.00    707  3.00
```

Rubber:
```
 15  2.00    166  3.00    190  3.00
```

Cyprus

Machines :
```
 1 Krag/Univ 0.50    2 Krag/Univ 0.50    3 Krag/Univ 0.50    21  1.00
```

Steel:
```
 61  0.50    147  0.50    201  0.50    482  0.75    775  0.50    947  1.00    1001  1.00
 76  0.50    148  0.50    218  0.75    514  0.50    797  0.75    949  0.75    1014  0.75
113  0.50    149  0.50    220  0.50    515  0.75    937  1.00    966  1.00    1025  1.00
121  1.00    164  0.25    245  0.75    567  0.75    938  0.75    967  1.00    1041  1.00
123  0.50    168  0.50    246  0.75    570  1.00    941  1.00    969  0.75    1042  2.00
124  0.75    169  0.75    250  1.00    600  0.75    942  0.75    970  1.00    1043  2.00
129  0.50    171  1.00    257  0.75    656  0.50    943  0.75    971  1.00    1045  1.00
137  1.00    186  0.75    260  1.00    658  1.00    944  0.75    998  0.75    1053  1.00
140  1.00    187  0.75    388  0.75    718  0.75    945  0.75    999  1.00    1054  0.75
141  1.00    197  0.50    461  0.50    757  1.00    946  0.75    1000  1.00    1055  0.75
```

Rubber:
```
 49  1.00     91  1.00    104  1.00    111  1.00    116  1.00    123  1.00    182  1.00
 68  1.00     99  1.00    105  1.00    112  1.00    117  1.00    124  1.00    189  1.00
 83  1.00    101  1.00    106  1.00    113  1.00    118  1.00    152  1.00    192  1.00
 85  1.00    102  1.00    107  1.00    114  1.00    119  1.00    156  1.00    199  1.00
 86  1.00    103  1.00    110  1.00    115  1.00    122  1.00    160  1.00    200  1.00
 90  1.00
```

Dominica

Steel:
558 12.00

Dubai

Steel:
121 4.00   514 2.00   1013 2.00   1057 1.75

Rubber:
164 6.00

Egypt

Machines:
  1 (Krag) 0.50   2 (Krag) 0.50

Steel:

13 0.75	124 0.75	171 1.00	218 0.75	266 0.75	445 0.75	576 0.75
15 0.75	136 1.50	172 0.75	234 0.75	293 0.75	461 0.75	714 0.75
17 0.75	137 0.75	174 0.75	235 1.00	299 1.00	518 0.75	777 1.00
67 1.00	141 1.00	186 0.75	245 0.75	309 1.00	532 0.75	938 20.00
76 1.00	168 0.75	187 0.75	246 1.00	316 0.75	551 0.75	953 25.00
113 0.75	169 0.75	190 0.75	255 0.75	375 0.75	552 0.75	1020 20.00
123 0.75	170 0.75	191 0.75	257 0.75	443 10.00	567 0.75	

Rubber:
172 2.00

Ethiopia

Steel:
 35 5.00   143 5.00   375 7.50   958 10.00

Rubber:
 50 10.00

Falkland Islands

Machines:
 40 3.00   655 1.00   666 1.00

Steel:
141 1.00   170 2.00   252 1.50   941 2.00

Rubber:
 10 10.00   41 3.00   157 3.00   166 3.00

Fiji

Steel:
 80 7.00   149 7.00   233 10.00   708 10.00   1038 10.00   1044 7.50

Rubber:
135 12.00

France

Steel:

128 3.00	305 3.00	777 3.00	915 1.50	956 2.00	979 2.00	1012 3.00
155 3.00	716 1.50	791 3.00	941 3.00	968 2.50	981 3.00	1045 3.00
235 3.00	768 2.00	816 3.00	950 1.00	975 2.00	989 2.00	1046 3.00
265 3.00	774 5.00	907 1.50	951 1.50			

Rubber:
  1 3.00   2 3.00   3 3.00

Gambia

Steel:
129 7.50   143 7.50
141 7.50   243 7.50

15/121

Germany (excluding Berlin & TPO's) - values 0.20 to 0.50

Machines of existing design, see 15/117:
 9   10   11   15   17   18   19   20   23   24   25   26   28   29   30   31   32   33   774

From 1994 "meter style" machines 15/121 were used (some initially in red, with/without lines at left &
value 000 at right) at the following BFPOs with location shown (except 140) : 15, 16, 17, 22, 25,
26 (Casteau, Belgium), 31, 34, 35, 36, 38, 39, 40 (Rhinedahlen spelling error, slightly different
"frank" at right), 140 (also at Rheindahlen), 43 (Laarbruck spelling error), 44, 47

Steel:

76	218	256	299	339	383	501	606	731	774	841	909	957	974	986	994	1020	1033
116	220	262	305	340	414	508	607	734	783	843	911	958	975	987	995	1021	1035
128	222	264	307	350	424	521	619	740	790	850	914	959	976	988	996	1022	1036
137	223	265	308	351	431	530	620	746	791	867	915	960	978	989	1004	1023	1043
154	230	266	309	352	432	535	694	748	792	870	916	961	980	990	1011	1026	1044
168	235	267	318	358	445	556	716	752	798	893	950	962	982	991	1015	1027	1048
172	245	280	319	359	461	575	717	755	800	899	952	963	983	992	1016	1028	1052
177	246	283	328	361	463	588	718	764	813	901	954	968	984	993	1019	1032	1053
209	251	286	331	382	493	594	729	768	816	907	956	973	985				

Rubber:

1	9	17	24	33	40	47	54	62	68	74	80	88	98	114	123	137	180
2	11	18	25	34	41	48	55	63	69	75	81	90	100	116	127	140	183
4	12	19	26	35	42	49	58	64	70	76	82	92	101	117	129	143	187
5	13	20	27	36	43	50	59	65	71	77	83	95	105	119	131	146	188
6	14	21	28	37	44	51	60	66	72	78	84	96	108	120	135	148	192
7	15	22	29	38	45	52	61	67	73	79	87	97	110	122	136	149	197
8	16	23	32	39	46	53											

Germany (Berlin)

Machine:
16

Steel:
128 359 382 493 606 737 909 911 916 987 994 1011

Rubber:
37 45 60 65 66 114 128

15/122   15/123   15/124

15/125

15/126   15/127   15/128

```
BFPO BERLIN (British type)  15/122, 15/123   machine & steel 1-6 ....................... 3.00
                            15/124           rubber 1-6 ............................... 3.00
             (German type)  15/126, *15/127  machine & steel 1-6 ....................... 0.50
                            15/128, 15/129   rubber 1-6 ............................... 0.75
```

Note : a philatelic version of this handstamp (above date) was used on special covers marking the last date of British Forces in Berlin 16 December 1994.

TPOs steel FPO handstamps 908 910 912 8.00 each

15/131

15/129   **15/130**

Special ACE (Allied Command Europe(NATO)) **15/130** (also smaller lettering) 5.00

Ghana

Steel:
574 7.50

Gibraltar (local stamps normally used to 1995 then GB stamps)

Steel:
123 1.00   186 1.00   475 0.50   958 0.75   976 1.00   1061 0.75

Rubber:
 52 1.00   130 2.00   133 1.00   145 2.00   169 1.50

Gilbert and Ellice Islands (Christmas Island)

Steel:
 158 20.00   **15/131** BFPO Christmas Island 2.00

Greece

Steel:
 69 2.00   375 3.00   567 3.00   991 3.00   1043 3.00   1044 4.00   1062 3.50
316 3.00   514 2.00   783 1.00   1042 3.00

Rubber:
159 4.00

15/132

Gulf War 1990-1992 - see notes at start of listing

Machine (meter **15/132**):
  Gulf 2   5.00

Steel:
 40 5.00   375 4.00   482 4.00   755 4.00   791 4.00   990 2.00   1012 4.00
222 4.00

Rubber:
  7 4.00   46 4.00

Hong Kong

Machines:
  5 (Krag) 1.00   12 (Univ) 1.00

Steel:
 67 1.00   129 0.75   146 0.50   375 0.75   708 0.75   945 0.50   998 0.75
 69 0.75   136 0.75   164 0.75   385 1.00   746 0.50   948 0.50   1037 0.75
 80 0.75   142 0.50   168 0.75   701 0.50   790 0.50   964 0.50   1038 0.75
121 1.00   145 0.75   233 0.75   707 0.50   816 1.00   970 0.50   1044 1.00

  BFPO Hong Kong (due to close 1997) **15/133** steel 1-8, 10 each 0.50

Rubber:
 20 1.00   108 1.00   123 1.00   127 1.00   138 1.00   191 1.00   195 1.00
 71 1.00   110 1.00   124 1.00   131 1.00   168 1.00   194 1.00   198 1.00
107 1.00   122 1.00   125 1.00   135 1.00   184 1.00

  BFPO Hong Kong rubber **15/134** (large) 1-6 2.00   **15/135** (small, with variations) 1-7 1.00

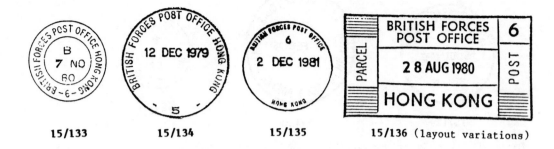

15/133   15/134   15/135   15/136 (layout variations)

Iceland

Steel:
316 10.00

Iraq (see also Gulf War)

Steel:
171 1.00   515 1.00   567 1.50   756 1.50   942 2.00

Israel

Steel:
136 5.00

Italy (* denotes 1990s FPOs for RAF operations over Bosnia)

Steel:
136 3.00   174 1.00   246 1.50   *574 2.00   *795 2.00   953 1.50   1041 1.00
148 3.00   186 2.00   534 2.50   *707 2.00   *940 1.50   971 0.50   1051 2.00
164 0.75   190 1.50   558 2.00   777 3.00   942 0.50

Rubber:
 57 2.00   87 2.00   *103 3.00

Jamaica

Steel:
129 5.00   243 5.00   250 7.50   375 5.00   443 5.00   574 5.00   940 5.00
136 5.00

Rubber:
 98 7.50

Japan

Steel:
260 5.00   376 3.00   946 2.50   949 2.00

Jordan

Steel:
 61 1.00   121 1.00   140 3.00   155 1.50   174 10.00   201 1.00   575 1.50
113 1.00   137 2.00   149 1.00

Kenya

Steel:
123 0.75   157 2.00   250 1.00   443 2.00   940 2.00   1002 1.00   1055 1.50
124 0.50   164 1.00   254 1.00   532 1.00   947 2.00   1039 1.00   1056 1.00
129 2.00   186 1.00   256 0.50   567 1.00   967 2.00   1040 1.50   1057 1.00
136 2.00   218 1.00   375 2.00   576 0.75   970 1.50   1041 1.50   1063 1.50
140 2.00   243 1.50   376 2.00   656 0.50   997 1.50

Rubber:
 96 1.00   99 1.00   115 1.00   134 1.00   194 1.00   198 1.00   200 1.00
 98 1.00   100 1.00   121 1.00

Korea

Steel:

80	2.00	136	2.00	707	2.00	740	2.00	766	3.00	798	3.00	1006	1.50
121	3.00	406	2.00	734	2.50	746	2.00	790	2.00	948	2.50	1044	2.00

Rubber:

122	2.50	126	2.50

Kuwait (see also Gulf War)

Steel:

941	15.00	1039	10.00	1040	7.50	1043	5.00	1062	10.00

Lebanon

Steel:

1055	5.00

Rubber:

102	5.00	172	5.00	174	5.00

Libya

Steel:

1	2.00	142	0.75	190	0.50	267	0.75	558	1.00	782	1.00	1001	1.50
28	0.75	147	0.75	191	0.75	461	0.75	576	1.00	942	1.00	1015	2.50
61	0.75	149	0.75	197	0.75	518	0.75	656	0.75	944	1.00	1019	2.50
76	0.75	168	0.75	246	0.75	532	0.75	658	1.00	953	1.00	1020	2.50
113	0.50	171	1.00	257	0.75	534	0.75	756	0.75	971	1.00	1051	1.50
141	0.75	174	0.50	258	0.75	552	0.75	757	0.75	998	1.50	1062	2.00

Rubber:

66	2.00	83	2.00	84	2.00	85	2.00	86	2.00	88	2.00

Malawi

Steel:

443	10.00

Malaya

Steel:

129	3.00	148	5.00	746	2.00	1003	2.00	1007	2.00	1010	2.00	1058	5.00
142	3.00	223	2.00	964	5.00	1004	3.00	1008	3.00				

Rubber:

133	4.00	145	4.00

Maldive Islands

Steel:

51	2.00	142	2.50	166	2.00	1000	3.00	1013	2.00	1025	1.00	1048	5.00
140	2.00	146	2.00										

Rubber:

129	5.00	140	5.00

Malta

Machine:

21	1.50

Steel:

61	1.00	149	1.00	186	1.50	254	1.00	532	1.00	746	1.50	953	1.50
76	0.50	151	1.00	187	1.50	258	1.00	534	1.50	757	1.00	1001	1.00
121	1.00	158	1.00	191	1.00	266	1.00	558	2.00	782	0.75	1040	2.00
147	1.00	168	1.50	220	1.00	443	1.50	570	2.00	942	1.00	1047	1.50
148	1.00	171	1.50	246	1.00	515	1.00	573	1.50	944	1.00	1051	1.50

Rubber:

82	2.00	88	2.00	103	2.00	109	2.00	152	2.00	161	2.00	169	2.00
84	2.00	89	2.00	107	2.00	112	2.00	156	2.00	167	2.00	189	2.00

Special 1000 5.00

Mauritius

Steel:

255	10.00	1008	10.00

Namibia

Steel:

940	5.00

Rubber:

189	7.00

Nepal

Steel:
146 2.00	186 5.00	443 5.00	600 5.00

Rubber:
123 3.00

Netherlands

Machine:
18 1.00

Steel:
164 2.00	307 1.50	340 1.50	358 1.50	376 1.50	961 1.00	983 2.00
305 2.00	331 2.00					

Rubber:
52 2.00	53 2.00	70 2.00	121 2.00

New Hebrides

Steel:
941 10.00

New Zealand

Steel:
576 7.50	656 7.50	707 7.50	708 7.50	989 7.50

Rubber:
103 10.00

North Borneo

Steel:
154 5.00	169 3.50	573 3.00	948 2.50	1030 5.00	1035 5.00	1061 4.00
166 3.00	450 5.00	766 3.00				

Rubber:
146 4.00	164 5.00	190 5.00

Northern Ireland

Machines:
8 (figure 8 damaged, resembles 6) 0.25   27 0.50

Note : "Meter style" machines similar to 15/121 were used in red at "Aldergrove" & "Lisburn" from 1996, with/without lines at left

Steel:
316 0.50	551 0.50	553 0.50	658 0.50	714 0.50	771 0.50	772 0.50
385 0.50	552 0.50	576 0.50	659 0.50	770 0.50		

Rubber:
3 1.00	158 1.00	161 1.00	170 1.00	175 1.00	177 1.00	181 1.00
72 1.00	159 1.00	162 1.00	171 1.00	176 1.00	179 1.00	185 1.00
116 1.00						

Norway

Steel:
129 2.00	157 1.50	222 2.00	376 2.00	740 1.50	941 2.00	1044 2.50
136 1.50	158 2.00	234 2.00	443 2.00	777 2.00	951 2.00	1062 2.50
141 2.00	172 2.00	243 2.00	532 2.00	797 2.00	1042 2.50	1063 3.00
148 2.00	190 2.00	375 1.50	707 1.50	867 0.75	1043 2.50	

Rubber:
29 3.00	50 2.50	103 2.50	163 2.50	170 2.50	178 2.50	ACE 7.50
30 1.50	97 2.50	113 2.50	165 2.50			

Oman

Steel:
143 5.00	190 2.00	406 1.50	567 2.00	740 4.00	766 2.50	953 2.00

Rubber:
50 7.00	98 3.00

Poland

Steel:
968 4.00

Portugal

Steel:
67 0.75	186 3.00	464 3.00	574 3.00	718 2.50	791 3.00	1017 4.00
157 2.50	221 5.00	558 3.00				

Rubber:
78 3.00	119 3.00	139 2.50

Rhodesia and Zimbabwe

Machine (meter 15/137) :
632 8.00

Steel:
234 5.00   532 5.00   1053 3.00

Rubber:
 94 5.00   191 5.00   194 5.00

Rwanda

Steel:
375 5.00

15/137

St Lucia

Steel:
443 10.00

Sarawak

Steel:
67 4.00   136 2.00   948 2.50   1005 4.00   1035 6.00   1048 6.00   1059 3.00
69 4.00   156 3.00   964 5.00   1025 4.00   1044 3.00   1059 3.00

Rubber:
131 4.00

Saudi Arabia

Machine:
 40 2.00

Steel:
190 3.00   574 4.00   764 4.00   1025 4.00   1042 3.00   1058 4.00   1059 4.00
234 4.00

Rubber:
 95 5.00   132 4.00   165 4.00   186 4.00

Sharjah

Steel:
186 2.00   234 2.00   255 2.00   514 2.00   936 1.50   1056 2.00   1057 3.00
190 2.50   235 2.00   293 2.00

Rubber:
 93 3.00   107 3.00   112 3.00

Singapore

15/138   **15/139**   **15/140**

15/141

Machine:
 28 1.00   ANZUK **15/138** 1.50

Steel:
 66 2.00   142 3.00   156 1.50   258 2.00   570 6.00   965 3.00   ANZUK 2.00
123 3.00   154 1.50   254 2.00   514 2.00   (15/139)

Rubber:
 26 3.00   27 3.00   145 3.00   154 3.00   156 2.50   188 3.50   ANZUK 4.00
                                                                                  (15/140)

Sudan

Steel:

141 5.00	158 5.00	221 10.00	443 5.00	718 3.00	777 5.00	782 3.00

Swaziland

Steel:

124 3.00	656 3.50	997 3.00	1019 4.00	1041 3.00

Tanganyika

Steel:
1062 5.00

Thailand

Steel:

66 2.00	573 2.00	1003 3.00	1005 0.75	1006 1.50	1058 3.00	1061 3.00

Rubber:
147 2.50

Trieste

Steel:

136 2.00	530 2.50	594 2.00	600 2.50

Turkey

Steel:

376 2.00	513 2.50	516 2.00	773 2.00

Uganda

Steel:

201 4.00	218 3.00

Rubber:
112 5.00

USA

Steel:

66 1.00	154 2.50	375 2.00	707 2.00	777 2.00	965 2.00	1043 2.00
136 2.00	188 0.75	443 2.00	766 2.00	941 2.00	990 2.00	1063 2.00
141 2.00	234 2.00	532 2.00				

Rubber:

58 1.00	143 2.00

Zaire

Steel:
444 3.00

Rubber:
72 4.00

Zambia

Steel:

143 5.00	777 8.00	1018 10.00	1062 7.00

Rubber:

20 8.00	195 8.00

Zanzibar

Steel:

254 5.00	970 6.00	1041 5.00

FPOs used at Sea

Steel:

188 40.00	941 50.00	1020 50.00	1055 20.00

Section VI : Camps and other military establishments

In this simplified listing detailed variations in wording are excluded (and BO omitted too, see single circle below for example). The post town or county shown in brackets is sometimes included in the handstamps, sometimes not so. For Naval and RAF/RNAS establishments see chapters 14 and 16 respectively. * denotes entries for which confirmation is required.

A	Scroll	G	Krag Machine
B	Double Arc	H	Universal Machine
C	Duplex	I	Rubbers/Packet handstamps
D	Single Circle	J	Parcel handstamps
E	Double Circle	K	Registered handstamps
F	Skeleton	S	SID (self inking datestamp)

B   15/142
Double Arc

C   15/143
Duplex

D   15/144
Single circle
(Several types)

E   15/145
Double circle
(Several types)

F   15/146
Skeleton

I   15/147
Rubber

S   15/148
Self inking
datestamp

(Irish skeletons are double rim)

England, Scotland, Wales

Acreknowe Camp, Hawick F	15.00	Barry Camp D	5.00	Bettisfield Park Camp,	
Aldershot Camp B	35.00	(Dundee or Carnoustie)		Whitchurch E	5.00
C (046,96)	10.00	Barton Stacey Camp,		F	25.00
D	4.00	Winchester Hants D	3.00	J	7.00
E	3.00	J	5.00	Bisley Camp, Woking C (J62)	5.00
J	8.00	Bassingbourn Barracks E	3.00	D	3.00
Arborfield Camp (Berks) D	4.00	(for earlier see chap 16)		E	2.00
Arncott Depot, Oxford D	4.00	Bears Rail Camp, Windsor F	20.00	J	4.00
E	5.00	(rubber skeleton)		K	10.00
Ashley Walk Camp F	15.00	Beaulieu Camp, Lymington F	15.00	Blackdown Camp, Aldershot D	3.00
(Hants)		Beaulieu Heath Camp, Hants		E	3.00
Ashwick Camp F	15.00	F	20.00	F	8.00
(Dulverton or Tiverton)		Camp Beauly (Inverness-shire)		J	6.00
Auchengate Camp, Troon D	5.00	F	20.00	Blackpool Military Hospital	
Bagshot Moor Camp, Hants		Belhus Park Camp, Aveley E	4.00	D	7.00
(Brockenhurst) F	20.00	F	15.00	I	15.00
Balmer Camp, Lewes F	20.00	Belton Camp, Grantham D	4.00	J	15.00
Bangour War Hospital,		I	6.00	Blandford Camp, Blandford D	3.00
West Lothian E	8.00	J	7.00	E	3.00
F	25.00			J	5.00
Barnstaple Camp F	25.00			Blandford Field Force D	50.00

The Camp, Bodmin E	6.00
Bordon Camp, E Liss Hants D	4.00
E	3.00
Field PO, Bordon F	10.00
Bourley Camp, Aldershot E	4.00
F	10.00
Bovey Tracey Camp (Devon) F	20.00
Bovington Camp D	3.00
(Poole or Wareham)	
E	2.00
F	15.00
G	10.00
I	5.00
J	4.00
Bowood Camp E	5.00
Bow Street Camp F	8.00
Boyton Camp, Wilts D	4.00
E	3.00
I	4.00
J	5.00
Bramshott Camp (Liphook) D	3.00
E	3.00
F	6.00
G	10.00
J	6.00
Camp, Bridestowe RSO Devon D	3.00
Brocton Camp, Stafford D	5.00
E	3.00
J	6.00
Brough Camp, Catterick F	20.00
Buddon Camp (Carnoustie) D	4.00
E	3.00
F	6.00
Bulford Barracks, Salisbury D	3.00
E	3.00
G	1.50
H	10.00
I	3.00
J	8.00
K	8.00
Paid handstamp	8.00
Bulford Camp, Salisbury D	4.00
E (& FPO)	3.00
F (& Field PO)	8.00
J	5.00
Bullswater Camp, Woking F	8.00
Burley Camp, Ringwood F	7.00
Burrowhead Camp, Newton Stewart	
E	5.00
Bushey Down Camp F	10.00
(Southampton)	
Bustard Camp, Devizes D	4.00
F (or Salisbury)	5.00
(The) Bustard Field PO F	7.00
Royal Military College,	
Camberley D	8.00
1st Eastern Gen. Hospital,	
Cambridge D	12.00
F	20.00
The Camp, Camelford E	5.00
Cannock Chase FPO C (G19)	50.00
Caterham Barracks D	3.00
J	5.00
Catterick Camp, Yorks D	3.00
E	2.00
G	10.00
H	1.50
J	3.00
K	8.00
later Catterick Garrison D	3.00
E	4.00
K	8.00
Chelsea Barracks SW D	4.00
Pimlico Rd Chelsea Barracks SW	
D	3.00

Chisledon Camp, Wilts D	4.00
E	3.00
F (and Swindon)	7.00
J	10.00
Chobham Camp B	150.00
Churn Camp, Oxford D	4.00
F	7.00
Chyngton Camp, Seaford D	4.00
E	3.00
F	10.00
J	8.00
Claughton Territorial Camp	
(Cheshire) F	8.00
Clipstone Camp, Notts E	3.00
F	20.00
J	5.00
Clochkeil Camp, Campbeltown	
F	25.00
Codford St Mary Camp J	8.00
Colchester Garrison E	5.00
Colsterdale Camp, Yorks E	5.00
F	7.00
Comrie Camp, Perthshire E	8.00
Cooden Camp, Bexhill-on-Sea	
E	5.00
J	10.00
Cothill Camp (Forres) F	10.00
Crookham Camp, Aldershot Hants	
D	3.00
E	3.00
J	6.00
Crowborough Camp D	3.00
F	4.00
J	6.00
K	8.00
Camp Hill Camp, Crowboro F	7.00
J	8.00
Cuckfield Camp (Sussex) F	12.00
Darnley Camp (Glasgow) F	8.00
Dartmoor FPO C (G17)	50.00
RST C (G18)	100.00
Deepcut Camp D	2.00
(Aldershot or Farnborough)	
E	2.00
J	5.00
Deganwy Camp (Conway) F	10.00
Detling Camp, Maidstone E	4.00
The Barracks, Devizes E	6.00
Devizes, Military Camp E	3.00
J	4.00
Dibgate Camp, Shorncliffe E	4.00
F	10.00
Dolphinholme Camp (Lancs) F	15.00
Doonfoot Camp, Ayr F	20.00
Duke of York's School, Dover	
D	4.00
E	3.00
Draycott Camp, Swindon E	5.00
F	20.00
Dundonald Camp, Troon Ayrshire	
D	4.00
J	6.00
Durrington Camp, Salisbury D	4.00
E	3.00
F	6.00
J	10.00
East Anstey Camp (Devon) F	8.00
E Boldre Camp, Brockenhurst	
F	10.00
East Down Camp, Devizes E	4.00
*East Marton Camp ?F	15.00
Flower Down Camp, Winchester	
D	5.00
E	4.00

Fort George (Inverness)	
concave 'Fort George'	40.00
str line	40.00
circular	30.00
circular mileage	25.00
boxed/unframed mileage	20.00
mileage removed	10.00
boxed Too Late	100.00
numeral (149)	10.00
D	4.00
E	2.00
F	8.00
J	6.00
Fovant Camp, Salisbury D	4.00
E	3.00
F	10.00
J	4.00
Frensham Camp, Farnham F	20.00
Frensham Common Camp, Farnham	
D	4.00
E	3.00
F	15.00
Gailes Camp, Irvine =602= E	6.00
F	6.00
*Gargrave Camp ?F	15.00
Glamis Camp F	8.00
Glanrheidol Camp (Cardiganshire)	
F	15.00
Guards Camp, Goodwood F	20.00
Gosforth Park Camp,	
Newcastle-on-Tyne D	4.00
Grazeley Camp, Reading Berks	
D	4.00
Greenhill Camp, Sheffield D	4.00
Gypsy Bottom Camp, Aylesbury	
F	20.00
Hagley Park Camp (Staffs) F	12.00
Halton Camp/Tring D	3.00
(later Bucks or Aylesbury)	
(Army to 1917 then RAF)	
E	2.00
F	8.00
I	4.00
J	6.00
K	10.00
Halton Camp North D	3.00
(see note re Halton above)	
Hampton Court Camp F	40.00
I (Kingston-on-Thames)	6.00
Harrowby Camp, Grantham D	4.00
J	7.00
Haynes Park Camp, Bedford D	5.00
Hazeley Camp, Winchester D	5.00
E	4.00
J	7.00
Heytesbury Camp, Wilts E	3.00
I	5.00
J	6.00
Hindlow Camp, Buxton F	8.00
Holkham Camp, Wells Norfolk	
F	8.00
Hollingbury Camp, Brighton F	10.00
Hollinside Camp NB (Co Durham)	
F	25.00
Hollom Dn Barn Camp, Hants F	10.00
Holmsley Camp, Ringwood F	10.00
Horsebridge Camp, Hants F	20.00
Houghton Down Camp, Hants F	15.00
Hunmanby Camp, Yorkshire F	8.00
Hurdcott Camp, Salisbury D	5.00
E	5.00
F (Hardcott Camp)	15.00
J	7.00

Hursley Camp, Winchester D	4.00	
Hursley Park Camp D	4.00	
E	5.00	
F	10.00	
Ibsley Camp (Ringwood) F	10.00	
Royal Hospital School, Ipswich		
Suffolk D	7.00	
Kensington Gdns Camp W2 D	5.00	
F	10.00	
K	8.00	
King Edward VII Sanatorium,		
Midhurst D	6.00	
E	6.00	
Kinmel Park Camp, Rhyl D	4.00	
E	3.00	
F (Registered/Kinmel Park		
not Camp)	20.00	
J	6.00	
Kinross Camp F	10.00	
Knockaloe Camp, Peel (1908)		
F	100.00	
The Camp Knockaloe, Peel		
(1915 POW Camp) E	50.00	
Lamphey Camp, Pembroke		
F (rubber skeleton)	20.00	
Landguard Camp, Felixstowe E	4.00	
Lark Hill Camp, Salisbury D	4.00	
E	2.00	
F	7.00	
J	8.00	
Lathom Park Camp, Ormskirk D	4.00	
E	4.00	
Littlemore Camp, Weymouth F	8.00	
Lodmore Camp, Weymouth F	8.00	
Longmoor Camp, Liss Hants D	3.00	
E (East Liss)	3.00	
F	8.00	
J	5.00	
Lopcombe Camp, Salisbury F	10.00	
Lovesgrove Camp, Aberystwyth		
F	8.00	
Lulworth Camp, Wareham F	7.00	
Lydd Camp, Kent D	4.00	
E	4.00	
F	15.00	
Maresfield Park Camp, Uckfield		
E	6.00	
Marlborough Lines, Aldershot		
D	2.00	
E	2.00	
F	7.00	
J	6.00	
Camp, Marske by Sea Yk F	10.00	
Martinhoe Camp, Barnstaple		
F	15.00	
Milford Camp, Stafford F	15.00	
Milton Depot, Steventon		
Berks E	4.00	
*I	7.00	
The Camp, Minehead Som D	4.00	
Morfa Camp, Conway D	4.00	
J	4.00	
Morn Hill Camp, Winchester D	4.00	
E	3.00	
F	8.00	
Mytchett Camp F	8.00	
(Aldershot or Farnborough)		
Nettlebed Camp, Henley Ths F	8.00	
*North Denes Camp (Norfolk) F	?	
North Leam Camp NB		
(Co Durham) F	25.00	
North Sway Camp (Hants) F	6.00	
Norton Barracks, Worcester D	8.00	
Okehampton Camp, Okehampton		
D	5.00	
E	3.00	
Orsett Camp, Grays Essex D	4.00	
J	6.00	
*Osterley Park Camp, Isleworth		
E	?	
Otterpool Camp (Kent) E	4.00	
F	6.00	
Oxney Camp, Bordon Hants F	20.00	
Panfield Camp, Braintree F	15.00	
Parham Park Camp (Sussex) F	12.00	
Park Hall Camp, Oswestry D	4.00	
E	4.00	
F	10.00	
J	6.00	
Park Hall West Camp, Oswestry		
D	4.00	
E	4.00	
J	6.00	
Park House Camp, Salisbury E	4.00	
Park Royal Camp NW D	15.00	
Pease Pottage Camp, Crawley		
E	5.00	
Peel Camp, Douglas F	200.00	
Penkridge Bank Camp,		
Stafford E	4.00	
Penley Hall Camp, Wrexham		
Denb E	5.00	
Perham Down Camp, Andover D	4.00	
E (& APO/FPO Perham Down)	4.00	
F	10.00	
J	8.00	
Pewsey Field Force D	50.00	
Pirbright Camp, Woking D	4.00	
E	2.00	
Pitt Camp, Winchester D	5.00	
E	5.00	
Plessey Camp, Cramlington F	10.00	
Pond Farm Camp, Devizes D	4.00	
F (Salisbury)	8.00	
Popham Camp, Winchester F	10.00	
Portobello Barracks F	8.00	
Experimental Ground/Stn, Porton		
Salisbury E	10.00	
Prees Heath Camp, Whitchurch		
(Salop) D	4.00	
E	3.00	
F	10.00	
J	8.00	
Barracks, Preston D	4.00	
J	7.00	
Puddaven Camp (Devon) F	8.00	
Purfleet Camp, Grays D	5.00	
F	7.00	
Ranikhet Camp, Reading Berks		
D	4.00	
Ravensworth Camp, Gateshead		
F	20.00	
The Barracks, Reading D	3.00	
S	2.00	
Reedhall Camp, Colchester D	4.00	
E	4.00	
F	20.00	
J	6.00	
Regents Park Camp NW1 F	10.00	
Remount Depot, Romsey D	5.00	
Rhayader Military Camp		
F (rubber skeleton)	20.00	
Richborough Camp, Sandwich		
Kent D	5.00	
Richmond Camp, Yorks D	4.00	
E	3.00	
J	6.00	
Ripon Camp D	3.00	
E	3.00	
J	6.00	
Rockford Camp (Ringwood) F	10.00	
Roehampton Camp SW D	5.00	
Rollestone Camp, Salisbury D	4.00	
E	4.00	
F	15.00	
J	8.00	
Romsey Camp, Romsey E	4.00	
F	10.00	
J	8.00	
Roomer Camp, Masham F	15.00	
Rugeley Camp, Stafford D	4.00	
E	4.00	
F	6.00	
J	6.00	
Rushmoor Camp, Aldershot E	4.00	
F	15.00	
St Anthony Camp, Falmouth E	4.00	
I	8.00	
St Giles Camp, Wimborne Dst		
F	8.00	
St John's, Crowborough Camp		
F	15.00	
J	7.00	
St Leonards Camp, Ringwood F	8.00	
Sand Hill Camp, Wilts E	3.00	
F	15.00	
I	8.00	
J	6.00	
Sandling Camp E	3.00	
(Folkestone, Hythe or Shorncliffe)		
F	15.00	
K	8.00	
Scarborough Race Course Camp		
E	8.00	
Seaford Camp, Lewes F	10.00	
Seaford North Camp, Sussex D	4.00	
The Camp, Seaford F	8.00	
Sedbury Camp, Chepstow E	4.00	
Sheepcot Camp, Wallingford		
F	25.00	
Sherrington Camp F	8.00	
(Warminster, Wilts)		
Shoreham Camp, Sussex D	4.00	
E	3.00	
F	6.00	
Shorncliffe Camp, Folkestone		
C (F46)	5.00	
D	8.00	
E	2.00	
J	5.00	
K	8.00	
Sling Camp, Salisbury E	4.00	
F	7.00	
J	10.00	
Sling Plantation Camp F	8.00	
Stanhope Lines, Aldershot D	3.00	
E	2.00	
F	7.00	
J	6.00	
*Stobs Camp, Hawick D	6.00	
Stowe Park Camp, Bucks		
(or Buckingham) F	8.00	
Strensall Camp, York C (930)	5.00	
D	3.00	
E	3.00	
Summerdown Camp, Eastbourne		
D	4.00	
J	5.00	

Sunningdale Camp, Ascot E	5.00	Trenchard Lines D	2.50
Sutton Mandeville Camp,		(prev RAF Stn Upavon)	
Salisbury D	4.00	Twezeldown Camp D	4.00
E	4.00	(Aldershot or Farnham)	
J	6.00	E (or Tweseldown)	3.00
Sutton Veny Camp, Wilts D	5.00	F (or Tweseldown)	6.00
E	3.00	Wareham Field Post Office D	20.00
F	8.00	Welbeck Camp, Worksop F	15.00
I	8.00	FPO West Down Camp E	5.00
J	8.00	West Down North Camp, Devizes	
Swanage Camp, Poole D	4.00	D (or Salisbury)	3.00
F	7.00	(or FPO West Down North)	
Tadworth Camp, Epsom D	4.00	West Down South Camp, Devizes	
E	4.00	D (or Salisbury)	3.00
Tain Camp, Ross-shire F	10.00	(or FPO West Down South)	
Thetford Camp or		West Lavington Camp E	5.00
Army Camp, Thetford D	4.00	I	6.00
E	4.00	West Lulworth Camp, Wareham	
F	8.00	E	3.00
Tidworth Barracks, Andover		F	8.00
(or Hants) D	4.00	West Parley Camp, Wimborne	
E	2.00	F	12.00
F	8.00	Whitchurch Down Camp	
J	7.00	(Tavistock Devon) F	10.00
Tidworth Park Camp, Andover		White Hill Bordon Camp, Hants	
D	4.00	D	4.00
F (Tidworth)	15.00	Whitmoor Camp, Woking F	20.00
Tidworth Pennings Camp, Andover		Whittington Barracks (Lichfield)	
D	4.00	D	2.00
J	6.00	E	3.00
Townfoot Camp, Denny F	10.00	F	15.00
Trawsfynydd Camp D	4.00	Wicklesham Camp, Swindon F	20.00

Willsworthy Camp F	10.00
(Bridestowe Devon)	
Wiltshire TF Assn Trowbridge	
E	15.00
Wimbledon Camp C (801)	35.00
D	15.00
Windmill Hill Camp, Andover	
D	4.00
E	4.00
J	7.00
Wing Camp, Leighton Buzzard	
F	10.00
Witley Camp, Godalming E	4.00
Woodbury Camp, Exeter	
F (rubber)	20.00
F (steel)	25.00
Woodbury Common Camp	
F (rubber)	20.00
Woodcote Camp, Epsom E	4.00
Woodhead Camp (Aberdeen) F	12.00
Woolsington Camp, New on T	
F	15.00
Woolwich RA Barracks SE18 D	8.00
Woolwich Royal Arsenal D	6.00
Worgret Camp (Poole or Wareham)	
D	4.00
E	4.00
F	8.00
Worthy Down Camp, Winchester	
Hants D	3.00
F	10.00
The Camp, Yarmouth D	5.00

Ireland

Aglish Camp, Fermoy F	20.00	C	10.00	Kilbride Camp, Dublin D	5.00
Ballinvonear Camp, Buttevant		D	2.00	Kilworth Camp, Cork D	5.00
E	6.00	E with cross pattee	3.00	F	15.00
F	20.00	E double arc with gap	5.00	Lisnegar Camp	
Ballykinler Camp, Co Down D	2.50	F	10.00	F (rubber skeleton)	25.00
E	4.00	I	4.00	Magilligan Camp, Londonderry	
Bere Island MTO F	30.00	Finner Camp, Ballyshannon D	8.00	D	4.00
Clandeboye Camp F	15.00	Glen Imaal Camp D	8.00	Malahide Camp, Co Dublin D	4.00
Coolmoney Camp, Co Wicklow F	20.00	F	15.00	Moore Park Camp F	10.00
Cork Barracks Mil Tel Off D	8.00	Glen Imaal Artillery Camp F	7.00	Shanes Park Camp, Belfast F	6.00
Curragh Camp A	600.00	Gormanston Camp, Co Meath F	10.00	(single rim skeleton)	
B	50.00	Hare Park, Curragh Camp D	10.00		

Section VII : Special Events (see chapter 12 for further details)

15/152

15/149 Colonial & Indian Exhibition, 1886 .... *
15/150 Royal Military Exhibition, 1890 .... *
15/151 BFPS 1000 (Aldershot Army Display), 1967 .... 0.40
   (this was the first of many uses of BFPS 1000 handstamps)
15/152 Royal School of Military Engineering (Open Day), 1967 .... 0.50
15/153 The Royal Tournament BFPS 1068, 1968 .... 1.50

Note : from this point military BFPS handstamps burgeoned including use for
events with RAF, Royal Naval and Royal Marines connections, see chapter 12 and
"Special Event Postmarks of the UK" for details

16. Aviation

The chapter covers air mail postmarks, also Airport and RAF Post Office postmarks though applied to covers that are not normally transmitted by air.

The field of "Aero Philately", connected with study of flown covers, is a large subject beyond the scope of this handbook. This is because first flights, special air meetings and other special flights utilised special envelopes and special cachets, not necessarily with "different" postmarks. Listed below, however, are some of the "classic" special postmarks.

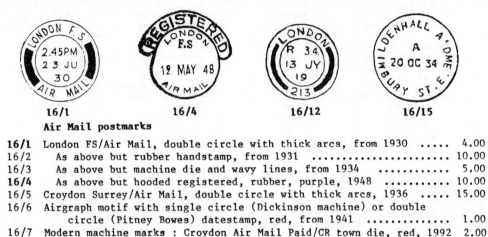

| 16/1 | 16/4 | 16/12 | 16/15 |

Air Mail postmarks

16/1 London FS/Air Mail, double circle with thick arcs, from 1930 ..... 4.00
16/2   As above but rubber handstamp, from 1931 .... 10.00
16/3   As above but machine die and wavy lines, from 1934 .... 5.00
16/4   As above but hooded registered, rubber, purple, 1948 .... 10.00
16/5 Croydon Surrey/Air Mail, double circle with thick arcs, 1936 ..... 15.00
16/6 Airgraph motif with single circle (Dickinson machine) or double
        circle (Pitney Bowes) datestamp, red, from 1941 .... 1.00
16/7 Modern machine marks : Croydon Air Mail Paid/CR town die, red, 1992 2.00
16/8   London FS/Great Britain, 1st Paid Airmail in wavy lines, 1995 . 2.50
16/9   Southampton "By air mail" slogan, red, 1996 .... 2.50

Special Events (a selection of "classic" events, see chap 12 for details)

16/10 First United Kingdom Aerial Post London, numbered 1-6, 1911 ..... 17.50
16/11   As above but Windsor, numbered 1-2 .... 45.00
          (16/10 and 16/11 only applied to special envelopes and postcards)
16/12 Airship flight from USA, double circle with R34 above date, 1919 1300.00
16/13 Calshot Aerodrome/Sthmptn, skeleton, Schneider Trophy Race, 1931 . 30.00
16/14 Air Post Exhibition London SW1, 1934 .... 5.00
16/15 Mildenhall A'drome/Bury St.E, skeleton, UK-Australia Air Race 1934 25.00
16/16 International Air Transport Association 7th AGM London, 1951 ..... 25.00
16/17 Farnborough SBAC/Hts Ex (Farnborough Air Display), skeleton, 1951 30.00

Aerodromes and airports

Notes : (1) Croydon name changed from Waddon in 1928 then closed in 1940 and re-opened as "Airport" 1947-60 (2) 16/5 was used at Croydon Head Office (3) Gatwick used from 1934 but re-opened in 1958 (4) Heathrow opened 1946 and the PO was located in a hut until the 1960s, and address had meanwhile changed from Feltham to Hounslow. Later the 3 terminals each had a post office (not shown in handstamps) but rationalisation in 1980s closed two of these, though opening of terminal 4 in 1987 made the total two again, plus Cargo Centre (5) Some data comes from an article in British Postmark Society Bulletin of 1960: it refers to five current post offices including Manchester and Prestwick, thus leaving uncertain the status at that time of postmarks at Dalcross East (Inverness Airport 1941-74, civilian use except 1943-44) and Renfrew (1954-71 then replaced by Glasgow airport) (6) Dates are earliest known not necessarily start dates, but other reports are welcome (7) for Digby see next section (RAF)

| 16/18 | 16/19 | 16/20 | 16/21 | 16/22 |

16/23   16/24   16/25   16/26   16/27

(for key see RAF & RNAS Establishments on next page, also S = SID)

Croydon		I (L.A Mail Unit)	6.00
Waddon Aerodrome (1921)		J	5.00
D **16/18**	50.00	K	8.00
Croydon Aerodrome D	20.00	Heathrow Airport B.O./	
E	10.00	Hounslow Middx D (1983)	3.00
Aerodrome B.O. Croydon Surrey/		Heathrow Airport/	
Air Mail E (1936)	15.00	Terminal 4 D (1987)	2.00
Croydon Airport D **16/19**	8.00	J	3.00
J	17.50	S	1.50
Gatwick		Heathrow MSPO (terminal 2)	
Gatwick Airport/Horley, Surrey		D (1991) **16/22**	1.50
E (1936)	6.00	I	2.50
D (1958)	5.00	J	3.00
J (1958)	10.00	S	1.50
London (Gatwick) Airport,		Heathrow Airport Cargo Area/	
Horley, Surrey D	1.50	Hounslow D (1987)	2.00
I	5.00	J	5.00
J	6.00	**Other airports**	
Gatwick Airport W Sussex		Belfast Airport LSO **16/23** I	3.00
I (1982)	5.00	(new sorting office 1990)	
Gatwick Surrey S	2.00	Dalcross East/Inverness E	5.00
Heathrow		(Inverness Airport, see note)	
The London Airport,		Glasgow Airport.Paisley/	
Feltham Middx D (1946)	20.00	Renfrewshire D **16/24**	2.00
K (purple) **16/20**	15.00	J	5.00
London Airport North,		Airport.Manchester 22	
Hounslow Middx D	4.00	D (1956) **16/25**	2.00
J	12.00	J	8.00
K	15.00	Northolt Airport, Ruislip	
The London Airport,		(see RAF listing below)	
Hounslow Middx E (1957)	8.00	Airport.Prestwick/Ayrshire D	8.00
I	10.00	J	15.00
London Airport D (1971)	5.00	Prestwick Airport/Prestwick 2	
London (Heathrow) Airport,		Ayrshire E **16/26**	6.00
Hounslow Middx E (1971)	5.00	Airport, Renfrew D	15.00
I	8.00	Southampton Airport	
London (Heathrow) Airport		D (1937 only)	30.00
Central (variations)		Tees-side Airport/Darlington	
D **16/21**	2.00	D (1968-92) **16/27**	5.00

16/28

Second World War - "Numbered" RAF Post Offices

There were a good number of these; only the initial ones are shown here

RAFPO 001 single circle	- Iceland		15.00
002 single circle	- Iceland	**16/28**	15.00
004 ?	- Azores		30.00
005 double circle	- Iceland		10.00

Second World War - Air Force Censor Marks (see note in chapter 14)

16/29 (R4) 2.00	**16/30** (R6) 1.00	**16/31** (R14) 2.00	**16/32** (R20-3) 10.00
Middle East, Africa 1939-41	Azores, Malaya, Iceland etc 1942-45	Algeria, Sicily 1943-44	N Ireland 1944

RAF and RNAS Establishments

This list is largely compiled with the aid of "Postal Markings of RAF, RFC and RNAS Stations in the UK 1918-1968" by Bill Garrard, and published by the Forces Postal History Society in 1990. This data is used with permission. Additional data and corrections were kindly provided by Derrick Burney. Inscriptions are abbreviated and shown without punctuation; also not all changes of designation are included eg Aldergrove exists shown both as Lisburn and Crumlin. Some of the post offices are civilian ones but on RAF premises; some are open to the public but others are not.

Most RAFPOs have circular rubber cachets which are easily mistaken for rubber packet stamps but are usually undated; these are RAF Post Room marks and usually only appear on official mail. All values should be DOUBLED for registered covers, and the presence of interesting registration labels and the Post Room cachets referred to here further enhances the value of such covers.

D	Single Circle	I	Packet handstamps
E	Double Circle	J	Parcel handstamps
F	Skeleton handstamps	K	Registered handstamps

D

E

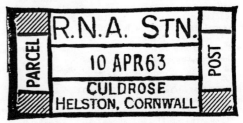

16/33 Single circle   **16/34** Double circle   **16/35** Parcel handstamp **J**

England, Scotland, Wales

Abingdon RAFPO/Berks D	3.00	
(later RAF Stn	3.00)	
Acaster Malbis RAFPO/York D	8.00	
E	8.00	
Acklington RAFPO/Morpeth,		
N'thbd D	3.00	
J	10.00	
Alconbury RAFPO Station/		
Huntingdon E	6.00	
Alness RAFPO/Alness,		
Ross-shire D	10.00	
Amport RAFPO/Andover,		
Hants E	6.00	
Andrews Field RAFPO/		
Braintree E	10.00	
Ashbourne Dys/RAFPO D	10.00	
Aston Down,Stroud,Glos D	8.00	
J	12.00	
Ayr RAFPO/Ayr D	10.00	
Babdown RAFPO/Tetbury E	8.00	
Balderton RAFPO/Newark,		
Notts D	8.00	
Balivanich/Lochboisdale		
D (poss used at RAFPO)	?	
then Benbecula RAFPO E	10.00	
Banff RAFPO D	8.00	
Bardney RAFPO/Lincoln D	8.00	
Barrow in Furness RAFPO/		
Lancs D	6.00	
Bassingbourn RAFPO/Royston,		
Herts E	6.00	
then RAF Stn Bassingbourn E	3.00	
J	6.00	
(later Bassingbourn Barracks		
- see chapter 15)		

Bawdsey Ferry/Woodbridge,		
Suffolk (RAF Bawdsey) E	4.00	
Beaulieu RAFO/Brockenhurst,		
Hants E	8.00	
Bentley Priory RAFPO/		
Stanmore,Middx D	5.00	
Bicester RAFPO/Oxon D	4.00	
J	8.00	
Biggin Hill RAFPO/Westerham,		
Kent E	5.00	
Binbrook RAFPO/Lincoln D	3.00	
E	4.00	
Bircham Newton RAFPO/		
Kings Lynn,Nfk D	4.00	
J	6.00	
Blakehill RAFPO/Swindon,		
Wilts D	6.00	
Blyton RAFPO/Gainsborough,		
Lincs D	8.00	
Boscombe Down RAFPO/		
Salisbury D	3.00	
Bourn RAFPO/Cambridge E	6.00	
Brackla RAFPO/Nairn D	10.00	
Bramcote RAFPO/Nuneaton,Wks D	6.00	
RNAS Brawdy/Haverfordwest,		
Pembs D	5.00	
Breighton RAFPO/Selby,Yorks D	8.00	
Bridgnorth,Shropshire/RAFPO D	6.00	
E	4.00	
Brize Norton RAFPO/Oxford D	5.00	
Stanmore Cres,Carterton/Oxford		
(RAF Brize Norton) D	2.50	
J	5.00	
Bruntingthorpe RAFPO/Rugby,		
Wks D	8.00	
USAF Base,Warrington/Lancs D	8.00	
(RAF/USAF Burton Wood)		
Calshot/Southampton D	3.00	
(RAF Calshot)		

Calveley RAFPO Nantwich/		
Cheshire D	8.00	
Camelford RAFPO/Cornwall E	6.00	
(RAF Davidstowe Moor)		
Carew Cheriton RAFPO/Tenby,		
Pembs D	8.00	
Castle Bromwich RAFPO/		
Birmingham D	8.00	
Castle Camps RAFPO/Cambridge		
D	8.00	
Catfoss RAFPO/Hull,Yorks D	5.00	
I	6.00	
Catterick Camp, see chapter 15		
Charterhall RAFPO/Duns D	8.00	
Chedburgh RAFPO/Bury St.Edmunds		
Sfk D	8.00	
Chicksands RAFPO/Shefford,Beds		
D	8.00	
Chigwell RAFPO/Essex D	8.00	
Chilbolton RAFPO/Stockbridge		
Hants D	8.00	
Chivenor RAFPO/Barnstaple,		
Devon D	3.00	
Church Fenton RAF Stn/		
Tadcaster,Yks D	6.00	
Church Lawford RAFPO/		
Rugby Wks D	8.00	
Clay Lane,Oxford/-		
(RAF Benson) D	3.00	
E	3.00	
Colerne RAFPO/Chippenham		
Wilts D	3.00	
E	7.00	
Coltishall RAFPO/Norwich,		
Norfolk D	5.00	
E	3.00	
J	6.00	
K	10.00	

Compton Bassett Camp/		
Calne,Wilts E	6.00	
J	8.00	
Cosford Camp,Wolverhampton/		
Staffs (or W Mids) D	3.00	
J	5.00	
Cottesmore RAFPO/Oakham,		
Rutland D	8.00	
E	3.00	
J	4.00	
Crabtree RAFPO/Warminster,		
Wilts (RAF Warminster) D	8.00	
Cranage RAFPO/Middlewich,		
Cheshire D	8.00	
Cranfield RAFPO/Bletchley,		
Bucks D	7.00	
Cranswick RAFPO/Driffield D	8.00	
(RAF Hutton Cranswick)		
Cranwell/Sleaford,Lincs D	4.00	
E	3.00	
Creca RAFPO/Annan		
Dumfriesshire D	8.00	
Crimond RNASPO/Lonmay E	?	
Crosby on Eden RAFPO/		
Carlisle E	10.00	
Crossapol/Isle of Tiree D	20.00	
(later RAFPO Tiree)		
Culdrose RN Air Stn/		
Helston,Cornwall D	4.00	
E	2.00	
J	8.00	
Culmhead RAFPO/Taunton,Som D	8.00	
Dalcross East/Inverness E	5.00	
(also with RAFPO added)		
(see Airport listing above)		
Dallachy RAFPO/Spey Bay		
Morayshire D	10.00	
Defford RAFPO/Worcester D	5.00	
Detling RAFPO/Maidstone,		
Kent D	8.00	
Digby Aerodrome/Lincoln D	5.00	
E	6.00	
J	8.00	
Dishforth RAFPO/Thirsk,Yks D	6.00	
(later North Hill E 4.00)		
E	10.00	
Downham Market RAFPO/		
Norfolk D	8.00	
Drainie,Lossiemouth/		
Morayshire D	4.00	
(RNAS Lossiemouth)		
E	5.00	
J	8.00	
Driffield RAFPO/Yorkshire D	3.00	
J	6.00	
Duxford Camp D	15.00	
Duxford RAFPO/Cambridge D	6.00	
E	3.00	
Earls Colne RAFPO/Colchester,		
Essex D	8.00	
East Fortune RAFPO/Drem		
East Lothian D	10.00	
East Kirkby RAFPO/Spilsby,		
Lincs D	8.00	
Edzell RAFPO/Brechin,Angus D	5.00	
Elgin RAFPO/Morayshire D	10.00	
(also Bogs of Mayne E	8.00)	
Elsham Wolds RAFPO/Barnetby,		
Lincs D	7.00	
Elvington RAFPO/York E	10.00	
Errol RAFPO/Perth D	8.00	
Eshott RAFPO/Morpeth,Nthbd D	8.00	
Evanton RAFPO/Evanton		
Rossshire D	8.00	
Exeter RAFPO/Devon D	8.00	
Fairford RAFPO/Fairford,		
Glos E	5.00	

Faldingworth RAFPO/Lincoln D	8.00	
Fauld RAFPO/Burton-on-Trent,		
Staffs D	8.00	
Fazakerley RAFPO/		
Liverpool 9 D	8.00	
Feltwell RAFPO/Thetford,		
Norfolk D	4.00	
J	8.00	
Fenton Barns,Drem/East Lothian		
(RAF) J	?	
Butlins Camp/Filey,Yorkshire		
(RAF Filey) E	15.00	
Filton RAFPO/Bristol D	8.00	
Finningley RAFPO/Doncaster,Yks		
D	3.00	
E	3.00	
J	5.00	
Fiskerton RAFPO/Lincoln D	8.00	
Ford RNAS,Arundel/Sussex D	8.00	
Forres RAFPO/Morayshire D	10.00	
Foulsham RAFPO/Dereham,Nfk D	8.00	
Fulbeck RAFPO/Grantham		
Lincs D	8.00	
Full Sutton RAFPO/York E	5.00	
Fylingdales RAFPO/Pickering,		
Yks E	4.00	
J	5.00	
Gamston RAFPO/Retford,Notts		
D	8.00	
Gaydon RAF Stn/Leamington Spa,		
Wks D	3.00	
E	3.00	
Graveley RAFPO/Huntingdon D	8.00	
Gt Dunmow RAFPO/Dunmow,		
Essex D	10.00	
E	10.00	
Gt Massingham RAFPO/Kings Lynn,		
Nfk D	6.00	
Grimsby RAFPO/Lincs D	8.00	
Halfpenny Green RAFPO/		
Stourbridge D	8.00	
Halton Camp - see chap 15		
(RAF Cardington)		
E	3.00	
Harwell RAFPO/Didcot,Berks D	8.00	
Haverfordwest RAFPO/Pembs E	10.00	
Hawarden RAFPO/Chester D	4.00	
Hednesford Camp,Hednesford/		
Staffs D	4.00	
J	6.00	
Hemswell Aerodrome/Lincoln E	8.00	
(later RAFPO E	3.00)	
Henlow Camp/Beds D	3.00	
E	3.00	
J	5.00	
Hinton in the Hedges RAFPO/		
Brackley D	8.00	
Hixon RAFPO/Stafford D	8.00	
Holme Moor RAFPO/York E	8.00	
Holmesley Sth RAFPO/		
Christchurch,Hants D	8.00	
Honeybourne Grounds/		
Evesham,Worcs D	10.00	
Honington RAFPO (later Camp)/		
Bury St.Edmunds Sfk D	4.00	
E	3.00	
J	5.00	
Hornchurch RAFPO/Romford,		
Essex D	10.00	
(later South Hornchurch)		
Horsham St.Faiths RAFPO/		
Norwich D	4.00	
Houndstone Camp,Yeovil/		
Somerset D	4.00	
J	6.00	

Hullavington RAFPO/		
Chippenham,Wilts D	3.00	
J	8.00	
Husbands Bosworth RAFPO/		
Rugby,Wks D	8.00	
Ingham RAFPO/Lincoln D	8.00	
Jurby RAFPO/Ramsey,		
Isle of Man D	30.00	
parcel 17/191	40.00	
Keevil RAFPO/Trowbridge,		
Wilts E	6.00	
J	8.00	
Air Ministry Unit RAF/		
Kenley,Surrey D	5.00	
Kidlington/Oxford D	3.00	
(RAF Kidlington)		
E	3.00	
Kinloss RAFPO/Forres,		
Morayshire D	4.00	
J	6.00	
Kirkham Camp/Preston,Lancs D	4.00	
J	6.00	
Lakenheath Camp/Brandon,		
Suffolk D	2.50	
E	2.50	
Langar RAFPO/Barnstone,		
Nottingham D	8.00	
Larton RAF Camp,Wirral/		
Cheshire (RAF W Kirby) D	4.00	
E	3.00	
F (no RAF Camp)	20.00	
Leconfield RAFPO/Beverley,Yks		
D	8.00	
K	10.00	
Leechmoor Cross/Cowbridge,		
Glam (RAF Llandow) D	10.00	
Leeming RAFPO/Northallerton,		
Yks D	8.00	
(later Gatenby RAF Stn E	4.00)	
Lee-on-Solent - see chap 14		
The Leys/Oxford (RAF Upper Heyford)		
D	5.00	
E	5.00	
Lichfield RAFPO/Lichfield,		
Staffs D	4.00	
Lindholme RAFPO/Doncaster,		
Yks D	5.00	
J	6.00	
Linton-on-Ouse RAFPO/York D	6.00	
Lissett RAFPO/Driffield,Yks		
D	8.00	
Little Onn RAFPO/Stafford D	8.00	
Little Rissington RAF/		
Cheltenham,Glos D	5.00	
(also Rissington RAFPO D	4.00)	
J	8.00	
Little Staughton RAFPO/		
Huntingdon D	8.00	
Loch Doon Camp/Ayrshire		
(RNAS) E	10.00	
Locking Camp,Weston-super-Mare/		
Som D	5.00	
J	8.00	
Long Marston RAFPO/Stratford-		
on-Avon D	10.00	
Longparish RAFPO/Andover,		
Hants D	8.00	
Ludford Magna RAFPO/Lincoln E	8.00	
Lyneham RAFPO/Chippenham,		
Wilts (later RAF Stn) D	5.00	
J	8.00	
Machrihanish North/		
Campbeltown (RAF) D	4.00	
E	5.00	
Manby/Louth,Lincs (RAF) E	5.00	
RAF Stn/Manston,Ramsgate D	3.00	

Marham RAFPO/Kings Lynn, Nfk D	2.00
E	2.00
J	5.00
Market Harborough RAFPO/ Leics D	8.00
Marston Moor RAFPO/York E	8.00
Marsworth RAFPO/Tring E	8.00
Medmenham RAFPO/Marlow, Bucks D	3.00
Melbourne RAFPO/York E	8.00
Melksham Camp/Melksham,Wilts D	3.00
J	7.00
Metheringham RAFPO/Lincoln D	8.00
Methwold RAFPO/Thetford, Norfolk D	8.00
Middleton St.George RAFPO/ Darlington D	4.00
J	6.00
Middle Wallop RAFPO/ Stockbridge,Hants E	3.00
Mildenhall RAFPO/Bury St. Edmunds,Sfk D	8.00
Milfield RAFPO/Alnwick D	10.00
Mill Green RAFPO/Hatfield, Herts D	8.00
Millom RAFPO/Cumberland D	8.00
Milltown RAFPO/Elgin, Morayshire D	10.00
Milton RAFPO/Abingdon, Berks D	8.00
Mona RAFPO/Holyhead,Anglesey D	10.00
Moreton RAFPO/Moreton-in-Marsh, Glos D	8.00
Netheravon RAFPO/Salisbury, Wilts D	5.00
Newton RAF Station/ Nottingham D	3.00
Newtownards RAFPO/Co.Down D	10.00
North Cotes RAFPO/Grimsby, Lincs D	3.00
J	6.00
North Creake RAFPO/Egmere Wells,Nfk D	10.00
North Killingholme RAFPO/ Grimsby D	8.00
North Luffenham RAFPO/ Oakham,Rutland D	4.00
Northolt Airport,Ruislip/ Middlesex (RAF Northolt) D	10.00
North Weald RAFPO/Epping, Essex D	3.00
Norton Disney RAFPO/Lincoln D	8.00
Oakington RAFPO/Cambridge D	4.00
Old Sarum RAFPO/Salisbury, Wilts D	8.00
Ossington RAFPO/Newark,Notts D	8.00
Oulton RAFPO/Norwich,Norfolk D	8.00
K	10.00
Ouston RAFPO/Newcastle-on-Tyne D	4.00
J	8.00
Padgate Camp/Warrington,Lancs D	5.00
(also Cowlane RAFPO D	5.00)
J	6.00
Pembrey RAFPO/Burryport, Carm D	8.00
Pembroke Dock RAFPO/ Pembroke Dock D	8.00
Penrhos RAFPO/Pwllheli, Caern D	10.00

Peplow RAFPO/Market Drayton, Salop D	8.00
Pershore/Worcs,RAFPO D	5.00
Peterhead RAFPO/Aberdeenshire D	10.00
Pocklington RAFPO/York E	8.00
Port Ellen RAFPO/ Isle of Islay D	15.00
Rattlesden RAFPO/ Bury St Edmunds,Sfk D	8.00
Rednal RAFPO/Oswestry, Salop D	8.00
Redruth RAFPO/Cornwall D	8.00
Riccall Common RAFPO/Selby, Yorks D	10.00
Rivenhall RAFPO/Witham, Essex D	8.00
Rufforth RAFPO/York E	6.00
St.Athan Main Site/Barry, Glam D	2.00
(also St. Athan Station D	3.00
and RAF Stn D	4.00)
J	5.00
St.David's RAFPO/ Haverfordwest Pemb D	12.00
St.Eval RAFPO/Wadebridge, Cornwall D	4.00
E	3.00
J	6.00
St.Mawgan RAFPO/Newquay, Cornwall D	3.00
J	6.00
Saltby RAFPO/ Melton Mowbray Leics E	8.00
Sandtoft RAFPO/Doncaster,Yks E	8.00
Scampton RAFPO/Lincoln D	3.00
J	5.00
Scapa RAFPO/Kirkwall,Orkney D	20.00
Sculthorpe RAFPO Fakenham/ Nfk D	4.00
E	4.00
Sealand RAFPO/Chester D	5.00
J	6.00
Seighford RAFPO/Stafford D	8.00
Shenley Rd RAFPO Bletchley/ Bucks D	10.00
Silloth RAFPO/Cumberland E	8.00
Silverstone RAFPO/Towcester, N'thants D	8.00
Skeabrae RAFPO/Kirkwall, Orkney E	25.00
Skitten RAFPO/Wick,Caithness D	10.00
Sleap RAFPO/Shrewsbury, Shropshire D	8.00
Snailwell RAFPO/Newmarket, Sfk D	8.00
Snitterfield RAFPO/Stratford- on-Avon D	8.00
South Cerney RAFPO/ Cirencester E	3.00
South Down RAFPO/High Wycombe, Bucks D	8.00
J	8.00
(later RAFPO/High Wycombe, Bucks D	5.00)
Spilsby RAFPO/Spilsby,Lincs D	8.00
Spitalgate RAFPO/Grantham, Lincs D	5.00
Stafford RAFPO/Stafford D	4.00
J	6.00
Stoke Heath RAFPO/Market Drayton, Salop D	6.00

Stoke Orchard RAFPO/ Cheltenham D	10.00
Stoney Cross RAFPO/Lyndhurst, Hants E	8.00
Stormy Down RAFPO/Pyle,Bridgend, Glam (RAF Porthcawl) D	8.00
Stornoway RAFPO/ Isle of Lewis D	25.00
Stradishall Camp/Newmarket Suffolk (also RAFPO) D	4.00
E	2.00
J	5.00
Stretton Sugwas/Hereford D	3.00
J	5.00
(later RAF Stn/Hereford D	5.00)
Strubby RAFPO/Alford,Lincs D	8.00
Sturgate RAFPO/Gainsborough Lincs D	10.00
Sullom Voe RAFPO/Lerwick, Shetland D	25.00
Sutton-on-Hull RAFPO/Hull, Yks D	5.00
Swannington RAFPO/Norwich, Nfk D	8.00
Swanton Morley RAFPO/ Dereham,Nfk D	3.00
J	6.00
Swinderby RAFPO/Lincoln D	3.00
J	6.00
Syerston RAFPO/Newark,Notts D	4.00
J	8.00
Tain RAFPO/Ross-shire D	8.00
Talbenny RAFPO/Haverfordwest, Pembs E	8.00
Tangmere RAFPO/Chichester, Sussex D	8.00
J	10.00
Tarrant Rushton RAFPO/ Blandford D	8.00
(then Tarrant Rushton/ Blandford Forum E	15.00
used with Tarrant Rushton Airfield registration label)	
Tealing RAFPO/Dundee,Angus D	8.00
Tempsford RAFPO/Sandy,Beds E	8.00
Ternhill RAFPO/Market Drayton, Salop D	3.00
J	5.00
Thorney Island RAFPO/Emsworth, Hants D	5.00
Tinwald Downs RAFPO/ Dumfries (RAF Dumfries) D	6.00
Titchfield RAFPO/Fareham, Hants D	8.00
Topcliffe RAFPO Thirsk, Yorkshire D	4.00
(later Thistle Hill E	3.00)
Tuddenham RAFPO/Bury St.Edmunds, Suffolk D	8.00
Turnberry RAFPO/Girvan, Ayrshire E	8.00
Turnhouse RAFPO/Edinburgh 12 D	8.00
Central Flying School/Upavon D (variations)	20.00
F	50.00
RAF Station/Upavon, Marlborough,Wilts E	4.00
(later Pewsey)	3.00
J	10.00
later Trenchard Lines see ch 15	
Upwood RAFPO/Huntingdon D	3.00
E	4.00
Uxbridge Common/Uxbridge, Middx (RAF Uxbridge) D	8.00

Valley RAFPO/Holyhead,			Wigbay RAFPO/Stranraer E	8.00	Wythall RAFPO/Birmingham D	5.00
Anglesey D	5.00		J	10.00	J	6.00
E	5.00		Wigsley RAFPO/Newark,Notts		Wyton RAFPO/Huntingdon E	3.00
J	10.00		D	8.00	J	6.00
Waddington RAFPO/Lincoln D	5.00		Wigtown RAFPO/Wigtown D	6.00	Yatesbury Camp/Calne,Wilts	
E	2.00		Wilmslow RAFPO/Manchester		D	3.00
Warboys RAFPO/Huntingdon D	8.00		(later Cheshire) D	5.00	E (RAF Camp)	8.00
Watchet RAFPO/Watchet,			J	8.00	J	8.00
Somerset E	8.00		Windrush RAFPO/Oxford D	8.00	Yeovilton/Yeovil,Som D	3.00
Waterbeach RAFPO/Cambridge D	3.00		Wing RAFPO/Leighton Buzzard,		(later RNA Stn D	4.00)
Watton RAFPO/Thetford,			Beds D	8.00	J	7.00
Norfolk D	3.00		Winthorpe RAFPO/Newark,Notts			
E	3.00		D	8.00	**Ireland**	
J	5.00		Wittering Camp RAFPO/			
Weeton Camp,Preston/Lancs			Peterborough D	6.00	Aldergrove/Crumlin,	
D	4.00		Woodbridge RAFPO/Woodbridge,		Co.Antrim D	5.00
J	8.00		Sfk D	6.00	E	6.00
Welford RAFPO/Newbury,Berks			Woodside/Arbroath,Angus		Ballyhalbert RAFPO/- D	15.00
E	8.00		(RNAS Arbroath) D	5.00	Ballykelly RAFPO/	
Wellesbourne RAFPO/Warwick D	4.00		Woodvale RAFPO Formby/		Londonderry E	10.00
(RAF Wellesbourne Mountford)			Liverpool D	8.00	Bishops Court RAFPO/	
Westcott RAFPO/Aylesbury,			Woolfox Lodge RAFPO/Oakham,		Downpatrick D	7.00
Bucks D	8.00		Rutland D	8.00	E	6.00
West Freugh RAFPO/Stranraer			Worksop RAFPO/Worksop,Notts		Castle Archdale RAFPO/	
D	10.00		D	4.00	Enniskillen D	10.00
West Malling RAFPO/Maidstone,			Wratting Common RAFPO/		HQ RAF/Northern Ireland D	10.00
Kent D	4.00		Cambridge D	8.00	Killadeas RAFPO/Enniskillen,	
West Raynham RAFPO/Fakenham,			Wroughton RAF Hospital/		Co.Ferm D	10.00
Nfk D	4.00		Swindon,Wilts D	5.00	Limavady RAFPO/Londonderry	
E	3.00		F	25.00	E	10.00
J	4.00		Wymeswold RAFPO/Loughborough,		Long Kesh RAFPO/Lisburn,	
West Wickham RAFPO/Cambs D	8.00		Leics D	8.00	Co Antrim D	15.00
Wickenby RAFPO/Lincoln D	8.00		J	8.00	Nutts Corner RAFPO/	
					Co.Antrim E	12.00

16/41

16/42

SALVAGED MAIL
AIRCRAFT CRASH
PRESTWICK 25-12-54

16/48

Instructional and other markings:

16/36 Air Mail/Express, unframed two line cachet, 1919 .... 25.00
16/37   As above but single line Air Mail, 1920 .... 20.00
16/38 No Flight/sent by/ordinary service, c1920......................... 20.00
16/39 Air Mail/London FS, undated rubber stamps (various sizes), 1920s 20.00
16/40   As above but Reading, 1960s-80s, purple 2.00
16/41 Air Mail or By Air Mail, applied by machine (Glasgow 1935-36) 3.00
        (see "Collecting Slogan Postmarks" for details)
16/42   As above but symbol "not filled in", handstamp used on registered 20.00
16/43 "All letters go by air" slogan-type marks 1938-39 on incoming mail 10.00
        (note : this and the next item - both Empire Air Mail - were
            applied by machine, for details see "Collecting Slogan Postmarks")
16/44 Please Advise Sender that letters should be prepaid 1½d for each
            half ounce (see above) 20.00
16/45 Over .... oz Insufficiently Prepaid for Transmission by Direct
            India Air Mail 10.00
16/46 Insufficiently paid for transmission by air mail 4.00
16/47 Postage Deficiency/Paid/(Reading Dutch Scheme)(claimed from sender) 5.00

Disaster or Crash cachets

See end of chapter 14 for general remarks concerning disasters and crashes.
Shown as **16/48** is an example of a cachet used on salvaged mail - value 25.00

17. Islands

The first part of the chapter covers the Channel Islands and the Isle of Man, both before and after their separation from the British PO from 1 October 1969 (Channel Islands) and 5 July 1973 (Isle of Man). The chapter continues with islands of England, Wales, Northern Ireland and Scotland.

The Channel Islands

There have been differing opinions concerning the locations and use of (possibly) two distinctive Maltese Crosses. For a long time they were associated only with Alderney. It is now known there was only one distinctive cross and it is referred to as the "Channel Islands Cross". Its use is recorded between 1843 and 1845. It is very scarce and has a current value of approx £4000. Parcel post labels (from 1890) are generally beyond the scope of this handbook, but it is worthy of note that those of Channel Islands sub-offices are valued from 100.00, and Alderney and Sark 250.00.

Jersey (this page shows "Jersey" postmarks used at St Helier(s))

| 17/4 | 17/12 | 17/15 | 17/17 | 17/42 |

17/1	Concave Jersey, 1794-99	350.00
17/2	Straight line Jersey, 1797-1810	300.00
17/3	Ship letter types, 1802-53	500.00
17/4	Scroll types, 1810-30	100.00
17/5	Jersey/Penny Post, boxed, 1831-40	250.00
17/6	Double arc handstamps, 1830-58	20.00
17/7	Handstruck numerals: 1, 2 etc (red, black), 1842-68	275.00
17/8	Skeleton ("travelling") handstamps, 1843-45	400.00
17/9	Maltese cross, 1840-44	35.00
17/10	Numeral handstamps (409), 1844-1904	25.00
17/11	Duplex handstamps (409), 1858-86	20.00
17/12	Squared circles, 1881-1905	1.00
17/13	Crown registration marks, 1855-70	200.00
17/14	Double circles with cross or 1 at base, 1897-1929	2.00
17/15	Double circles with or without "St. Heliers" in brackets, 1930-	1.00
17/16	Single circles, 1858-1926	5.00
17/17	modern single circle counter handstamps, 1935-	1.00
17/18	Parcel handstamps, barred circle, 1886-1911	30.00
17/19	similar but double circle, 1892-1915	15.00
17/20	rectangular types with/without "St. Heliers" in brackets, 1915-	4.00
17/21	Paid handstamps, with/without Gt Britain at foot, red, 1919-	3.00
17/22	Rubber packet handstamps, 1893-	1.50
17/23	Oval registered handstamps, 1879-	3.00
17/24	Paquebot marks, 1896-1908 (less for 1970s usage)	150.00
17/25	Krag machine marks, 1923-30	2.50
17/26	similar but Paid die, red	8.00
17/27	Universal machine marks, 1930-	0.10
17/28	with Square Paid die, red, 1932	10.00
17/29	with circular town die, "Paid" within wavy lines, red, 1937-	0.50
17/30	with triangle 409 and wavy lines or slogan	5.00
17/31	with Telephone slogan, 1931-32	1.50
17/32	with other slogans, 1946-63	0.50
17/33	with Holiday slogans, 1963-73	0.20

From 1969 (postal independence):

17/34	Machine postmark with boxed lines	0.15
17/35	with "Jersey stamps worth collecting" slogan 1978- or "Jersey Post First Class" 1989-	0.15
17/36	with other slogans (most were short lived), 1970-	0.30
17/37	with circular town die, "Paid" within wavy lines, red	0.20
17/38	with "Air Mail Postage Paid" slogan type mark, 1991-, red ..	2.50
17/39	Rubber packet handstamps	1.00
17/40	Circular rubber "Parcel Post" handstamps	3.00
17/41	Paid steel handstamp, or "Postage Paid" rubber on parcels, red	4.00
17/42	Continental style handstamp (used at Philatelic Bureau), 1984-	1.00
17/43	Handstamps inscribed "Philatelic Bureau" or "Philatelic Service"	0.20
17/44	"Stamp Invalid xxp to pay" surcharge mark (UK stamp used)	2.50

Other Instructional marks and "First Day of Issue" handstamps are not listed

Other Jersey Offices - for code details see next page

Augres (1894-1980)
C undated	150.00
C	10.00
D	2.50

Beaumont (1853-) A 250.00
C	4.00
F	1.50

Beresford St. (1909-72)
C	60.00
D	2.50
mailbag seal	100.00
K	7.50

Carrefour Selous (1891-1978)
B	8.00
F	4.00

Central Market (1972-)
G no arc	3.00
K	4.00

Cheapside (1888-) C 60.00
D	4.00

Colomberie (1905-20)
C	300.00

Conway Street (1903-10)
C	250.00

David Place (1874-1914)
C	50.00

Faldouet (1893-1972)
B	6.00
F	5.00

First Tower (1885-) B 4.00
D	3.00
H	400.00

Five Oaks (1889-) C 5.00
F	3.00

George Town (1882-)
C	90.00
D	3.00

Gorey (1830-) A 300.00
Jersey Penny Post	150.00
C (20mm)	50.00
C (22mm)	3.00
F	1.50
H	350.00
K	5.00

Gorey Village (1893-1940)
C	5.00
D	80.00

Grands Vaux (1960-)
D	4.00

Great Union Road (1903-24)
C	400.00

Greve d'Azette (1927-74)
D	6.00
mailbag seal	100.00

Grouville (1853-)
A	400.00
B	6.00
D	4.00
F	4.00

Havre-des-Pas (1889-1962)
C	80.00
D	5.00

La Rocque (1892-) C 5.00
F	3.00

Le Squez (1974-) D 3.00
Maufant (1983-) D 3.00

Millbrook (1851-)
A	250.00
B	200.00
C	4.00
F	3.00

Pontac (1898-1904)
E	450.00

Quennevais (1950-) G 3.00

Roseville St (1962-)
D	3.00
K	4.00

Rouge Bouillon (1890-)
C	80.00
D	3.00

St.Aubin (1830-)
Jersey Penny Post	200.00
A	250.00
C	5.00
F	3.00
H	250.00

St.Brelade's Bay (1890-1977)
C	25.00
E	130.00
G	4.00

St.John's (1852-1932)
A	400.00
C	8.00

St.John's Church (1891-)
B	6.00
D	3.00
F	5.00

St.Lawrence (1854-60)
A	450.00

St.Martin's (1850-)
A	350.00
C	4.00
F	3.00

St.Mary's (1853-)
A	450.00
C	8.00
F	3.00

St.Owens/Ouen's (1852-)
B	3.00
C	8.00
C (code P)	200.00
F	3.00

St.Peter's (1851-)
A	400.00
C	5.00
D	3.00
F	5.00
H	400.00

Samares (1887-) B 5.00
F	3.00

Sion (1932-77) D 15.00
F	8.00

Stopford Road (1914-73)
C	100.00
mailbag seal	100.00
D	6.00
G	4.00

Town Mills (1903-21 & 1973-)
C	200.00
D	3.00

Trinity (1852-) A 350.00
E	70.00
F	3.00

We gratefully acknowledge the help of David Gurney in providing added information in the Channel Islands listing. For further reading we recommend the books by David Gurney listed in the Bibliography.

Codes used in detailed listings in this chapter

A	Undated double arc	H	Skeleton handstamps
B	Single circle without Island name	J	Undated double circle parcel mark
C	Single circle with Island name (or post town)	K	Label type parcel handstamp
		L	Guernsey PO lower case s/c
D	Single circle with Island name and Ch. Is. (or post town & island name)	L*	As L but upper case lettering
		M	As L but larger
E	Rubber handstamps	N	Boxed parcel mark, Guernsey PO
F	Double circle with thick arcs	O	As N but unboxed
G	Double circle with thin arcs	S	Self inking datestamp

Guernsey (this page shows "Guernsey" postmarks used at St Peter Port)

17/45	17/52	17/81	17/85

17/45 Concave Guernsey, 1794-1803 .... 350.00
17/46 Scroll types, 1802-30 .... 125.00
17/47 Ship letter types, 1802-49 .... 300.00
17/48 Handstruck numerals: 1, 2 etc (red or black), 1843-47 .... 275.00
17/49 Maltese cross, 1840-44 .... 35.00
17/50 Double arcs, 1830-58 .... 25.00
17/51 Skeleton ("travelling") handstamps, 1843 & 1847 .... 500.00
17/52 Numeral 324 types, 1844-1890s 30.00
17/53 Duplex 324 types, 1858-88 .... 30.00
17/54 Small single circles, 1858-1900s 4.00
17/55 Squared circles, 1887-1905 .... 1.00
17/56 Oval Express mark, 1891 .... 80.00
17/57 Paquebot marks, 1903-28 (less for 1960s usage) 400.00
17/58 Double circles with cross at base, 1905-27 .... 2.50
17/59 Double circles with/without "St Peter Port" in brackets, 1929-69 1.50
17/60 Paid handstamps, with/without Gt Britain at foot, red, 1920-69 3.00
17/61 Rubber packet handstamps, 1932-69 .... 1.00
17/62 Single circle, counter stamp with "St Peter Port" in brackets 1.00
17/63 Krag machine marks, 1923-31 .... 2.00
17/64   similar but Paid die, red 8.00
17/65 Universal machine marks, 1931- 0.10
17/66   with triangle 324 with wavy lines or slogan 5.00
17/67   with Royal Wedding slogan, 1947 .... 2.00
17/68   with 'British Holiday Abroad' slogan 1966-69 .... 0.15
17/69   with other slogans, 1950-69 .... 0.50
17/70 Parcel handstamps, barred circle type, 1886-89 .... 30.00
17/71   similar but double circle types, 1889-1915 .... 10.00
17/72   similar but rectangular label types, 1915- 3.00
       (with/without "St Peter Port" or "Smith St" in brackets)
17/73 Oval registered handstamps, 1938- 3.50
17/74 Note : covers/cards with 2d bisects Dec 1940 - Feb 1941 ..... 8.00

From 1969 (postal independence), marks inscribed "Guernsey Post Office" :

17/75	Universal machine postmark with two horizontal bars	0.50
17/76	with "Paid" in wavy lines, red	0.30
17/77	with "New stamps" slogans 1974-75 only in red on paid mail .	10.00
17/78	with long running slogans, ie "Collect Guernsey Stamps", "First Class", "Stamps & Coins", "St Peter Port" (pictorial)	0.15
17/79	with other slogans, 1970-	1.00
17/80	with 7 continuous wavy lines, 1990s	0.40
17/81	New style handstamps in lower case lettering (type M)	0.50
17/82	Paid handstamps in lower case lettering, red	3.00
17/83	Rubber packet handstamps in lower case lettering, 1969-71 ...	3.00
17/84	Rubber packet handstamp, upper case, 32mm/40mm diam, 1980s/90s	0.30
17/85	Oval registration marks in lower case lettering	5.00
17/86	Boxed parcel handstamps, "Head Office"/"Sorting Office" (type N)	3.00
17/87	Postal Museum handstamp 1971-82	1.50
17/88	"Stamp Invalid xxp to pay" surcharge mark (UK stamp used) ...	3.50
17/89	"Accepted after last collection at sender's request", 1980s ..	5.00

Other Instructional marks and "First Day of Issue" handstamps are not listed

Other Guernsey Offices

Arcade (1987-)	G	3.00
	L*	3.00
	N 17/90	3.00
Bouet (1888-93)	E	400.00
Braye Road (1938-76)		
	D	35.00
	L	4.00
	N	6.00
Bridge (1988-)		
	L*	3.00
	N	3.00
Camp du Roi (1925-40)		
	F	150.00
Catel (1849-1986)		
	A	450.00
	B	8.00
	D	3.00
	L	20.00
	N	3.00
Cobo (1888-)	E	30.00
	F	6.00
	H	400.00
	L	3.00
	L*	3.00
	N	2.00
Collings Rd (1974-86)		
	H	200.00
	L	3.00
	N	6.00
Forest (1899-)	E	45.00
	F	6.00
	H	600.00
	L	3.00
	N	3.00
Les Baissieres (1952-68)		
	D	100.00
Les Gravées (1890-1986)		
	C	6.00
	D	30.00
	L	3.00
	N	3.00
L'Islet (1891-)	C	8.00
	E	250.00
	F	8.00
	L **17/91**	3.00
	N	3.00

Market Place (1883-1987)		
	C	80.00
	D	6.00
	J	150.00
	K	20.00
	L	3.00
	L*	3.00
	M	3.00
	N	3.00
	O	6.00
Mount Row (1895-96)		
	E	500.00
Pleinmont Rd (1958-65)		
	D	50.00
Quay BO (1932-53)	D	45.00
	F	45.00
Rocquaine (1967-69)		
	D	50.00
Rohais (1985-)		
	L* 17/92	3.00
	N	3.00
St.Andrew(s) (1887-1989)		
	B	150.00
	C	4.00
	F	8.00
	H	450.00
	L	3.00
	N	3.00
St.Johns (1935-1986)		
	D	15.00
	L	3.00
	N	3.00
St.Martin(s) (1849-)		
	A	400.00
	C	10.00
	D	10.00
	F	10.00
	L	3.00
	M	3.00
	N	3.00
St.Peters (1852-)		
	A	350.00
	C	60.00

then		
St.Peter-in-the-Wood (1886-)		
(St.Pierre-du-Bois 1994-)		
	B	6.00
	F	6.00
	L	3.00
	N	3.00
St.Sampson(s) (1849-1987)		
	A	400.00
	B	3.00
	C	100.00
	D	10.00
	F	8.00
	J	150.00
	K	20.00
	L	3.00
	M	3.00
	N	3.00
St.Saviour(s) (1906-)		
	E	35.00
	F	8.00
	L	3.00
	N	3.00
The Vale/Vale (1893-1988)		
	B	8.00
	F	6.00
	H	400.00
	L	3.00
	N	3.00
Torteval (1930s-)	F	10.00
	L	3.00
	N	3.00
Vale Road (1895-1988)		
	C	8.00
	D	8.00
	E	250.00
	F	10.00
	L	3.00
	N	3.00
	O	8.00
Ville au Roi (1936-)		
	D	8.00
	L	3.00
	N	3.00

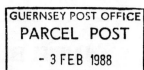

17/90   **17/91**   **17/92**

Alderney (1843-)

17/97   **17/103**   **17/105**

17/93 Undated double arc, 1848-55 .... 1500.00
17/94 Numeral 965, 1848-60s 100.00
17/95 Dated double arc, 1851-60 .... 300.00
17/96 Alderney single circles, 1860-98 .... 100.00
17/97 Alderney double circle with cross at base, 1895-1934 .... 10.00
17/98 Oval Post Office/R.E.Office/Alderney c1907 .... 350.00
    (probably used by Royal Engineers detachment)
17/99 Alderney skeleton handstamp, 1922 .... 850.00
17/100 Alderney/Ch. Is., double circle, thick arcs, 1930-66 .... 6.00
17/101 Alderney/Guernsey Channel Islands, double circle no arcs, 1966-69 10.00
17/102 Alderney/Ch. Is., single circle, 1936-55 .... 8.00
17/103 Alderney/Guernsey, Channel Islands, single circle, 1955-69 .. 6.00
17/104 Rubber packet handstamps, various wordings, 1955-69 .... 10.00
17/105 Parcel double circle, Alderney or Alderney/Ch'l Islands, 1911-12 75.00
17/106 Parcel handstamp, rectangular label type, 1947-69 .... 25.00
17/107 Post-1969 new style single circle (type L) 4.00
17/108   As above but larger (type M) 5.00
17/109   As above but "ordinary" lettering (type L*), 1985- 3.00
17/110   As above but boxed parcel marks (type N) 4.00
17/111 Rubber packet handstamps, upper case lettering, 1970- 3.00
17/112 Guernsey Post Office/Alderney double circles, 1975-
            (with or without arcs) 3.00
17/113 Large rubber handstamp, 1990s 2.50

Note : for 1990s machine postmarks see chapter 10

Sark (1857-)

17/114 Undated double arc, 1858 .... 4000.00
17/115 Sark 29mm rubber handstamp, 1888 .... 500.00
17/116 Sark single circle, code A, 1885-1900 .... 5.00
17/117   As above but code B 350.00
17/118   As above but code C 750.00
17/119 Sark, Guernsey/Channel Islands, double circle thick arcs, 1926-66 4.00
17/120 Double circle, thin arcs, 1966-69 .... 3.00
17/121 Sark.Guernsey/Channel Islands, single circle, 1960-69 .... 8.00
17/122 Post-1969 new style single circle (type L) 3.00
17/123   As above but larger (type M) 4.00
17/124   As above but boxed parcel marks (type N) 4.00
17/125 Rubber packet handstamps, upper case lettering, 1970- 3.00
17/126 Guernsey Post Office/-Sark- double circle, 1979- 2.00
17/127 Guernsey Post Office/Sark single circle, 1996- 1.50

| 17/116 | 17/119 | 17/126 | 17/128 | 17/130 |

Herm (1925-)

17/128	Herm Guernsey/Channel Islands, d/c, thick arcs, 1925-38	300.00
17/129	Meter postmark, 1948	500.00
17/130	Post-1969 new style single circle (type L)	5.00
17/131	As above but larger (type M), 1971-	3.00
17/132	As above but boxed parcel mark (type N)	5.00
17/133	Rubber packet handstamps, upper case lettering, 1970-77	15.00
17/134	Guernsey Post Office/Herm single circle, 1996-	1.50

Isle of Man

The first section shows postmarks used at Douglas, inscribed Isle of Man or Douglas or Regent Street.

ISLE OF MAN

| 17/135 | 17/140 | 17/145 | 17/187 |

17/135	Isle of Man, straight line handstamps, 1767-1829	150.00
17/136	Isle of Man, horseshoe, blue or black, 1796-1808	150.00
17/137	Ship letters, 1802-43	3000.00
17/138	Isle of Man, double arc types, undated, 1829-39	100.00
17/139	Penny Post types, 1838	1000.00
17/140	1840 Penny Post, P1 or 2 in red, 1840-49	200.00
17/141	Double arc types, dated, Douglas or Isle-of-Man, 1839-57	15.00
17/142	Maltese Cross, 1840-44	40.00
17/143	Skeleton ("travelling") handstamp, Douglas or Isle of Man, 1843	500.00
17/144	Numeral 407 types, 1844-79	30.00
17/145	Duplex 407 types, 1857-1900	6.00
17/146	Oval registered handstamps, 1880-	5.00
17/147	Squared circles, 1892-1901	1.00
17/148	Single circles with Isle of Man or I of Man at foot, 1858- ..	3.00
17/149	similar but modern counter handstamps, 1940-	0.75
17/150	Double circles with Isle of Man, I of Man or cross at foot, 1901-	0.25
17/151	Rubber packet handstamps, 1903-	1.00
17/152	Paid handstamps, red, 1905-	3.00
17/153	similar but skeleton, 1947	250.00
17/154	Posted in Advance for Xmas, 1906-09	275.00
17/155	Parcel handstamps, single circle with PP, 1883	50.00
17/156	barred circle, 1886-88	15.00
17/157	similar but double circle types, 1889-1909	15.00
17/158	similar but rectangular label types, 1895-	3.00
17/159	Krag machine postmarks, 1910-25	1.00
17/160	similar but Paid die, red, 1922-25	80.00
17/161	similar but with "Feed the Guns" slogan, 1918	120.00
17/162	Hey Dolphin machine postmarks, 1925-33	1.50
17/163	rectangular boxed Paid die without wavy lines, red, 1926-33	45.00
17/164	Universal machine postmarks, 1933-	0.05
17/165	with square Paid die, red	15.00

17/166	Universal, with triangle 407 .... 12.00
17/167	with circular IOM or GB die, with Paid in wavy lines, red . 10.00
17/168	Slogans : some examples - British Goods 1926 .... 3.00
17/169	- Join The King's Roll 1926 .... 60.00
17/170	- Post Early 1937-39 .... 2.50
17/171	- V-bells, Royal Wedding, Fest of Britain 40.00
17/172	- Jubilee TT Races 1957 .... 25.00
17/173	- Holiday/Retirement slogans 1963- ... 0.40

From 5 July 1973 (inscribed Douglas unless shown otherwise) :

17/174	Slogans : "First day" 1973 (Douglas, more for Ramsey) 4.00
17/175	"Manx Decimal coins" 1975-76 .... 5.00
17/176	"Congratulations" (birth of Pr William/Harry 1982/84) 1.50
17/177	long-running slogans, 1973- 0.15
17/178	Paid machine postmarks, in red 0.20
17/179	New style double rim/single rim circular parcel marks, 1973- . 4.00
17/180	ditto but rectangular, Douglas or "Regent St" inscription .. 3.00
17/181	Packet handstamps, rubber, 1980s-, ... 0.50
17/182	Paid handstamp, rubber, 1990s, in red 1.00
17/183	Philatelic Bureau handstamps 0.30
17/184	Postal Museum handstamps 1.00
17/185	Paquebot handstamp, double circle with thin arc, 1973 only ... 100.00
17/186	Surcharge mark "Stamps invalid" (various)(UK stamps used) 3.50

Other Instructional marks and "First Day of Issue" handstamps are not listed

Douglas Town Offices

Anagh Coar (1990-) D	2.00	D	1.50	Strand Street (1880-87)	
K	3.00	G	1.50	C	100.00
Athol St (1887-91)		K	3.00	The Crescent (1851-1989)	
D	100.00	Market Place (1884-1912)		A	250.00
Brunswick Rd (1898-)		C	50.00	D	2.00
D	1.50	Prospect Hill (1895-1984)		K	4.00
K	3.00	C	10.00	The Esplanade (1928-33)	
Bucks Rd (1885-1965)		D	2.50	D	50.00
C	15.00	G	2.50	The Palace (1907-15)	
D	5.00	K	4.00	C	50.00
Crosby Terrace (1941-)		Pulrose (1930-) D	1.50	Victoria Street (1884-1921)	
D	1.50	E	50.00	C	40.00
K	3.00	K	3.00	D	60.00
Derby Road (1933-65)		Royal Avenue (1911-)		Villa Marina (1936-89)	
D	15.00	C 17/187	1.50	D	2.00
Duke St (1858-80)		E	50.00	K	4.00
A	250.00	K	3.00	Willaston (1954-) D	1.50
Undated s/c	75.00	Saddlestone (1996-)		K	3.00
D	50.00	E	2.00	Windsor Rd (1975-)	
Falcon Street (1886-97)		St Ninians (1931-36)		G no arcs	2.50
E	80.00	D	40.00	G	1.50
Grandstand (1972-)		E	75.00	H	20.00
H	40.00	Shore Road (1857-1915)		K	3.00
special	3.50	undated	75.00	Woodburn Rd (1857)	
Holiday Camp (1949-63)		C	60.00	A	250.00
D	40.00	D	25.00	Woodbourne Rd (1965-75)	
IOM Holiday Centre		South Quay (1874-1913)		D	4.00
(1964-66) G	40.00	C (The Quay)	75.00	York Road (1912-40)	
Kirk Onchan (1855-)		D	70.00	D	50.00
B	35.00	Station (1889-1940)			
C	6.00	C	35.00		
		D	50.00		

17/188

17/189

17/190

17/191

Other IOM Offices

Abbeylands (1898-1941)		
	E	65.00
	F	40.00
Baldrine (1897-)	E	40.00
	F	25.00
	G	1.50
Baldwin (1884-1946)		
	E	60.00
	F	40.00
Ballabeg (1862-)	C	10.00
	E	50.00
	F	4.00
	G	1.50
	K	3.00
Ballafesson (1907-73)		
	D	7.00
	E	50.00
Ballasalla (1848-)		
	A	175.00
	single arc	85.00
	C	8.50
	F	16.00
	G	1.50
	H	60.00
	Univ + slogans	0.60
Ballaugh (1845-)		
	A **17/188**	200.00
	B	50.00
	C	1.50
	F	7.50
	G	1.50
Castletown (1832-)		
	boxed **17/189**	500.00
	unframed	500.00
	A seriffed	75.00
	A dated	50.00
	Numeral 037	50.00
	Duplex 037	10.00
	B	40.00
	C	1.50
	E	1.00
	F	3.00
	G	0.50
	Paid h/s	12.00
	Krag	3.00
	Krag Paid	20.00
	Krag (one line)	5.00
	Univ + slogans	0.20
	Pitney Bowes m/c	5.00
	J	30.00
	K	3.00
Colby (1858-)		
	undated **17/190**	300.00
	C	10.00
	F	5.00
	G	1.50
	K	3.00
Crosby (1854-)	A	200.00
	C	2.50
	E	60.00
	F	6.00
	G	1.50
Derbyhaven (1898-1974)		
	E	50.00
	F	6.00
Four Roads (1904-81)		
	D	4.00
	E	65.00
Foxdale (1858-)		
	undated	300.00
	C	15.00
	F	6.00
	G	2.00
Glen Auldyn (1930-44)		
	D	50.00
	E	50.00
Glenmaye (1858-)		
	undated (Glenmoy)	300.00
	D	1.50
	E	40.00

Jurby (1856-1909)		
	A	300.00
	and (1983-) G	1.50
Jurby RAFPO (1951-63)		
	D	30.00
	parcel **17/191**	40.00
Kirk Andreas (1855-)		
	A	200.00
	B	35.00
	D	15.00
	G	1.50
Kirk Bride (1858-1990)		
	small B	150.00
	D	1.50
	E	50.00
	F	7.50
Kirk Maughold (1858-)		
	undated	250.00
	E	50.00
	F	1.50
Kirk Michael (1845-)		
	A	150.00
	C	2.50
	F	1.50
	G	1.00
	H	60.00
Knockaloe Camp (1908)		
	H	100.00
The Camp, Knockaloe (1915)		
	F	50.00
Laxey (1853-)	A	150.00
	C	1.50
	F	2.00
	G	1.50
	H	50.00
Lower Foxdale (1896-1978)		
	D	4.00
	E	50.00
North Ramsey (1887-)		
	D	5.00
	E	50.00
	G	1.50
Old Laxey (1905-93)		
	D	3.00
	E	55.00
	G	3.00
Peel (1832-)		
	boxed Peeltown	300.00
	A Peeltown IOM	100.00
	A Peeltown	100.00
	A Peel	80.00
	Numeral D51	50.00
	Dupl D51 **17/192**	10.00
	B	30.00
	C	5.00
	D	1.00
	Sq circle	5.00
	E	0.50
	F	3.00
	G	0.50
	Paid h/s	15.00
	Krag	1.00
	Univ	0.30
	Pitney Bowes m/c	5.00
	J	30.00
	K	3.00
Peel Camp (1908) H		200.00
Port Erin (1858-)		
	undated	300.00
	B	7.50
	C	0.75
	E	1.00
	F	2.50
	G	0.50
	H	100.00
	J	25.00
	K	2.50
	Univ + slogans	0.30

Port St Mary (1852-)		
	A	100.00
	B	25.00
	C	1.00
	F	5.00
	G	0.50
	H	80.00
	J	25.00
	K	3.00
	Pitney Bowes m/c	5.00
	Univ + slogans	0.30
Port Soderick (1886-1979)		
	C	12.50
	E	50.00
	F	5.00
Quarter Bridge (1855-63)		
	A	300.00
Ramsey (1832-)		
	Boxed	200.00
	Unframed	1000.00
	A undated	100.00
	A **17/193**	25.00
	dated single arc	60.00
	Num 036 **17/194**	40.00
	Duplex 036	10.00
	C	1.00
	Sq circle	30.00
	E	0.50
	F	1.50
	G	0.25
	Paid h/s	10.00
	Triangle RAX h/s	30.00
	Krag	3.00
	Univ + slogans	0.20
	+ triangle 036	10.00
	+ GB die	20.00
	J	30.00
	K	3.00
	circ parcel(1973)	5.00
Regaby Gate (1898-1977)		
	E	60.00
	F	7.50
St John's (1853-)		
	A	150.00
	C undated	75.00
	C	12.50
	F	3.00
	G	0.75
	H	60.00
St Marks (1857-1978)		
	A	250.00
	D	5.00
	E	65.00
Sandygate (1909-68)		
	E	65.00
	F	25.00
Santon (1857-)		
	undated (St Anns)	100.00
	C (St Anns)	40.00
	C (Santon)	20.00
	E (St Anns)	60.00
	G	1.50
Southern PDO (1993-)		
	E	3.00
	G	3.00
	Univ + slogans	1.50
Sulby (1853-) A		150.00
	C	15.00
	D	1.50
	E	50.00
	F	6.00
The Green (1855-63)		
	A	300.00
Union Mills (1853-)		
	A	250.00
	B	30.00
	C	1.50
	E	75.00
	K	3.00

17/192	17/193	17/194

Isles of Scilly

Note : the main office is on the island of St Mary's (1804-) and "Scilly" postmarks were used there, but replaced by "St Mary's Isles of Scilly" postmarks from 1925.

17/195	Straight line, Scilly, 1804-40	150.00
17/196	Scilly double arc, 1840-	100.00
17/197	Numeral 610, horizontal, 1844-75	120.00
17/198	Numeral 610, vertical, 1878-93	80.00
17/199	Scilly, single circle with Scilly across centre, 19mm, 1859-60s ..	40.00
17/200	Scilly, single circles, 20-26mm, 1878-?1925	8.00
17/201	Scilly, double circle with cross at foot, 1895-1925	4.00

17/201	17/202	17/203

Bryher (1888-) E	40.00		St Mary's (see above)	
F	15.00		C	2.00
G	2.00		E	1.50
St Agnes (1880-) C	20.00		F **17/202**	3.00
F	10.00		G	1.00
G	1.50		Krag	0.60
St Martin's (1879-)			Universal	0.20
C	20.00		K	3.00
F	5.00		Tresco (1868-) B	25.00
G	1.50		F	10.00
			G **17/203**	1.50

Isle of Wight

17/204	17/205	17/206	17/207

Notes : (1) Dates are years of offices' opening, not necessarily when postmarks recorded (2) Ship letters not included for IOW, see chapter 14 for these.

Apse Heath (1937-) C 1.00
Arreton (1843-) A 50.00
  C 5.00
  E 30.00
  G 1.00
Bembridge (1834-) A 30.00
  B 20.00
  C 1.00
  F 5.00
  G 2.00
  H 20.00
  K 2.00
  Krag 1.00
Blackwater (1843-)
  A 50.00
  E 5.00
  G 1.00
  H 25.00
Brading (1834-) A 30.00
  B 5.00
  numeral C54 15.00
  duplex C54 3.00
  C 1.00
  F 4.00
  K 2.00
Brighstone (1843-) C 1.00
  F (circ spacers) 1.00
  H 30.00
Brook (1886-1995) C 2.00
  E 20.00
  G 2.00
Calbourne (1843-) A 50.00
  C 5.00
  E 20.00
  G 2.00
Chale (1849-1991) A 50.00
  B 20.00
  F 1.00
Chale Green (1912-)
  E 15.00
  F 10.00
  G 1.00
Chillerton (1853-)
  A 50.00
  E 20.00
  F 2.00
  G 1.00
Cowes (1769-)
  mileage 15.00
  A undated 30.00
  A dated 4.00
  numeral 225 5.00
  duplex 225 3.00
  B 3.00
  C 1.00
  E 1.00
  F 2.00
  G 1.00
  H 30.00
  J 10.00
  K 2.00
  registered oval 3.00
  Paid h/s 1.50
  Krag 0.20
  Univ + slogans 0.20
  Univ Paid 1.00
Arctic Road (1894-1923)
  B 8.00
  E 15.00
Medina (1918-) B 8.00
  C 1.50
  K 3.00

Cowes (continued)
  Medina Road (1876-1918)
    B 8.00
  Pallance Road (1921-)
    C 1.50
    E 15.00
  Tennyson Road (1923-)
    B 1.50
  Victoria Road (1886-1983)
    B 5.00
    C 2.00
    K 5.00
Cranmore (1952-) G 2.00
East Cowes (1843-)
  A 30.00
  B 5.00
  C 1.00
  E 10.00
  F 3.00
  G 1.00
  J 10.00
  K 3.50
  Clarence Road (1898-1917)
    E 20.00
  Meadow Road (1958-)
    C 1.50
Freshwater (1843-93 & 1933-)
  A 25.00
  B 3.00
  C 1.00
  F 2.00
  G 1.00
  K 2.00
  Paid h/s 2.00
  Registered oval 3.00
  Krag 0.60
  Krag Paid 4.00
  Univ 0.20
  Univ Paid 1.00
  Church (1902-34 & 1950-)
    C 2.00
    E 15.00
  School Green (1848-93)
    A 35.00
    B 10.00
    duplex H06 20.00
  Station Road (1934-50)
    C 5.00
Freshwater Bay (1893-)
  C 5.00
  F 2.00
  G 1.50
  H 25.00
Freshwater Gate (1843-60)
  B 10.00
Freshwater Station (1893-1933)
  C 2.00
  duplex H06 5.00
  F 1.50
  H 8.00
Godshill (1838-) A 25.00
  numeral C52 6.00
  duplex C52 2.00
  B 20.00
  F 5.00
  G 1.00
Gurnard (1866-) C 5.00
  F 2.00
Haven Street (1853-)
  B 10.00
  C 2.00

Nettlestone (1893-)
  B 5.00
  C 1.00
  E 15.00
Newbridge (1899-) E 15.00
  F 3.00
  G 1.00
Newchurch (1852-) C 1.00
  E 12.00
  F 5.00
Newport (1673-)(includes
"Isle of Wight" to 1762
and 1977-)
  str line 75.00
  mileage 10.00
  A serif **17/204** 10.00
  A 2.00
  penny post 100.00
  H 'traveller' 60.00
  numeral 560 4.00
  duplex 560 1.00
  C 1.00
  E 1.00
  F 2.00
  G 1.00
  H skeleton 25.00
  J 10.00
  K 2.00
  Krag 1.00
  Krag Paid 2.50
  Paid handstamp 1.50
  Univ + slogans 0.10
  Univ '6' error 4.00
  Univ square paid 2.00
  Univ circ Paid 0.60
Carisbrooke (1843-)
  A 20.00
  B 5.00
  C 1.50
  E 4.00
  K 3.00
Castle Road (1903-85)
  C 2.00
Coppins Bridge (1885-1982)
  C 2.00
Hunny Hill (1885-)
  B 10.00
  C 2.00
Pan (1982-) C 1.50
Parkhurst (1887-)
  C 1.50
Shide (1892-) C 1.50
  E 10.00
  G 4.00
Upper St James St (1877-1985)
  C 1.50
  K 2.50
Whitepit Lane (1936-81)
  C 2.00
Niton (1838-)
  A dated 40.00
  A single 40.00
  C **17/205** 1.00
  F 5.00
Niton Undercliff (1912-)
  B 4.00
  G 1.00
Norton (1844-1919)
  E 15.00
Norton Green (1897-)
  C 7.00
  F 5.00
  G (no arcs) 2.00

Osborne (1904-22) C	5.00	
F	4.00	
(see also chap 22)		
Porchfield (1887-)		
E	20.00	
F	5.00	
G	2.00	
Rookley (1853-) C	15.00	
E	25.00	
F	2.00	
Ryde (1786-)		
str line	50.00	
A double	30.00	
A single	2.00	
mileage	15.00	
penny post	150.00	
too late	50.00	
missent	100.00	
numeral 666	5.00	
dupl 666 **17/206**	3.00	
sq circle	2.00	
B	3.00	
C	1.00	
E	1.00	
F	2.00	
G	1.00	
H 'traveller'	100.00	
J	10.00	
K	2.00	
Krag	1.00	
Univ + slogans	0.20	
Univ Paid	1.00	
Binstead (1853-)		
A	50.00	
B	10.00	
C	1.00	
F	1.00	
H	60.00	
Elmfield (1884-) C	1.50	
G	1.50	
K	4.00	
Esplanade (1871-1900)		
C	10.00	
George St (1900-80)		
B	5.00	
C	3.00	
Haylands (1895-) C	1.50	
E	20.00	
High St (1880-) B	8.00	
C	1.00	
K	2.50	
Oakfield (1853-)		
A	50.00	
B	6.00	
C	1.50	
Strand (1881-) C	1.50	
F	15.00	
K	3.00	
Upper West St (1871-80)		
B	10.00	
West St (1880-) C	1.50	
G	1.50	
K	3.00	
St Helens (1834-) C	1.00	
F	4.00	
G	3.00	
St Lawrence (1889-)		
B	10.00	
E	20.00	
F	2.00	

Sandown (1835-) A	20.00	
numeral B88	8.00	
B	3.00	
sq circle	1.50	
C	1.00	
E	2.00	
F	2.00	
G	1.00	
J	10.00	
K	2.00	
Krag	2.00	
Univ + slogans	0.20	
Avenue Road (1894-)		
B	5.00	
C	2.00	
Lake (1843-) A	60.00	
C	1.50	
E	25.00	
K	3.00	
Station Avenue (1909-82)		
C	5.00	
G	1.50	
K	2.50	
Seaview (1834-) A	20.00	
B	5.00	
C	2.00	
F	3.00	
G	1.00	
H	20.00	
K	3.00	
Shalfleet (1843-1903 & 1947-)		
B	10.00	
G	2.00	
Shanklin (1843-)		
A undated	15.00	
A dated	10.00	
numeral B89	8.00	
sq circle	1.00	
B	3.00	
C	1.00	
E	1.00	
F	2.00	
G	1.00	
H (RSO)	20.00	
J	10.00	
K	2.00	
Registered oval	4.00	
Univ + slogans	0.20	
Atherley Rd (1908-71)		
C	5.00	
Esplanade (1892-1904)		
B	10.00	
Hope Road (1889-1908)		
B	10.00	
Regent St (1934-78)		
C	3.00	
Wilton Pk Rd (1940-)		
C	1.50	
Shorwell (1843-) B	7.00	
E	15.00	
F	6.00	
G	1.00	
H	30.00	
Totland Bay (1880-)		
B	5.00	
C	1.00	
F	4.00	
K	3.00	

Ventnor (1837-)		
A undated	15.00	
A dated	8.00	
B	3.00	
numeral 971	5.00	
duplex 971	2.00	
C	1.00	
E	1.00	
F **17/207**	2.00	
G	1.00	
J	10.00	
K	2.00	
Registered oval	3.00	
Paid h/s	3.00	
Krag	2.00	
Univ + slogans	0.20	
Univ Paid die	1.00	
Bonchurch (1843-)		
A	50.00	
B	6.00	
C	1.50	
Lowther (1886-) C	2.00	
E	10.00	
Madeira Rd (1880-1980)		
B	15.00	
C	3.00	
Wellow (1899-) E	20.00	
F	5.00	
G	2.00	
Whippingham (1843-)		
A (or St)	50.00	
C	2.00	
E	25.00	
Whitwell (1851-) C	5.00	
E	15.00	
F	1.00	
Wootton Bridge (1837-)		
Penny post	100.00	
B	5.00	
numeral C55	20.00	
C	1.00	
F	3.00	
(also with circ spacers)		
H	30.00	
K	3.00	
Wroxall (1853-) B	8.00	
sq circle	2.00	
C	1.00	
F	2.00	
J	20.00	
Yarmouth (1800-)		
mileage str	30.00	
mileage circ	10.00	
A dated	4.00	
numeral 486	10.00	
duplex 486	2.00	
C	1.00	
F	2.00	
G	1.00	
H	25.00	
K	2.50	

OTHER ENGLISH ISLANDS

In this section are listed the relevant offices with dates of opening/closing but without details of the postmarks used. The start dates shown are "earliest known listed" dates, for which we thank Ken Smith. The list is restricted to genuine islands, thus Isle of Dogs, Grain and Thanet are excluded.

Foulness (Essex) (1857-)

Holy Island (Northumberland)(1847-)

Lundy (1887-1927, local stamps
  and postal service from 1929)

Whale Island (RN)(Portsmouth) (1907-85)

17/208   17/209

Barrow in Furness
Barrow Island (1885-1985)
  (confirmed part of Barrow Docks)
Ramsden Dock Road (1905-)
  (also on Barrow Island)
Piel (1895-1990) (post office not on
  Piel island, but confirmed as being
  on nearby Roa island, and deliveries
  to Piel were made from this PO)
Walney Island
  Douglas Street (1924-, see note)
  Mikasa Street (1924-, see note)
  Mill Lane (1981-)
  Vickerstown (1902-24)
  Vickerstown South (1904-24)
  Note : the last two offices were
  replaced in 1924 by Douglas St
  and Mikasa St, possibly in same
  locations

17/210   17/211

Canvey Island (Essex) (1896-)
Canvey on Sea (1907-)
Canvey Village (1931-)
Furtherwick (1941-60)
Maurice Road (1955-)
Winter Gardens (1955-72, 1978-)

Hayling Island (Hants) (1838-)
Eastoke (1896-)
Gable Head (1893-1946/55)
Manor Road (1901-)
Sandy Point (1955-85)
Sea Front (1955-78)
Stoke (1894-)
West Town (1891-)

Mersea Island (Essex)
East Mersea (1855-)
West Mersea (1855-)

Sheppey (Kent)
Eastchurch (1845-)
East Minster (1973-)
Halfway Houses (1904-)
Leysdown-on-Sea (1926-)
Minster-on-Sea (1850-)
Queenborough (1726-)
Sheerness (1799-)
  Blue Town (1876-1984)
  High St E (1926-)
  Marine Town (1878-1926)
  Mile Town (1845-76)
  Queensway (1958-)
Warden Point (1931-)
West Minster (1907-76)

WALES

Barry Island (1898-)
Caldy (1896-), later Caldey Island

17/212

Anglesey

In bringing the Anglesey listing up to the same standard of detail as that of Channel Islands and Isle of Man (earlier in the chapter) we are delighted to have had the assistance of John Cowell, of the Welsh Philatelic Society, in providing much of the detailed data. Many of the dates were provided by Ken Smith, as with English islands shown on the previous page. Spellings can vary at one location over the years eg "Penny post" at Llan(n)erchymedd pictured below.

Codes used in Anglesey listing

A Undated double arc
B Single circle without Island name
C Single circle with Island name (or Gwynedd from 1976)
E Rubber handstamps

F Double circle with thick arcs
G Double circle with thin arcs
H Skeleton handstamps
K Label type parcel handstamp

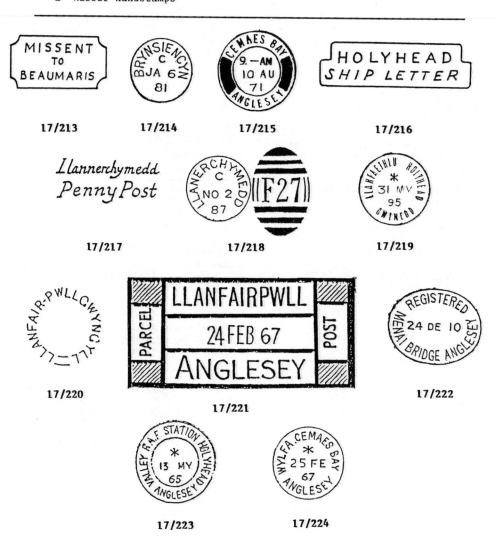

17/213 17/214 17/215 17/216

17/217 17/218 17/219

17/220 17/221 17/222

17/223 17/224

Aberffraw (1843-)

A	30.00
B	3.00
C	2.00
F	1.00

Amlwch (1826-)

Penny post	50.00
Boxed No.5	10.00
H/struck 1	35.00
Numeral (B49)	25.00
Duplex (B49)	2.00
B	2.00
C	1.00
E	0.50
F	1.00
G	1.00
H	8.00
Krag	0.40
Univ	0.20
K	3.00
registered	4.00

Amlwch Port (1891-1985)

B	5.00
C	2.00

Beaumaris (1705-)

str line	15.00
st line mileage	15.00
circ undated	5.00
circ dated	2.00
h/struck 1	150.00
h/struck 2	100.00
Paid 1	150.00
Traveller	60.00
Missent 17/213	150.00
Ship Lre	250.00
Ship letter	200.00
India lett	300.00
A	5.00
A dated	2.00
Num'l (58) vert	10.00
Num'l (58) horiz	5.00
Duplex (58)	1.00
B	1.00
C	1.00
E	0.50
F	0.50
G	0.50
H	8.00
Krag	0.40
Univ	0.40
K	3.00
Registered	4.00

Benllech (1975-) C 1.00

Bethel (1850-1991)

A	30.00
B	5.00
C	1.00

Bodedern (1833-)

Penny post	30.00
Boxed No.3	25.00
B	4.00
C	2.00
F	2.00

Bodffordd (1868-) B 5.00

C	3.00
F	2.00

Bodorgan (1887-1972)

Duplex (J60)	6.00
B	2.00
C	1.00
F	1.00
K	3.00

Bryngwran (1852-) A 30.00

B	4.00
C	2.00
F	2.00

Brynllanfair (1845-55)

A	30.00

(renamed Llanfairpwll)

Brynsiencyn (1850-)

A	30.00
B 17/214	2.00
C	1.00
G no arcs	1.00

Brynteg (1884-) E 10.00

F	3.00
G	2.00

Bull Bay (1896-1993)

B	4.00
C	1.00
E	5.00
F	1.00

Caergeiliog (1895-)

C	2.00
F	1.00

Capel Gwyn (1930-77)

C	3.00
F	2.00

Carmel (1912-76) C 3.00

F	2.00

Carreglefn (1877-) B 5.00

C	2.00
E	10.00

Cemaes (1843-1912)

A	30.00
B	1.00

(renamed Cemaes Bay)

Cemaes Bay (1912-)

C	1.00
F 17/215	1.00

Cerrigceinwen (1864-1978)

B	5.00
C	3.00
G no arcs	2.00

Dulas (1873-?1977) B 5.00

C	3.00
F	2.00

Dwyran (1857-) A 30.00

B	3.00
C	2.00
F	1.00

Four Mile Bridge (1914-)

B	5.00
C	3.00
E	10.00
F	2.00

Gaerwen (1846-) A 30.00

Numeral (F26)	25.00
B	4.00
C	2.00
F	1.00
K	3.00

Glyn Garth (1887-1946)

B	2.00
F	2.00

Gwalchmai (1852-) A 30.00

B	4.00
C	2.00
F	1.00

Gwyndy (1785-1867)

266 Gwyndu	100.00
H'shoe (Gwyndee)	50.00
Gwindee 266	30.00
Boxed No.2	15.00
A	30.00

Holyhead (1780-)

Str line	50.00
Mileage	30.00
Circ mileage	10.00
Erased	15.00
Horseshoe	50.00
Circ dated	2.00
H/struck 2	75.00

Ship Lre	250.00
Ship let 17/216	100.00
India lett	150.00
Numeral (374)	3.00
Duplex (374)	2.00
B	1.00
C	1.00
E	0.50
F	0.50
G	0.50
H	7.00
Krag	1.50
Univ	0.10
K	3.00
registered	4.00

Alderley Terrace (1938-77)

C	3.00

Church Terrace (1892-)

B	6.00
C	3.00

Kingsland (1924-66)

C	3.00

Llaingoch (1852-)

A	30.00
B	6.00
C	3.00
F	2.00

London Road (1902-70)

B	6.00
C	3.00

Morawelon (1973-)

C	2.00

Porthyfelin (1928-)

F	2.00

Llanbedrgoch (1886-)

B	4.00
C	2.00
E	10.00
F	2.00

Llanddaniel (1864-)

B	6.00
C	2.00
E	10.00

Llanddeusant (1860-)

B	4.00
C	2.00
F	2.00

Llanddona (1874-) B 6.00

C	3.00
E	10.00
F	2.00

Llandegfan (1859-) B 6.00

C	3.00
E	10.00
H	10.00

Llandyfrydog (1949-93)

C	2.00

(previously Tynypwll)

Llanedwen (1897-1971)

B	6.00
C	3.00
E	10.00

Llanerchymedd (1828-)

Penny post 17/217	30.00
Boxed No.4	20.00
Numeral (F27)	10.00
Duplex 17/218	4.00
B	4.00
C	2.00
F	1.00
K	3.00

Llanfachraeth (1859-)

A	20.00
B	4.00
C	2.00
F	2.00
H	20.00

Llanfaelog (1868-)
  Numeral (H89)   25.00
  B   5.00
  C   2.00
Llanfaethlu (1849-)
  A   30.00
  B   5.00
  C 17/219   2.00
Llanfairpwllgwyngyll (1855-)
(previously Brynllanfair)
(various abbreviations
eg Llanfair PG, for full
name see chapter 24)
  A 17/220   30.00
  Numeral (F25)   15.00
  Duplex (F25)   3.00
  B   4.00
  C   2.00
  F   2.00
  K 17/221   3.00
Llanfairynghoronwy (1859-)
(later Llanfairynghornwy)
  A   30.00
  B   6.00
  C   3.00
  E   10.00
  F   2.00
Llanfechell (1858-)
  A   30.00
  B   5.00
  C   2.00
  F   2.00
  H   10.00
Llanfihangel (1857-67)
  A   30.00
Llanfwrog (1935-?95)
  F   2.00
Llangaffo (1881-) B 6.00
  C   3.00
  F   2.00
Llangefni (1827-)
  Penny post   30.00
  Boxed No.1   15.00
  Numeral (B50)   25.00
  Duplex (B50)   2.00
  B   2.00
  C   1.00
  E   0.50
  F   1.50
  G   1.00
  H   10.00
  Univ   0.10
  K   3.00
  registered   4.00
Llangoed (1853-) A 30.00
  B   3.00
  C   2.00
  F   2.00
Llangristiolus (1978-?95)
  C   1.00
Llangwyllog (1890-?1985)
  Numeral (J53)   25.00
  B   5.00
  C   3.00
  F   2.00

Llanrhyddlad (1904-)
(later Llanrhuddlad)
  B   6.00
  C   3.00
  E   10.00
Llansadwrn (1887-1987)
  B   6.00
  C   3.00
  F   2.00
Maenaddwyn (1933-) C 2.00
Maldwyn (1949-) C   2.00
Malltraeth (1912-) B 5.00
  C   2.00
  E   10.00
Marianglas (1896-) E 5.00
  F   2.00
Menai Bridge (1841-)
  A   15.00
  Numeral (B51)   12.00
  Duplex (B51)   2.00
  B   2.00
  C   1.00
  E   0.50
  F   1.50
  G   1.00
  Univ (29.4.68 only) 2.00
  K   3.00
  registered 17/222 4.00
Moelfre (1851-) A   30.00
  B   4.00
  C   2.00
  F   2.00
Mynydd Mechell (1933-94)
  C   2.00
Newborough (1850-)
  A   30.00
  B   5.00
  C   2.00
  F   2.00
Paradwys (1909-75) B 6.00
  C   3.00
Pengorphwysfa (1897- later
  Pengorffwysfa -?1977)
  B   6.00
  C   3.00
Penmon (1931-76) F   2.00
Penmynydd (1863-) B   6.00
  C   3.00
  E   10.00
Pentraeth (1845-) A 15.00
  B   2.00
  C   1.00
  E   1.00
  F   2.00
  G   1.00
  K   3.00
Penysarn (1855-) A   30.00
  B   6.00
  C   2.00
Rhoscolyn (1888-?1990)
  B   4.00
  C   2.00
Rhosgoch (1887-1973)
  Numeral (H91)   25.00
  B   4.00
  C   2.00
  F   2.00

Rhosneigr (1895-) B   2.00
  C   1.00
  F   1.00
  K   3.00
Rhostrehwfa (1992-95)
  C   4.00
Rhosybol (1852-) A   30.00
  Numeral (F28)   12.00
  B   4.00
  C   2.00
  E   10.00
  F   2.00
Rhydwen (later Rhydwyn)
(1867-) B   4.00
  C   2.00
  F   2.00
Talwrn (1886-) B   6.00
  C   3.00
  E   10.00
Trearddur Bay (1898-)
  B   2.00
  C   1.00
  E   10.00
  F   1.00
  H   10.00
Tregele (1933-77) F   2.00
Trevor (later Trefor)
(1883-1981) B   6.00
  C   3.00
Ty Croes (1888-)
  Numeral (J21)   25.00
  B   4.00
  C   2.00
  F   1.00
  K   3.00
Tynlon (1895-) B   6.00
  C   3.00
  E   10.00
  F   2.00
Tynygongl (1855-1975)
  A   30.00
  B   2.00
  C   1.00
  F   1.00
  H   10.00
  K   3.00
(then renamed Benllech)
Tynypwll (1897-1946)
  E   10.00
(then Llandyfrydog)
Valley or The Valley
(1857-) A   25.00
  Numeral (D60)   20.00
  Duplex (D60)   3.00
  B   4.00
  C   2.00
  F   1.00
  K   3.00
Valley RAF Station
(prob 1940s-1960s) C 5.00
  G no arcs 17/223 5.00
  K   10.00
Wylfa (1964-73)(power
  station construction)
  C 17/224   10.00

NORTHERN IRELAND

Rathlin Island

Note : Greenisland, Carrickfergus is not an island, and is not to be confused
with the uninhabited Green Island near Greencastle

Postmarks from these island post offices vary in value considerably, some of them being extremely scarce. In the 20th century many post offices in the Scottish islands have handstamped mail (also with machines in some major towns). REMEMBER THESE ARE "FROM" PRICES, thus postmarks of smaller locations are worth substantially more.

EASDALE PENNY POST

MORNISH

17/225   17/226   17/231   17/233

17/234   17/236   17/237   17/240

17/225	Penny Post, boxed/unboxed	50.00
17/226	Scots local stamps, various	50.00
17/227	Ship letters - Kirkwall, Lerwick, Tobermory	150.00
17/228	Handstruck '1' eg Kirkwall	10.00
17/229	Handstruck '2' eg Kirkwall, Lerwick	50.00
17/230	Duplex handstamps	15.00

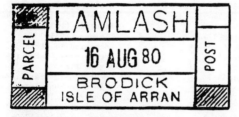 

17/243   17/244

17/231	Circular dated, double arcs	10.00
17/232	Baltasound (Isle of Unst) mailbag seal used as handstamp	20.00
17/233	Single circle, various sizes, value for 1890-1920 specimens	4.00
17/234	Double circle, incl Scottish types, value for 1900-30 specimens	5.00
17/235	Skeleton handstamps	20.00
17/236	Rubber handstamps, value for 1900-1930 specimens	10.00
17/237	Double circle, modern, on ordinary mail	0.30
17/238	as above, on registered cover	5.00
17/239	Krag machine, pre 1950 (see also chapter 10)	1.00
17/240	as above, but post 1950	0.40
17/241	Universal machine, pre 1950 (see also chapter 10)	0.60
17/242	as above, but post 1950	0.10
17/243	Parcel handstamps	2.50
17/244	Registered oval handstamps	3.00
17/245	SID handstamps	0.30

The list that follows shows Scottish island post offices, along with dates, but not details of their postmarks.

SCOTLAND (some "individual" islands then approx south to north)

Canna (1878-)
Coll (1805-)
Colonsay (1873-)
Eigg (1874-)
Gigha (1859-)
Kerrera (1879-1969)
Rum/Rhum (1891-)
St Kilda (1900-30, but used
   1957-62 on forces mail,
   latterly used at Nunton)
Stroma (1898-1958)
Arran
Blackwaterfoot (1883-)
Brodick (1827-)
Corrie (1853-)
Dippen/Dippin (1946-69)
Kildonan
   (1880-1946 then Dippen)
Kildonan Shore (1934-)
Kilmorie/Kilmory (1849-)
Kings Cross (1880-1978)
Lamlash (1807- init Arran)
Lochranza (1854-)
Machrie (1901-77)
Pirnmill (1872-)
Shannochie (1898-1977)
Shiskine (1854-1983)
Sliddery (1898-1981)
Whiting Bay (1860-)
Islay
Ballygrant (1854-)
Bonahaven (1895-1987)
Bowmore (1774-1859
   renamed Bridgend)
Bowmore Village (1847-59
   renamed Bowmore)
Bridgend (1859-)
Bruichladdich (1883-)
Gruinart (1862-1977)
Kildalton (1895-1975)
Portaskaig (1767-)
Port Charlotte (1847-)
Port Ellen (1854-)
Portnahaven (1867-)
Jura
Craighouse (1876-)
Inverlussa (1947-84)
Jura (1812-68 then Lagg)
Lagg (1868-1963)
Cumbrae
Millport (1835-)
Bute
Kerrycroy (1900-17)
Kilchattan Bay (1881-)
Kingarth (1848-1946)
Rothesay (1767-)
   Ardbeg Road (1889-)
   Ascog (1845-1968)
   Barone Road (1903-14)
   Columshill St (1914-72)
   Craigmore Pier (1884-1980)
   Gallowgate (1896-)
   High St (1903-19,1942-75)
Port Bannatyne (1834-)
Straad (1907-82)
Mull
Aros (at Salen) (1803-)
Auchnacraig (1792-1965
   then Lochdon)
Bellochroy (1830-40)
Bridge of Lussa (1864-77
   then Lochbuie)
Bunessan (1804-)
Calgary (1888-1967)

Carsaig (1891-1961)
Craiguire/Craignure (1881-)
Croggan (1900-65)
Dervaig (1880-)
Fionnphort (1873-)
   (various spellings)
Gribun (1909-71)
Gruline (1886-1965)
Iona (Isle of)(1851-)
Lochbuy/Lochbuie (1877-)
Lochdon (1965-)
Mornish/Morinish (1830s-80
   then Dervaig)
Pennyghael (1869-)
Tiroran (1893-)
Tobermory (1791-)
Torloisk (1898-1974)
Ulva (island)(1839-72)
Ulva Ferry (1884-)
Lismore
Achnacroish (1881-92
   then Lismore)
Bachuil (1898-1940)
Lismore (1892-)
Point (1945-55)
Seil
Balvicar (1897-)
Clachan Seil (1897-?1993)
Easdale (1825-)
North Easdale (1901-59)
   (Easdale island)
Luing
Blackmill Bay (1896-1929)
Cullipool (1896-)
Toberonochy (1896-1983)
Tiree
Balemartine (1894-)
Cornaig (1896-after 1974)
Middleton (1934-closed?)
Ruaig (1898-)
Scarinish (1898-)
Tyree/Tiree (1804-98
   then Scarinish)
Skye
Ardvasar (1863-)
Armadale (1822-39)
Arnisort (1857-)
Bernisdale (1892-)
Borreraig (1884-)
Bracadale (1835-44)
Breakish (1879-)
Broadford (1820-)
Camustinivaig (1899-)
Carbost (1842-)
Culnacnock (1887-)
Dunan (1881-1986)
Duntulm (1868-1985)
Dunvegan (1741-)
Earlish (1898-)
Edinbane (1857 then 1869-)
Elgol (1880-)
Glenbrittle (1937-)
Glendale (1855-)
Hallin (1935-)
Harlosh (1868-)
Isle Ornsay (1829-)
Kilmuir (1830-)
Kyleakin (1843-)
Linicro (1955-)
Ose (1938-76)
Penifiler (1899-)
Portnalong (1924-)
Portree (1809-)
Raasay (Isle of)(1833-)

Rhudunan (1884-1937
   then Glenbrittle)
Roskhill (1937-)
Sconser (1769-)
Skeabost (1855-92
   then Bernisdale)
Skeabost Bridge (1889-)
Skinidin (1900-87)
Sligichan/Sligachan (1875-1965)
Snizort (1868-)
Soay (island)(1891-1953)
Staffin (1868-)
Struan (1835-1987)
Tarskavaig (1898-)
Teangue (1898-)
The Braes (1873-)
Tighlone (1855-57 then
   Edinbane then Arnisort)
Torran (on Raasay)(1898-1967)
Torrin (1898-)
Uig (1845-)
Waternish (1855-)
Barra
Barra (1855-1923
   then Northbay)
Borve (1897-)
Castlebay (1875-)
Eoligarry (1931-78)
Northbay (1923-)
Skallary (1930-)
Vatersay (island)(1928-)
South Uist
Bornish (1916-)
Bualdubh (1956-66)
Daliburgh (1888-)
Eochar (1878-1976)
Eriskay (island)(1885-)
Grogarry (1890-1972)
Howmore (1843-1951, 1965-)
Kilbride (1839-)
Linique (1935-)
Lochboisdale (1878-)
Lochboisdale Hotel (1880-81
   then Pier)
Lochboisdale Pier (1881-1909
   then Lochboisdale)
Lochcarnan (1937-88)
Lochskipport (1912-68)
North Boisdale (1949-)
South Lochboisdale (1926-)
Stoneybridge (1951-)
West Gerinish (1935-77)
Benbecula
Balivanich (1943-44 & 1972-)
Benbecula RAFPO (1944-46)
Creagorry (1878-)
Gramsdale (1935-74)
Griminish (1938-)
Nunton (1843-1972, used at
   several locations then
   Balivanich)
North Uist
Balishare (Baleshare island)
   (1885-)
Bayhead (1877-)
Bernera (island)(1880-,
   spelling Berneray 1962-)
Carinish (1802-)
Clachan (1988-)
Claddach Kirkibost (1935-71)
Grimsay (island)(1880-)
Locheport (1881-1988
   then Clachan)
Lochmaddy (1829-)

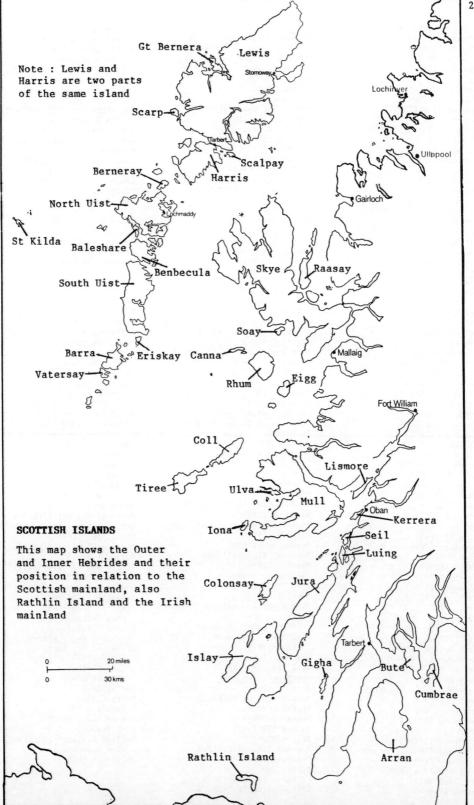

Gt Bernera

Lewis

Note : Lewis and
Harris are two parts
of the same island

Stornoway

Lochinver

Scarp

Ullapool

Tarbert

Scalpay

Berneray

Harris

North Uist

Gairloch

Lochmaddy

St Kilda

Baleshare

Benbecula

Skye

Raasay

South Uist

Soay

Mallaig

Barra

Eriskay

Canna

Vatersay

Rhum

Eigg

Fort William

Coll

Lismore

Tiree

Ulva

Mull

Oban

Kerrera

Iona

Seil

Luing

SCOTTISH ISLANDS

This map shows the Outer
and Inner Hebrides and their
position in relation to the
Scottish mainland, also
Rathlin Island and the Irish
mainland

Colonsay

Jura

Tarbert

Islay

Gigha

Bute

Cumbrae

0   20 miles

0   30 kms

Rathlin Island

Arran

Lochportan (1926-)
Newtonferry (1878-)
Sidinish (1934-)
Sollas (1879-)
Tigharry (1851-)
Harris
Amhuinnsuidh (1950-)
Ardhasaig (1950-)
Drinnishadder (1930-)
Finsbay (1914-)
Harris (at Tarbert)(1836-)
Kyles Scalpay (1930-)
    renamed Kyles Harris (1953-)
Leverburgh (1921-)
Manish (1879-)
Northton (1930-)
Obbe (1873-1921
    then Leverburgh)
Scalpay (Isle of) (1887-)
Scarista (1951-)
Scarp (island)(1931-69)
Seilebost (1946-)
Stockinish (1896-)
Strond (1950-)
Lewis
Achmore (1927-)
Arivruaich (1950-)
Back (1874-)
Balallan (1878-)
Barvas (1855-)
Bayble (1934-)
Bernera (1880-)
    (on Gt Bernera)
Borve (1886-)
Bragar (1910-)
Breasclete (1950-)
Callanish (1884-)
Carloway (1875-)
Cromore (1912-)
Crossbost (1874-)
Crulivig (1949-)
Eneclate (1931-)
Galson (1950-)
Garrabost (1855-)
Garrynahine (1873-84
    then Callanish)
Gravir (1884-)
Gress (1888-91, 1950-)
Grimshader (1947-)
Islivig (1892-)
Keose (1901-)
Kershader (1929-)
Knock (1892-)
Laxay (1884-)
Laxdale (1897-1989)
Lemreway (1930-)
Leurbost (1950-)
Marvig (1934-)
Miavaig (1857-1988
    then Valtos)
Ness (1875-)
North Tolsta (1879-)
Portnaguran (1888-)
Port of Ness (1888-)
Sandwick (1935-)
Sandwickhill (1897-1901)
Shader (1913-)
Shawbost (1883-)
Skigersta (1950-)
South Dell (1952-)
Stornoway (1756-)
    Bayhead (1951-)
Timsgarry (1933-)
Tolstachaolais (1909-)
Tong (1911-81)
Valtos (1988-)

Orkney
Backaland (1898-1970 then
    renamed Eday)(on Eday)
Balfour (on Shapinsay)(1848-)
Birsay (1849-)
Burray (1858-)
Burwick (1800-)
Deerness (1857-)
Dounby (at Downby)(1873-)
Eday (island)(1857-,
    at Backaland 1970-)
Egilshay/Egilsay (island)
    (1878-)
Evie (1844-)
Finstown (1844-)
Flotta (island)(1860-)
Graemsay (island)(1882-)
Harray (1849-73)
Holm (1934-)
Hoy (island)(1879-)
Kirkwall (1746-)
Lady (on Sanday)(1890-)
Longhope (on Hoy)(1835-)
Lyness (on Hoy)(1940-)
Melsetter (on Hoy)(1902-69)
Mire (on Sanday)(1935-82)
North Ronaldshay (island)
    (1855-, then N Ronaldsay
    1966-)
North Shapinsay
    (on Shapinsay)(1935-75)
Orphir (1848-)
Papa Westray (island)(1879-)
Quivals (on Sanday)(1898-)
Quoyburray (1898-1934
    then Toab)
Quoyloo (1879-)
Rendall (1869-)
Rousay (island)(1854-)
Rusness (on Sanday)(1898-)
St Margaret's Hope
    (on S Ronaldsay)(1826-)
St Mary's Holm (1856-1934
    then Holm)
Samson's Lane (on Stronsay)
    (1884-)
Sanday (1839-)
    (on Sanday at Kettletoft)
Sandwick (1858-)
Sourin (on Rousay)(1879-1969)
Stenness (1875-)
Stromness (1797-)
Stronsay (island)(1839-)
Swannay (1885-)
Tankerness (1893-)
Toab (1934-)
Twatt (1879-)
Valdigarth (on Westray)(1898-)
Veira (on Wyre)
    (1885-1933 then Wyre)
Wasbister (on Rousay)
    (1898-1969)
Westray (island)(1839-)
Wyre (island)(1933-)
Shetland
Aith (1911-)
Baltasound (on Unst)(1827-)
Bigton (1907-)
Bixter (1884-)
Boddam (1827-39)
Brae (1827-)
Bressay (island)(1857-)
Brettabister (1896-)
Bridge-end
    (Burra islands)(1943-74)
Bridge-of-Walls (1884-)

Brough (on Whalsay)(1936-95)
Buness (on Unst)(1839-57)
Burra (island)(1873-1943
    then Bridge-end)
Burravoe (on Yell)(1839-)
Camb (on Yell)(1933-)
Cullivoe (on Yell)(1839-)
Cunningsburgh (1847-)
Dalsetter (on Yell)(1878-1918
    then Sellafirth)
Dunrossness (1847-)
East Yell (on Yell)(1845-)
Eshaness (1895-)
Fair Isle (island)(1877-)
Fetlar (Isle of)(1858-)
Foula (Isle of)(1879-)
Garderhouse (1839-1981)
Gott (1943-)
Graven (1941-43)
Grutness (1885-93
    then Sumburgh)
Gutcher (on Yell)(1885-)
Hamar (1903-72)
Hamnavoe (Burra islands)
    (1898-)
Haroldswick (on Unst)(1827-)
Heylor (1892-)
Hillswick (1839-)
Hillwell (1933 then Quendale)
Lerwick (1763-)
    Freefield (1906-)
Levenwick (1884-)
Linkshouse (on Yell, 1827-84
    then Mid Yell)
Lochend (1906-)
Mid Yell (on Yell)(1884-)
Mossbank (1839-)
Nesting (1865-66)
North Roe (1880-)
Ollaberry (1827-)
Papa Stour (island)(1880-)
Quarff (1898-)
Quendale (1933-73)
Reawick (1884-)
Sandness (1839-)
Sandwick (1847-)
Scalloway (1856-)
Scousburgh (1896-)
Seafield (on Yell)(1844-)
Sellafirth (on Yell)(1910-82)
Skellister (1897-)
Skerries (islands)(1889-)
Sullom (1880-)
Sullom Voe RAF (1943-45)
Sumburgh (1893-1969)
Symbister (on Whalsay)(1942-)
Tangwick (1826-46)
Tingwall (1869-1943
    then Gott)
Tresta (1856-)
Ulsta (on Yell)(1827-)
Uyeasound (on Unst)
    (1827-1988)
Vidlin (1891-)
Virkie (1866-)
Voe (1827-)
Walls (1827-)
Weisdale (1839-)
Wester Skeld (1929-)
West Sandwick (Yell) (1839-)
Whalsay (island)(1866-1943
    then Symbister)
Whiteness (1850-)

Orkney and Shetland Islands

This map shows the relative positions of the Orkney and Shetland islands, in relation also to John O'Groats on the north coast of Scotland's mainland, and to Stroma which is just off the mainland. Also shown are the individual islands on which post offices exist or once existed. Note that in both cases the main island is referred to as "Mainland".

Haroldswick, the northernmost post office, is also shown in chapter 12.

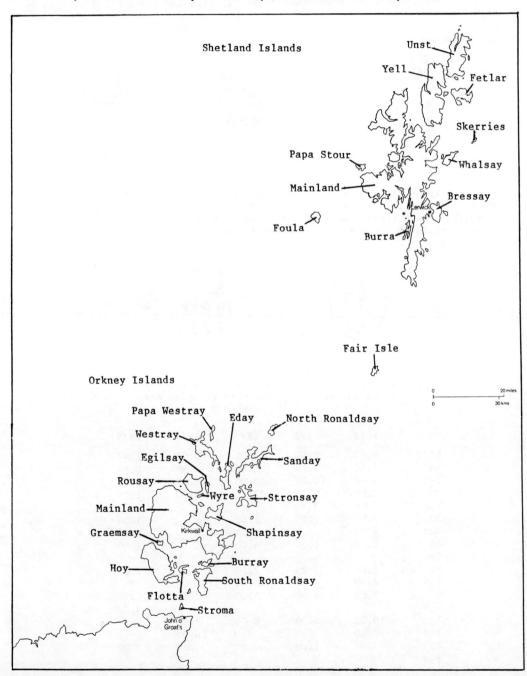

18. Charge, Instructional and Explanatory marks

This chapter shows a representative listing of these marks. It does not pretend to be a complete listing, partly as in modern times there are many non-standard marks as local post offices produce handstamps of their own layouts. Readers should therefore hesitate before submitting additions. From the 1980s self-adhesive labels have taken over to a certain extent. Meter date correction marks are not included; these are shown in chapter 27, with machine-applied slogans in chapter 11.

Charge Marks

18/1

From 1860s
Scottish types often have a Roman letter with full stop beneath. Irish types often have a capital D above a double line

18/2

From 1870s
With office number or London District initials above or below value

18/3

Circular Frame and office numbers

18/4

Oval frame and office numbers

18/5

Unframed with 'To Pay' Scottish or Irish are prefixed S or I

	18/1	18/2	18/3	18/4	18/5
½d	4.00	2.50	10.00	5.00	2.00
1d	1.50	0.75	5.00	2.50	0.60
1½d	10.00	10.00	10.00	10.00	3.00
2d	2.00	1.75	7.00	4.00	1.25
2½d	7.00	7.50			
3d	3.00	1.50	6.00		1.00
3½d	8.00		8.50		3.00
4d	5.00	1.75	6.00		1.00
4½d					
5d	3.00	1.25	2.50		2.00
5½d	10.00		10.00		
6d	3.00	3.00	5.00	2.50	1.50
6½d					3.50
7d	10.00	8.00	8.00	3.00	
7½d	10.00			10.00	
8d	6.00	1.00	8.00		2.00
8½d					

9d		6.00	7.00	7.00
9½d	12.00			
10d	6.50	8.50	10.00	
11d	12.00	12.00	12.00	
1/-	3.00	3.00	5.00	
1/1	10.00			
1/1½	12.50			
1/4	12.50			
1/5	12.50			
1/7		15.00		
1/8		15.00		
1/9		15.00		
1/10		15.00		
1/11		15.00		
2/-	10.00			
2/3	10.00			10.00
2/6		10.00		
3/-		10.00		
4/6	?			
5/-	?			

18/6	Circular frame without office numbers, late Victorian	from	5.00
18/7	Oval frame without office numbers	from	10.00
18/8	Square or rectangular frame without office numbers	from	5.00
	Circular types with H.C.S.W. (House of Commons) – see chapter 21		
18/9	Square or rectangular frame with office numbers	from	6.00
18/10	Charge marks with NPB (Newspaper Branch)	from	5.00
18/11	-------- D TO PAY/Number	from	1.00
18/12	Hexagonal frame with TO PAY and office number	from	10.00
18/13	Cross shaped frame with TO PAY and office number	from	10.00

Boxed T shaped marks with office numbers or London District Initials black, purple or green (double prices for red), from 1870s – these are difficult to value since some are still in use, clearly earlier specimens are worth more than the values stated:

Closed contrary to regulations 11 6	Gone Away 763B	Liable to Letter Rate 407
18/34	18/45	18/61

18/14	1D to pay	2.00
18/15	4D to pay	3.00
18/16	1D to pay/above .. oz	2.50
18/17	1D to pay/contains a letter in/Typewritten characters	3.50
18/18	1D to pay/Liable to/Postcard Rate	1.75
18/19	2D to pay/Liable to/Letter Rate	1.75
18/20	Above .. oz/More to pay	2.00
18/21	Above 1oz/1d/More to pay	2.00
18/22	Above 1oz/2d/More to pay	2.00
18/23	Above 2oz/3d/More to pay	4.00
18/24	Above 3oz/1d/More to pay	4.00
18/25	Above 4oz/1d/More to pay	5.00
18/26	Above .. oz/ /More to pay	6.00
18/27	Address Contrary to rule	5.00
18/28	Book Post/over	4.00
18/29	Charged for/re-direction	4.00
18/30	Circular in imitation type/writing. Posted out of course	3.50
18/31	Closed against inspection	3.50
18/32	Closed against/inspection	3.50
18/33	Closed against inspection/contrary to Regulations	3.50

18/34	Closed contrary/to regulations	2.00
18/35	Closed contrary to/regulations	2.00
18/36	Compulsorily Registered	5.00
18/37	Contains a communication/of the nature of a letter	3.50
18/38	Contains a letter in/type-writing characters	3.50
18/39	Contains writing in/the nature of a letter	3.50
18/40	Contrary to Regulations	2.00
18/41	Contrary to Regulations/Exceeds limits of size	3.00
18/42	Deceased	3.50
18/43	Exceeds limits of size	3.00
18/44	Firm not known	3.00
18/45	Gone Away	1.00
18/46	Gone No address	3.00
18/47	House empty	4.00
18/48	Imitation typewriting/posted out of course	4.50
18/49	Improper enclosure	5.00
18/50	Inadmissible at ½d rate	4.00
18/51	Inadmissible at printed paper rate	2.00
18/52	Inadmissible at .. rate	3.00
18/53	Incorrectly Addressed	2.00
18/54	Insufficient Address	2.00
18/55	Insufficiently Addressed	1.50
18/56	Insufficient Paid	5.00
18/57	Insufficiently paid	3.00
18/58	Insufficiently prepaid	2.00
18/59	Insufficiently Paid/over .. oz	2.50
18/60	Letter Rate/Above .. oz	2.00
18/61	Liable to Letter Rate	0.75
18/62	Liable to/Letter Rate	1.50
18/63	Liable to postcard rate	1.50
18/64	Misdirected	3.00
18/65	More to Pay/Above .. oz (line beneath 'More to Pay')	2.00
18/66	As above but without line	1.50
18/67	No Such Street	4.00
18/68	No Such Street in	4.00
18/69	No Such Street in Liverpool	4.50
18/70	No Trace	2.00
18/71	Not called for	2.00
18/72	Not certified as official	7.00
18/73	Not found	3.00
18/74	Not known	2.00
18/75	Not known as addressed	3.00
18/76	Not known at	4.00
18/77	Not paid in stamps	7.00
18/78	Not to be found	2.00
18/79	Not transmissible at the/Rate of Postage	4.00
18/80	Of the nature of a letter	15.00
18/81	Of the nature/of a letter	10.00
18/82	Over .. oz	2.50
18/83	Over .. ounces	2.50
18/84	Over .. oz/More to pay	3.00
18/85	Posted out of course	3.00
18/86	Posted out/of course	3.00
18/87	Posted without Late Fee	5.00
18/88	Posted without/Late Fee	5.00
18/89	Prohibited enclosure	5.00
18/90	Property demolished	2.50
18/91	Re-issued	5.00
18/92	Reposted more than one/clear day after delivery	5.00
18/93	Undelivered for reason stated/Return to Sender	3.00
18/94	Unpaid	2.00
18/95	Unpaid/above ..oz	2.50

Rectangular types in black, purple or green (Double prices for red)

| 18/96 | 18/101 | 18/106 | 18/111 |

18/96 ½D/Postage/due/for/return/to/Sender, boxed 1.00
18/97   As above but 1d 1.00
18/98   As above but 1½d 2.00
18/99   As above but 2d 1.50
18/100   As above but 3d 1.75
18/101 1D/to pay/Liable/to/Letter/Rate, boxed with office number 1.00
18/102   As above but 2d 3.00
18/103 More to Pay, Above .. oz types 3.00
18/104 Undelivered for/reason stated/½D/Postage Due/For Return/To Sender,
    boxed with office number 1.00
18/105   As above but 1d 1.00
18/106   As above but 1½d 1.50
18/107   As above but 2d 1.00
18/108   As above but 2½d 2.00
18/109   As above but blank value for completion 2.00
18/110 Unpaid 2D to pay/Posted too late for ½D rate, boxed 4.00

Boxed marks incorporating charge and explanation in brass or rubber.
Value inserted by separate brass piece, by hand or fixed rubber above
office number or London District Initials - black, violet, green or red.

Double frame from 1924

18/111 More to/Pay/letter rate/above .. oz 3.00
18/112 More to/Pay/Printed Paper Rate/above .. oz 3.00
18/113 More to/pay/letter rate/above .. oz 1.00
18/114 More to/pay/Newspaper/rate/contains .. newspapers 5.00
18/115 More to/pay/.. rate/above .. oz 1.00
18/116 To pay/contrary to/regulations/liable to/.. rate 2.50
18/117 To pay/Form not/appropriately/printed/Liable to/Letter rate 5.00
18/118 To pay/inadmissible/Sample rate/liable to/letter rate/above .. oz . 5.00
18/119 To pay/liable to/letter rate 2.00
18/120 To pay/liable to/postcard/rate 2.50
18/121 To pay/Posted/unpaid 2.00
18/122 To pay/Posted/Out of/course 5.00
18/123 To pay/posted/unpaid/above .. oz 1.00
18/124 To pay/posted/unpaid 1.00
18/125 To pay/Posted/Unpaid/Too Late For/½d Rate 5.00
18/126 To pay/Contrary to/Regulations/Liable to/.. rate 4.00

 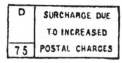 

| 18/132 | 18/136 | 18/145 | 18/167 |

Single frame: 1931-69

18/127	More to/Pay/Letter Rate/Above .. oz	0.75
18/128	More to/pay/letter rate/Above .. oz	0.75
18/129	As above but 1 oz	1.00
18/130	As above but 2 oz	1.00
18/131	More to/Pay/.. rate/Above 2 oz	1.50
18/132	More to/Pay/.. rate/Above .. oz	1.00
18/133	More to/Pay/Insufficiently/Prepaid	1.50
18/134	More to/pay/Printed Paper/Rate/above .. oz	2.00
18/135	More to/Pay/Newspaper/Rate/Contains ../Newspapers	2.00
	More to/Pay/Late Fee/Unpaid (see chapter 13)	
18/136	Surcharge Due/to Increased/Postal charges	1.00
18/137	To Pay/closed/contrary to/Regulations/Liable to/Letter rate	2.00
18/138	To pay/contrary to/regulations/liable to .. rate	1.50
18/139	To pay/imitation type/circular, not/specially posted/liable to/	
	.. rate	2.00
18/140	To pay/liable to/letter/rate	0.50
18/141	To pay/liable to/letter rate/.. oz	0.50
18/142	To pay/Liable to/postcard/rate	1.50
18/143	To pay/liable to/Printed Paper/rate/above .. oz	1.00
18/144	To pay/posted/underpaid	0.75
18/145	To pay/posted/unpaid	0.50
18/146	To pay/posted/unpaid/above .. oz	0.50
18/147	As above but without office number	1.00
18/148	To pay/Posted Unpaid/Too late for 1d rate	2.00
18/149	To pay/Posted Unpaid/Too late for 2d rate	2.00
18/150	To pay/Posted/Unpaid/Too late for 3d rate	2.00
18/151	To pay	1.75
18/152	To pay/Inadmissible/Sample Rate Liable To/Letter Rate/above .. oz	2.50
18/153	To Pay/Posted in/T.P.O./Late Fee/Not Paid	3.00
18/154	To Pay/Posted/Out of/Course	5.00
18/155	Undelivered for Reason/Stated/Postage Due For/Return to Sender	1.50

Boxed marks: decimal currency from 1971:

18/156	3p/More to/Pay/over .. oz, with office number	0.50
18/157	P/More to Pay/.. Rate/Above .. oz., as above	0.50
18/158	P/More to Pay/.. Rate/Above .. Grms., as above	0.50
18/159	P/Surcharged/To Increased/Postal charges	2.00
18/160	Surcharge due/To Increased/Postal charges	1.00
18/161	P/To pay/Insufficiently prepaid	2.00
18/162	P/To pay/More to Pay over/.. oz	0.50
18/163	P/To pay/Posted/Unpaid, blank panel above office number	0.50
18/164	Multipurpose charge box with fixed value	0.75
18/165	As above but blank panel for insertion	0.25
18/166	As above but oz removed after metrication	0.50
18/167	As above but with G or Gms	0.25

I.B. 10ᴰ

18/168

1ᴼ⁻ I.S.A.

18/169

3ᴰ⁻ I.S.

18/170

1ᴰ⁻ TO PAY F.B. G

18/171

1ᴰ⁻ F.B.A

18/172

1/- TO PAY F.S.

18/173

5½P. TO PAY F.S

18/174

	18/168	18/169	18/170	18/171	18/172	18/173	18/174
	Small IB	Large IS	Small IS	Small FB	Large FB	Small FS	Decimal FS
½d		4.00		5.00	4.00		1.00
1d	5.00	1.50	3.00	3.00	1.50	2.50	
1½d		2.00			3.00		
2d	4.00	2.00	2.50		2.00	2.50	0.80
2½d		5.00			3.00		1.00
3d		2.00	2.00		2.00	2.50	1.00
3½d		4.00				4.50	1.00
4d	2.00	2.00	2.50		3.00		0.80
4½d		4.00				1.20	
5d	6.00	2.00	2.00		4.00	2.00	1.50
5½d		5.00					1.00
6d		2.00	2.00		2.00	1.00	
6½d							1.50
7d	8.00	5.00		8.00	4.00	1.00	1.50
7½d		5.00			7.00		1.50
8d		5.00			5.00		1.50
8½d							2.00
9d		4.00		9.00	4.00		
9½d						3.00	
10d	10.00	8.00			5.00		
11d	12.00	8.00			10.00		
1/-	6.00	4.00				3.00	
1/0½d					15.00		
1/1d		10.00					
1/2d		10.00			10.00		
1/3d		10.00					
1/4d		10.00					
1/5d		10.00					
1/5½d					15.00		
1/6d		5.00					
1/7½d	15.00						
1/8d					8.00		
1/9d	15.00						
1/10½d	15.00						
2/-	12.00						
3/-	20.00						

Other IS/FS marks:

```
18/175  Above .. oz/1D/More to pay/I.S, boxed, T-Shaped .................    1.50
18/176  Address illegible/I.S. boxed. T-shaped ..........................    2.50
18/177  Charge not paid/I.S. boxed, T-shaped ............................    2.50
18/178  Contrary to Regulations/I.B. boxed, T-shaped ....................    3.00
18/179  Damaged by/Sea-water/M.P./I.S. ..................................   10.00
18/180  Delayed through being/posted in a letter box/for 'Country' letters/
            please advise sender, crinkly frame (used at ECDO) ..........    6.00
18/181  Delayed through being/posted in a letter box/for 'London' letters/
            please advise sender, crinkly frame .........................    6.00
        (the above two items were machine applied from 1927-68 - for full
            details see "Collecting Slogan Postmarks", for later see "This item")
18/182  Express/Fee Partly/Paid/To Pay/MP I.S. ..........................    6.00
18/183  Found Torn/and enclosed at/Inland Section, boxed, in purple .....    2.50
18/184  Insufficient Postage 1st Class/Transferred to 2nd Class, boxed ..    1.50
18/185  Insufficiently Addressed/I.S. boxed, T-shaped ...................    2.00
18/186  Invalid Stamps/Used/MP I.S., Postage Due ........................    5.00
18/187  I.S. in triangle, Inspector's mark ..............................    1.50
18/188  3D/I.S./More to/pay/ .. rate/above .. oz, boxed, in green .......    2.50
18/189  10D/I.S.M.P./To Pay/posted/underpaid, boxed in green ............    3.00
18/190  Liable to Letter Rate/I.B., boxed, T-shaped .....................    3.00
18/191  Liable to Letter Rate/I.S., boxed, T-shaped .....................    2.50
18/192  Liable to 2nd class rate/Unpaid Underpaid/Over...grammes/I.S.M.L.O.  2.00
18/193  More to pay/above .. oz/I.S., boxed, T-shaped, in green .........    1.50
18/194  Multipurpose charge box .........................................    0.50
18/195  8D/M.P.I.S./to pay/posted/unpaid/boxed ..........................    2.00
18/196  Not on board/Return to Sender, not boxed ........................    7.00
18/197  Posted on Board Ship Abroad/I.S., T-shaped ......................   10.00
```

18/186

18/206

```
18/198  Posted on Board Ship/I.S., T-shaped .............................   10.00
18/199  Posted on H.M.S./Abroad/I.S., boxed .............................   10.00
18/200  Posted out of course, boxed .....................................    3.00
18/201  Posted/out of/course/I.S. boxed .................................    3.00
18/202  Received/Posted Out/of course/London I.S.M.L.O. .................    5.00
18/203  R.L.D.I.S./Surcharge Duty/To pay, boxed .........................    3.00
18/204  Return to Sender/Address Insufficient/I.S., boxed, T-shaped .....    3.00
18/205  Stamp Disallowed/By Office of Posting/M.P. I.S./To Pay ..........    5.00
18/206  This item was not posted into the correct posting box....delay ..    2.50
            (applied by machine at ECDO before transfer to IS, see "Slogan
            Postmarks of the Eighties" for details of this and variations)
18/207  To Pay/I.S. boxed ...............................................    3.00
18/208  To pay/R.L.D.I.S., boxed ........................................    2.00
18/209  To Pay/Liable to Letter Rate/Posted Too Late/for Inclusion In/
            Printed Matter On/Day of Posting/D/I.S., boxed ..............    3.00
18/210  To pay/Postage cannot be/prepaid by means/of an incomplete/franking
            impression/liable to....rate/I.S. ...........................    2.00
18/211  1/- To pay/R.L.D.I.S., boxed ....................................    3.00
18/212  Undelivered for/Reason Stated/2D/Postage due/for return/to/Sender,
            in green ....................................................    1.50
18/213  Unpaid 2D to pay/Posted too late for ½d rate/I.S. boxed .........    5.00
18/214  W/X/Y/Z London ISMLO "lifebelt" style delayed code handstamp ....    3.00
```

18/214   18/216

18/222

(FS on this page)

18/215	Contrary to Regulations/F.B., boxed, T-shaped	3.00
18/216	Delayed - not fully paid, FS, "lifebelt" style handstamp (various)..	5.00
18/217	Exceeds Limits of size/F.S., T-shaped	3.00
18/218	Express Fee Paid, boxed	5.00
18/219	Insufficient/Address, boxed	2.00
18/220	Insufficiently Addressed, boxed, FS in panel at right	2.50
18/221	Liable to Letter Rate/F.S., boxed, T-shaped	4.00
18/222	Missent to/Great Britain/London Foreign Section, boxed	6.00
18/223	More to Pay/F.S.	2.50
18/224	More to/Pay/.. Rate/above .. /oz with F.S. and blank panel to left	2.00
18/225	No service/Return to sender, boxed, divided horizontally, purple ..	10.00
18/226	Not transmissible unpaid/Postage required, boxed	2.50
18/227	Postage stamps required/for overseas addresses (on Official Paid) ..	3.00
18/228	Posted out/of course, boxed	3.00
18/229	Returned for/better address, boxed, with FST inside right panel ...	4.00
18/230	Return to Sender/Open Panel F.S./Contrary to regulations, see page .. P.O. Guide, boxed, purple	5.00
18/231	Return to sender/No Transport links available/because of/Middle East Situation (1990) (variations)	10.00
18/232	Service suspended, boxed	10.00
18/233	Stamp not valid for overseas mail, boxed (uncertain where applied)	3.00
18/234	Stamps not valid, with F.S., boxed	3.00
18/235	This item stopped in transit. Postage stamps required overseas mail	4.00
18/236	Too Late/F.B.G.P.O., small circle	5.00
18/237	T/15c (or manuscript value) in hexagon, with L for London beneath ..	2.00
18/238	T/1d in hexagon, with FS beneath (see note below)	4.00

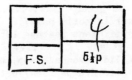

18/237   18/238   18/239

Note : the system for calculating surcharges on overseas underpaid mail varied over the years, the basis being the centime to 1965 (though sterling marks are also known, see above), then a fraction system took over with new surcharge marks of which the following is an example; the marks applied did not apply to FS alone, see next section.

| **18/239** | T/F.S./5½p in 4-part box | 2.00 |
| 18/240 | Undelivered for reason stated/Returned to Sender, with FSR inside panel to right | 1.50 |

Charge marks confined to mail from abroad (incl Channel Is):

18/241	Accountancy Marks (to 1875)	15.00
18/242	Cents marks used at Liverpool	5.00
18/243	Hexagonal marks with L for London	2.50

(see note above, similar to outgoing mail, these hexagonal marks also seen on incoming overseas mail)

18/244	Insufficiently Paid ...... to pay 258 (Dover)	3.00
18/245	Over grammes ...d more to pay/258 (Dover), boxed	3.00
18/246	It is regretted that/this item could not be/delivered because the/ addressee is reported/missing, boxed, purple	10.00
18/247	This Letter formed Part of Undelivered/Mails which fell into the hands of/The Allied Forces in Germany. It is/Undeliverable as addressed, and is/Therefore returned to you, boxed (W War II) ...	30.00
18/248	This letter has been returned by/The Swiss Post Office who were/ unable to forward it to Germany/because of the interruption of/ communications, boxed (World War II)	30.00
18/249	To pay/Channel Island/Stamps not/admissible when..873 (Weymouth) ..	5.00
18/250	To Pay, plus value, dated or undated, 1970s-	1.50

Charge Marks used countrywide (see note at end of section)

18/251	Charge Not collected/X/Fresh label required, boxed	0.50
18/252	CH, in circle	5.00
18/253	Contains enclosure liable to letter rate Manchester F.S.	4.00
18/254	..D to Pay, boxed	2.50
18/255	Delayed not fully paid, Manchester FS, "lifebelt" style handstamp ..	5.00
18/256	Imperfect impression/6d to Pay, boxed	2.00
18/257	Insufficiently stamped	2.50
18/258	Insufficiently Prepaid for airmail, boxed	4.00
18/259	Insufficiently Prepaid/For Transmission by Air, boxed	4.00
18/260	Insufficiently Paid boxed	2.00
18/261	Insufficiently paid/..d to pay, boxed with or without office number, in green	0.50
18/262	Insufficiently paid/.., to pay, boxed with office number, in green	0.50
18/263	Insufficient Postage 1st Class/Transferred to 2nd class, boxed, green	1.00
18/264	Invalid Revenue/Stamp, boxed, in green	5.00
18/265	Invalid Stamps Used/Postage Due .., boxed	3.00
18/266	Liable to Letter Rate, boxed	2.50
18/267	Liable to Postage surcharge/imperfect Meter franking, unframed in green	1.50
18/268	Liable to Surcharge/Imperfect/Meter franking, boxed with office number	1.50
18/269	LSD stamps/Now Invalid, boxed in green	5.00
18/270	£sd stamps/invalid/ to pay	5.00
18/271	More to pay (many types)	2.00
18/272	OS in double circle for 'Old Stamp' with 1840 Penny Black	750.00
18/273	Over Grammes/..d More to Pay, with office number	2.00
18/274	Postage cannot be/prepaid by means/of incomplete/franking impressions (variations, framed/unframed, usually in green) ..	1.50

18/251

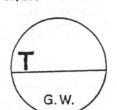

18/266

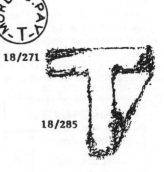

18/271

```
STAMP DISALLOWED
BY OFFICE OF POSTING
```

18/278

18/284

18/285

18/275	Short-Paid/Posted Unpaid/over .. g/T, with office number	3.00
18/276	Stamp Invalid, unframed	4.00
18/277	Stamps/Missing in/Transit, boxed, in red	4.00
18/278	Stamp disallowed/By office of posting, boxed	4.00
18/279	Surcharged/Amount underpaid etc	0.50
18/280	Surcharged/Stamps invalid, boxed	4.00
18/281	Surcharge/No licence held/Licence cancelled (on business reply) ...	3.00
18/282	Surcharge Fee/10p boxed	1.00
18/283	T/15c in small hexagon, with or without office number beneath (used on overseas items, see note above under FS listing)	2.00
18/284	T/G.W., overseas "fractional" taxe system from 1960s (Glasgow), but variety of designs from other offices	2.00
18/285	T marks (large), used largely in NE England, solid, outline or boxed, to indicate underpayment on INLAND mail, usually green	0.50
18/286	T incorporated into other surcharge marks (NE England)	1.50
18/287	To Pay/13p, boxed green (and other values)	0.50
18/288	To Pay/Ldn. RLB unframed 1d, 3d, etc.	2.00
18/289	20p to Pay (and other values), some dated	0.50
18/290	14p/to Pay/Posted/Unpaid/Second Class, boxed (and other values) ...	0.75
18/291	To Pay/liable to/Postcard Rate, rectangular with blank panel for amount and office number	2.50
18/292	To pay/on return/to sender/Postage/deficiency, in three sections with blank panel for amount and office number	1.00
18/293	To Pay/Postage cannot be/prepaid by means/of an incomplete/ franking impression/liable to .. rate, boxed with blank value tablet to left and office number or London District letters, green, black or purple	1.50
18/294	To Pay/amount/Postage Unpaid, boxed	0.50
18/295	Underpaid/Diverted to/Second Class	2.00
18/296	Unpaid, boxed or unboxed	0.50
18/297	Unpaid/Postage/And Fee/Due, boxed	2.50

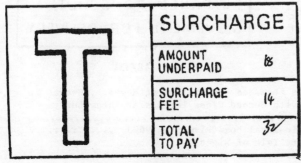

18/286

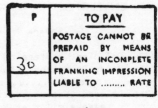

18/293

Note : modern surcharge marks are often produced locally and have no standard pattern and examples are shown below - **18/302** is a standard type in East Anglia however (usually red) from 1995. All value 0.50. From 1983 the surcharge system of "double deficiency" was replaced by the raising of a surcharge fee, initially 10p, added to the deficiency (and ½p rounded down). Details of later surcharge fees are given in the Postal Rates section at the end of this book. Illustration **18/303** shows a surcharge mark with a spelling error - value 2.50

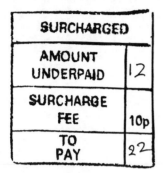

18/298

18/299

18/300

18/301

18/302

18/303

Instructional & Explanatory Marks used countrywide

18/304 Actually Posted on/date/Incorrectly Dated By/Sender. Use Correct/
         Date for L.I.S. Sampling, boxed 2.50
18/305 Address Defective/Please advise sender, boxed, in purple 2.00
18/306 Avoid delay - Undelivered mail....senders name etc 2.50
18/307 Business reply and/Freepost correspondence/docketed and charged ... 2.50
18/308 Correct Endorsement/Please, T-shaped 2.00

AVOID DELAY
UNDELIVERED MAIL IS
RETURNED WITH GREATER
SPEED (and unopened) IF THE
SENDERS NAME, ADDRESS
AND POSTAL CODE ARE
SHOWN ON OUTSIDE OF
ENVELOPE OR WRAPPER.

18/306

ITEM FOUND IN OFFICIAL
POSTAL SYSTEM.
RETURNED TO SCOUT
MOVEMENT FOR DELIVERY

18/331

18/309 Deficient postage on this item/has been raised at Newport, Gwent .. 3.00
18/310 Delay Regretted - Found/with Second Class letters/at Shrewsbury,
         boxed 3.00
18/311 Delayed through posting in local box (Plymouth 1969) 4.00
         (also similar at Newport Isle of Wight)
18/312 Demolished 1.00

```
18/313  Do not charge/Mistreated in Post  ..................................  3.00
18/314  Endorse and dispose, boxed  .......................................  2.00
18/315  Exceptionally this letter must not be redirected etc  .............  2.50
18/316  For correct/Endorsement please, boxed  ............................  3.00
18/317  Found Damaged In/A Pillar Box Fire/At .., boxed  ..................  5.00
18/318  Found-in-FNO (Foreign Newspaper Office)/without contents  .........  5.00
18/319  Found in mixed/bundle of first/and second class/meter items  ......  2.50
18/320  Found in WCDO/without contents, boxed  ............................  3.00
18/321  Gone away, boxed or unboxed  ......................................  1.00
18/322  Gone away/Address Not known, boxed  ...............................  1.50
18/323  Gone away/1/2, boxed  .............................................  1.50
18/324  Gone away/Left No Address  ........................................  2.00
18/325  Gone away/Return to Sender  .......................................  0.50
18/326  Gone away/Not known/Demolished, boxed  ............................  2.00
18/327  House/Unoccupied, boxed  ..........................................  2.00
18/328  Insufficiently Addressed, boxed  ..................................  0.75
18/329  Irregularly included by posted/in a bundle of late posted/meter-
            franked printed papers, framed in green  ......................  1.50
18/330  Item delayed due to/vague address, boxed  .........................  2.50
18/331  Item found in Official/Postal System./Returned to Scout/Movement
            for delivery, boxed (Sheffield)  ..............................  8.00
18/332  Items delayed/underpaid/Extra Revenue collected/by Derby Finance Dept  1.50
18/333  Late Fee/Paid, boxed  .............................................  5.00
18/334  Liverpool MLO/Trapped in Machinery, dated single circle  ..........  8.00
18/335  Mail opened and disposed/of at Liverpool (etc), boxed  ............  4.00
18/336  Misdirected To, unframed  .........................................  2.00
18/337  Moved/Please return/to sender  ....................................  1.50
18/338  No longer in residence/Return to sender  ..........................  2.50
18/339  No post town, boxed or unboxed  ...................................  2.00
18/340  No such street/Greenford Middx, many similar types, boxed or unboxed  2.00
18/341  No such street/(or place) in .. unframed  .........................  1.00
18/342  Not called for, boxed with office number  .........................  2.00
18/343  Not known, boxed or unboxed  ......................................  0.50
18/344  Not known at address stated/Forwarding particulars not available,
            boxed  ........................................................  5.00
18/345  Not known/Southport,/Lancs, many similar types, boxed or unboxed  ..  3.00
18/346  Open Panel/Return to sender/Inadmissible for/Transmission Abroad,
            boxed purple  .................................................  2.50
18/347  Please inform sender/of your correct address, boxed  ..............  2.00
18/348  Postage Refunded, straight line  ..................................  3.00
18/349  Posted after the last/collection of the Date/shown on the Postmark,
            unboxed (see chapter 27 for more related marks on meter mail)  ..  2.00
18/350  Posted in/Post Office/Posting Box/liable to surcharge  ............  5.00
18/351  Posted in/Second Class Pouch/Hull APC HU7 0AA (1993)  .............  1.50
18/352  Posted Out of Course, with London initials, boxed  ................  4.00
18/353  Premises boarded up/Unable to gain access/Date etc  ...............  2.50
```

POSTED IN SECOND CLASS POUCH 30 MAR 1993 HULL APC HU7 0AA

18/351

THE POST OFFICE REGRETS THAT THIS ITEM HAS BEEN DELAYED AS A RESULT OF INDUSTRIAL ACTION WHICH AFFECTED THE LIVERPOOL/BELFAST FERRY.

18/367

THIS ITEM WAS INCORRECTLY
INCLUDED WITH 2ND CLASS
ITEMS BY THE SENDER AND MAY
BE DELAYED

18/370

```
UNDELIVERED FOR REASON STATED
```
```
RETURN TO SENDER
```

18/378

THIS UNDELIVERABLE LETTER
WOULD HAVE BEEN RETURNED
TO YOU
(A) MORE QUICKLY
(B) UNOPENED

IF YOUR NAME AND ADDRESS
HAD BEEN SHEWN ON THE
REVERSE SIDE OF THE COVER

18/372

18/354	Present Location Uncertain (World War I)	10.00
18/355	Property boarded up/Initials Badge no. Date, boxed	1.50
18/356	P.T.O., boxed or unboxed	0.50
18/357	Received at Post Office London, in an otherwise empty bag from	4.00
18/358	Repaired in R.P.S. London Overseas Mail Office, boxed	2.00
18/359	Returned letter	0.50
18/360	Returned for/Endorsement please, boxed	2.00
18/361	Return sender/moved, boxed	1.50
18/362	Return to delivery officer/for endorsement/badge no. etc	2.00
18/363	Return to sender/Not known at this address, unboxed	1.50
18/364	Return to sender/Undelivered for reasons stated, boxed, without horizontal division, purple	0.50
18/365	Ship Sailed, boxed	10.00
18/366	Sorting Office (town name)/Returned for Endorsement, boxed	2.50
18/367	The Post Office regrets....delay....Liverpool/Belfast ferry (1981)..	8.00
18/368	This item has been/franked in Excess. For/Adjustment of the Account Please return cover to:-/District Postmaster (PB27) W.D.O. London, W1P 1AA/via your postman/Post Office	5.00
18/369	This item was found with with/2nd class items causing delay	2.00
18/370	This item was incorrectly included with 2nd class items (variations)	2.00
18/371	This item was posted/After the last collection/on the date shown, boxed (see "Posted after last collection..." on previous page)	2.00
18/372	This undeliverable letter...name & address on reverse side	3.00
18/373	Too late - ship sailed, unframed in black	5.00
18/374	Transferred to Second Class/Insufficient postage for first/class service 367	2.00
18/375	Unable to Deliver/Return to Sender, boxed	1.50
18/376	Unaddressed	1.50
18/377	Unclaimed, boxed or unboxed	2.00
18/378	Undelivered for reason stated/return to sender, boxed in two horizontal sections in purple, black or green (red 0.50)	0.20
18/379	As above but 'reasons' (see next section)	0.50
18/380	As above but unboxed	1.00
18/381	As above but also Returned from R.L.O. London	3.00
18/382	Undelivered for reason stated/to be returned to sender/at the address shown on cover, boxed in two horizontal sections	2.00
18/383	Undelivered for/reasons stated/Return to Sender/PHG Intls No, boxed	2.00
18/384	Word Postcard Omitted/Liable to Letter Rate, used Southampton 1905	20.00
18/385	Writer of a letter addressed/to	2.00
18/386	Wrongly Dated By/Poster Not to be/Sampled Under L.I.S., boxed	2.00
18/387	Your correct postal address is/Any other form of address may lead/to delay. Please advise sender	2.00

Multipurpose marks explaining non-delivery, framed or unframed

Illustrations **18/388** to **18/394** show examples of the range of these marks, some of which show the office name or number, or refer to the office in the text (see Ipswich in **18/393**); wording usually starts with "Return to sender" or "Undelivered for reason stated" – value 0.50.

Undelivered For Reason Stated.	18th.
Deceased	
Definitely Refused	
Gone Away	
Not Known	
Ship Sailed	
Insufficient Address	

18/388

Undelivered for reason stated	323		
Return to sender	GRIMSBY		
Premises demolished		Gone away	✓
Not to be found		No such Street	
Insufficient address		Deceased	
Not known at No.		Refused	

18/389

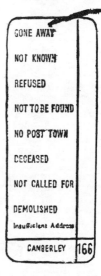

UNDELIVERED FOR REASONS STATED, BELOW
NO TRACE .... ✗
UNIT DISBANDED ....
INSUFFICIENTLY ADDRESSED ......
DATE 070750
LOCATIONS BRANCH B.F.P.O. LONDON

18/390

RETURN TO SENDER
UNDELIVERED FOR REASON STATED

Unoccupied .... Demolished ....
Not Called for.......... Deceased ....
Insufficiently Addressed ....
Addressee Not Known
Gone Away 60/65 Refused ....
Address Not Known
447

18/391

1. RETURN TO SENDER
UNDELIVERED FOR REASON STATED

GONE AWAY .... DECEASED ....

NOT KNOWN.......... REFUSED ....

NO ANSWER.......... NOT CALLED FOR...

NO SUCH ADDRESS IN ....

INSUFFICIENTLY ADDRESSED ....

NO POINT OF DELIVERY ....

HOUSE UNOCCUPIED ....

FOUND AT IPSWICH WITHOUT ADDRESS

ADDRESS UNREADABLE ....

18/393

GONE AWAY

NOT KNOWN

REFUSED

NOT TO BE FOUND

NO POST TOWN

DECEASED

NOT CALLED FOR

DEMOLISHED

Insufficient Address

CAMBERLEY	166

18/394

RETURN TO SENDER
UNDELIVERED FOR REASON STATED

GONE AWAY .... DECEASED ....

NOT KNOWN .... REFUSED ....

NOT OCCUPIED .... NOT CALLED FOR..

NO SUCH ADDRESS INSUFFICIENTLY ADDRESSED ....

18/392

RLB/RLO Handstamps

The marks described in this chapter are often accompanied by handstamps confirming details of location and date. Frequently these are specially inscribed and examples are shown below. Value 0.25 for modern items but rising to 5.00 for pre-1930 items.

18/395

EDINBURGH A JU 22 05 R.L.O.

RETURNED LETTER BRANCH 6 DEC 71 BELFAST

18/396

PORTSMOUTH 14 OCT 1992 SURCHARGE

18/397

REWRAP SECTION M.L.O. 21 SEP 1992 GLASGOW

18/398

LETTER DISTRICT OFFICE, LIVERPOOL L8 1AA REVENUE PROTECTION 30 NOV 1992 051 242 4336 SPL EXAMINER

18/399

BRITISH POSTMARK SOCIETY

always extends a welcome to enthusiastic collectors .... who might be ...

... raving over RSOs ...

... squiffy with squared circles ...

... crazy on Columbias ...

... terrific over Too Lates ...

... dotty over duplexes ...

... silly over slogans ...

... steamed up over stations ...

... potty over placenames ...

... mad about machines ...

... surrounded with surcharges ...

... titillated by TPOs ...

... insane over ink-jets ...

... freaked out with field post offices ...

... cuckoo on counter stamps ...

... krinkly over Krags ...

... foolish over first days ...

25 January - Robert Burns Death Bicentenary

S 271
26 February - Greetings

S 272
12 March Wi

PB 257
16 April

PB 258
14 May

d 259

PB 26

40 / 10

BRITISH POSTMARK SOCIETY
- B -
1 JAN 1958

BRITISH POSTMARK SOCIETY QUARTERLY BULLETIN

Volume 40

January 1997

Number 1

all correspondence on editorial matters to the Hon Editor
Reynolds, 24 Thirlmere Drive, Stowmarket, Suffolk IP14 1SE
Tel: 01449/613319 E-mail: 101654.3006@compuserve.com
Internet: http://ourworld.compuserve.com/homepages/Barry_Reynolds
items for 'Society News', advertisements and general correspondence to the Hon S
Thorp, Struanlea, 4 Haugh Road, Dalbeattie, Stewartry of Kirkcudbright, DG5 4A

MACHINE NEWS

(this section written by Colin Peachey - reports direct to him pleas)

1. ABERDEEN DROPS "ROYAL MAIL" FROM NEW TOWN DIES
Last year I put forward my theory concerning offices whose CFC dies w
totally illegible. Although, as I write these notes in November 1996,
Guildford soldier on with illegible dies, at least Aberdeen has come
It was one of three offices (the other two being Swindon and L
"Royal Mail" in (some of) the town die inscriptions, and
remains. The new dies show, I am pleased to say, some ma
Patrick Awcock to cover the CFC and FCT dies, and in the
(shown here) used in red on Paid mail.

2. NEW DIES AT EDINBURGH AND BOURNEMOUTH
It's as though Royal Mail read these columns! Indistinguishable town
dies have been used at Edinburgh, but since dropping "Lothian Fife
Borders" in 1995 there has been plenty of room to include a machine
identity. Now they have done so, and new dies show CFC and FCT -
one of the latter is shown here. The meaning of die letters probably
used in SCMs is less clear. F (shown here) and M having been seen so far - more repo
M has been seen on meter items with the date corrected so maybe that die is used on
Then Bournemouth did the same with its "Dorset & SW Hants" dies, and CFC1 ha
late November 1996, which I will leave Patrick Awcock to illustrate and include in his

3. GREAT BRITAIN DIES USED IN BLACK
I bring the 1996 list to a close with one more report, that of Hatfield use
shown here used in November. My convention has been to include all D
each year in the Christmas reserve list, and accordingly I plan to produce such a list
for the April Bulletin including December 1996 usages.

4. PAID MAIL STAMPE ... ACK (39/5, 39/61)
A number of membe
without I do n
worth noti   ed Wolverhampton in black, both with Great Britai
                 all the offices using black ink for Paid mail but I

ABERDEEN APC
18 NOV 1996

EDINBURGH
8 - PM
28 OCT 1996
FCT A

EDINBU
5 - 3
1996

HATFIELD,HERTS
27 NOV 1996
GT BRITAIN

40 / 1

For only £8 per annum (current subscription 1997, £8 extra for airmail postage outside Europe) members are offered a Quarterly Bulletin, an annual auction and sale, Exchange Packets, a Library, London and regional meetings, and so on ....

For details and application form please write to the Membership Secretary:
Ole Constantine, 9 Hillfield Road, Hawarden, Deeside CH5 3AB

19. Newspaper, Parcel, Registered, Express and Triangular Postmarks

Newspaper Branch (prices are for large pieces or Newspaper Wrappers)

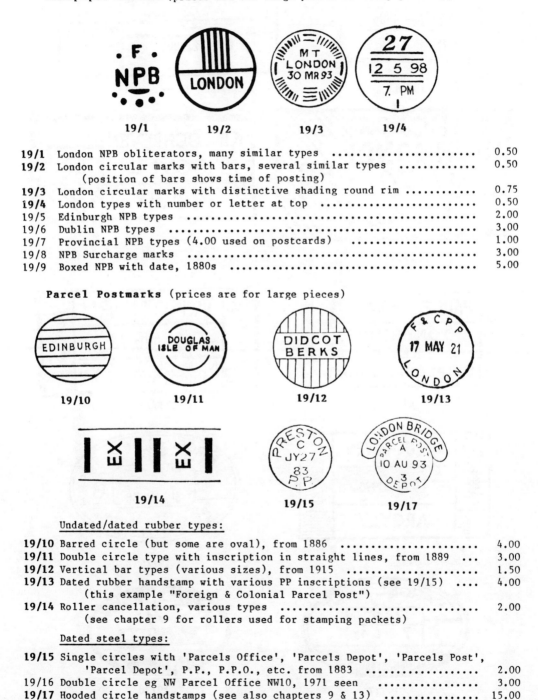

| | 19/1 | 19/2 | 19/3 | 19/4 |

19/1 London NPB obliterators, many similar types 0.50
19/2 London circular marks with bars, several similar types 0.50
    (position of bars shows time of posting)
19/3 London circular marks with distinctive shading round rim 0.75
19/4 London types with number or letter at top 0.50
19/5 Edinburgh NPB types 2.00
19/6 Dublin NPB types 3.00
19/7 Provincial NPB types (4.00 used on postcards) 1.00
19/8 NPB Surcharge marks 3.00
19/9 Boxed NPB with date, 1880s 5.00

Parcel Postmarks (prices are for large pieces)

| | 19/10 | 19/11 | 19/12 | 19/13 |

| | 19/14 | 19/15 | 19/17 |

Undated/dated rubber types:

19/10 Barred circle (but some are oval), from 1886 .... 4.00
19/11 Double circle type with inscription in straight lines, from 1889 ... 3.00
19/12 Vertical bar types (various sizes), from 1915 .... 1.50
19/13 Dated rubber handstamp with various PP inscriptions (see 19/15) 4.00
    (this example "Foreign & Colonial Parcel Post")
19/14 Roller cancellation, various types 2.00
    (see chapter 9 for rollers used for stamping packets)

Dated steel types:

19/15 Single circles with 'Parcels Office', 'Parcels Depot', 'Parcels Post',
    'Parcel Depot', P.P., P.P.O., etc. from 1883 .... 2.00
19/16 Double circle eg NW Parcel Office NW10, 1971 seen 3.00
19/17 Hooded circle handstamps (see also chapters 9 & 13) 15.00

Rubber Parcel handstamps (termed "label types" for **19/19** onwards since based on a facsimile of parcel labels used previously)

19/18

19/19

19/20

19/21

19/22

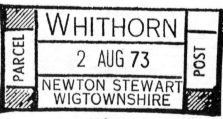

19/23

19/24

19/26

19/27

19/28

19/18	Concave corners	10.00
19/19	Label type, usually in violet, from 1887 (variations)	2.50
19/20	Revised design, from 1915, without arms but with telegraphic code ..	5.00
19/21	Revised design, from 1925, no arms or telegraphic code	2.00
19/22	Undated wartime "economy" parcel handstamp, 1940s	4.00
19/23	Revised design, from 1958, with date at centre, Parcel/Post at ends	1.00
	(date composed of loose type, year 2 digits)	
19/24	Shorter design, from 1979, with revolving date wheels, year 4 digits	0.50

Paid Parcel rubber handstamps (in red)

19/25	Concave corners	6.00
19/26	Large oval double rim design, from 1892, with coat of arms at top ..	6.00
19/27	As above but without coat of arms, from 1940	1.50
19/28	Undated wartime "economy" handstamp, 1940s	8.00
19/29	Label type, similar to **19/24**, with PAID, post-1979	5.00
	(now little used, PPIs having largely taken over the function)	

Registration

19/32   **19/42**   **19/45**

19/30	Money-Letter, straight line, 1830s	100.00
19/31	Crown with 'Registered' above, Foreign Office from 1820s	50.00
19/32	As above but crown above Registered, London and Provincial, 1836-71	25.00
19/33	As above, European Country above, 1850s-60s in red	50.00
19/34	Registered, straight line, from 1850s	20.00
19/35	As above but also with town name, e.g. Registered Scarbro oval ...	40.00
19/36	Single circle marks struck alongside numeral obliterator, from 1850s	15.00
19/37	Liverpool 466 registered spoon (see chapter 7)	150.00
19/38	Double circle marks, alongside obliterators or as obliterators, from	
	1860s	12.00
19/39	As above but with thick arcs, Scottish offices, from 1920s	4.00
19/40	As above but R breaking thin arcs	2.00
19/41	Oval, Registered/GPO and side arcs, 1856-7	75.00
19/42	Oval Registered marks, steel, from 1860s	2.00
	(date composed of loose type, month 2 characters, year 2 digits)	
	(value higher pre-1930, at least 15.00 pre-1900)	
19/43	As above but incorporating reference to 2d fee	5.00

Note : the following 3 items normally accompany other postmarks on cover thus the value has to be "combined" with that of these marks.

19/44	R in circle or oval, from 1885	3.00
19/45	As above but with Fee Paid, from 1892	3.00
19/46	Registered 2d straight line, boxed or unboxed	5.00
19/47	Single circle marks incorporating reference to 2d fee	7.50
19/48	Oval Registered marks, rubber, from 1890s (cf. steel **19/42**)	2.50
	(date composed of loose type, month 3 characters, year 2 digits)	
	(see valuation comments for "steel" above)	
19/49	Undated wartime "economy" registered handstamp, 1940s	6.00
19/50	Oval double-rim rubber handstamps from 1980, date on revolving wheels,	
	year four digits	2.00

19/48   **19/49**   **19/50**   **19/54**

19/51 Circular Registration handstamps, rubber (Climax, see **9/36**) 15.00
19/52 Skeleton Registration handstamps 20.00
19/53 Hooded Registration handstamps, steel (month 2 characters) 5.00
19/54   same but rubber (month 3 characters), double-rim, black/purple . 6.00
19/55 Small oval A.R. ('Avis de Reception') to denote reply required
           under the 'Advice of Delivery' service 5.00

Express (also "Priority Services", new term from 1993 to cover Guaranteed
Delivery and Registration Services)

19/57       **19/58**

19/56 Express - straight line types 20.00
19/57 Express - oval types 3.00
19/58 Priority Services rubber handstamps, from 1993 .... 1.50

Triangular Handstamps
(used to denote posting under specific printed paper regulations - to 1968)

19/59   **19/61**   **19/64**   **19/67**   **19/68**   **19/70**

19/59 With telegraphic code letters 1.50
19/60 With London District initials or London Head Office initials eg S.M.,
       K.E., M.T.P., F.B., F.S., I.S. 1.00
19/61 With provincial office numbers 1.50

"Inspectors' marks" (usually denoting an irregularity has been noted)

19/62 Diamond marks at Manchester, L.C. and L.C.O. at Letter Carriers' Office,
      H.O. at Head Office, 1876-1912 .... 5.00
19/63 Diamond marks with London District Office initials or I.S. c1900 .... 4.00

     Small inverted triangles denoting mail missorted to wrong stream
          (values higher pre-1902) :
19/64   G.E, MID, N.W, S.E, S.W, SUBN, all with numbers or + ... 1.50
19/65   G.W, with numbers 2.00
19/66   SCOTCH, WELSH or IRISH with numbers 3.00
19/67 Small triangle (still in use 1980s) 1.50
19/68 Small oval, district initials plus numbers 1.00
19/69 Rubber triangle, MR (Manchester), 1970s 2.50
19/70   similar sized rubber triangle, S42/APC/Glasgow, 1996 .... 2.50

    See chapters 9, 14 and 27 for further triangular handstamps.

20. Posted in Advance for Christmas Postmarks

In the late 1800s, Post Office officials became concerned about annual increases in the number of postings at Christmas. Their problem was the need to effect next day delivery for normal business mail as well as the large amount of seasonal greetings. Several alternative proposals were considered and in 1902 it was decided to experiment at Rochdale. For six days prior to Christmas week, greetings to local addresses could be handed in, for delivery on Christmas Day. Green ½d stamps were cancelled in red: red 1d stamps were cancelled in black. Special handstamps were designed for the purpose.

In 1903 the scope of the scheme was extended to a total of 28 towns. It was not a success, so in 1904 only 14 towns were included in the experiment. In 1905 the number dropped to 6. Further special efforts were made during each of the years 1906-9 by 27 offices, but after a total of eight years of modifications and trials, the experiment was eventually abandoned.

Known examples of the special handstamps (and one machine postmark) are listed. We are indebted to (the late) John Swanborough for a detailed analysis of auction realisations and dealers' prices. Only two specimens of the Cheltenham undated postmark are known to us, and the year is thought to be 1903 though not confirmed by the envelope contents.

20/1 Type 1   20/2 Type 2   20/3 Type 3 (parcels)

20/4 Type 4   20/5 Type 5: Columbia Machine

20/6 Type 6

Town (TC = telegraph code, type 2 only)	TC	Year	Type	Colour	Val'n
Altrincham	ADJ	1903	2		£300
		1904	2		£275
		1905	2		£250
		1906	4		£300
		1907	4		£300
		1908	4		£300
		1909	4		£300
Ashton Under Lyne		1906	4		£400
		1907	4		£400
		1908	4		£300
Birkenhead		1906	4		£200
		1907	4		£150
		1908	4		£150
		1909	4		£100
Bolton	BL	1903	2		£200
		1904	2		£200
Bradford	BD	1904	2	red	£400
Bury	BC	1903	2	red	£300
Carlisle	CE	1904	2		£500
Cheltenham		1903	6	red	£350
(see note opposite)					
Douglas IOM		1906	4		£300
		1907	4		£300
		1908	4		£275
		1909	4		£275
Dover	DR	1903	2		£600
Dukinfield		1909	4		£500
Eccles		1906	4		£300
		1907	4		£300
		1908	4		£200
		1909	4		£200
Glasgow	GW	1904	2		£200
Glossop		1907	4		£500
		1908	4		£500
Hull	HU	1903	2	red	£250
Hyde		1906	4		£600
		1907	4		£600
		1908	4		£500
		1909	4		£550
Knutsford		1906	4		£500
Leicester	LE	1903	2	red	£200
		1904	2	red	£200
		1908	4		£150
Leigh, Lancs		1907	4		£400
Liverpool		1906	4		£100
		1907	4		£100
		1908	4		£90
		1909	4		£90
Macclesfield	MC	1903	2	red	£300
Manchester	MR	1903	2		£100
		1904	2		£95
		1905	2		£80
		1905	3	violet	£200
		1905	3	black	£150
		1906	3	black	£200
		1906	4		£90
		1906	5		£100
		1907	4		£70
Manchester		1907	5		£100
		1908	4		£70
		1908	5		£100
		1909	4		£55
		1909	5		£100
Newton Le Willows		1906	4		£500
		1907	4		£500
Norwich		1907	4		£350
		1908	4		£200
Oldham		1906	4		£300
		1908	4		£200
		1909	4		£300
Ormskirk		1906	4		£500
		1909	4		£400
Prescot		1907	4		£500
		1909	4		£500
Preston	PR	1904	2		£400
Reading		1908	4	red	£400
		1908	4	black	£300
Rochdale	RO	1902	1	red	£450
		1902	1	black	£750
		1903	2	red	£250
		1904	2	red	£250
Runcorn		1907	4		£500
St. Helens		1906	4		£300
		1907	4		£300
Sale	SCR	1903	2		£400
		1904	2		£250
		1905	2		£250
		1906	2		£200
		1907	2		£200
		1908	2		£150
		1909	2		£150
Southport	SP	1903	2		£400
Stalybridge		1907	4		£500
Stockport		1906	4		£200
		1907	4		£300
		1908	4		£200
		1909	4		£200
Wakefield	WF	1903	2	red	£300
Walsall	WL	1903	2	red	£200
Warrington	WA	1903	2		£300
		1904	2		£300
		1905	2		£200
		1906	4		£200
		1907	4		£200
		1908	4		£200
		1909	4		£150
Widnes	WIP	1904	2		£450
		1905	2		£450
		1906	4		£500
Wigan	WI	1903	2		£250
		1904	2		£200
		1905	2		£150
		1906	4		£150
		1907	4		£150
		1908	4		£150
		1909	4		£150

21. Parliamentary

For many years members of both Houses of Parliament were able to post letters without charge, using the Free Frank system. This system ceased upon the adoption of the Uniform Penny Post. Thereafter, to have the benefit of free postage, Members were required to use specially printed envelopes which could be posted only from Parliament. Letters were bagged and taken to the Post Office, where they received a Crown Paid handstamp. Later, special postmarks were introduced.

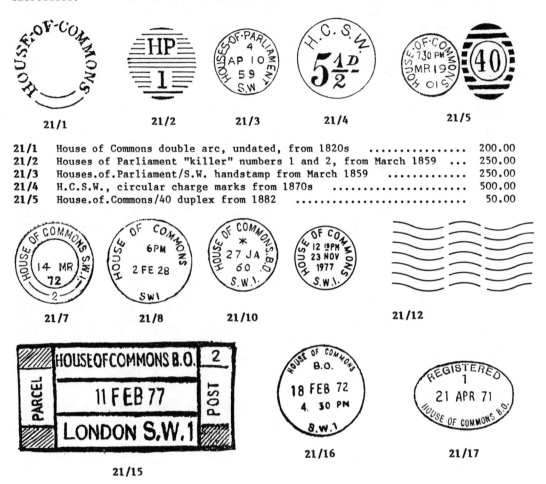

21/1	21/2	21/3	21/4	21/5

21/1   House of Commons double arc, undated, from 1820s 200.00
21/2   Houses of Parliament "killer" numbers 1 and 2, from March 1859 ... 250.00
21/3   Houses.of.Parliament/S.W. handstamp from March 1859 .... 250.00
21/4   H.C.S.W., circular charge marks from 1870s 500.00
21/5   House.of.Commons/40 duplex from 1882 .... 50.00

21/7	21/8	21/10	21/12

21/15	

21/16	21/17

21/6   House of Commons S.W.1, double circle, thick arcs (several), 1912-60   5.00
21/7   As above but -1- and -2-, with thin arcs 1.00
21/8   House of Commons skeleton handstamp, 1928 .... 100.00
21/9   House of Commons B.O. S.W.1./Official Paid, double circle, red ...   2.00
21/10 House of Commons B.O./S.W.1. single circle (variations) 5.00
21/11   As above but SID handstamp, from about 1995 ....   2.00
21/12 House of Commons/S.W.1 (later SW.1.) universal machine 0.50
21/13   As above but with Official Paid sideways in bars, red 3.00
21/14   As above but 'House of Commons/SW', red, from 1991 (used on mail
             from outstationed parliamentary offices in Westminster) 1.00
21/15 House of Commons B.O. rubber parcel handstamp (variations) 20.00
21/16 House of Commons/B.O./S.W.1, rubber packet handstamp (variations)   3.00
21/17 Registered/1/House of Commons B.O. oval handstamp (variations) ... 25.00

H.P   H:P.

21/18   **21/19**   **21/20**   **21/21**

21/18	H.P (House of Peers), small with dot between letters, 1820s/30s .	550.00
21/19	H:P (ditto), larger with 2 dots between letters, 1830s-1843	850.00
21/20	House of Lords S.W.1./-1-, double circle with thin arcs (variations)	3.00
21/21	House of Lords S.W.1/Official Paid, double circle, red	4.00

Cachets:

21/23   **21/27**   **21/28**   **21/31**

21/22	House of/Commons, oval certifying stamp with crown from 1909	5.00
21/23	House of Commons/Speaker, upright oval with crown (varieties)	1.00
21/24	Vote Office/House of Commons, oval with coat of arms	8.00
21/25	Parliamentary Counsel/Office, double oval	8.00
21/26	Office of/Parliamentary/Commissioner, triangular	8.00
21/27	Clerk of the Parliaments/House of Lords, oval with coat of arms ..	5.00
21/28	As above but small double circle, crown above (two diff crowns)	3.00
21/29	Black Rod/House of Lords, oval with central coat of arms	8.00
21/30	Staff Superintendent/House of Lords, with central coat of arms ...	8.00
21/31	Lord Great Chamberlain/House of Lords, double circle (varieties) ..	5.00
21/32	The Lord Chancellor, straight line script lettering (various colours)	2.00
21/33	Fees Office/House of Commons/London SW1A 0AA	8.00
21/34	Postmaster/House of Commons, 1970s-	5.00

Note : it is difficult to give values to the above cachets since some were used over many years. Some, though still in use in the late 20th century, are not easy to find. Suggested valuation scale is as follows :

     1960 to date - as listed above
     1940-1960 - above values times 2
     1930s   - above values times 3
     1920s   - above values times 5
     prior to 1920 - scarce; prior to 1910 extremely scarce

22. Royalty

Throughout the developments of the mails described in earlier chapters, Royal letters were carried free in the post. But Queen Victoria paid postage on many of her letters after abolition of the Free Franking system on 10 January 1840. Edward VII also paid postage on some of his letters. In the 20th century most royal covers bear a cachet, usually featuring the royal cypher, as a means of authorising the mail as official. This includes personal letters from the royal family as well as business mail from the Royal Household. Postmarks are mainly "Official Paid" handstamps or machine marks. There are also special handstamps which include a crown or the name of a royal residence. * denotes items of rarity.

Royal Residences (some for short visits only) :

| 22/1 | 22/2 | 22/5 | 22/9 |

Queen Victoria (first two items used on mail from London royal residences)

22/1	London hooded circle handstamp, code A, with VR (serif) at centre .	150.00
22/2	similar but with VR (serif) at base, 1882-1900	100.00
22/3	Osborne/I. of Wight, single circle, 1900	150.00
	(not Osborne BO/Cowes, which opened 1904)	
22/4	Sandringham/Norfolk, single circle, 1900-19	50.00

**Note: There were other single circles, e.g. 'Osborne' and 'Cumberland Lodge', which were issued for telegraphic purposes and which may also have been used on postal items, possibly "by favour". Some of those shown in the Sixth Edition are excluded, but three are shown below, also 'King's Special Wire' and 'Westminster Abbey' double circle (see next page). Hampton Court, seen as a backstamp pre-1900 and for stamping postcards 1908-15, is now thought to have no Royal connections.

King Edward VII

22/5	London hooded circle handstamp, code A, with ER (non serif) at base	*
22/6	**Buckingham-Palace, single circle, 1903-23	50.00
22/7	**Frogmore, single circle, 1907	*
22/8	Official Paid/Sandringham RSO Norfolk, single circle, red, 1902-24	20.00
22/9	**Windsor Castle, single circle, 21mm, 1903-26	75.00

King George V

Postmarks listed under K Edward VII at approx same values.

Additional marks :

22/10	London hooded circle handstamp, code A, with GR at base	250.00
22/11	Royal Pavilion, Aldershot, single circle with crown, red, 1915 ..	750.00
22/12	Balmoral Castle, single circle with crown at base, 26mm, 1911-, with or without code, or second handstamp 24mm, 1950-	25.00
22/13	Registered/Buckingham Palace, oval, 1920- (or with SW1 1938-) ...	40.00
22/14	London SW1 (later SW) Official Paid, double circle thick arcs, red	15.00
22/15	Dublin Castle, single circle with cross at base, 1911 only	350.00
22/16	Holyrood Palace, single circle with cross at base, 1911-	150.00
22/17	Sandringham/Norfolk PAID handstamp, red, 1924	75.00
22/18	Sandringham/Norfolk, double circle (long/short arcs), 1934-68 ...	25.00
22/19	Official Paid/Sandringham.Nfk., single circle, red, 1925-50	25.00
22/20	Official-Paid/Windsor, single circle, red, 1920	20.00

King Edward VIII

Postmarks listed under K George V but approx double values.

22/11   22/12

22/13

22/15

King George VI

Postmarks listed under K George V but approx 25% of value.

Additional marks :

22/21	Official Paid/Ballater, double circle with thick arcs, red, 1940-91	25.00
22/22	Balmoral Castle/Aberdeenshire, label type parcel handstamp (various)	50.00
22/23	Buckingham Palace/S.W.1., single circle, 1951-	20.00
22/24	Buckingham Palace S.W.1./Paid, undated univ machine die, black, 1940	60.00
22/25	Buckingham Palace/SW1, label type parcel handstamp, 1951- (various)	40.00
22/26	Official Paid/Windsor Berks, double circle & thick arcs, red, 1943-	10.00
22/27	Windsor Great Park, Windsor/Berks, single circle, 1949-	20.00

22/18   22/19   22/21   22/24   22/27

Queen Elizabeth II

Postmarks listed under K George VI but approx 50% of value.

Additional marks :

22/28	Registered/Buckingham Palace SW1, double rim oval 1987- (as **19/50**)	40.00
22/29	As above but large (55mm long) rubber oval 1990-	30.00
22/30	Abergeldie Castle/Aberdeen, skeleton, 1955 only	30.00
22/31	Official Paid/Balmoral Castle, single circle, red, 1953-81	25.00
22/32	Registered/Balmoral Castle, oval, 1952-	50.00
22/33	Official Paid/Ballater, rubber, red, 1991- (replaced **22/21**)	10.00
22/34	Official Paid/King's Lynn, single circle, red (on Sandringham mail)	10.00
22/35	Sandringham House/Norfolk, double circle, 1972-	10.00
22/36	Official Paid/Sandringham House.Nfk, single circle, red, 1974- ..	20.00
22/37	Windsor Castle Windsor/Berks, single circ (1979 but issued earlier)	10.00

Other Royal Postmarks:

22/38   22/40   22/41   22/42

22/38	HMY Osborne/Cowes, skeleton for Cowes Regatta, 1901	1000.00
22/39	His Majesty's Yacht, single circle with crown at base, 1904-34 ..	200.00
22/40	**King's special wire, as above, 1904-10	300.00
22/41	Official-Paid, single circle with crown at base (variations,	
	with or without hyphen), red (or * in black), 1901-11 ...	80.00
22/42	**Westminster Abbey, 1911 double circle with cross (B rarer than A)	800.00
	(covers without address are probably stamped by favour)	

312 **Royal Cachets:**

22/44   **22/45**   **22/46**   **22/48**   **22/49**   **22/51**

22/43	Circular type with ER VII cypher, surmounted by crown	60.00
22/44	As above but GVR	45.00
22/45	Boxed type with ERI/VIII cypher	60.00
22/46	Circular type with GRI/VI	80.00
22/47	As above but GVIR "script" lettering again as 22/43-44, 1939- .	30.00
22/48	As above but EIIR (later single circle)(various)	1.00
22/49	same but with E11R in error (single circle), 1996-	2.50
22/50	HM Yacht Britannia, rectangular (various types)	8.00
22/51	The Royal Yacht, double circle (rubber), 1977-	5.00
22/52	The King's Flight/Royal Air Force, large double circle (rubber) ..	30.00
22/53	The Queen's Flight, double circle similar to **22/51**, 1977-95	10.00

OFFICE OF
HRH THE DUKE
OF GLOUCESTER
Kensington Palace
London W8

22/55   **22/59**   **22/64**

22/54	Privy Purse/Buckingham Palace, oval with crown, 1904-52	5.00
22/55	PH/EIIR/Buckingham Palace, oval with crown, 1953-	3.00
22/56	Lord Steward/M.H./Buckingham Palace, oval with crown, 1904-40 ...	8.00
22/57	Master of The Horse/(The) Royal Mews, S.W., oval with crown, 1902-	4.00
22/58	Buckingham Palace Court Postmaster, rubber, 31mm, 1993-	15.00
22/59	Lord Chamberlain/St James's Palace, oval with crown, 1902-	6.00
22/60	Central Chancery of the Orders/of Knighthood/8 Buckingham Gate/London SW1, oval with crown 1960- (later St James's Palace, larger oval)	8.00
22/61	Office of/Kensington Palace/HRH Princess Marina Duchess of Kent, double oval, 1962	15.00
22/62	Office of/Kensington Palace/HRH The Princess Margaret, oval, 1976	10.00
22/63	Office of/St James's Palace/HRH The Duke of Gloucester, oval, 1963	10.00
22/64	Office of/HRH The Duke/of Gloucester/Kensington Palace/London W8, 1971	8.00
22/65	Office of the/Court Postmaster, double circle with GVR cypher used on mail ex Royal Yacht, magenta, 1933	200.00
22/66	Master of the Horse/The Royal Mews Windsor, oval with crown	10.00
22/67	Master of the Household's Department/Windsor Castle, double oval with crown, 1955-, later single oval	15.00
22/68	Privy Purse/Windsor, oval with crown, 1908-40	10.00
22/69	Royal Gardens/Windsor, oval with crown, 1976-90	10.00
22/70	HM's Representative/Ascot Office/St James's Palace SW1A 1BP, 1979-	10.00
22/71	The Royal Collection/St James's Palace SW1A 1JR, 1988-	6.00
22/72	Sandringham/Estate, circular rubber, 31mm, 1979	10.00

Note : the above cachets are difficult to price since some were used over many years. Most, even if still in use in the late 20th century, are not easy to find and are thus priced higher than "EiiR" and "PH" (Paymaster of the Household) which are comparatively common. Uses of 22/54 onwards (exc 22/65) pre-1940 should be priced at double the figures shown and for pre-1920 prices should be trebled.

For further cachets not shown above see Glenn Morgan's book listed in Bibliography

Meters at Royal Residences/Estates (see chapter 25)

22/74

22/73   Meters used "incognito" at London W8 (Kensington Palace),
       Sandringham, Windsor (see Morgan for details), 1984- 2.00
       (no indication of source, town only shown, no slogan)
22/74 "Aberdeen" meter with Crown EiiR ex Balmoral Estate, 1983-94 ....   5.00
22/75 "Forfar" meter with Glamis Castle slogan, 1986-88 ....   4.00
22/76 "Kings Lynn" meter with "The Royal Studs Crown EiiR" slogan, 1990-   5.00
22/77 "Sandringham" meter & "The Estate Office Sandringham" slogan, 1990   4.00
       (note this is the Sandringham meter from 22/73 with slogan added)
22/78 "Slough" meter with "St George's School Windsor Castle" slogan, 1993   5.00

22/76

23. British Post Offices Abroad

In colonies and countries lacking efficient postal administration, some British Consulates were authorised to provide postal services (some from the late 1700s) and later to supply GB stamps. By 1890, most of these arrangements had officially been terminated, although a few continued until the 1920s.

In a departure from previous editions, this chapter now lists only markings used as cancellations on complete covers franked solely with GB adhesive stamps ie NOT GB overprints nor mixed GB and foreign.

Values below £100 are based on Exchange Packet prices and dealers' lists. Higher values are from auction results. ** means "more than £1000". Collectors requiring a more detailed account of this subject are advised to refer to John Parmenter's book shown in the Bibliography.

Ovals with codes C,G,M and S

23/1   23/5

23/1	"C." horizontal oval - Constantinople	10.00
23/2	As above but upright oval	500.00
23/3	"G" horizontal oval - Gibraltar	60.00
23/4	"M" horizontal oval - Malta	100.00
23/5	"S." upright oval (with full stop) - Stamboul	100.00

Ovals/duplexes with numeric and alpha-numeric codes

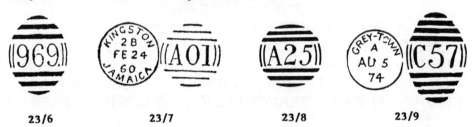

23/6   23/7   23/8   23/9

		Horizontal oval	Upright oval	Circular duplex	Oval duplex
247	Fernando Po		**		
582	Naguabo, Porto Rico		**		
942	Larnaca, Cyprus		£100		
969	Nicosia, Cyprus **23/6**		£500		
974	Kyrenia, Cyprus		**		
975	Limassol, Cyprus		£500		
981	Papho, Cyprus		**		
982	Famagusta, Cyprus		**		
A01	Kingston, Jamaica	£60		£60 **23/7**	
	("twin" horizontal oval £300)				
A02	St John's, Antigua	£300			
A03	Demerara/Georgetown, Br Guiana	£60			
A04	Berbice/New Amsterdam, Br Guiana	£300			
A05	Bahamas	£300			
A06	Belize, British Honduras	£200			
A07	Dominica, Leeward Is	£300			
A08	Montserrat	£500			
A09	Nevis	£500			
A10	St Vincent, Windward Is	£100			

		Horizontal oval	Upright oval	Circular duplex	Oval duplex
A11	St Lucia	**			
A12	St Kitts	£500			
A13	Tortola, Virgin Is	**			
A14	Tobago	£200			
A15	Grenada	£60			
A18	English Harbour, Antigua	**			
A25	Malta	£100 23/8	£300	£20	£30
A26	Gibraltar	£20	£800	£20	£40
A27	Alexandria, Jamaica	£500			
A28	Annotto Bay, Jamaica	£300			
A29	Bath, Jamaica	£300			
A30	Black River, Jamaica	£100			
A31	Brown's Town, Jamaica	£500			
A32	Buff Bay, Jamaica	£500			
A33	Chapelton, Jamaica	£300			
A34	Claremont, Jamaica	£500			
A35	Clarendon, Jamaica	£500			
A36	Dry Harbour, Jamaica	£500			
A37	Duncans, Jamaica	£500			
A39	Falmouth, Jamaica	£100			
A40	Flint River, Jamaica	£300			
A41	Gayle, Jamaica	£300			
A42	Golden Spring, Jamaica	£500			
A43	Gordon Town, Jamaica	£500			
A44	Goshen, Jamaica	£100			
A45	Grange Hill, Jamaica	£200			
A46	Green Island, Jamaica	£300			
A47	Highgate, Jamaica	£500			
A48	Hope Bay, Jamaica	£500			
A49	Lilliput, Jamaica	£200			
A51	Lucea, Jamaica	£300			
A52	Manchioneal, Jamaica	£500			
A53	Mandeville, Jamaica	£200			
A54	May Hill, Jamaica	£200			
A55	Mile Gully, Jamaica	£300			
A56	Moneague, Jamaica	£300			
A57	Montego Bay, Jamaica	£100			
A58	Montpelier, Jamaica	£200			
A59	Morant Bay, Jamaica	£200			
A60	Ocho Rios, Jamaica	£300			
A61	Old Harbour, Jamaica	£200			
A62	Plantain Garden River, Jamaica	£200			
A64	Port Antonio, Jamaica	£300			
A65	Port Morant, Jamaica	£200			
A66	Port Maria, Jamaica	£200			
A67	Port Royal, Jamaica	£500			
A68	Porus, Jamaica	£200			
A69	Ramble, Jamaica	£300			
A70	Rio Bueno, Jamaica	£300			
A71	Rodney Hall, Jamaica	£200			
A72	Saint David, Jamaica	£500			
A73	St.Ann's Bay, Jamaica	£200			
A74	Salt Gut, Jamaica	£300			
A75	Savanna-la-Mar, Jamaica	£100			
A76	Spanish Town, Jamaica	£100			
A77	Stewart Town, Jamaica	£500			
A78	Vere, Jamaica	£300			
B01	Alexandria, Egypt	£40	£40		£60
B02	Suez, Egypt	£40			
B32	Buenos-Ayres, Argentina	£40	£60	**	
C28	Montevideo, Uruguay	£100			
C30	Valparaiso, Chile		£30		£60
C35	Panama, Colombia	£60			£60
C36	Arica, Peru	**	**		
C37	Caldera, Chile	£100			
C38	Callao, Peru	£200	£30		**
C39	Cobija, Bolivia	£300	**		
C40	Coquimbo, Chile	£100			
C41	Guayaquil, Ecuador	£40			
C42	Islay, Peru	£100			
C43	Paita/Payta, Peru	£300			

		Horizontal oval	Upright oval	Circular duplex	Oval duplex
C51	St.Thomas, Danish W Indies	£40	£40		£40
C56	Cartagena, Colombia	£60			
C57	Grey-town, Nicaragua		**	23/9	£400
C58	Havana, Cuba	£200			£150
C59	Jacmel, Haiti	£150			
C60	La Guayra, Venezuela	£150			
C61	Porto Rico	£150	£150		£150
C62	Santa Martha, Colombia	£200			
C63	Tampico, Mexico	£300			
C65 (error)	Cartagena, Colombia		£300		
C81	Bahia, Brazil		£100		
C82	Pernambuco, Brazil		£150		
C83	Rio de Janeiro, Brazil		£150		
C86	Porto Plata, Dominica		£300		
C87	San Domingo, Dominica		£200		
C88	St.Jago-de-Cuba (Santiago), Cuba		£800		
D22	Ciudad Bolivar, Venezuela		**		
D74	Pisco, Peru		**		
D87	Iquique, Peru		£450		
E53	Port-au-Prince, Haiti		£200		
E88	Colon, Colombia		£300		
F69	Savanilla, Colombia		£200		
F83	Arroyo, Porto Rico		£300		
F84	Aguadilla, Porto Rico		£250		
F85	Mayaguez, Porto Rico		£150		
F87	Smyrna		£30		
F88	Ponce, Porto Rico		£350		
G06	Beyrout, Levant		£50		

Postmarks in "clear English" - in alphabetical sequence

| 23/12 | 23/15 | 23/16 | 23/17 | 23/18 |

23/10	Ascension, single circle (until 1922)	100.00
23/11	Beyrout/British Post Office, hooded circle (until 1906)	25.00
23/12	British Post Office/Constantinople, single circle (until 1923) ..	5.00
23/13	Grey-Town, Nicaragua, single circle (until 1882)	200.00
23/14	Jacmel, Haiti, single circle (until 1850)	600.00
23/15	British Post Office/Salonica, single circle (until 1905)	20.00
23/16	As above but double circle (until 1905)	15.00
23/17	Smyrna, small single circle (until 1893)	50.00
23/18	British Post Office/Smyrna, single circle (until 1905)	10.00

24. Tourist cachets

Cachets are normally rubber stamps applied to an envelope or postcard <u>away from</u> the stamp. They are NOT postmarks. We have limited the scope of the listing below to the popular tourist cachets, excluding (a) cachets used on official mail from Government departments (b) slogan type messages advertising political parties or "protest messages" eg "Permit Sunday trading" (c) the plethora of modern cachets used on philatelically prepared covers, including Postal Museums "Posted at ..." or "carried on mail coach" etc.

This chapter is restricted to privately produced "tourist cachets" which are or were available on postcards posted by visitors at the appropriate location, not on a "one off" occasion or connected with a special or philatelic posting. Some cachets that do not strictly meet this definition were in the fifth or sixth edition but are now excluded. Some cachets are applied to cards before purchase, hence unused cards are available and these can be posted at other locations. Cacheted cards should ideally bear local postmarks, otherwise values should be reduced by half, which applies also to unused cards. Values given are for cards or covers with stamps, local postmarks, and clear cachets. Dates shown are for the earliest known specimen in each case though a range of years is shown particularly where the cachet was used over a long period. Further reports are always welcome, with a photocopy of the whole postcard please. However we do not intend to maintain a complete listing of locations producing too many modern cachets eg Land's End and Llanfairpwll.........

Some cachets are <u>printed</u> on postcards; these are excluded. Some are applied only to, or intended for use with privately produced labels, eg Caldey Island and Llechwedd Caverns and these too we have excluded along with those intended for use on or with railway letter stamps. The 1987 Snowdon Summit entry is, however, retained. Cachets produced primarily for use on "tourist passports", but which can also be used on postcards, we have excluded. This includes National Trust and National Trust for Scotland cachets listed in the Sixth Edition. Of the Dartmoor cachets only the Cranmere Pool cachets are listed, not the hundreds of other "log book" cachets.

We acknowledge the considerable assistance given by John Holman in checking details and adding some entries. John Owen, who produced the recent Land's End book (see Bibliography), has kindly provided a summary for inclusion here.

Beachy Head

BEACHY HEAD.

24/1	**24/4**	**24/6**

24/1	Beachy Head, straight line, with seriffed or sans serif lettering, unframed, purple/black, 1905	5.00
24/2	Watch Tower/on/Beachy Head/England/Harry Randal, circular, black, 1909	6.00
24/3	Watch Tower/Beachy Head/year, 3 straight lines, purple, 1910	6.00
24/4	The Watch Tower/Beachy Head, belt/buckle design, purple/black, 1913	4.00
24/5	Watch Tower/Beachy Head, double framed diamond, black/purple 1921	2.50
24/6	Watch Tower/Beachy Head, oval, purple or black, 1930	2.00
24/7	As above but with lighthouse in centre, purple, 1931	2.00
24/8	Posted at/Beachy Head Hotel, framed, purple, 1954	4.00

Blackpool Tower

24/11

24/12

24/13

24/9	Tiny Town/Post Office/Tower Blackpool, double oval, purple, 1933	20.00
24/10	Posted at John Lester's/Midget Town/The Tower/Blackpool, boxed, date required	10.00
24/11	Posted from Top of/Blackpool/Tower/518 feet high, double rim oval, black or purple, 1949	1.50
24/12	Posted/from/the/top/of/Blackpool/Tower/Height 518 feet, purple red, black or blue, 1957-92	1.00
24/13	Similar to **24/11** but Centenary Year, turquoise, 1994	3.00

Cranmere Pool and other Dartmoor cachets   Note : Cranmere Pool is Britain's remotest letter box and the only one marked on Ordnance Survey maps – cards usually bear postmarks of Bridestowe, Sticklepath, Okehampton or Plymouth

24/14

24/16

24/18

24/20

24/21

24/14	Cranmere/Dartmoor double circle, 25mm, black, 1900s	25.00
24/15	Cranmere, double rim circle, 20mm, purple/black, 1914-18	25.00
24/16	Cranmere/+, double circle, 24mm, red/purple/blue/black, 1916-30s	20.00
24/17	Cranmere/Pool/Dartmoor, double rim circle, 35mm, purple, 1939-47	20.00
24/18	Cranmere/Pool/Dartmoor, double circle, 35mm, blue/purple, 1952-56	8.00
24/19	Cranmere Pool/Dartmoor, large, two straight lines, purple, 1953	10.00
24/20	Cranmere/Pool/Dartmoor, double circle, 29mm, purple, 1959	10.00
24/21	Cranmere Pool Dartmoor 1825 feet, black/red/purple, 1960s-1970s	2.50
24/22	similar wording but rectangular, red, 1966	4.00
24/23	Cranmere Pool/Dartmoor, hexagonal, black, 1991-	3.50
24/24	Other Dartmoor cachets eg Duck's Pool, 1952 oval, or 1960 circle, and others arranged by scouts c1970	3.00

Note : there are many hundreds of Dartmoor cachets but they are designed for applying to "log books" or other documents and are seldom used on postcards

24/25	Museum of Dartmoor Life Okehampton, circular 73mm, 1980s-1990s	2.50

Island Cachets

24/26	Ailsa Craig, single circle with star, 1908	8.00
24/27	similar but without star, violet, 1920	10.00
24/28	Ailsa Craig in oval (different sizes), violet, 1928	8.00
24/29	Ailsa/Craig in oval, black, 1952,	5.00
24/30	Burgh Island/Bigbury-on-Sea/South Devon/TQ7 4AU UK, large double rim oval, black or violet, 1989	2.00
24/31	Posted at/Ettrick Bay, Bute, boxed, purple, 1906	15.00
24/32	Posted at/date/Ettrick Bay, larger than 24/31, purple, 1909	15.00

24/26	**24/32**	**24/36**	**24/48**

24/33 Fingal's Cave Staffa, large double circle, purple, 1969 .... 2.50

24/34 St. Kilda/date, unframed, 1931 .... 12.00
24/35   As above but boxed with indented corners, purple 10.00
24/36 St. Kilda/The furthest station west, circular with puffin, violet
         or red, 1960 .... 4.00
24/37   As above but double rimmed circle (variations), purple, blue or
         red, 1970s-1990s 2.00

24/38 St. Mary's Island Whitley Bay, shows lighthouse, pink, 1991 ..... 2.00

24/39 St. Michael's Mount., boxed, with decorative border, 1920s 10.00

24/40 Honeybills/South Stack Tea Rooms/Holyhead, double box, black, 1935 10.00
24/41   similar but pictorial, showing lighthouse, 1939 .... 15.00

Island Cachets – Channel Islands

24/42 Herm, single line, black, 1903 .... 100.00

24/43 Wolf Caves, Jersey, double circle, violet or red, 1905 .... 30.00

24/44 Jethou Island/date, straight line, black, 1907................. 75.00
24/45 Jethou Island/Chan.Isles, circular, violet, 1909 .... 50.00

Island Cachets – Isle of Man

24/46 Posted at Cunningham Holiday Camp Douglas IOM boxed, purple, 1923 75.00

24/47 Peel Castle/Isle of Man, horizontal diamond, purple, 1913 .... 60.00

Snaefell Summit:
24/48 Upright diamond in black 1904, or purple 1907 .... 6.00
24/49   As above but green 1926, or red 1927 .... 25.00
24/50 Horizontal diamond in purple (several types) red 1933, green 1934 6.00
24/51   As above in black, 1935 .... 0.75
24/52   As above in blue, 1977 .... 1.50
24/53   As above plus height 2036FT in red, 1992 .... 2.00
24/54   As above but with "Centenary 1895-1995" added, 1995 .... 4.00
24/55   As above but with "Centenary" and "1895" removed, 1996, red 3.00

24/56 Tholt-y-will/Sulby Glen, upright diamond, black/purple, 1909 ..... 40.00
24/57   As above in green, 1922 .... 60.00

Note: modern, chiefly philatelic, uses of IOM cachets are not listed
(numbers 24/58-80 reserved for future use)

John O'Groats

24/81	**24/82**	**24/83**	**24/85**	

24/92

24/81 John O'Groats/N.B./House, NB in script, in triangle, black, 1898 . 30.00
24/82 John O'Groats/N.B./House, in triangle, black/purple, 1904 .... 10.00
24/83 John O'Groats House Hotel, single circle, purple, 1931 .... 4.00
24/84 John O'Groats House, single circle (diff sizes), purple, 1930s ... 3.00
       (24/83 with "Hotel" removed, also later new cachets without Hotel)
24/85 John O'Groats/House, octagonal, purple, 1950 .... 2.50
24/86 John O'Groats House Hotel, straight line, purple, 1957 .... 2.00
24/87   As above but small circle, purple, 1970 .... 2.00
24/88   As above but oval (variations), purple/black, 1978 .... 2.00
24/89 John O'Groats/Scotland, double rim circle, purple, 1959 .... 2.00
24/90   As above but oval with space for inserting date, black, 1984 .. 2.00
24/91 Last House/John O'Groats, straight line, blue, 1981 .... 1.50
24/92 First & Last in Scotland, large octagonal pictorial, black, 1989 . 2.50
24/93 The Last House/in Scotland/John O'Groats, three straight lines,
          purple or black, 1991 .... 1.50

Land's End

24/95

24/111

24/115

24/119

24/120

24/123

24/124

24/94 From the/Old Man at the/Land's End, rectangle with indented corners,
          purple, blue or green, 1901-10 .... 4.00
24/95 Land's End, triangle with blocked border, black, purple or blue,
          1901-78 .... 1.00
24/96 Land's End/Hotel,/Cornwall., rectangle with indented corners,
          purple, 1903 .... 8.00
24/97 First and Last Refreshment House/By E. James/Lands End, double oval,
          black, 1905 .... 5.00
24/98   As above but without words 'By E. James', black, 1907 .... 5.00
24/99 Lands End, small double circle, black, 1905 .... 8.00
24/100 Lands End/Post Office, large double circle, black, 1913 .... 5.00
24/101 Lands End, small double rim oval, blue, purple or green, 1911-13 . 2.00
24/102   As above but large single oval, purple, 1920 .... 4.00
24/103   As above but large double rim oval, 1921-25 .... 3.00
24/104 First & Last House/Lands End, unframed 2-line, purple, 1912-25 .. 3.00
24/105   As above, variety of cachets, diff sizes/colours, 1929-35 ..... 3.00
          (many versions of this cachet were printed, not listed here)
24/106 Sennen/Post Office/Lands End, single circle, black, 1924 .... 6.00
24/107 Lands End, single triangle, purple, 1925-29 .... 1.50
24/108 Lands End, boxed with blocked border, 1928 .... 6.00
24/109 First & Last House/Lands End, two lines, boxed, red/black, 1931-76 2.50
24/110 First and Last House/In England/Land's End, 3 lines, boxed, red,
          1931-38 .... 2.50

24/111 Lands End, shield with lighthouse, scroll below, purple, 1935-39 . 2.00
24/112 Lands End between pairs of 4 wavy lines, black, 1939-47 .... 2.00
24/113   As above but pairs of 2 wavy lines, black, 1947-49 .... 2.00
24/114 Lands End, double triangle (apex downward) with scrolls, black,
        1950-64 .... 1.50
24/115 Last/Inn/Lands/End, boxed, purple, 1953-54 .... 4.00
24/116 The Land's End Hotel Ltd/Land's End, 38mm circle with shield,
        black, 1950 .... 4.00
24/117 The First & Last House/In England/Lands End, 3 straight lines in
        two colours, Lands End in red, remainder in blue, 1976-77 ..... 4.00
24/118 Breathtaking/Lands End, large boxed, 51mm wide, black, 1982 ..... 7.50
24/119 Land's End, single circle, 31mm, black, 1982 .... 3.00
24/120 Land's End/Man & the Sea, with waves, lighthouse and shipwreck,
        blue, 1983 .... 3.00
24/121 Lands End, unframed with star attached to E, black/blue, 1984-88 . 3.00
24/122 Lands End, large 71mm oval with picture of house within, black, 1985 3.00
24/123 Lands End, semi-circle showing lighthouse & rays of light, red,
        blue or black, 1989-93 .... 2.00
24/124 Lands End/date/You know the way, large oval, black, 1992-93 ..... 2.00

plus several in 1994 not listed (numbers 24/125-140 reserved for future use)

Llanfair P.G.

24/147   **LLANFAIRPWLLGWYNGYLLGOGERYCHWYRNDROBWLLLLANDYSILIOGOGOGOCH**

24/141

24/150

24/154

24/141 Village name round rim of double circle with 'Posted at' or 'Post
        Office' in centre, many types, blue, black or violet, 1956 .. 1.00
24/142   As above but map or dragon in centre 1.50
24/143 Village name round rim of single circle (some with double rim),
        dragon at centre (variations), several types/colours, c1960 .. 1.00
24/144   As above but 'Posted From', 'Posted at' or blank centre
        (variations, sizes vary 27-37mm), 1961 .... 1.00
24/145   As above but picture of station at centre, red/black, 1985 .... 3.00
24/146   As above with dragon and "Siop Betsan" inscription, several types,
        red, 1983, and 2-colour version red/green, 1990 .... 2.50
24/147 Village name, unboxed straight line, several sizes/colours, 1964 . 1.50
24/148 Village name round rim of double oval with blank centre, ?1968 ... 2.00
24/149   As above (vert) but large "Marquess of Anglesey's Column", 1980 . 3.00
24/150   As above (horiz) but "Siop Garnedd Wen" at centre, purple, 1985 . 2.50
24/151 Large unframed 95x40mm "Siop.Betsan" with 2 dragons, pink, 1990 . 2.50
24/152 Large vert oval with "Siop Betsan" & "longest named railway station
        the world", green, & red/black Welsh lady at centre, 1990s ... 2.50
24/153 Circular village name in single circle with "Siop Betsan" at centre,
        Wales at foot, red, 1995 .... 2.50
24/154 Village name (lower case) round rim (but no rim) with added wording
        "Isle of Anglesey Ynys Mon", and either "James Pringle", 1990,
        or dragon (used in Pringle shop), black (diff sizes), 1991 .. 1.50

(numbers 24/155-170 reserved for future use)

322

Snowdon

24/171   24/174   24/178
                                24/175

24/171 Summit/of/Snowdon, single circle, 23mm, blue/purple, 1902-35 .... 2.00
24/172   As above but double rim circle, 37mm, purple/black/red, 1926-32 . 2.50
24/173   As above, single circle, 21mm, purple/black/red, 1930s 2.50
24/174   As above, double rim circle, 24mm, purple, 1945-52 .... 2.00
24/175   As above, single circle, 32-35mm, variations, purple or black,
         1950s-80s 1.00
24/176 Half-way House/G. Williams/Snowdon, double oval, blue, 1930s-50s . 5.00
24/177 Mount Snowdon, boxed, violet (details required) 8.00
24/178 Snowdon Summit 1085 metres etc, circular (on labels), 1987- 2.00
24/179 Snowdon/Railway, circular 25mm, ?1930s (more reports required) .. 10.00
24/180 Snowdon/blank, possibly above item with "Railway" removed, probably
         1930s but further reports required 10.00

Ship's cachets (all are static displays open to the public)

24/186   24/190   24/192

24/181 Posted on board HMS Belfast (River Thames London), 40mm double rim
         circle, black, 1973 .... 1.50

24/182 Cutty Sark 1869 (Greenwich), circular, black, 1959 .... 2.00
24/183 Cutty Sark/Off No.63557/1869/London, black, 1991 .... 2.00

24/184 SS Great Britain Bristol (ship pointing right), black, 1978 ...... 2.00
24/185   similar but ship pointing left, black or blue, 1985 (variations) 1.50
24/186   similar but "150 Years 1843-1993" wording, violet, 1993-94 ..... 2.00

24/187 The Frigate Unicorn/Victoria Dock Dundee, pictorial, black, 1989 . 3.00

24/188 Posted In/H.M.S. Victory (Portsmouth), blue, unframed, 1949,
         or Posted/in H.M.S. Victory, purple, 1954 .... 2.00
24/189 Illustration of HMS Victory, no wording, blue, 1951 .... 2.00
24/190   As above but smaller with Posted/on board/H.M.S. Victory wording
         (variations), blue, violet or black, 1952 .... 0.50
24/191 Large boxed ship illustration with name of HMS Victory Commanding
         Officer, red, 1978 .... 1.50
24/192 Posted on board/HMS Victory, circ, 35mm, violet/blue/black, 1982 . 1.00

24/193 HMS Warrior/1860 (Portsmouth), double rim oval, black, 1988 ..... 2.50

Other cachets - England

24/194

24/195

24/212

24/217

POSTED IN THE VICTORIAN
LETTERBOX   AT   THE
MUSEUM OF LINCOLNSHIRE LIFE
BURTON ROAD LINCOLN.
ENGLAND.

24/214

24/194 Posted at the/Grand Pump Room/Bath, boxed, 1915	10.00
24/195 Posted at the/Pump Room/Bath, England, boxed, purple/black, 1958 .	1.00
24/196 Posted at/Cape Hill/Brewery/Birmingham, pictorial, pink, 1938 ...	10.00
24/197 Chatterley Whitfield Mining Museum (Tunstall Stoke on Trent), circular, dated, black, 1981	2.50
24/198 Central Spa/Town Hall, rectangle with indented corners, used at Cheltenham (details of dates required)	7.50
24/199 Posted in Coronation Street (TV studio set, Manchester), 1970s ..	1.00
24/200 Posted at Crewe Heritage Centre, circular, red, 1991	1.50
24/201 Posted at Tramway Museum Crich Derbyshire, circular, red, 1974 ...	2.00
similar but large "stamp shaped", red or green, 1973	3.00
24/202 Carried by tramcar (same location), pictorial, red, 1989	2.00
24/203 Small Relics Museum Didcot, triangular, red, 1982	3.00
24/204 Posted at the Black Country Museum, Dudley, black, 1987	2.50
24/205 Haddon Hall/date/Bakewell, single circle, black or violet, 1953 .	4.00
24/206 Royal Pump Room Museum (Harrogate), circular, black, 1970	2.50
24/207 Royal Pump Room Museum/Harrogate Yorkshire, circular, 1989	2.00
24/208 Hell's/Mouth/Cornwall, triangular, pink, 1951	3.00
24/209 Holmfirth/Postcard/Museum, framed in square, black, 1987	2.00
24/210 Posted on the World's 1st Cast-Iron Bridge, Ironbridge, red, 1989	1.50
(on souvenir cover with full set of Industrial Arch stamps 7.50)	
24/211 Posted at Blists Hill Ironbridge Shropshire, red, 1989	1.50
24/212 Posted at Jodrell Bank, circular, 25mm, 1967	2.50
(also dated version used 19 Sept 1966, Technology stamp issue day)	
24/213 similar but large unframed 52mm, pictorial, 1972	2.50
24/214 Museum of Lincolnshire Life Lincoln, black, 1978	2.00
24/215 Penny Park/House/Coventry, double circle, 1970s	2.00
24/216 Portsmouth City Museum/Dickens Birthplace, circular, 1969	1.50
24/217 Ragley/Hall., small double rim circle, blue/black/violet, 1960s .	2.00
24/218 RAF Museum Hendon, circular, 1970s	1.00
24/219 Ryedale Folk Museum/Posted at, with sheaf, black, 1991	2.00
24/220 Posted End of Pier/Southend, red, 1913	30.00
24/221 Tan Hill, England's Highest Inn, purple, 1930s-58 (Kendal pmk) ..	5.00

CAIRNGORM CHAIRLIFT
POST BOX
HIGHEST IN BRITAIN

24/266

24/269

24/222

THIS CARD WAS
POSTED ON
LLANDUDNO PIER

24/278   24/281   24/282

24/222 The Old Post Office/Tintagel, large circle (variations), green/
black/blue, 1971-1990s (also used on labels) 1.00
24/223   as above but with "NT Centenary 1895 1995" added 2.50

24/224 Underground/Post Box/Wheal/Roots/Mine/Wendrow, oval, black, 1979 1.50
24/225 Poldark/Mining Ltd/Posted/Underground, black, 1979 .... 1.50
24/226 Posted underground/at Poldark Mine, circular, black, 1995 .... 2.00

24/227 Upleatham Old Church, smallest church in England, black, 1960s .. 2.50

24/228 Posted at the Upminster Windmill, purple, 1949 .... 5.00

24/229 Posted at/Wannock (gardens at Eastbourne), unframed, violet, 1937 8.00

24/230 Posted at the/Wedgwood/Visitor/Centre, circular, black/blue, 1982 1.50

24/231 Posted in/Wookey/Hole, boxed, & witch on broomstick, blue, black,
green or red, 1962-86 .... 1.50

24/232 Wrekin Hill/Wellington Salop, decorated two line cachet, ?date .. 7.50

24/233 NRM (National Railway Museum, York), small, black, 1979 .... 2.00

(numbers 24/234-260 reserved for future use)

Other cachets – Scotland

24/261 Aonach Mor, Fort William, Britains Highest Postbox, boxed, 1993 .. 3.00

24/262 Santa Claus Land/Aviemore Centre, double circle, red, 1983 ...... 3.00

24/263 Tam O'Shanter/Museum/Ayr, oval, black, ?1960s 6.00

24/264 Ben Nevis/Observatory, double oval with centre blank, c1902 ..... 10.00
24/265 Ben Nevis Summit/J. Miller/Hotel, double oval, purple, 1905 ..... 10.00

24/266 Cairngorm Chairlift/post box/highest in Britain, framed, black,
green or red, 1963-82 .... 1.00
24/267 Cairngorm Chairlift/Car Park 2150ft/Top Station 3647ft, unframed,
blue, black, red or green, 1969-79 .... 1.00

24/268 Culloden Battlefield NTS, circular 26mm pink, 1969 .... 2.50
24/269   similar but 28mm, black, 1974-1990s 1.50

24/270 Glasgow Museum of Transport, Oldest Pillar Box in Scotland, unframed,
red, 1968 .... 1.50
24/271   similar but framed, black, 1978-1990s 1.00

24/272 First House in Scotland/Sark Bridge/Gretna, boxed, violet, 1973 .. 2.00

24/273 Posted from Livingstone Memorial Blantyre, red or green, 1973-93 1.50

24/274 Loch Ness Visitors Centre, Drumnadrochit, pictorial, black, 1989   1.50
24/275 Loch Ness Official Exhibition Centre, circular, black, 1993 ..... 1.50

24/276 Posted at/Sanquhar/The Oldest/Post Office/in Britain/Est 1763,
       unframed, red, 1986 .... 3.00
24/277 Sanquhar.... the world's oldest working post office, pictorial,
       black or green, 1993 .... 2.50

24/278 Shell Grotto (Burns Memorial Gardens Alloway), black, 1905 only . 10.00

24/279 Nat Trust for Scotland/White Lady Shieling 2525 feet, black, 1966   5.00

Other cachets - Wales

24/280 Llythyrdy/Bethlehem (old post office), circular, red/black, 1991   2.00

24/281 Cader Idris Summit, Refreshment Room, oval, violet, 1939 .... 7.00

24/282 This card was/posted on/Llandudno Pier ?1950s, details required .. 5.00
24/283 This Card was Posted/at the Summit of the/Great Orme, Llandudno,
       boxed, blue, black or red, 1964 .... 1.50
24/284 Posted from the/Great Orme Summit, boxed, red, 1986 .... 2.50

24/285 Llywernog Silver Lead Mine, circular, c1984 .... 2.50
24/286   similar but with Ponterwyd location included, pictorial, with
       "Posted underground in Mid-Wales", 1993 .... 2.50

24/287 St. Davids "Britain's smallest city", boxed, 82x23mm, 1970 .... 3.00

Note: The "Sark Quatercentenary" item has been omitted since it is a Post Office
cachet. The "Cruise of the Northern Belle" railway cachet has been moved to
chapter 13.

25. Meter marks

Companies, local authorities and other users purchase or license meter machines to stamp their own mail, making appropriate payments to the Post Office. They were first used in the UK in 1922 and in general they are struck in red to denote "prepaid mail" and contain the inscriptions "Great Britain" (except Channel Islands & Isle of Man after postal independence) and "Postage paid". They should not be confused with Post Office "Paid" postmarks struck in red by means of hand-stamps or machines (see chapters 9, 10, 11, 21 and 22) on Post Office premises.

Since used only for the mail of one company, advertising slogans or patriotic and "appeal" legends can be used freely within the normal bounds of acceptability. Covers with slogans are priced at up to 10 times the value of postmarks without slogan though for low value post-1950 items this will only apply to slogans with a particular thematic appeal.

In the early days there were three manufacturers of meter machines but after 1968 the number increased. Letters and numbers included in the postage paid emblem (which we term "frank") distinguish the manufacturer and/or the machine model but the initial Pitney Bowes series had none. Once in use in a machine the frank can remain unchanged for years. Thus, for example, a GviR frank may be found used during the reign of EiiR. We show here most of the types used showing manufacturers but not machine models. For further reading see Mann's book (listed in Bibliography) and articles by Jack Peach in Postal Mechanisation Study Circle Newsletters.

For convenience parcel post labels are included at the end of the chapter, also the postmark of the 1912 Wilkinson "penny in the slot" machine.

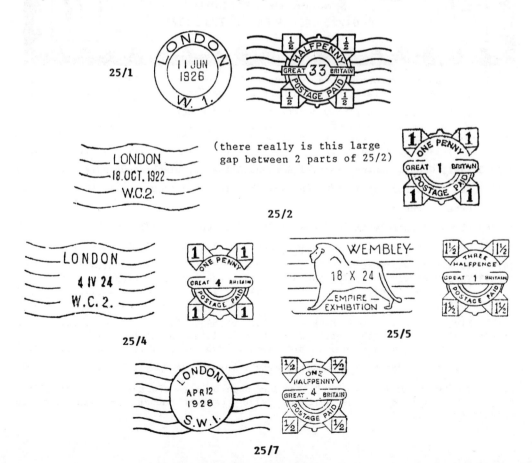

25/1

(there really is this large gap between 2 parts of 25/2)

25/2

25/4

25/5

25/7

25/8 *The Universal Midget 3*
PRINTS FRANK-POSTMARK & *YOUR OWN* ADVERT.=

25/9

25/11

25/1	Pitney Bowes 1922 (valuation is for 1922, 2.00 from 1923)	5.00
25/2	Universal NZ 1922, frank 25x25mm, town die black 5 bars, spaced at distance to left	40.00
25/3	Closer spaced, town die black 6 bars, frank 25x22mm, from 1923 .	4.00
25/4	similar but town die red	3.00
25/5	As above but special Wembley town die in black or red, 1924-25 . (used in NZ Pavilion at Wembley exhibition)	90.00
25/6	As above but circular town die within 6 wavy lines, from 1923 ..	30.00
25/7	similar but within 7 wavy lines ("High speed"), from 1923	2.00
25/8	Neopost machine with N below number in centre, or Universal "Midget" (M), circular town die, from 1925 .... (valuation higher with slogan as shown at **25/8**)	1.00
25/9	New frank design from 1927, circular town die .... - manufacturers and codes were Pitney Bowes (PB,H), Universal (M, NZ, NZA), Neopost (N)	0.50
25/10	As above but with small cypher at foot, from 1932 .... - Universal (U) from 1932, Pitney Bowes (P) from 1935 (Note : there are other variations in the frank design eg position of "Post Paid" wording, which are not listed here)	0.30
25/11	EviiiR cypher, from 1936 - Pitney Bowes (PB,P), Universal (M,U), Neopost (N) (8.00 with slogan of thematic appeal)	1.50
25/12	GviR cypher, from 1937 - Pitney Bowes (PB,H), Universal (NZ,M), Neopost (N)	0.20
25/13	As above but with small cypher at foot, as 25/10 - Pitney Bowes (P), Universal (U,UA etc, S,SA)	0.20
25/14	EiiR cypher, from 1953 - Pitney Bowes (PB), Universal (NZ,M), Neopost (N)	0.20
25/15	As above but with small cypher at foot, as 25/10 - Pitney Bowes (P,PA), Universal (U,UA etc,S,SA,SB,SV,SX,SY,SZ,SL,A,AA), Neopost (NA-ND)	0.20
25/16	As any of 25/12-25/15 with slogan of thematic appeal	1.00

25/16

| 25/17 | New floral emblems frank design, from 1959 .... - Universal/Pitney Bowes (P, PA-PC, RT, S, SA etc, U, UA etc, AA-AH), Roneo-Neopost (N, NA-NR, J, TN) | 0.20 |

25/18 New frank design, from 1967 .... 0.50
— Postage & Revenue Franking Machines (fm1)

25/17   25/18

25/19

25/32

25/33

25/34

From 1968 a new frank design was introduced in readiness for decimalisation with values in pence/½ pence only. Suppliers as follows:

25/19	a) Acral (Francotyp machine) (AC.A, ACA)	0.40
25/20	b) Addressing Systems International (Secap machine)(ASA, ASM)	0.20
25/21	c) Envopak/Francotyp-Postalia (EGS, ENV, EMD, EFS)	0.20
25/22	as above but (T) printed by *thermal transfer, from 1992	0.30
25/23	d) Friden (G)	0.30
25/24	e) Hasler/Ascom Hasler (HGB, HAS, HF, HM, HB, HT, HS)	0.05
25/25	f) Mailing & Mechanisation (Frama machine) (MMC)	0.20
25/26	g) Pitney-Bowes (PBC,PBS,PBA,PBR,PBT,PBL,PBE,PB,PBT,PBD,PBH, PBK,PBM,PBN,PBF,PBG,PBO,PBV,PBW,PBC,PBJ,PBP,PBQ,PBB)	0.05
25/27	as above with coloured slogan (black, green, blue)	0.20
25/28	similar but colour error eg slogan/frank reversed ..	1.50
25/29	h) Postage & Revenue Franking Machines (Hasler m/c)(fm1, FML)	0.40
25/30	i) Roneo/Alcatel/Neopost (N,J,JA-JZ,NA-NZ,PX,TN,RN,RM,RR,RV, W,2N, 1-9NE incl 4NE by *thermal transfer from 1996) .	0.05
25/31	j) Scriptomatic/Cheshire Mailing/Frama (FSC, 5 or 6 digits)	0.10
25/32	Any of the above with slogan matching a Post Office slogan	0.50
25/33	Pitney Bowes "Post Perfect" (PB7) printed by *thermal transfer, and encrypted code to left of town die, from 1995	0.20
25/34	New designs for Channel Islands, 1969- , and Isle of Man, 1973- ...	0.30

*Note: thermal transfer postmarks have a glossy finish

THE NEW FACE OF FRANKING

25/35

Computacenter

25/36

New "bar code" design - has bar code in place of Great Britain/Postage Paid,
"United Kingdom" in town die, and "Royal Mail" above value

25/35 Sample postmarks for collectors provided by Royal Mail 0.50
(seen dated Feb-Aug 1996, with Watford town die, one machine only, not
to be confused with test mail since these items passed through mail)

25/36 Trial in Watford/St Albans/Hatfield area, 1996-97 .... 1.00
(used in 100 meter machines in the area, in connection with IMP trial
at Watford, see chapter 10, illustration shows earliest date seen)

(Numbers 25/37-90 reserved for future use)

Parcel post labels

25/91

25/92

25/93

25/91 Parcel post labels sold at PO counters, 1947-c1963 .... 1.50
(variety of manufacturers and designs, some worth much more)

25/92 As above, "TIM" special design at Festival of Britain, 1951 .... 20.00

Wilkinson "Penny in the slot" machine

25/93 Wilkinson "Postage Paid" postmark on cover, dated 25 January 1912 . 75.00
As above, other 1912 dates 100.00
(no date is shown in machine impression and all were struck towards
the centre of the cover, in red, but all were additionally handstamped "London EC"
etc, dated between 25 January and 31 August when the sole machine was withdrawn)

26. Printed Postage Impressions

For large companies and magazine distributors, the postmarking of mail, either by the customer (meter mail) or by the Post Office (Paid mail) is a time-consuming process. This could be avoided by means of regulations introduced in 1965, whereby a "Printed Postage Impression" could be printed beforehand on the envelope. Later, magazine plastic wrappers were developed and PPIs were printed on these too. PPIs heralded what later became known as "junk mail".

The principle of a PPI is that the words "Postage paid" are shown, along with a town name and a "serial" that identifies the sender. A "PHQ" series (Postal Headquarters) is used for major users, printers and magazine distributors with multiple outlets. Although there are some standard types, there are many exceptions, in terms of design and inscription. Colourful variations followed as senders attempted eye-catching designs, and to avoid their mailshots being discarded as unwanted "junk mail" by the recipient.

Although most PPIs are printed, others are applied by rubber stamp or machine. Charities often use adhesive stamps on their appeal envelopes, again to avoid being discarded as junk mail, and from 1992 PPIs applied to adhesive stamps are known. In 1996 PPI rubber stamps were seen used for pre-cancelling stamps on charity mail (ie the postmark appeared on the stamp not on the envelope as well).

The first PPI type was used up to the introduction of the "two tier" system in 1968, and shows no "1" or "2" - see **26/1**. **26/2** is one of various types used on some of the Post Office's own mail. These are not really PPIs but, like PPIs, such envelopes do not usually attract another postmark.

26/1

26/2

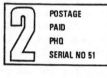

26/3

26/4

26/1 1965-68 First type, with serial number but without "class" 0.25
26/2 from 1960s Other "Post Paid" symbols used on Post Office envelopes .. 0.10
26/3 to 26/13 from 1968 as **26/1** but with "1" or "2" etc. 0.10

26/5

REMEMBER
to use the
POST CODE!

PARCEL POST ✦ POSTAGE PAID
      ✷   PHQ 13
   ✷✷✷✷✷✷✷✷✷✷✷✷✷✷

26/6

POSTAGE
PAID
BRIGHTON 41
GREAT BRITAIN

26/7

POSTAGE PAID
1
PADD
733

26/8

26/9

1 POSTAGE PAID
SOUTHAMPTON 324

26/10

26/11

Although all PPI designs require to be approved, from the outset there were many non-standard designs. **26/4** shows a "stamp simulation", and **26/5** was probably machine applied and is struck in red. **26/6** shows an early (1968) computer-printed PPI for parcel post. In the post-1968 PPIs, "1" and "2" denote first and second class mail, "R" mail which attracts a rebate, and "P" parcel mail.

In the 1970s a series of about eight standard designs was developed, and these included triangular and octagonal designs as well as the long format shown at **26/10**. There are many exceptions to these layouts, and in some cases simulations of "normal" Post Office postmarks are used. **26/12** shows a machine postmark simulation. Similarly, the Chester example (**26/13**) is printed (in black) as a simulation of a meter postmark (though this would have been in red).

From 1989 Mailsort was introduced for bulk mailings, and this is usually indicated by the "stylised M", the Mailsort logo, and this, as shown in **26/9** and **26/11**, replaced R. MHQ (Mailsort Headquarters) was also introduced (as in **26/12**). From 1994 there was a requirement to include "Royal Mail" in all PPIs.

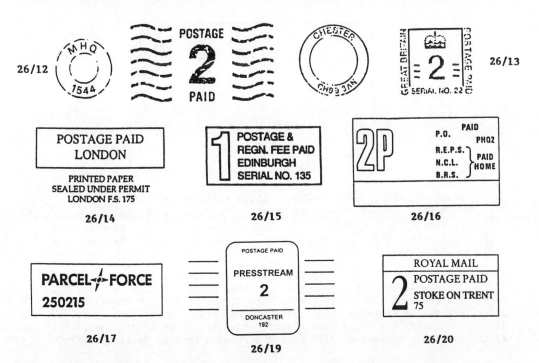

Three further variations are shown at **26/14** - **26/16**. One is the inclusion of "Sealed under permit" inscriptions; these sometimes show a different location from the PPI location. Second is inclusion of a registration fee. The "multiple carrier" parcel PPI is shown at **26/16**; here "P.O." (this is pre-"Parcel Force") is shown as one of a number of options for carriage of the parcel concerned.

26/14	Sealed under permit marks, usually with PPIs	0.10
26/15	PPI with recorded delivery or registration fee	0.50
26/16	Multi-carrier parcel marks	0.20
26/17	Parcel marks with contract number, "Parcel Force" 1990s	0.20
26/18	Mailsort marks with "stylised M" (see **26/9** or **26/11**)	0.10
26/19	Presstream mark, 1990s, another new service, development of Mailsort	0.20
26/20	PPIs with "Royal Mail", 1994-	0.10

Further reading : PPI listing produced as supplements to British Postmark Society Bulletin 1987-94, thanks to the efforts of Dr Michael Gould.

27. Postal Mechanisation

Successful automation of the postmarking process spurred the Post Office to mechanise the letter sorting process. This chapter summarises developments from the 1930s up to the massive changes to letter handling that have followed from about 1970. Test/dummy mail and philatelic covers are omitted. After listing the "marks" to be found on envelopes, some other mechanisation oriented postmarks are then shown. A glossary of terms and a reading list complete the chapter.

Early sorting marks

Trials of a Transorma machine started at Brighton as early as 1935. Operator identity codes A to Z, later lower case letters and numerals, were applied to the front of envelopes.

Between 1952 and 1956 trials took place at Mount Pleasant of a six-position Letter Sorting Machine (LSM) with Roman numeral idents I to VI. From 1955 single position machines (SPLSMs) were used at several offices.

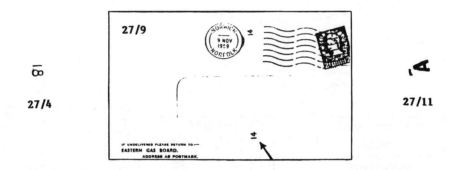

Transorma mark, letter/number applied at Brighton:

27/1	trials prior to 7 October 1935	50.00
27/2	operational in red, 1935	9.00
27/3	similar, 1936-37	3.00
27/4	similar, 1938-45	2.00
27/5	used in black or red/black mixture, 1945-46	15.00
27/6	in red, 1946-50	1.00
27/7	in red, 1951-68 (when use of machine ended)	0.50
27/8	Six-position LSM idents (roman I to VI) at London (Mt Pleas) 1952-56	80.00
27/9	SPLSM with operator code, 1959-64 (red, black, or violet)	40.00
27/10	similar but later double-digit codes at London Foreign Sec, 1971	80.00
27/11	single character (diff sizes) at London Foreign Section, 1977-89	4.00

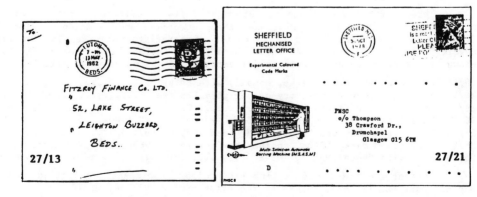

Dots representing postcodes and related idents

In 1959 a 2-stage sorting system was introduced at Luton. At a coding point phosphor dots were printed vertically on envelopes, which were then sorted mechanically. A similar system was later used at other mechanised offices, as postcodes were introduced countrywide, to apply two rows of dots horizontally in binary code representing the two halves of the postcode.

27/12	Coding dots at Luton - vertical at right, clear, 1960-65	80.00
27/13	similar with added red SPSLM operator marks	150.00
27/14	horizontal dots at foot of envelope, 1965-68	30.00
27/15	Coding dots at Norwich - rectangular, clear, 1966-68	40.00
27/16	experimental white raised dots, 1966	*
27/17	similar but "wax" dots, 1966-67	150.00
27/18	Large clear dots eg London EC, Croydon, 1970-	1.00
27/19	Rectangular dots (but London EC 20.00)	1.00
27/20	Small dots	0.30
27/21	Blue dots, early dates (first used Sheffield 30 Oct 1978)	0.50
	(illustration is of a philatelic item, value 2.00)	
27/22	later blue dots	0.10
27/23	Colour variations : turquoise	0.50
27/24	turquoise opacified	0.30
27/25	blue opacified	0.20
27/26	Upper row of dots only, overseas mail, 1991-	1.50

Idents are usually black, the following are variations:

27/27	clear "phosphor" ident at right : Cardiff, 1977-78	5.00
27/28	similar from Chelmsford, 1983-84	2.00
27/29	ident inside start dot eg London IS, 1980	20.00
27/30	coloured idents eg red/black at Romford, magenta at Huddersfield	0.30
27/31	commem ident T/50 in red at Brighton, 1985 (on PO postcard SEPR46)	
	(this is a philatelic item, commercial *)	2.50
27/32	Q of S ident eg 3 figures at Birmingham	0.40
27/33	italic ident at London Mt Pleasant (London and incoming overseas	
	mail destined for the provinces)	0.20
27/34	large ident from Slough, top of envelope, repeated 58mm, 1995-	0.50

Further marks from "manual" coding

27/35	Coding desk ink-jet ident at top left - Reading inland mail, 1987	*
27/36	similar but without zeros, 1987-88	2.00
27/37	similar without zeros, London FS (overseas mail), 1988-	1.00
27/38	similar at FS but pink or yellow (ditto), 1989	25.00
27/39	similar on Jersey mail to UK, 1991-	0.30
27/40	similar at Canterbury, March 1990 (office+day+operator+desk) .	20.00
27/41	Ink-jet pre-sorter slogan imprints at Liverpool, 1989-93	0.20
27/42	same but blue, June-July 1989	*
27/43	short-lived messages eg Valentine 1990-92	2.00
27/44	spelling errors eg CAMCER (note: 27/41-44 are on front of env'pe)	2.00

27/35   **27/37**   **27/40**

27/43

334

Bars from OCR process

Following an extended trial at London EC, the automatic, or optical, reading of
postcodes on letters soon became operational; the process prints bars as opposed
to dots, on the envelopes, but the bars are composed of a number of minute dots.

27/45	OCR trials - clear ink-jet bars at Guildford, 1980	*
27/46	London EC trial, blue, 1983	5.00
27/47	Operational use at London EC & other offices, blue, 1984-	0.20
27/48	revised (thinner) bars, 1992-95	0.10
27/49	as above but one-eighth inch pitch instead of ¼", 1994-	0.20
27/50	as above but red (more for red/blue on one envelope), 1995- ..	0.10
27/51	Four-state OCR bars in blue, Preston trial (and others), 1994 ...	*
27/52	as above but operational at Glasgow, April-May 1995	1.00
27/53	as above but in red, Scotland & Belfast 1995-, others 1996- ..	0.10
27/54	as above but colour variations eg red-brown, purple	0.20

(numbers 27/55-80 reserved for future use)

27/53 |ₗ|||ₗ|||ₗ|ₗₗₕₙ|ₗₚₚₙ|ₗₕ|ₗₕₗₕₗₚₚ|ₗ||ₕₕₗ|

Other marks from OCR process

27/81	Ink-jet imprint top left, firstly Reading 1988 (RG + day of week)	1.00
27/82	other offices eg GL (office + day of month) 1989-93	0.20
27/83	extended print for engineers but used on live mail	5.00
27/84	Q of S imprints at Liverpool on reverse of envelopes, black, 1991	1.50
	(size varies, also printed is "Liverpool MLO" in phos blue at left)	
27/85	as above but in clear phosphor, 1991	6.00
27/86	as above but in phosphor blue (almost invisible) 1991	5.00
27/87	"Serial product counter" blue phos messages (used at 6 towns), 1991	3.00
	(eg IIItownIII or "this letter was processed at W1" on reverse)	
27/88	Slogan imprints or date/time at Liverpool and others, 1991-	0.20

(note: similar to 27/41 pre-sorter marks at Liverpool but leaning to
left; these were printed at a number of towns, London SE1 and some
at Dartford on the front, leaning to right, but generally on reverse
of envelopes, and some are in red eg Croydon; see Patrick Awcock's
Volume 2 in Bibliography for lists)

27/89	same but short-lived or with spelling errors	2.00
27/90	same but used in error eg "Get your message across here", 1991	1.50
27/91	Reading bar code trial, black, 1990 (on reverse of envelope)	*

(numbers 27/92-120 reserved for future use)

For ink-jet messages on "large flats" see chapter 10.

GL 28   AA:50 L2-03-32 TU 81

27/82   **27/83**

27/86 Total length (day number + hour) 43mm and 65mm

IIIEDINBURIII10040858   HAPPY CHRISTMAS F
                               FROM THE POST OF ICE

27/87   **27/89**

Mechanisation oriented postmarks (for Glossary see next page)

27/121 Early ALF machines.   Value: 0.40 each

27/122 Generic postmarks used at MLOs. Value: from 0.05

27/123 MLO machine and handstamp postmarks. Value: from 0.05

27/124 Postcode slogans. Value: 0.75   Value: 0.05

  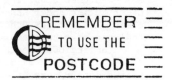

27/125 Philatelic handstamps on postcode theme. Value: 1.50 each on souv cover

27/126 Operational postmarks including postcodes. Value: from 0.10 each

Quality of Service explanatory cachets - used to correct dates on meter mail, alternatively machine applied slogans carry out the same duty, for these see chapter 11; for further explanatory marks see chapter 18.

Value: 1.00 each

Glossary of some mechanisation-related terms/abbreviations

ALF - Automatic Letter Facing machine, first introduced 1957 at Southampton
APC - Automated Processing Centre, the latest (1992-97) term for MLO (then
      "Mail Centre" used instead)
ASM - Automatic Sorting Machine, uses the phosphor dots/OCR bars once applied
CFC - Culler Facer Canceller, 1990s generation of automated cancelling machine
clear - colourless "phosphor" marks only visible if held at angle to light
Coding desk - the machine which, when an operator keys postcode, applies dots
         (unlike OCR, see below, which is automatic and an operator is required only
         when the OCR is unable to confirm the postcode)
Coding dots - rows of dots which represent the postcode (or town) in binary code
FCT - Facer Canceller Table, 1970s generation of semi-automated cancelling
Ident - numbers/letters showing either coding desk or operator or both, or date!
IMP - Integrated Mail Processor
Imprints - other Q of S messages printed on envelopes
Ink jet - fast modern printer using small jets to form characters from dots
MLO - Mechanised Letter Office, the result of concentration of letter traffic
      in the relevant catchment area (term introduced 1976)
MTT - Mail Transport ie the mechanism for passing mail through sorting equipment
OCR - Optical character recognition, resulting bars on envelopes are ink jet
      printed (larger on brown or dark envelopes), unlike blue coding dots; bars
      generally of same size, later 4-state code bars of diff sizes see 27/53
Opacified - added to the blue dot is a white chalky-looking substance to make
      blue dots opaque when applied to window envelopes & shiny substances
Phosphor blue - pale blue barely visible colour used for some marks on envelopes
Q of S - Quality of service, postmarks to show date/time of stages of letter
      sorting, or confirmation of date of posting (eg of meter mail)
SPLSM - Single position letter sorting machine
Transorma - name of sorting machine at Brighton (name means "TRANsporting" and
      "SORting", plus MA = design company Marchand-Andriessen Engineering Co.)

Although this chapter summarises a complex topic, we have covered it without mention of third generation, tag codes, OCR/VCS, AEG or transitional coding. Readers who wish to delve further should contact the Postal Mechanisation Study Circle, details of which are shown opposite.

28.   Post Office Names

For much of this book we have concentrated on TYPES of postmark. Many
collectors are interested in postmarks of specific post offices regardless of
type, so for simplicity we confine ourselves here to handstamps (single or
double circle, rubber or SID): the point is purely the inscription. Our
intention is to give some ideas for the basis of a collection.

Towns or counties

| 28/1 | 28/2 | 28/3 | 28/4 |

Collectors usually like to collect the postmarks of post offices in their local
town or county and many Postal History Societies are devoted to the postal
history of specific counties or regions. As an example some handstamps of POs
in the Stranraer area are shown above. Counter datestamps are usually obtained
either on registered letters or on certificates of posting, a cheap and
legitimate way of obtaining Post Office datestamp impressions.

Interesting places

Post offices can be found in stations, castles, schools, hospitals, super-
markets, on islands and at famous landmarks (some are in earlier chapters).
Some are illustrated here and others are shown in the list that follows :

| 28/5 | 28/6 | 28/7 | 28/8 | 28/9 |

Ampleforth College   Royal Courts of Justice   Hotel Cecil
Canal Bridge   Stock Exchange   Royal Automobile Club
Savacentre (supermarket) Giant's Causeway   Bethlehem Llandeilo
Smithfield Market   London Bridge Station   Universities (several)
Harrods   Portland Harbour   Isle of Iona
Northern Parliament Belfast Botanic Gardens Belfast Law Courts Belfast

Thematic Collecting

| 28/10 | 28/11 | 28/12 |

In chapter 12 we featured the idea of thematic collecting based on slogans and
special event postmarks. Similarly a collection can be formed with operational
postmarks and shown here are some examples of Colliery postmarks. These are
from the work of Fred Taylor who in 1997 published his book on this topic,
details of which are shown in the Bibliography.

Amusing Place-names

28/13   28/14   28/15   28/16   28/17

Searching for postmarks of locations with amusing names is a fun way to start collecting. Here are a few to get you going :

Ugley	Twatt	Upper Slaughter	Sandwich
Barking	Bicker	Yelling	Clatter
Halfpenny Green	Tooting	Bunny	The Lizard
Nomansland	Clock Face	Loggerheads	Foxholes
Freezywater	Isle of Dogs	Battlefield	Hanging Ditch
Flint	Piddletrenthide	Newton Blossomville	Cross Houses

The longest/shortest name and maximum characters in a handstamp

28/18   28/19   28/20   28/21

Llanfairpwllgwyngyllgogerychwyrndrobwllllantysiliogogogoch is well known as Britain's longest town/village name and not surprisingly its name is not shown in full in Post Office datestamps, as shown above. For the full name (various spellings) see the cachets in chapter 24. The shortest name of Ae is also shown here. The handstamps of Walton Road and Cwmfelinfach shown here are almost certainly not the longest inscriptions to be found in datestamps. We will leave collectors to find their own "longest inscriptions" with the suggestion that anything longer than 40 characters (depending if you count spaces as one or ½) - less in a SID - constitutes a pretty lengthy inscription!

Temporary/mobile datestamps

28/22   28/23   28/24   28/25

These can be of several sorts including skeleton datestamps which are covered in chapter 9. The Reading datestamp shows one used at the Henley Regatta Post Office (similar to others covered in chapter 12). The Manchester Emgy (Emergency) and Oxford datestamps were used at normal post offices for short periods, and clearly could have at other times been used elsewhere. The Mobile PO datestamp is used at a new post office (it started in July 1996) housed in a van which moves from village to village in the Carlisle area, somewhat different from the Mobile Post Offices featured in chapter 12.

Inscriptions with errors

Post Office Counters Ltd are not as fastidious as they once might have been in terms of including a full address in each inscription. Having said that we can only regard it as an error when no city is shown at all, such as "Lower Sydenham" showing neither London nor SE26 and Newcastle upon Tyne absent from "St Nicholas". The "Limekilns" specimen is mis-spelt and so is "Shipston on Stour" in the Tredington handstamp.

| 28/26 | 28/27 | 28/28 | 28/29 |

Offices opening or closing

Collectors feel a sense of loss when a post office closes and a sense of excitement when a new one opens. Some examples from London are shown here. Euston Centre closed for site redevelopment in 1996 while in 1992 Canary Wharf Post Office opened. Southampton Row BO closed in 1992 to be replaced by the post office at nearby Russell Square. Shown here are "almost the last day" of one and the first day of the other.

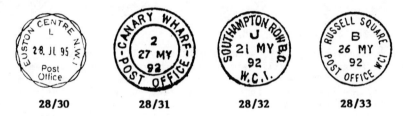

| 28/30 | 28/31 | 28/32 | 28/33 |

.... and lastly .... **The Extremes**

Which post offices that are furthest north, east, south and west depend on whether you include the Isles of Scilly, Shetland, Northern Ireland, Channel Islands and so on, so we will leave collectors to work out their own answers. Just as a couple of examples shown here Kilchoan on the Ardnamurchan peninsula, the western most point of the British mainland, and Sennen the nearest village to Land's End.

| 28/34 | 28/35 |

We acknowledge the assistance of the British Postmark Society Quarterly Bulletins as the source of some of the illustrations in this chapter.

Abbreviations

Care should be taken in interpreting abbreviations in postmarks; for example there are now two meanings of FPO! This list omits abbreviations of place names (eg IOW = Isle of Wight) and telegraphic codes (eg BHK = Bishop Auckland). Other abbreviations, such as UPF ("Universal Postal Frankers", the former name of a manufacturer of stamp cancelling machines), have not to our knowledge appeared in operational postmarks.

ADO	Aston District Office (Birmingham)	F & CPP	Foreign and Colonial Parcel Post
ALF	Automatic Letter Facer	FB	Foreign Branch
AM/AMDO	Aston Manor (District Office Birmingham)	FBO	Foreign Branch Office
		FC/FCT	Facer Canceller Table
AMDO	Army Mail Distribution Office	FD	Foreign Dept (of PO)
APC	Automated Processing Centre	FMO	Fleet Mail Office
APO	Army Post Office	FNM	French Night Mail? Foreign Night Mail?
BA	British Association	FNO	Foreign Newspaper Office
BAPO	Base Army Post Office	FNS	Foreign Newspaper Section
BC & FPP	British Colonial and Foreign Parcel Post (prev I & FPP)	FO	Flag Officer, also Foreign Office (dept of PO)
BFPO	British Forces Post Office	FPO	Field Post Office or (modern) Franchised Post Office
BFPS	British Forces Postal Service		
BMM	British Military Mission	FRH	Floating Receiving House
BO	Branch Office	FS	Foreign Section
BP	Bulk Posting		
BT	Bag Tender	GNR	Great Northern Railway
		GP	General Post
CDO	Counters District Office	GPO	General Post Office
CF	Compensation Fee	G(R)SD	Giro (Remittance) Services Dept.
CFC	Culler Facer Canceller		
CH	Clearing House or Camp Hill (District Office, Birmingham)	H	Hockley (District Office Birmingham)
CL	Late Matter Collection	H & K	Holyhead and Kingstown
CO	Chief Office	HD	Home Depot
Co.	County	HMY	His/Her Majesty's Yacht
CP	Competition Posting (football pools)	HO	Head Office
		HP	House of Peers
CR	Caledonian Railway	HPO	Head Post Office
CS	Church of Scotld Assembly		
CX	Charing Cross	IB	Inland Branch
		IE	International Exhibition
DALO	Director of Army Letters Office	IPS	Inward Primary Sorting
		IS	Inland Section
DLS	Dead Letter Section	IVO	Inward Vouching Office
DO	District Office		
DOM	Delivery Office Manager	KE	King Edward St.
DP	Deferred or Discount Posting	L	Late
DSC	District Sorting Carriage	LB & SC	London, Brighton and South Coast
EC	East Central	LDO	Letter District Office (1986-92)
ED	Eastern District		
EDO	Eastern District Office	LIS	Letter Information Sample
EX	Exchange	LOMO	London Overseas Mail Office (E16)

LPD	Local Parcel Depot	R	Rebate or Registered
LPR	London Postal Region	RDO	Rural/Railway Distribution Office
LPS	London Parcel Section	RH	Receiving House
M	Mailsort	RHAS	Royal Highland Agricultural Society
MB	Movable Box	RHS	Royal Highland Show
MHQ	Mailsort Headquarters	RL	Ride Letter
MLO	Mechanised Letter Office	RLB	Returned Letter Branch
MO & SB	Money Order & Savings Bank	RLE	Registered Letter Enclosure
MOO	Money Order Office	RLO	Returned Letter Office
MP/MTP	Mount Pleasant	RLS	Returned Letter Section
MPO	Mobile Post Office	RNAS	Royal Naval Air Service
MPPO	Mount Pleasant Parcel Office	RNC	Royal Naval College
MS	Missent	RO	Receiving Offices or Railway Office
MSPO	Modified (contract) sub post office	RPO	Railway Post Office
MT	Motor Transport	RRH	Rural Receiving House (Office)
MTO	Military Telegraph Office	RSC	Railway Sorting Carriage
MTP	Mount Pleasant	RSO	Railway Sorting Office or Railway Sub Office
NB	North Britain	RST	Railway Sorting Tender
NDO	Northern District Office	RWPO	Railway Post Office
NE(TPO)	North Eastern TPO		
NILD	Northern Ireland Letter Dist	SC	Sorting Carriage
NMT	Night Mail Tender	SDO	Southern District Office or Sub District Office
NPB	Newspaper Branch		
NR	Northern Railway	SDSO	Sub-district sorting office
NSB	National Savings Bank		
NSD	National Savings Dept.	SEDO	South Eastern District Office
NWTPO	North Western TPO		
OCR	Optical Character Recognition	SM	St Martins Le Grand
OCS	Old Cavendish Street	SMP	St Martins Place
OS	Old Stamp	SO	Station Office or sub office or Sorting Office
OVO	Outward Vouching Office		
P (in PPIs)	Parcel	SPDO/SPSO	Scale payment Delivery Office/Sub-Office
PB	Parcel Branch		
PC	Prison Censor	SSO	Station Sorting Office
PCO	Parcels Concentration Office	ST	Sorting Tender
PD	Paid to destination or Paid	SW(R)	South Western Railway
PDO	Postmen's delivery office, or Parcel Delivery Office	SWDO	South Western District Office
PHG	Postman Higher Grade	SY	Show Yard
PHQ	Postal Headquarters		
PL	Paid Late	T	Taxe (ie postage underpaid)
PO	Post Office	TD	Telegraph Department
POC/POOC	Posted out of Course	TO	Telegraph Office
POW	Prisoner of War	TP	Two Penny
PP	Penny Post or Parcel Post or Post Paid	TPO	Travelling Post Office
		TSO	Town sub-office
PPI	Printed Postage Impression		
PPO	Parcel Post Office	W	Window Letter
PS	Parcel Section	WC	Western Central
PSC	Parcel Sorting Carriage	WDO	Western District Office
PSO	Postmen's Sub Office	WR	Willesden Ride
PTO	Please turn over		

Postal Rates

Inland Letters Rates 1638-1839

All rates quoted are for single letters, i.e. letters written on a single sheet
of paper tucked round as an 'Entire'. Double and treble letters were charged
at double and treble rates. Quadruple rates applied per ounce.

1638	2d under 80 miles	1801	3d 15 miles
	4d 80-140 miles		4d 15-30 miles
	6d over 140 miles		5d 30-50 miles
	8d London to Scotland		6d 50-80 miles
	9d London to Ireland		7d 80-120 miles
			8d 120-170 miles
1653	2d under 80 miles		9d 170-230 miles
	3d over 80 miles		10d 230-300 miles
	4d London to Scotland		
	6d London to Ireland	1805	4d 15 miles
			5d 15-30 miles
1711	3d 80 miles		6d 30-50 miles
	4d over 80 miles		7d 50-80 miles
	6d London to Edinburgh		8d 80-120 miles
	6d London to Dublin		9d 120-170 miles
			10d 170-230 miles
1765	1d One Post Stage		11d 230-300 miles
	2d between one and two Post stages		1d each additional 100 miles or part
	3d between two Post stages and 80 miles	1812	4d 15 miles
	4d over 80 miles		5d 15-20 miles
	6d London to Edinburgh		6d 20-30 miles
			7d 30-50 miles
1784	2d One Post Stage		8d 50-80 miles
	3d between one and two Post stages		9d 80-120 miles
	4d between two Post stages and 80 miles		10d 120-170 miles
	6d 80-150 miles		11d 170-230 miles
	7d London to Edinburgh		1/- 230-300 miles
			1d each additional 100 miles or part
1796	3d 15 miles		
	4d 15-30 miles	1838	2d 8 miles
	5d 30-60 miles		4d 8-15 miles
	6d 60-100 miles		Other rates as for 1812
	7d 100-150 miles		
	8d over 150 miles		

Scotland

1710	2d under 50 miles		4d 50-80 miles
	3d 50-80 miles		5d 80-150 miles
	4d over 80 miles		6d above 150 miles
	6d Edinburgh to London		7d Edinburgh to London
1765	1d One Post stage	1796	3d One Post stage
	2d between one Post stage and 50 miles		4d between one Post stage and 50 miles
	3d 50-80 miles		5d 50-80 miles
	4d over 80 miles		6d 80-150 miles
	6d Edinburgh to London		7d above 150 miles
			8d Edinburgh to London
1784	2d One Post stage		
	3d between one Post stage and 50 miles	1801	Scottish rates made same as English

Ireland (1660-1839) Rates were for Irish miles except for a brief period Jan. 1826-July 1827.

1660	2d 40 miles
	4d over 40 miles
	(1/- per ounce over 40
	    miles, raised to 1/4
	    in 1711)
			1813	2d under 10 miles
				3d 10-20 miles
				4d 20-30 miles
				5d 30-40 miles
				6d 40-50 miles
				7d 50-60 miles
				8d 60-80 miles
				9d 80-100 miles
				10d over 100 miles

1765	1d One Post stage 2d between One Post Stage and 40 miles 4d over 40 miles			
1768	2d One Post stage 4d over 40 miles		1814	2d under 7 miles 3d 7-15 miles 4d 15-25 miles 5d 25-35 miles 6d 35-45 miles 7d 45-55 miles 8d 55-65 miles 9d 65-95 miles 10d 95-120 miles 11d 120-150 miles 1/- 150-200 miles 1/1 200-250 miles 1/2 250-300 miles 1d each additional 100 miles
1773	Dublin local post established			
1784	2d under 15 miles 3d 15-30 miles 4d over 30 miles			
1797	2d under 15 miles 3d 15-30 miles 4d 30-50 miles 5d 50-80 miles 6d over 80 miles			

1805	3d under 15 miles
	4d 15-30 miles
	5d 30-50 miles
	6d 50-80 miles
	7d over 80 miles
			1826	Jan. 6
				English rates and currency
				    introduced.
				Previous Irish rates reduced
				    by 1d

1810	4d under 15 miles 5d 15-30 miles 6d 30-50 miles 7d 50-80 miles 8d over 80 miles		1827	July Irish rates of 1814 restored but in English currency.

1832 Provincial Penny Posts
      established throughout
      the U.K.

By the 1830s postal charges had become insupportable. To send a single sheet from London to Edinburgh cost 1/1½d while sending a letter the same weight as the 1990 minimum charge cost 8/8½d. About 2 weeks pay was required to send a letter of the same weight inside Great Britain! Opposition came from the newly enfranchised middle classes and the agitation led by Robert Wallace MP and Rowland Hill. A House of Commons Select Committee, appointed November 1837, reported in August 1838 and recommended the adoption of Hill and Wallace's proposals. A uniform rate was to be charged, regardless of distance. After a brief experimental rate of 4d, a penny rate was introduced from 10th January 1840. Handstamps were used from this date, adhesive stamps and printed stationery being issued on 6 May 1840. In 1890 an anniversary publication commented, 'one of the greatest social reforms ever introduced was, to speak plainly, given as a bribe by a tottering Government to secure political support'.

1839-1968

From			First stage:	Subsequent stages:
1839, Dec 5th	4d	½ oz		4d per ½ oz; the 2d rate still applied up to 8 miles; pre-paid London local letters were charged at 1d, unpaid at 2d or 3d
1840, Jan 10th	1d	½ oz		1d for next ½oz, 2d for each subsequent ounce (or part) to maximum of 16 oz; unpaid letters were charged double
				1847, 16 oz limit abolished
				1865, 1d for next ½ oz and each succeeding half oz
				1872, initial weight step raised to 1 oz, ½d for each succeeding 2 oz (or part) to 12oz, thereafter 1d per oz
				1882, 12 oz limit abolished
				1897, initial weight step raised to 4 oz, ½d for each succeeding 2 oz (or part)
				1915, initial weight step reduced to 1 oz; 2d between 1 oz and 2 oz; ½d for each succeeding 2 oz (or part)
1918, June 3rd	1½d	4 oz		½d for each succeeding 2 oz
1920, June 1st	2d	3 oz		½d for each succeeding ounce
1922, May 29th	1½d	1 oz		2d for 3 oz; ½d each succeeding ounce
				1923: initial weight step raised to 2 oz; ½d each succeeding 2 oz
1940, May 1st	2½d	2 oz		½d each additional 2 oz
				1952: ½d for next 2 oz, 1d for each 2 oz thereafter
1957, Oct. 1st	3d	1 oz		1½d for each succeeding 2 oz
1965, May 17th	4d	2 oz		2d for each succeeding 2 oz up to 1 lb, then 3d per 2 oz

1968 to present day

Date of new charge	Max weight for minimum charge	First class minimum charge	Second class minimum charge
1968, 16 September	4 oz.	5d	4d
1971, 15 February (decimalisation)	4 oz.	3p	2½p
1973, 10 September	2 oz.	3½p	3p
1974, 24 June	2 oz.	4½p	3½p
1975, 17 March	2 oz.	7p	5½p
1975, 29 September (metrication)	60g	8½p	6½p

1977, 13 June	60g	9p	7p
1979, 20 August	60g	10p	8p
1980, 4 February	60g	12p	10p
1981, 26 January	60g	14p	11½p
1982, 1 February	60g	15½p	12½p
1983, 5 April	60g	16p	12½p
1984, 3 September	60g	17p	13p
1985, 4 November	60g	17p	12p
1986, 20 October	60g	18p	13p
1988, 5 September	60g	19p	14p
1989, 2 October	60g	20p	15p
1990, 17 September	60g	22p	17p
1991, 16 September	60g	24p	18p
1993, 1 November	60g	25p	19p
1996, 8 July	60g	26p	20p

Postcards:

1870	½d	1940	2d
1918	1d	1957	2½d
1921	1½d	1965	3d
1922	1d		

A separate postcard rate disappeared with the advent of Two Tier post in 1968.

Surcharges on unpaid/underpaid mail

Until 1983 unpaid/underpaid mail was subject to a surcharge equal to double the deficiency, and this was charged to the recipient. Subsequently a new system was introduced, with a surcharge fee added to the deficiency and ½p (if there was one) then rounded down. Thus, for example, with a rate of 12½p at the time (underpaid items always charged as second class), and with a surcharge fee of 10p, on an unpaid item 22p would have been charged. The surcharge fees were as follows:

1983, 5 April	10p	1991, 16 September	14p
1988, 5 September	11p	1993, 1 November	15p
1989, 2 October	12p	1996, 8 July	20p
1990, 17 September	13p		

From 1914 "To pay" labels were used as a receipt for surcharges paid, but from the mid 1990s these seem to have been discontinued with little publicity. Shown here is a 1997 "Surcharge paid" marking which has the same purpose. The amount involved is shown in the "to pay" marking shown elsewhere on the envelope.

TPO late fees

1860	2d	1971, 15 February	½p
1880	½d	1974, 24 June	1p
1969, 1 July	1d	1976, 27 September	no fee payable
			(but service for 1st class letters only)

Bibliography

"The Classics"

Modern writers, including ourselves, are greatly indebted to the research and scholarship of the writers whose works are listed below. These early publications still have much of interest and value to collectors wishing to specialise. Our background knowledge and many of our illustrations come (with permission) from them. The books are collectable in their own right and collectors search for them at book sales, auctions etc.

The History of the Early Postmarks of the British Isles, J.G. Hendy, 1906
The History of the Postmarks of the British Isles 1840-1876, J.G. Hendy, 1909
The Postmarks of Great Britain and Ireland, R.C. Alcock and F.C. Holland,
        pub. R.C. Alcock, 1940
(Note : an abridged version of the whole work is :
        British Postmarks: A Short History and Guide, R.C. Alcock & F.C. Holland,
        Revised Edition, pub. R.C. Alcock, 1977)

The Encyclopaedia of British Empire Postage Stamps, Vol. 1 Great Britain and
        The Empire in Europe, written and published by Robson Lowe, Second
        Edition 1952, reprinted in two parts by HJMR as Billig Philatelic
        Handbook Vols 34 & 35
The Postmark Slogans of GB, George Brumell, pub. R.C. Alcock Ltd, reprinted
        from The Philatelic Adviser, 1938
The Maltese Cross Cancellation of the United Kingdom, R.C. Alcock and F.C.
        Holland, pub. R.C. Alcock Ltd, Second Edition 1970
British Post Office Numbers 1844-1906, G. Brumell, originally pub. 1946, reprint
        pub. R.C. Alcock Ltd, 1979
The Local Posts of London 1680-1840, G. Brumell, 1938
Postal cancellations of London 1840-1890, H.C. Westley, pub. H.F. Johnson, 1950
Naval Mails 1939-49, J. Goldup, pub. TPO and Seapost Society, 1950
British Army Field Post Offices, 1939-1945, Locations and Assignments,
        G.R. Crouch and N. Hill, pub. Lava, 1951
A Christmas Story, C.W. Meredith and C. Kidd, pub. R.C. Alcock, 1954
The Spoon Experiment, 1853-58, R.M. & R.W. Willcocks & W. Bentley, pub. the
        authors, 1960, then similar but R.M. Willcocks and W.A. Sedgewick,
        pub. the authors, 1980
The Maritime Postal Markings of the British Isles, A. Robertson, pub. the
        author, 1958. Reprinted in 2 vols by James Bendon Ltd., 1993
British Slogan Cancellations 1917-1958, V. Swan, pub. the author, No.3 in
        series "The British Specialist", 1959
The Skeleton Postmarks of Great Britain, G.F. Crabb, pub. British Postmark
        Society, 1960
Handbook and Catalogue of the Stamps and postmarks of the Islands of Great
        Britain, pub. Woodcote Stamps, 1961
A Priced Catalogue of British Exhibitions 1840-1940, W.G. Stitt Dibden, pub.
        Argyll Stamp Co. Ltd, 1962
Current Machine Postmarks of the United Kingdom, J. Bruce Bennett, C.R.H.
        Parsons, G.R. Pearson, pub. British Postmark Society, 1963
Early Stamp Machines, W.G. Stitt Dibden, pub. The Postal History Society, 1964
Squared Circle Postmarks, W.G. Stitt Dibden, 1964, reprinted Harry Hayes, 1974
A History of Wreck Covers originating at Sea, on land and in the air
        A.E. Hopkins, pub. Robson Lowe, c1968
Fifty years of British Air Mails, 1911-1960, N.C. Baldwin, pub. F.J. Field,
        reprinted 1969
Camp Postmarks of the United Kingdom, R.A. Kingston, pub. Forces Postal
        History, 1971. Supplement 1974
Newspaper Branch Cancellations, W.G. Stitt Dibden, pub. The Postal History
        Society, 1971
Meter Stamps of Great Britain and Ireland, John C. Mann, pub. the author,
        Second Edition 1972
Posted in Advance for delivery on Christmas Day, C. Kidd, pub. Robson Lowe,
        1974

"The Moderns" (this section grouped approx in line with preceding chapters)

Most of "The Classics" are out of print and have been superseded and updated by more recent works. In the preparation of the Sixth and Seventh Editions we have drawn extensively (with permission) on many of them.

There are more works of James A. Mackay than indicated here. All were published by the author except the 1996 work published by British Postmark Society.

Postmarks of England and Wales, James A. Mackay, Second Edition 1988
Scottish Postmarks from 1693 to the Present Day, James A. Mackay, Second Ed 1995
Irish Postmarks since 1840, James A. Mackay, 1982
- all with supplements in Postal History Annual published each year 1979-89

England's Postal History to 1840, R.M. Willcocks, pub. the author, 1975
The Postal History of Great Britain and Ireland, A Summarised Catalogue to 1980,
         R.M. Willcocks and B. Jay, pub. the authors, Second Edition 1980
Postal Markings of Scotland to 1808, Bruce Auckland, 1978
Handbook of Irish Postal History to 1840, David Feldman and William Kane,
         pub. D. Feldman Ltd, 1975
Herewith my Frank, J.W. Lovegrove, pub. the author, Second Edition 1989
The Provincial Local Posts of England 1765-1840, G.F. Oxley, ?date
Welsh Post Towns before 1840, P. Scott Archer, 1970
The Scottish Additional Halfpenny Mail Tax, K. Hodgson & W.R. Sedgewick, pub.
         the authors, Second Edition 1984
The Early Days of the Postal Service, Tony Gammons, pub. Nat Postal Museum, 1986

British County Catalogue, R.M. Willcocks & B. Jay, Vols 1/2 (combined & updated)
         1996; Vol 3 1983; Vol 4, 1988; Vol 5, 1990
Wiltshire and its Postmarks, J. Siggers, pub. Sandcliff Press, 1982
Postmarks of the Date Impression Books, Section one (Vols. 1 and 2), W. Raife
         and H. Wellsted 1979; Section Two (Vols 3 and 4) by E.W. Proud 1983,
         pub. Proud-Bailey Co. Ltd
A Provisional Guide to the Valuation of the Numeral Cancellations of the
         British Isles, Part 1 England and Wales, M.R. Hewlett, Picton
         Philatelic Handbook No.1, 1979
The Sideways Duplex Cancellations of England and Wales, R.G. Traill and F.C.
         Holland, pub. R.C. Alcock, 1975
Priced check list of horizontal oval single cancellations with the number in a
         circle, J.C. Parmenter, pub. the author, 1974
London Cancellations, L. Dubus, pub. Robson Lowe Ltd., 1969-70
British Post Office Numbers, 1924-69, J.A. Mackay, pub. the author, 1981
British Post Office Numbers by County, K. Chapman, pub. Harry Hayes, 1985
Scottish Numeral Postmarks, J.A. Mackay, pub. the author, 1987
Barred Numeral Cancellations, J. Parmenter, Vol One, Wales 1984; Vol Two,
         England, Bedfordshire to Durham 1985; Vol Three, Essex to Kent, 1986;
         Vol Four, Lancs to Notts 1986; Vol Five, Oxfordshire to Sussex, 1987;
         Vol Six, Warwicks to Yorks, 1988, all pub. the author
Spoon Cancels 1853-1870, The Spoon Study Group, pub. Richard Arundel Ltd, 1992
Brunswick Star Cancels, R. Arundel, pub. Richard Arundel Ltd, 1993
Collecting British Squared Circle Postmarks, S.F. Cohen, pub. the author, 1987,
         with supplements 1990, 1993 and 1996
London Fancy Geometric Postmarks, M. Barette, pub. London Postal Hist Grp, 1994

Sub Office Rubber Datestamps of England and Wales, James A. Mackay, 1986
Sub Office Rubber Datestamps of Scotland, James A. Mackay, 1985
Sub Office Rubber Datestamps of Ireland, James A. Mackay, ?date
Official Mail of the British Isles, James A. Mackay, 1983
Scottish Post Offices, James A. Mackay, 1989
Skeleton Postmarks of Scotland, James A. Mackay, 1978
Skeleton Postmarks of England and Wales, James A. Mackay, compiled by Colin G.
         Peachey, pub. British Postmark Society, Second Edition 1996

UK Machine Marks, J. Peach, pub. Vera Trinder Ltd, Second Edition 1982
Machine Cancellations of Wales 1905-1985, Paul Reynolds, pub. Welsh Philatelic
        Society, 1985
Machine Cancellations of Scotland, James A. Mackay, 1986
English Provincial Krags, James A. Mackay, 1987

Collecting Slogan Postmarks, Cyril R.H. Parsons, Colin G. Peachey & George R.
        Pearson, pub. the authors, 1986 (includes full listing to 1969)
Slogan Postmarks of the Seventies, details as above, 1980
Slogan Postmarks of the Eighties, details as above, 1990
Slogan Postmarks of the Nineties: part 1 1990-94, details as above, 1995
        (part 2 due in 2000)
(Note : Supplements to the above in Bulletins of British Postmark Society)
In-depth UK Slogan Postmark Listings (four volumes covering 1960-99, 10 years
        each vol), Colin G. Peachey, pub. the author : Vol 1 The Sixties, 1996;
        Vol 2 The Seventies, 1997; Vol 3 The Eighties, 1997; (Vol 4 due in 2000)

Special Event Postmarks of the United Kingdom: Vol 1, George R. Pearson,
        Fourth Edition, compiled by Colin Peachey and John Swanborough,
        pub. British Postmark Society, 1991 (covers years 1851-1962);
        Vol 2, 1996 (covers years 1963-83); Vol 3, 1994 (covers years 1984-93),
        vols 2 & 3 both compiled by Alan Finch and Colin Peachey (based on
        earlier work by George R. Pearson), pub. British Postmark Society
(Note : Supplements to the above in Bulletins of British Postmark Society)
The lion roars at Wembley (The British Empire Exhibition 1924-25), Donald R.
        Knight and Alan D. Sabey, pub. D.R. Knight, 1984
Twenty Years of First Day Postmarks, Brian Pask and Colin G. Peachey, pub.
        British Postmark Society, 1983 (covers years 1963-83)
(Note : Supplements to the above in Bulletins of British Postmark Society)
Collect GB First Day Covers 1997, 25th edition, First Day Publishing Co, 1997
Collecting British First Day Covers, N.C. Porter, 16th edition 1997, pub.
        A.G. Bradbury, 1996
Regus Guide to British Regional Cards and Covers, 5th edition, Regus
        Publications, 1984

Railway Station Postmarks, D.P. Gowen, pub. Railway Philatelic Group, 1978
The Railway Sub Offices of Great Britain, A.M. Goodbody, pub. Railway
        Philatelic Group, Second Edition 1983
An Introduction and Guide to the Travelling Post Offices of Great Britain,
        A.M. Goodbody, pub. Railway Philatelic Group, Second Edition 1983
History of Travelling Post Offices of Great Britain & Ireland, H.S. Wilson,
        pub. Railway Philatelic Group, 1996 (previously in three volumes)
The Railway TPO's of GB & Ireland 1838-1975, Norman Hill, pub. Harry Hayes
        Philatelic Pamphlets, 1977
GB & Ireland Travelling Post Office Postmarks, Frank J. Wilson, pub. Railway
        Philatelic Group, 1991
TPO Postmarks of Great Britain 1962-1990, R.M. Stubbs and G.P. Roberts,
        pub. TPO & Seapost Society, 1992
Postmarks of British Railway Stations, W.T. Pipe & G.J. Blackman, pub. Railway
        Philatelic Group, 1994

Paquebot Cancellations of the World, Roger Hosking, pub. the author, Second
        Edition 1987
Floating Post Offices of the Clyde, James A. Mackay, 1979
The Transatlantic Post Office, Roger Hosking, pub. the author, 1979
Royal Mail Steam Packet Company, Michael Rego, Cockrill Series Booklet No.49,
        1987

The Postal History of the British Army in World War I, A. Kennedy and G. Crabb,
    pub. Forces Postal History Society, 1977
History of British Army Postal Service, Vol. 1 1882-1902, Vol. 2 1903-27,
    Vol. 3 1927-60, E.B. Proud, pub. Proud-Bailey Co. Ltd., 1982
Field Censor System of the Armies of the British Empire, 1914-18: Unit
    Allocations, i. War Office Based types 1,2,3,4 and 7, F.W. Daniel,
    pub. the author, 1984.
World War II Censor Marks, J.A. Daynes, pub. Forces Postal History Society,
    1984
The Royal Naval Air Service, Dr M.H. Gould, pub. Forces Postal History Society,
    1984
Postal Markings of R.A.F., R.F.C. and R.N.A.S. Stations in the United Kingdom
    1918-68, W Garrard, pub. Forces Postal History Society, 1990

The Channel Islands Sub-Post Offices and their Postmarks, David Gurney, pub.
    CISS Publishing, 1983; update 1990
The Post Office in the Smaller Channel Islands, David Gurney, pub. CISS
    Publishing, 1993
Channel Islands Postal History Catalogue, Stanley Gibbons Publications Ltd, 1991
Isle of Man Stamps and Postal History (YPM4), Dr J.T. Whitney, pub. BPH
    Publications, third edition, 1978
Islands Postal History - Series of 12 volumes, J.A. Mackay.

Catalogue of Great Britain Surcharge and Explanatory Dies, C.M. Langston,
    pub. the author, 1964
Surcharged Mail of the British Isles, J.A. Mackay, 1984

Telegraphic Codes of the British Isles, 1870-1924, J.A. Mackay, 1981
The Parcel Post of the British Isles, J.A. Mackay, 1982
Registered Mail of the British Isles, J.A. Mackay, 1983

Royal Household Mail, G. Morgan, pub. British Philatelic Trust, 1992

GB Used Abroad: Cancellations and Postal Markings, John Parmenter, pub. the
    author, 1993

The Postal History of the Manx Electric Railway, A. Povey and J.T. Whitney,
    pub. the authors, 1979
Cachets of Land's End, J.D.B. Owen, pub. the author, 1994, an update of previous
    book of similar name by G. Beckwith and J. Lawrence, Second Edition 1982
Dartmoor Letterboxes (and others), Anne Swinscow, pub. BPCC Wheatons Ltd Exeter,
    1984, revised 1987

An Introduction to British Postal Mechanisation, D.N. Muir & M. Robinson, pub.
    Postal Mechanisation Study Circle, 1979 with supplements 1981, 1983, 1992
British Postal Mechanisation, edited by Douglas N. Muir, pub. Postal
    Mechanisation Study Circle (being published in sections and housed in
    ring binder), part 1 1993, part 2 1996, further parts to follow
Automatic Letter Sorting in the UK, P.G. Awcock, pub. the author;
    Vol 1, 12th (final) edition, part 1 1996; Vol 2, 2nd edition, 1996
Brighton Transorma 1935-1968, Patrick G. Awcock, pub. the author, 1996

Colliery Postmarks 1854-1995, F.W. Taylor, pub. the author, 1997
Post Offices of the United Kingdom, The Post Office (last edition 1977)
Postal Directory 1850, reprint by London Postal History Group, 1987
Irish Post Offices 1600-1990, H. Frank & K. Stange, pub. F.A.I., 1990

"General"

Postmark Collecting, R.K. Forster, pub. Stanley Paul, 1960
Collecting Postmarks, R.K. Forster, pub. Stanley Gibbons Guides, 1977
Introducing Postal History, A. Branston, pub. Stanley Gibbons Guides, 1978
The Guinness Book of Stamp Facts & Feats, James A. Mackay, pub. Guinness
    Superlatives Ltd, 1982

INDEX OF ADVERTISERS

Societies Note : we have adopted a policy of offering inexpensive advertising space for Societies, included if possible at appropriate points in the book; Societies interested in being included in a future edition should write for details - address as on page 1